W9-AWU-779

Instructor's Guide to Text and Media for

Biology
Concepts & Connections

Fifth Edition

Campbell • Reece • Taylor • Simon

David Reid
Blackburn College

Edward J. Zalisko
Blackburn College

PEARSON

Benjamin Cummings

San Francisco   Boston   New York
Cape Town   Hong Kong   London   Madrid   Mexico City
Montreal   Munich   Paris   Singapore   Sydney   Tokyo   Toronto

Editor-in-Chief: Beth Wilbur
Acquisitions Editor: Chalon Bridges
Project Editor: Joan Keyes, Dovetail Publishing Services
Assistant Editor: Nora Lally-Graves
Managing Editor, Production: Erin Gregg
Production Supervisor: Jane Brundage
Marketing Manager: Jeff Hester
Manufacturing Buyer: Stacy Wong
Compositor: TechBooks/GTS

Cover Credit: James Balog, The Image Bank

⚠ **This work is protected by United States copyright laws and is provided solely for the use of instructors in teaching their courses and assessing student learning. Dissemination or sale of any part of this work (including on the World Wide Web) will destroy the integrity of the work and is not permitted. The work and materials from it should never be made available to students except by instructors using the accompanying text in their classes. All recipients of this work are expected to abide by these restrictions and to honor the intended pedagogical purposes and the needs of other instructors who rely on these materials.**

ISBN 0-8053-7161-3

Copyright © 2006 Pearson Education, Inc., publishing as Benjamin Cummings, 1301 Sansome St., San Francisco, CA 94111. All rights reserved. Manufactured in the United States of America. This publication is protected by Copyright and permission should be obtained from the publisher prior to any prohibited reproduction, storage in a retrieval system, or transmission in any form or by any means, electronic, mechanical, photocopying, recording, or likewise. To obtain permission(s) to use material from this work, please submit a written request to Pearson Education, Inc., Permissions Department, 1900 E. Lake Ave., Glenview, IL 60025. For information regarding permissions, call (847) 486-2635.

Many of the designations used by manufacturers and sellers to distinguish their products are claimed as trademarks. Where those designations appear in this book, and the publisher was aware of a trademark claim, the designations have been printed in initial caps or all caps.

PEARSON

Benjamin Cummings

7 8 9 10—TCS—09 08

www.aw-bc.com

Contents

About This Book

This *Instructor's Guide to Text and Media* is designed to help you organize and integrate the many different student and instructor supplements that are available with *Biology: Concepts & Connections,* Fifth Edition. These supplements are described on the following pages. In addition, an introductory chapter provides some tips on using technology to effectively teach Introductory Biology. The Appendix highlights major changes made in the Fifth Edition of *Biology: Concepts & Connections,* making it easier to update your syllabus and lecture notes.

The following sections are included for each chapter:

- The **Objectives** list the key teaching and learning goals for each main section of the chapter. The objectives are also on the *Biology: Concepts & Connections* website at the beginning of each chapter to guide student learning.

- **Key Terms** includes a convenient list of all boldfaced terms that appear in the text. The key terms are also on the *Biology: Concepts & Connections* CD-ROM and website, where they are linked to the glossary. The Key Terms are also provided as Flash Cards on the CD-ROM and website.

- **Word Roots** includes key word roots for each chapter, giving the meaning of each root and an example of a term from the text. The Word Roots are also on the *Biology: Concepts & Connections* website in the Key Terms section.

- The **Lecture Outline** is an extensive outline of the text that includes references to the figures, tables, and key terms for each chapter. In addition, this section provides numerous ways to incorporate what students have learned via a review and also signal future material via a preview.

- **Class Activities** provide numerous activities to engage students in the lecture and topic.

- **Transparency Acetates,** which include all the art and tables from the book, are listed to help you prepare for lecture.

- The **Media** section provides a quick reference to the animations and videos available on the Campbell Media Manager and a list of the student media Activities and the Thinking as a Scientist investigations for each chapter.

- All of these sections are also available in Word format on the *Biology: Concepts & Connections* website in the Instructor Resources area.

Supplements for the Instructor

New! Campbell Media Manager (0-8053-7110-9)

The new Campbell Media Manager combines all the instructor and student media for *Biology: Concepts & Connections* into one easy-to-use, chapter-by-chapter resource. Features include: the Image Presentation Library (containing all photos, art, and tables from the text); Power-Point® presentations (including Lectures, Layered Art, and Art Slides with editable labels and leaders); the Introductory Biology Lecture Launcher (Discovery Channel) Videos; Word files for the Detailed Lecture Outlines, Test Bank, and Instructor's Guide; student media activities and investigations; animations and videos; and new Active Lecture Questions in PowerPoint® for use with Classroom Resource Systems.

Instructor's Guide to Text and Media (0-8053-7161-3)

David Reid and Edward J. Zalisko, *Blackburn College*

This comprehensive guide provides chapter-by-chapter references to all the media resources available to instructors and students plus a list of Transparency Acetates. The guide also includes objectives, key terms, word roots, lecture outlines, and class activities. A separate chapter offers suggestions for effective uses of technology in teaching introductory biology.

Campbell Biology Website Instructor Resources (www.campbellbiology.com)

The Instructor Resources section of the Campbell Biology Website provides one convenient location for adopters to download the materials they need to teach their course: the Campbell Image Presentation Library, the PowerPoint Lectures, the Instructor's Guide to Text and Media (in Word), and additional critical thinking questions for class discussion or assignments (in Word). The Instructor Resources section also includes suggested answers to the Thinking as a Scientist media investigations. An Instructor's Access Code, found at the beginning of each Professional Copy of the text, is required to enter the Instructor Resources section of the website.

Transparency Acetates (0-8053-7162-1)

Over 650 full-color acetates include all illustrations and tables from the text, many of which incorporate photographs. New to this edition are selected figures illustrating key concepts broken down into layers for step-by-step lecture presentation.

Printed Test Bank (0-8053-7164-8)
Computerized Test Bank (0-8053-7163-X)

Edward J. Zalisko, *Blackburn College*

Thoroughly revised and updated, the test bank for the Fifth Edition now contains more than 2,100 multiple-choice questions. The Test Bank also includes an optional section with questions that test students on the Web/CD Activities. The test bank is available in print, on a cross-platform CD-ROM, and in the instructor section of CourseCompass™, Blackboard, and WebCT.

New! Course Management Systems

The content from the Campbell Biology Web Site and Computerized Test Bank is available in these popular course management systems: CourseCompass™, Blackboard, and WebCT. Visit http://cms.aw.com for more information.

Annotated Instructor's Edition for Laboratory Investigations for Biology, Second Edition (0-8053-6792-6)

Jean Dickey, *Clemson University*

This instructor's version of the lab manual includes the complete student version plus margin notes with instructor overviews, time requirements, helpful hints, and suggestions for extending or supplementing labs; answers to questions in the Student Edition; and suggestions for adapting the labs to a two-hour period.

Preparation Guide for Laboratory Investigations for Biology, Second Edition (0-8053-6771-3)

Jean Dickey, *Clemson University*

This guide helps the instructor to correctly order materials and to plan, set up, and run labs smoothly.

New! Instructor's Lab Manual for BiologyLabs On-Line (0-8053-7018-8)

Michael A. Palladino, *Monmouth University*
www.biologylabsonline.com

This printed manual provides the assignments and group assignments from the Student Lab Manual for BiologyLabs On-Line with suggested answers. Includes a subscription to BiologyLabs On-Line.

New! Symbiosis: The Benjamin Cummings Custom Laboratory for Biology (0-321-10049-2)

Build a customized lab manual, choosing the labs you want, importing artwork from our graphics library, and even adding your own notes, syllabi, or other material. Visit http://www.pearsoncustom.com/database/symbiosis.html for more information.

Supplements for the Student

New! Campbell Biology CD-ROM and Website (www.campbellbiology.com)

The student CD-ROM and website included with each book contain 7 new You Decide Activities and a customized quizzing feature, plus approximately 200 Activities, 56 Thinking as a Scientist investigations, 30 Connections, Flashcards, Word Roots, Key Terms linked to the glossary, over 3,000 quiz questions (a Pre-Test, Activities Quiz, a Chapter Quiz, and new Key Concept quizzes for each chapter), and a Glossary with pronunciations. Responses to questions can be e-mailed. In addition, the web site provides access to all the art from the book, with labels and without labels, 85 videos, the Tutor Center, Web Links, News Links, News Archives, Further Readings, Instructor Resources, and Syllabus Manager. The website content is also available in CourseCompass™, Blackboard, and WebCT.

Student Study Guide (0-8053-7116-8)

Richard M. Liebaert, *Linn-Benton Community College*

Students can master key concepts and earn a better grade with the thought-provoking exercises found in this study guide. Engaging chapter introductions relate biology to students' own lives. A wide range of questions and activities help students test their understanding of biology. The *Student Study Guide* also includes references to student media activities on the Campbell Biology CD-ROM and website.

Laboratory Investigations for Biology, Second Edition (0-8053-6789-6)

Jean Dickey, *Clemson University*

An investigative approach actively involves students in the process of scientific discovery by allowing them to make observations, devise techniques, and draw conclusions. Twenty carefully chosen laboratory topics encourage students to use their critical thinking skills and the scientific method to solve problems. This edition includes two new labs: Lab 8, Chromosomes and Cell Division, and Lab 10, Forensic Application of Molecular Genetics.

Biology Labs On-Line (www.biologylabsonline.com)

Robert A. Desharnais, *California State University, Los Angeles,* and Jeffrey R. Bell, *California State University, Chico*

These 12 virtual lab exercises enable students to perform potentially dangerous, lengthy, or expensive experiments in a safe electronic environment. The labs are available separately or in a 12-pack with the Student Lab Manual.

Student Lab Manual for Biology Labs On-Line (0-8053-7017-X)

Michael A. Palladino, *Monmouth University*

This printed student manual provides background information, instructions, assignments, and group assignments for Biology Labs On-Line. Includes a subscription to Biology Labs On-Line.

Tutor Center (www.aw-bc.com/tutorcenter)

This service provides one-to-one tutoring in four different ways—phone, fax, email, and the Internet—during evening hours and on weekends. Qualified college biology instructors are available to answer students' questions and provide instruction regarding self-quizzes and other content found in *Biology: Concepts & Connections,* Fifth Edition. The Tutor Center is free when bundled with a new book; a standalone access code card is available for purchase (0-201-72170-8).

CourseCompass™ Standalone Access Code Card (0-8053-7111-7)

Blackboard Premium Course Standalone Access Code Card (0-8053-7114-1)

WebCT Premium Course Standalone Access Code Card (0-8053-7115-X)

The Benjamin Cummings Special Topics Series

These booklets, each 32 to 48 pages long, provide up-to-date information on topics of current interest. Michael Palladino of Monmouth University serves as the series editor.

Understanding the Human Genome Project (0-8053-4877-8)

Michael Palladino, *Monmouth University*

This booklet explains the Human Genome Project in accessible language, presenting the background, the findings, and the social and ethical implications.

Stem Cells and Cloning (0-8053-4864-6)

David A. Prentice, *Indiana State University, Terre Haute*

In this booklet, embryonic and adult stem cells and mammalian cloning are discussed, along with scientific, political, and ethical ramifications of their use in research and medicine.

Biological Terrorism (0-8053-4868-9)

Steve Goodwin and Randall W. Phillis, *University of Massachusetts, Amherst*

This booklet presents a brief history of the use of biological weapons, highlights the major microorganisms used in bioterrorism, and examines the research being conducted to develop vaccines for these pathogens.

The Biology of Cancer (0-8053-4867-0)

Randall W. Phillis and Steve Goodwin, *University of Massachusetts, Amherst*

In this booklet, the causes, growth patterns, and possible treatments of various types of cancers are described in a clear and concise format. The authors discuss the major characteristics of the cancerous cell and the research being conducted on the hereditary and behavioral factors that contribute to the development of the disease.

HIV and AIDS (0-8053-3956-6)

Michael Palladino, *Monmouth University*

This booklet will help students learn about the biology of the human immunodeficiency virus as the cause of acquired immunodeficiency syndrome (AIDS), and AIDS as a disease will be explained from basic science, medical, and societal perspectives.

Emerging Infectious Diseases (0-8053-3955-8)

Michael Palladino, *Monmouth University*

This booklet provides students with an introduction to the origin, spread, and treatment of modern emerging infectious diseases such as Lyme disease, SARS, avian flu, and mad cow disease.

The Chemistry of Life CD-ROM (0-8053-8150-3)

Robert M. Thornton, *University of California, Davis*

Animations, interactive activities, and self-quizzes are used to teach the essentials of chemistry to biology students

An Introduction to Chemistry for Biology Students, Seventh Edition (0-8053-3075-5)

George J. Sackheim, *University of Illinois, Chicago*

This unique workbook takes students step-by-step through the chemistry necessary for success in life sciences courses.

Effective Uses of Instructional Technologies in Teaching Introductory Biology

By Eric J. Simon
New England College
Email: esimon@nec.edu

Technology is a funny thing. During the last decade, methods of teaching and learning have changed faster than during any time in the history of organized education. What is responsible for this rapid reformulation? Technology, of course. As educators, we hear about it all the time. The myriad benefits of instructional technologies have been stated and restated so many times that they are approaching mantra, if not dogma.

Yet, almost every educator has a favorite story about how technology can be overemphasized, inappropriately glorified, or just plain misused. Here is mine. A few years ago, my wife and I were in Hawaii (she on business, me as the grateful spouse). We decided to visit the observatories at the top of Mauna Kea, nearly 14,000 feet above the sea. The trip to the top is precarious enough to require a 4-wheel-drive jeep, so we rented one for the occasion. On our way down the mountain, when we returned to paved road, I needed to take the jeep out of 4-wheel drive and back into 2-wheel drive for the highway. My efforts failed and caused a terrible grinding of the gears. In a flash of inspiration, I decided to check the driver's manual. I opened the glove compartment, smiling at my cleverness. Inside, however, I found no driver's manual. What I found was an instructional video.

I could just imagine a committee patting each other on the back for the excellent way they had used technology to help jeep drivers. But at the top of a Hawaiian mountain, I was less impressed. The point was clearly noted: Technology should not be haphazardly applied across the whole spectrum of educational situations, but should be used in a thoughtful manner that always supports preestablished learning objectives.

Biology: Concepts & Connections, Fifth Edition, by Neil Campbell, Jane Reece, Marty Taylor, and Eric Simon, has a number of technology supplements for students and instructors. First, every new copy of the book includes a student CD-ROM and an access code to the *Biology: Concepts & Connections* website (www.campbellbiology.com). The website includes the same materials that are on the CD-ROM plus additional web-only content. Instructors also have the option of establishing an online course website for their students using Campbell-specific content in a course management system. CourseCompass™ provided by Pearson Education, is a nationally hosted course management system. Alternatively, instructors can download a Blackboard course or WebCT course for local hosting. All of these websites are password-protected and contain the same content that is on the *Biology: Concepts & Connections* website. Students who purchase a new copy of the textbook receive an access code card for the online course with their textbook. Students who buy a used book can purchase access to a website separately.

The purpose of this introduction is to present ways that these instructional technology tools for students can be used to enhance teaching and learning in introductory biology courses that use *Biology: Concepts & Connections*, Fifth Edition. I will present issues to consider and ideas gained from my own experience. In keeping with the lesson cited above, this introduction also discusses the possible pitfalls of technology use. Most importantly, this guide to technology is firmly grounded in one fundamental learning objective: teaching introductory biology using *Biology: Concepts & Connections*, Fifth Edition.

A quick word on what this introduction does not cover: This introduction will not discuss details of implementation. Visit http://cms.aw.com for information on specific course management systems (CourseCompass™, Blackboard, and WebCT). The ideas presented in this introduction are general enough to apply to multiple course management systems and related technologies such as CD-ROMs, the *Biology: Concepts & Connections* website, and e-books. The purpose of this introduction is to stimulate thought and provide ideas on how any instructor might gain the advantages of technology use in the classroom while, hopefully, avoiding the types of inappropriate uses that form the basis of so many apocryphal tales.

General Considerations

This section will discuss some general issues related to the use of instructional technologies in the introductory biology classroom.

The most important general point to be made about using technology tools is the one already stated: Don't let the technology tail wag the learning dog. Before implementing any specific technology, make sure to pause and ask yourself a few questions: Is this technology appropriate for my classroom? Is the proposed use firmly grounded in one or more of my course objectives? Will the technology under consideration enhance my ability to teach and/or the students' ability to learn? If the answer to any of these questions is "no," then perhaps using the new technologies under consideration should be reconsidered or saved for another course or semester.

Today's students are, in general, technology literate. We've all heard the cliché of a young child teaching his/her parents how to use a VCR or computer, and many classroom instructors may feel that the students are as comfortable (or more) with particular technologies as they are. While this may often be true, instructors need to acknowledge that some students may be very uncomfortable, perhaps even functionally illiterate, with certain technological learning aids. In particular, adults or returning students, international students, and economically disadvantaged students might be behind their peers in experience with new technologies. In addition, no matter how good they are at certain specific uses of the Internet, nearly every student needs guidance on the proper use of technology as an educational tool.

Thus, it is important for the instructor to introduce technology to the students and to carefully evaluate if it is serving all students. This introduction and evaluation can be accomplished in several ways. First, circulate a questionnaire to determine the level of computer literacy and comfort among your students. If you plan to make heavy use of instructional technologies during your course, poll your students on the first day of class to determine their comfort level. These polls and questionnaires can help guide the instructor regarding the pace of introducing new technologies, indicating which technologies the students are very comfortable with (e.g., email), and which might require more training or supervision (e.g., presentation software). The polls can also be used to establish teams of students by pairing less savvy students with those who are more competent. Figure 1 (page xxiv) contains a sample technology questionnaire that can serve as the basis for your own.

A similar poll can be used at the end of the course (or at the end of the first semester of a two-semester course) to evaluate the technology experience of your students. This poll can provide helpful information to the instructor regarding adapting the technologies for future courses or semesters. I have often found the students' comments to be insightful with respect to how the technologies were used and any perceived benefits and drawbacks. Figure 2 (page xxv) contains a sample end-of-semester technology questionnaire.

A useful method for introducing students to the technologies you plan to use is to create assignments that combine course material with technology usage. For example, ask students to track down certain specific information on the Internet (e.g., "How many organisms have had their genomes sequenced?" or "How many different species of mammal have been cloned?"). Require students to provide both the answer and a proper citation for their source. This assignment will help to familiarize students with Web-based biology resources and can also turn into a sophisticated lesson on how to critically evaluate Internet sources, a crucial skill as the Internet gains prominence as a scholarly tool. Other possible assignments can be based on the content provided on the *Biology: Concepts & Connections* CD-ROM and website. In each case, the assignment serves a dual purpose: to guide the students in a biology-related inquiry, and to ensure their proper use of the technology involved.

Many students, particularly those less familiar with technology, will experience two learning curves in a technology-heavy course: one for the curricular material itself and another for the technologies. Students can thus benefit from the stepwise introduction of instructional technologies into the classroom. A recommended approach is to use a series of assignments that gradually introduce the different instructional technologies. The first technology-related assignment should use an easy and familiar resource, such as email. Future assignments should build upon each other with respect to the technologies required. A second assignment, for example, might involve emailing a report, thus combining email and word processing skills. Future assignments can involve the course bulletin board, Internet, CD-ROMs, websites, and other resources. A capstone assignment for the course might involve creating a multimedia presentation on some relevant subject, requiring skills in presentation software, word processing, graphics, Internet searches, etc. The important point is to make sure that no particular assignment introduces more than one new technology component at a time and that the assignments build upon each other with respect to both curricular and technology content.

A final general piece of advice is to use both incentives ("carrots") and requirements ("sticks") to encourage students to participate in the technology components of the course. Assignments are a great way to ensure that every student is benefiting from the technologies, but remember to toss out some carrots as well. I have found that the prompt posting of grades to an online gradebook provides incentive for students to access the course website, particularly for once-a-week courses or at the end of the semester. Providing hints for an exam (through, for example, a virtual chat study session or postings to a bulletin board) is an excellent way of increasing participation. Providing fun links to multimedia such as videos, cartoons, and songs is another way to capture student interest. For example, point students toward content-related songs (such as Weird Al Yankovic's "I Think I'm a Clone Now" or Pearl Jam's "Do the Evolution"— email me for a list of dozens of biology-related popular songs) available as free samples on some retail websites (e.g., http://www.amazon.com). Or provide links to movie websites that connect to the curriculum, such as those for the *Jurassic Park* movies or *Gattaca.* I often allow students to earn extra credit by completing small technology projects, such as creating a slide for my in-class PowerPoint presentations or compiling and critically evaluating a list of Web links related to a course topic. Remember that to be used to its maximum potential, the technology, like the material itself, must be both informative and interesting to the students.

Technology alternatives to standard media have many potential benefits to the teaching and learning processes. Some of these benefits include:

- Multimedia capabilities
- Improved assessment
- Ability to present timely material
- Improved communication
- Customization of curriculum
- Portability

The following sections will discuss each of these advantages in detail. Specific suggestions will be made on using course management systems and related technologies to gain each advantage. In addition, tips on avoiding certain pitfalls of technology use will also be discussed.

Multimedia

One of the most obvious and powerful advantages that technology offers over the printed medium is the ability to display multimedia such as video, animation, hyperlinks, and sound. Movement is one of the characteristics of life, and explaining certain complex biological processes using only static visuals often proves difficult. Metabolic pathways, anatomical configurations, ecological systems, pronunciations of difficult words, and cell cycles are just a few of the topics that benefit from multimedia exposition.

Biology: Concepts & Connections, Fifth Edition, comes loaded with multimedia supplements. They fall into two general categories: those for the students and those for the instructor. Each chapter in this *Instructor's Guide to Text and Media* includes a list of the media assets available for that chapter.

Student Media

Multimedia student materials can be found on the CD-ROM, *Biology: Concepts & Connections* website, and Campbell course management websites. The student media include the following:

- Each chapter opens with a Chapter Guide, which clearly lays out all the media resources available within each chapter.

- Activities contain animations, interactive exercises, audio, and digital video to convey key concepts. Investigations involve students in interactive laboratory activities that teach them to follow the scientific method by making observations, formulating a hypothesis, designing and performing an experiment, collecting data, and drawing conclusions.

- There are over 80 videos available for student viewing. Videos are in easy-view Flash format and include video scripts.

- Each chapter contains four different types of multiple-choice quizzes: a Pre-Test to diagnose current knowledge, an Activities Quiz that tests understanding of the media Activities in the chapter, a comprehensive Chapter Quiz,* and multiple Key Concept quizzes to test understanding of the concepts in the chapter. Each quiz contains hints and immediate feedback. Results from each quiz can submitted to an electronic, online gradebook. A Cumulative Test allows students to build their own multiple-choice self-assessment test on any or all chapters by selecting questions from any chapter. Questions include concept number references and hints, and offer immediate feedback.

- Art from the book is provided both with labels and without labels. Students can print out the art to take to class for note-taking, and they can use the version without labels as a self-quiz.

- Study Tools for each chapter include Word Roots and Key Terms to improve vocabulary skills. Key Terms also include selected audio pronunciations. A Flashcards game allows students to practice terms, definitions, and word roots.

- The Glossary includes every boldface term from *Biology: Concepts & Connections,* Fifth Edition, with audio pronunciations of selected terms. Terms in the Activities are linked to the Glossary, and students can also access the Glossary independently.

- The Web Links and References section includes links to news stories that present recent developments related to the chapter content, and also to further readings.

- About the Book provides more information about *Biology: Concepts & Connections,* Fifth Edition, the authors, and the supplements.

Instructor Media

Nothing captures student interest during lengthy lectures more than lively presentations with informative multimedia elements. The Campbell Media Manager, available as a set of eight instructor CD-ROMs and via the Instructor Resources section of the *Biology: Concepts & Connections* website, aids the instructor in improving classroom lectures and presentations. This chapter-by-chapter visual archive of images is for the exclusive use of adopters of *Biology: Concepts & Connections,* Fifth Edition. All of the diverse images—art and tables, photos, videos, and animations—are organized by chapter. All file formats have been thoroughly tested in large lecture halls. The Media Manager includes:

- 1,600 photos, including the photos from the text, plus additional photos collected from a variety of sources that have been especially chosen to match the content of each chapter.

- All the art and tables from the text. Art figures are provided both with and without labels for maximum flexibility in lecture presentations. The version without labels can be customized for lecture, used to create a quiz, or used to create step-by-step presentations. All of the art and tables have been reformatted to be larger and clearer when used for lecture presentation.

- Selected art figures are layered for step-by-step presentation.
- PowerPoint Slides. All of the photos, art, and tables have been imported into PowerPoint.
- PowerPoint Active Lecture Questions. These questions, drawn from book content, can increase interactivity during lecture by testing student comprehension of key topics.
- Discovery Video Lecture Launchers. 29 three- to five-minute video clips from the Discovery Channel embedded in PowerPoint presentations.
- More than 80 video clips. Instructors can enhance their lectures with videos on a variety of biological concepts. Scripts are provided for background information. The videos are available in large (640 × 480) and small (320 × 240) formats.
- Over 100 animations. Animations can be used in lecture to help students understand key biological concepts.
- Lecture Outlines. Available in Microsoft Word format, these outlines can be edited, printed, and distributed electronically to help students focus on important study goals.
- A Quick Reference Guide summarizes all available resources in a fold-out format.

Fully prepared PowerPoint Lectures with lecture outlines, art, tables, and photos are also available. The PowerPoint Slides or Lectures can be customized for an instructor's course. If desired, the PowerPoint files can be printed out and duplicated for students to use for taking notes during lecture. Customized lecture notes can be published through Pearson Custom Publishing. (See www.pearsoncustom.com for more information.)

Assessment

One of the most challenging and time-consuming aspects of teaching is creating and grading tests and quizzes. Many teachers find it to be the most frustrating aspect of the job, from keeping track of old exam questions to calculating and recording grades. Technology can alleviate some of this frustration by doing what computers do best: repetitive tasks. There are also, however, some interesting problems that arise when using technology-based assessment tools.

The assessment tools available with *Biology: Concepts & Connections,* Fifth Edition, fall into two basic categories: those intended to help students test their knowledge of the material, and those intended to aid the instructor in the assessment process. For the students, the CD-ROM and the *Biology: Concepts & Connections* website include multiple self-assessment aids organized by chapter. Every chapter includes a Pre-Test of ten multiple choice questions which can be used by the instructor to gauge student understanding before lecture. A Chapter Quiz of 30–50 multiple-choice questions helps students test their new knowledge. Each quiz has hints and feedback for students, and answers can be submitted to an online gradebook.

The Cumulative Test is a feature new to *Biology: Concepts & Connections,* Fifth Edition. It is a Flash-based multiple-choice self-assessment test that allows students to choose the chapter or chapters they would like to be tested on and the number of questions. Each question includes feedback and hints. At the end of their test, students receive their personal score as well as a list of the concepts that may require further study.

The Key Concept Quizzes are also new to this edition of *Biology: Concepts & Connections*. These quizzes are organized by concept inside the chapter, and allow students to test their understanding of the big picture while synthesizing multiple topics.

Several of the features included on the CD-ROM and website have their own internal assessment tools. The multimedia Activities section associated with each chapter, for example, includes a multiple-choice quiz of 15–25 questions, many of which include graphics from the activities themselves. This quiz reinforces the materials presented in that chapter's Activities, thereby reinforcing important curricular concepts. Assigning the Activities Quiz is a good way to ensure that students successfully complete the Activities section. Answers can be submitted to an online gradebook. Also, student understanding of the Investigations can be measured by requiring students to email their responses. Suggested answers to the Questions can be found in the Instructor Resources section of the website. For instructors who assign any of the Biology Labs On-Line (www.biologylabsonline.com), students can email responses to assignments from within the *Biology: Concepts & Connections* website.

The Computerized Test Bank for instructors includes 50–60 multiple-choice questions per chapter that students do not have access to. In addition, the Test Bank includes five multiple-choice questions per chapter on the Media Activities so that instructors can encourage students to use these features by including questions on tests if they would like to.

All of these same assessment tools from the *Biology: Concepts & Connections* website are included in the CourseCompass™, Blackboard, and WebCT course management systems, giving the instructor great flexibility in preparing and presenting quizzes and tests. The Assessment Manager tools (in CourseCompass™/ Blackboard) control the pre-written quizzes for each chapter: Self-Quiz, Essay Questions, Pre-Test, Activities Quiz, and Chapter Quiz (all taken from the *Biology: Concepts & Connections* website) and Test Bank questions (taken from the Instructor's Computerized Test Bank). In each case, the instructor has the ability to preview, modify, or remove the pre-loaded question set. The modifications that an instructor can make are quite extensive. Every question can be altered to include text, images, or links. The number of answer choices can be set and the text and image for each answer modified. The specific feedback given upon a correct or incorrect answer can be changed for each question. The questions can be grouped into categories for easier selection. The instructor can use all of the questions provided or a subset of them, and the instructor can add original questions and answers.

Once a quiz/test has been created, the instructor has many options for making the quiz available to the students. The instructor controls when to make the quiz/test available to students. The correct answer can be revealed or not, depending on whether the instructor wishes the students to take a quiz multiple times. The customized feedback can be displayed or not. Students may be permitted multiple attempts at each question. A time limit can be set for the quiz, and it can be password-protected. All of these options allow the instructor to tailor each quiz to a particular learning goal. Taken together, these assessment tools provide great convenience in managing the creation and distribution of quizzes and tests while also providing great flexibility.

Once quizzes are made available to students, the Assessment Manager (in CourseCompass™/Blackboard) makes grading very convenient for the instructor.

The students submit their answers electronically. The quizzes can be automatically graded, with grades sent to the instructor and/or recorded in the online gradebook. The instructor has the ability to view each student's quiz results from anywhere with Internet access, removing the requirement of physical proximity to the office. The online gradebook can calculate averages and create a variety of reports, and is exportable to spreadsheet programs. Students also have access to their own grades on the website so that they can easily keep track of their standing in the course.

No matter which quiz format is being used, online assessment always involves issues of security. Secure online testing is one of the most vexing problems currently facing instructors who deliver courses electronically, and I know of no solution that is fully satisfactory for every teaching situation. The course management Assessment Manager (in CourseCompass™/Blackboard) does include some security features. A timer can be set to limit the amount of time a student has to complete a quiz. Setting the timer to a sufficiently low value can reduce the chances that a student can consult non-permitted materials (i.e., the book) but obviously does not eliminate that possibility. A password can be associated with each quiz, thereby controlling access, starting from the time the instructor makes that password available and ending when the instructor removes access to the quiz. Neither of these features allows for total confidence, however. Probably the most secure method of online testing can be found in schools with a testing center, i.e., a computer facility with a proctor. Such a facility gives students great flexibility of when to take their quiz while also ensuring a high level of security. Some distance learning formats allow students to visit a testing center at a local institution, or with a previously established proctor. Some day, I can imagine secure online testing being achieved through the use of Web cameras that will allow students to take a quiz at home under the scrutiny of an electronic eye that keeps them honest.

Another way to avoid the issue of test security is to design assessments that preclude cheating. For example, I have moved to a format of weekly online quizzes. I prepare a set of 30–50 questions using the electronic Test Bank and import them to my class website (part of the Blackboard course management system). When students take the quiz, they are assigned ten questions at random from the larger pool. This ensures that every student takes the quiz independently, since each student receives a different set of questions. I allow students access to all available study materials during the quizzes. At the end of the quiz, students receive their score only, no indication of which questions were answered correctly/incorrectly, and no hints or correct answers. Students may then repeat the quiz as many times as they like, but they will receive a different set of ten questions each time. Only the grade of the final attempt is recorded, so students may repeat the quiz as often as they like until they achieve their desired score. Besides mitigating questions of test security, this method provides some interesting insights into students' goals (e.g., which students are happy to stop at a 70, and which will take the quiz eight times to raise a 90 to a 100?).

Timeliness

No subject in the curriculum is more affected by recent advances than biology. We live in a time when biology seems to be in the news every day. Recent advances in cloning, genetically engineered foods, stem cells, genomes, fertility, and DNA technologies easily capture student attention. In addition to being very interesting, students see the relevance of these topics to their lives. Students, particularly introductory students, always appreciate when connections are made between the subject matter at hand and current events or popular culture. Biology instructors are uniquely positioned to take advantage of our current biology-centric society to improve the climate of learning in their classrooms.

Several technology resources available with *Biology: Concepts & Connections,* Fifth Edition, allow for the introduction of timely material. The *Biology: Concepts & Connections* website contains several timely content areas, and nearly identical materials are also built into the pre-loaded online course for *Biology: Concepts & Connections,* Fifth Edition, in the three course management systems. Even better, the timely materials available on each of these resources (the website and course management system offerings) are pre-sorted by the relevant *Biology: Concepts & Connections* textbook chapter, making it easy for the instructor to incorporate current events into classroom activities.

The website that comes with the printed text and the course management websites contain three sets of particularly timely materials: News Links that cover recent advances, Web links that point to timely Internet resources, and the Research Navigator, which offers unlimited access to scientific journals and websites. There is at least one relevant News Link associated with every chapter. On average, each chapter has about ten Web Links, with descriptions of the sites. In the course management systems, instructors can also add their own News Links and Web Links.

An advantage of using the online resources for recent news is that it avoids any copyright conflict. Most instructors know that photocopying articles and handing them out in class raises issues of copyright violation. Reprinting an article electronically on a course website raises identical issues. The Internet offers a way to avoid this potential problem through News Links and Web Links. A local link to a remote article that has been publicly posted by the producer poses no risk of copyright violation. Instructors can thus provide access to online versions of recent news articles without the possibility of recrimination.

Communication

Effective communication is important in every classroom. There are several avenues of communication that must be maintained: between professor and student, student and student, and student and teaching assistant. Many introductory biology courses have large enrollments, thus making effective communication simultaneously more important and more difficult.

Computer resources have the potential to vastly improve communication among all participants. Many instructors have found that the nature of the electronic medium encourages some students to speak up who otherwise might not. Students who may be intimidated to participate during lecture are often more comfortable participating via email and online discussions wherein they can compose and edit their comments before submitting them. The asynchronous nature of these forms of electronic communication (email and bulletin boards) provides greater access for all students but is particularly helpful for part-time or nontraditional students who are not on campus as often as their traditional peers. Multiple forms of electronic communication can also be used to create a sense of community and overcome the somewhat impersonal nature of the electronic medium. Creating a learning community is particularly helpful when teaching distance learning courses that lack the close in-person contact of the classroom environment. Students and instructors also benefit from the more global nature of electronic communication. Outside experts, colleagues, and other students can join in the forum, providing resources that are generally not available in a traditional classroom setting.

Within the course management systems, there are seven major communication vehicles: announcements, email, bulletin boards, live chat, home pages, digital drop box, and online gradebook. All of these resources will be discussed below.

Announcements

The most immediate way to communicate with students is through the Announcements feature. All students see announcements from their instructor as soon as they log into the course website. Announcements can include text, images, and links. I usually post at least one announcement per week. A typical announcement will remind students about upcoming assignments, lab activities, study sessions, or quizzes/exams. They can also be more whimsical, such as mentioning important dates in the history of science as they occur, or displaying digital photos taken during recent class activities. It is important to check your particular course management system to find out if announcements disappear from the front page after a certain amount of time and are then only visible if the student clicks on a tab to show older messages. I have found it useful to include a permanent announcement reminding students to look for older announcements.

Email

Email is the most widely used form of electronic communication. It is effective because it is asynchronous, thereby allowing students to read your comments whenever they have time (often, it seems, late at night). Email also allows students and instructors to archive conversations and exchange documents. Personally, I prefer to receive electronic files from my students via email because it is easier to detect and avoid viruses; floppy disks from college students are notoriously prone to invisible viruses. Email makes for a good first technology assignment because most students are very comfortable with it. During the first week of the semester, have every student email you with a simple hello message, or perhaps answers to a questionnaire that you have sent them. The successful completion of this simple assignment ensures that every student has access to a working computer and an email account, and that every student knows how to contact the instructor via email. The instructor can then check the email addresses received against the email database maintained by the course management software to make sure they match. This step is important because some students maintain multiple accounts, and the course management software may use their school account or an internal email address as default. Within the course management system, it is easy to send email to an individual, the entire class, or any subset thereof. This feature is available to all users so that students can easily email each other. Informing students that they should expect regular email from you will ensure effective communication in most cases.

Bulletin Boards

While email simulates a private office meeting, bulletin boards offer a reasonable simulation of classroom question-and-answer sessions. The bulletin board allows everyone in the class to "hear" the question and answer. I typically expect every student to participate verbally at least once during each in-class lecture. Similarly, I expect every student to participate at least once a week in the class bulletin board, either by posting a question/comment or by responding to a classmate's question/comment. Some instructors require students to post a number of questions and a number of answers in a given time period. In a typical bulletin board assignment, I will bring up an important biological issue (such as the use of DNA forensic evidence to examine old criminal cases or the ethics of reproductive technologies) and assign half the class to each side of that issue. I am often impressed with the enthusiasm and sophistication with which students participate in these discussions. The course management systems include a good threaded discussion system in their bulletin boards. Students can start new discussion topics and can include Internet links in their postings. The instructor can create new threads and has the option of allowing students to create them. I usually create a new thread for each week, so that the topmost level of the bulletin board has a link to each week and subject (such as "Week #3: The cell"). Within each week, I then create some standard subthreads that appear every week: questions/comments, homework assignments, and extra credit. Students are also free to create their own additional subthreads to raise issues of importance to them. The instructor can monitor the discussion and remove repeated, blank, erroneous, or inappropriate postings. I try to read the bulletin board every day during the school week so that I can answer questions, correct misconceptions, and keep the discussion focused on the subject. I find the bulletin board is used most heavily during the weeks before exams. This electronic forum can stimulate interesting questions, debates, and discussions among the students. The class bulletin board is particularly important when teaching distance learning courses because it can go a long way toward supplying interaction among the participants that might otherwise be absent. It also provides a good forum for working on group projects where progress can be monitored in real time.

Live Chat

In-class study sessions can be supplemented or replaced by a virtual discussion held in an online chat room. Such virtual chats have the additional benefit of being logged and archived for students who could not participate. The course management software includes an easy-to-use but sophisticated virtual chat room. The instructor can monitor who is present and everyone can read everyone else's comments. I have found that students often need to "warm up" and to be encouraged to participate, so I always have several practice questions prepared, just as I would for an in-person study session. The virtual chat forum is particularly handy before an exam and can also be used to facilitate virtual office hours. I always schedule two virtual chats during the week before an exam to accommodate a wide range of schedules. Classes comprised largely of traditional on-campus students probably fare better with live meetings. In classes with significant numbers of nontraditional, part-time, or off-campus students, however, the virtual meetings are often much more convenient for the students and may significantly increase participation levels.

Home Pages

Home pages offer a good way for members of the class to get to know each other. The course management systems provide an easy-to-use tool that guides even the most novice users to create a home page in a few minutes. For the more sophisticated, home pages can include images, links, or any other HTML code. Having every student create their own home page with answers to standard questions ("What is your major?" "What are your hobbies and interests?") is a good early technology assignment. Students always appreciate a detailed home page from the instructor and teaching assistants. I have found that students truly enjoy the chance to get to know me better, both personally and professionally, through my home page. I tend to add many personal details, such as photos of my children and pets, links to my favorite websites. etc.

Digital Drop Box

Much communication within a class, particularly a large class, centers on the receipt and acknowledgement of assignments. The course management systems offer a "Digital Drop Box" feature that allows students to submit assignments electronically. The students submit their assignments as electronic files into the drop box and receive a receipt. The instructor can remove assignments at any time, from any location with Internet access. This method is much more convenient for both parties than having a fixed location for students to turn in their assignments. Materials placed in the drop box have an attached link that allows an instructor to send an email to the student with one click. I usually send a quick email note to let the student know that his or her materials have been successfully received.

Online Gradebook

While an online gradebook may not seem like a form of communication, it is, and it can have a great impact. The course management systems offer an online gradebook with many organizational features. Only the instructor can view the entire set of results and modify them, but each student can see his or her own grades. Instructors can add, edit, or remove gradebook entries at will. Online grade posting allows for rapid communication of grades, and students can track their progress during the course. By viewing the gradebook as a spreadsheet, exporting the grade database to an external tool, or using various analysis tools included in the course management software, instructors can view trends, compare students, and search for weaknesses and strengths within the class.

Customization of the Curriculum

There is probably no introductory biology course that teaches the entire curriculum covered in *Biology: Concepts & Connections,* Fifth Edition. Printed textbooks are, by necessity, designed to carry the superset of possible materials covered in any individual course. Different courses will cover only a subset of these materials based on the interests of the students, the instructor, and the program. One advantage of technology is that it can help focus the curriculum from the full range of possible subject matter to just the subset covered in any particular course.

Students appreciate it when their study materials are concise and focused. The recent popularity of custom printed texts that incorporate just a portion of the possible materials confirms this need. Some instructors prepare their own self-written materials in order to make them more focused, but this approach requires a large start-up cost and will usually not reach the quality of professionally prepared learning aids.

Course management software provides an opportunity to have the best of both worlds: to pick and choose appropriate high-quality pre-written materials for your course from a large set prepared by the publisher. The ability to customize curricular materials lies within the course management systems. When instructors copy the *Biology: Concepts & Connections* CourseCompass™ course, building upon it to create their own course website, or when they download the *Biology: Concepts & Connections* Blackboard or WebCT courses, they will find courses pre-loaded with the content of the *Biology: Concepts & Connections* website, such as Internet links, quizzes, and interactive activities, as well as the entire computerized test bank. An optional e-book is available.

Instructors have the ability to customize these pre-loaded materials in several ways. First, any unwanted materials (e.g., those that cover chapters not included in the course) can be deleted from the course website. Students will thus be assured that all of the material on the course website is directly applicable to their particular course, as opposed to the CD-ROM or *Biology: Concepts & Connections* website which contain the full set of materials. The instructor can also modify some of the default material; for example, the instructor can change quiz questions or answers. Finally, instructors always have the ability to create new materials to upload to the site, either from scratch or by using external utilities such as Word or the TestGen software to prepare new quizzes. Instructors can thus simply and effectively customize the instructional materials available to students in ways that are impossible with the standard printed medium.

Conclusions

As technology plays an increasingly larger role in the modern biology classroom, two general types of features are emerging. The first are those that simply increase convenience for the student and/or the instructor. Examples include being able to access learning materials from multiple locations, the online gradebook, and the ability to customize a set of learning materials for a particular course. The second category of technology features includes those technologies that actually increase the potential for teaching and learning. Examples include the ability to provide access to very timely materials (i.e., News Links), multimedia explanations of important concepts, and access to outside resources via the Internet.

The instructional technologies included with *Biology: Concepts & Connections*, Fifth Edition, address both categories described above. Through proper implementation of the CD-ROM, the *Biology: Concepts & Connections* website, and Media Manager, and/or the course management systems, a lively and informative learning atmosphere can be created that benefits all students and the instructor.

Name _____ Course _____ Section _____

1. How comfortable are you with each of the following? (circle one)

    1 = not at all comfortable → 5 = extremely comfortable

A. Computers in general	1	2	3	4	5
B. Email	1	2	3	4	5
C. Word processing	1	2	3	4	5
D. Bulletin boards	1	2	3	4	5
E. CD-ROMs	1	2	3	4	5
F. Internet searches	1	2	3	4	5
G. Presentation software (e.g., PowerPoint)	1	2	3	4	5
H. Chat rooms	1	2	3	4	5

2. How comfortable are you using computers as an educational tool?

    1   2   3   4   5

3. How would you rate your computer literacy compared to your peers? (circle one)

    way below average   below average   average   above average   way above average

4. Are there any computer technologies that give you particular difficulties?

5. Do you think you need training in the use of any of the computer technologies listed above? If so, which ones?

Figure 1 A sample questionnaire that can be distributed at the start of a course to determine the level of computer literacy among students. The results can be used to guide the pace of technology usage, determine necessary levels of training and supervision, and guide in the creation of teams of students.

Course _____ Section _____

1. Please rate your overall level of satisfaction with the instructional technologies used in this course.

       1 = not at all satisfied → 5 = extremely satisfied

       (circle one)   1   2   3   4   5

2. Please rate your level of satisfaction with each of the following specific technologies used in this course:

A. Email	1	2	3	4	5
B. Word processing	1	2	3	4	5
C. Bulletin boards	1	2	3	4	5
D. CD-ROMs	1	2	3	4	5
E. Internet	1	2	3	4	5
F. Presentation software (e.g., PowerPoint)	1	2	3	4	5
G. Chat rooms	1	2	3	4	5

3. What were the advantages of using technology in this course?

4. What were the disadvantages of using technology in this course?

5. Which technologies would you like to see emphasized more in this course? Less?

6. Please make specific suggestions for how technology usage in this course can be improved.

7. Did you feel unprepared for any of the technologies used?

Figure 2 A sample questionnaire that can be distributed at the end of a semester or course to determine the level of satisfaction with instructional technologies.

Activities and Thinking as a Scientist Investigations on the Student CD-ROM and Website for *Biology: Concepts & Connections,* Fifth Edition

Module	Web/CD Activities
1.1	1A The Levels of Life Card Game
1.5	1B Classification Schemes
2.1	2A The Levels of Life Card Game
2.4	2B Structure of the Atomic Nucleus
2.6	2C Electron Arrangement
2.6	2D Build an Atom
2.7	2E Ionic Bonds
2.8	2F Covalent Bonds
2.9	2G Nonpolar and Polar Molecules
2.10	2H Water's Polarity and Hydrogen Bonding
2.11	2I Cohesion of Water
2.15	2J Acids, Bases, and pH
3.1	3A Diversity of Carbon-Based Molecules
3.2	3B Functional Groups
3.3	3C Making and Breaking Polymers
3.4	3D Models of Glucose
3.7	3E Carbohydrates
3.9	3F Lipids
3.11	3G Protein Functions
3.14	3H Protein Structure
3.16	3I Nucleic Acid Structure
4.1	4A Metric System Review
4.3	4B Prokaryotic Cell Structure and Function
4.4	4C Comparing Prokaryotic and Eukaryotic Cells
4.4	4D Build an Animal Cell and a Plant Cell
4.8	4E Overview of Protein Synthesis
4.13	4F The Endomembrane System
4.15	4G Build a Chloroplast and a Mitochondrion
4.17	4H Cilia and Flagella
4.18	4I Cell Junctions
4.19	4J Review: Animal Cell Structure and Function
4.19	4K Review: Plant Cell Structure and Function
5.2	5A Energy Transformations
5.3	5B Chemical Reactions and ATP
5.4	5C The Structure of ATP
5.6	5D How Enzymes Work
5.12	5E Membrane Structure
5.13	5F Signal Transduction
5.13	5G Selective Permeability of Membranes
5.14	5H Diffusion
5.15	5I Facilitated Diffusion
5.17	5J Osmosis and Water Balance in Cells
5.18	5K Active Transport

13.1	13A Darwin and the Galápagos Islands
13.1	13B The Voyage of the Beagle: Darwin's Trip Around the World
13.4	13C Reconstructing Forelimbs
13.9	13D Causes of Microevolution
13.12	13E Genetic Variation from Sexual Recombination
14.7	14A Polyploid Plants
14.8	14B Exploring Speciation on Islands
14.11	14C Mechanisms of Macroevolution
14.12	14D Paedomorphosis: Morphing Chimps and Humans
15.1	15A A Scrolling Geologic Record
15.5	15B Mechanisms of Macroevolution
15.10	15C Classification Schemes
16.1	16A The History of Life
16.10	16B Prokaryotic Cell Structure and Function
16.13	16C Diversity of Prokaryotes
17.1	17A Terrestrial Adaptations of Plants
17.3	17B Highlights of Plant Phylogeny
17.5	17C Moss Life Cycle
17.6	17D Fern Life Cycle
17.8	17E Pine Life Cycle
17.10	17F Angiosperm Life Cycle
17.14	17G Connection: Madagascar and the Biodiversity Crisis
17.16	17H Fungal Reproduction and Nutrition
17.17	17I Fungal Life Cycles
18.13	18A Characteristics of Invertebrates
18.21	18B Characteristics of Chordates
18.22	18C Animal Phylogenetic Tree
19.2	19A Primate Diversity
19.6	19B Human Evolution
20.1	20A Correlating Structure and Function of Cells
20.2	20B The Levels of Life Card Game
20.3	20C Overview of Animal Tissues
20.4	20D Epithelial Tissue
20.5	20E Connective Tissue
20.6	20F Muscle Tissue
20.7	20G Nervous Tissue
20.14	20H Regulation: Negative and Positive Feedback
21.11	21A Digestive System Function
22.5	22A The Human Respiratory System
22.10	22B Transport of Respiratory Gases
23.4	23A Mammalian Cardiovascular System Structure
23.4	23B Path of Blood Flow in Mammals
23.7	23C Mammalian Cardiovascular System Function
24.13	24A Immune Responses
24.17	24B HIV Reproductive Cycle
25.8	25A Structure of the Human Excretory System
25.10	25B Nephron Function
25.10	25C Control of Water Reabsorption

Module	Web/CD Thinking as a Scientist Investigations
1.6	How Do Environmental Changes Affect a Population?
1.8	The Process of Science: How Does Acid Precipitation Affect Trees?
2.1	Connection: How Are Space Rocks Analyzed for Signs of Life?
2.16	Connection: How Does Acid Precipitation Affect Trees?
3.16	Connection: What Factors Determine the Effectiveness of Drugs?
4.2	Connection: What Is the Size and Scale of Our World?
4.19	Connection: How Are Space Rocks Analyzed for Signs of Life?
5.7	How Is the Rate of Enzyme Catalysis Measured?
5.13	How Do Cells Communicate with Each Other?
5.17	How Does Osmosis Affect Cells?
6.12	How Is the Rate of Cellular Respiration Measured?
7.6	How Does Paper Chromatography Separate Plant Pigments?
7.11	How Is the Rate of Photosynthesis Measured?
8.6	How Much Time Do Cells Spend in Each Phase of Mitosis?
8.18	How Is Crossing Over Measured in the Fungus *Sordaria*?
9.23	How Is the Chi-Square Test Used in Genetic Analysis?
10.4	What Is the Correct Model for DNA Replication?
10.6	How Are Nutritional Mutations Identified?
10.16	Connection: How Do You Diagnose a Genetic Disorder?
10.20	Connection: Why Do AIDS Rates Differ Across the U.S.?
10.21	Connection: What Causes Infections in AIDS Patients?
11.6	How Do You Design a Gene Expression System?
11.13	How Can the "Head" Gene Be Regulated to Alter Development?
12.3	How Can Antibiotic-Resistant Plasmids Transform *E. coli*?
12.10	How Can Gel Electrophoresis Be Used to Analyze DNA?
13.2	How Do Environmental Changes Affect a Population?
13.7	How Can Frequency of Alleles Be Calculated?
13.13	Connection: What Are the Patterns of Antibiotic Resistance?
14.6	How Do New Species Arise by Genetic Isolation?
15.9	How Is Phylogeny Determined Using Protein Comparisons?
16.3	How Might Conditions on Early Earth Have Created Life?
16.11	What Are the Modes of Nutrition in Prokaryotes?
16.24	What Kinds of Protists Are Found in Various Habitats?
17.6	What Are the Different Stages of a Fern Life Cycle?
17.14	How Are Trees Identified by Their Leaves?
17.17	How Does the Fungus *Pilobolus* Succeed as a Decomposer?
18.12	How Are Insect Species Identified?
18.20	How Does Bone Structure Shed Light on the Origin of Birds?
18.22	How Do Molecular Data Fit Traditional Phylogenies?
21.11	What Role Does Amylase Play in Digestion?
23.10	Connection: How Is Cardiovascular Fitness Measured?
24.12	Connection: What Causes Infections in AIDS Patients?
24.12	Connection: Why Do AIDS Rates Differ Across the U.S.?
25.2	How Does Temperature Affect Metabolic Rate in *Daphnia*?
25.10	What Affects Urine Production?
26.5	How Do Thyroxine and TSH Affect Metabolism?
27.3	Connection: What Might Obstruct the Male Urethra?
27.14	What Determines Cell Differentiation in the Sea Urchin?
28.4	What Triggers Nerve Impulses?
30.10	How Do Electrical Stimuli Affect Muscle Contraction?

CHAPTER 1

Biology: Exploring Life

Teaching Objectives

Introduction   Describe the feeding habits of pelicans. Explain how recent human activity has impacted pelican populations.

The Scope of Biology

1.1   Define the levels of biological organization from molecules to the biosphere, noting the relationship each level has to the others.

1.2   Explain how the web of relationships gives an ecosystem its structure.

1.2   Compare the flow of chemical nutrients and the flow of energy in an ecosystem.

1.3   Explain how cells are the structural and functional units of life. Compare prokaryotic and eukaryotic cells.

1.3   Define emergent properties.

Evolution, Unity, and Diversity

1.4   Explain how DNA encodes a cell's information.

1.4   Describe seven properties that are common to all life.

1.5   Compare the three domains of life. Distinguish between the three multicellular kingdoms within Eukarya.

1.5   Explain why the old five-kingdom system of classification has been revised. Describe the unresolved problems of this new classification.

1.6   Describe the process and products of natural selection. Explain why individuals cannot evolve.

The Process of Science

1.7   Describe the goals and limits of scientific investigations. Compare discovery science and hypothesis-based science.

1.7   Define a hypothesis, and compare inductive and deductive reasoning.

1.8   Explain how deductive reasoning is part of hypothesis-based science.

1.8   Define a control, and describe an example.

Biology and Everyday Life

1.9   Compare the goals of science and technology. Explain why an understanding of biology is essential to all of our lives.

Key Terms

adaptation	biology	consumers
Archaea	biosphere	controlled experiment
atom	cell	decomposers
Bacteria	community	domains

ecosystem	natural selection	prokaryotic cell
emergent properties	organ system	species
Eukarya	organelle	system
eukaryotes	organism	taxonomy
eukaryotic cell	organs	technology
hypothesis	population	theories
kingdoms	producers	tissues
molecule	prokaryotes	

Lecture Outline

Introduction *A Big-Billed Bird Rebounds*

A. Self-introduction.

B. Administrative details.

C. Introduction to class content and course organization.

D. Introductory comments about the science of biology.

E. Core themes in biology.

1. How do biologists organize their subject matter?

Biology is a broad collection of subdisciplines such as evolution, ecology, zoology, cell biology, and genetics.

2. Can we uncover some common concepts that underlie all biological study?

Evolution is the unifying theory of biology. All living organisms are composed of cells, which are the basic units of life. All life forms are related and use DNA and RNA. The genetic code is virtually universal. Biological study unifies the concepts of structure and function.

NOTE: As a preface to your review of the themes and characteristics of life, ask your students what they hope to get from the course, and discuss how the material to be covered in the course is relevant to their lives.

F. To begin, we start our study of biology by focusing on the relationship between the brown pelican, the fish they eat, and the humans with whom the brown pelican must compete for space and resources.

I. The Scope of Biology

Module 1.1 Life's levels of organization define the scope of biology.

A. The levels at which life is organized are (from most to least inclusive): **biosphere, ecosystem, community, population, organism, organ system, organs, tissues, cell, organelles, and molecules** (Figure 1.1).

NOTE: Ask your students for examples, other than those in Figure 1.1, of each level of organization. Distinguish between unicellular and multicellular organisms.

B. These levels represent a hierarchy because each level is built of parts at successively lower levels of organization.

C. Biological researchers investigate the full spectrum of life, from the biosphere to the biochemical reactions within a cell.

Preview: The dynamics of higher levels of organization are discussed in Chapters 36 (populations) and 37 (communities and ecosystems).

Module 1.2 Living organisms and their environments form interconnecting webs.

    A. Living things do not exist in isolation from their environment. An organism's environment includes both living and nonliving components.

    B. Plants, as well as certain prokaryotes and protists, use carbon dioxide, water, minerals, and the energy of sunlight to make food for themselves by the process of photosynthesis. Organisms that can make their own food are called **producers.**
    Preview: The process of photosynthesis is discussed in detail in Chapter 7.

    C. All animals are ultimately dependent upon plants for food and are called **consumers.** Animals use oxygen and give off carbon dioxide. Animals return minerals to the environment when they defecate or die.

    D. **Decomposers,** such as prokaryotes, fungi, and small animals, are important for the recycling of complex organic matter and changing it into simple mineral nutrients that plants can use.
    Preview: Nutrient cycles can be divided into separate chemical or molecular cycles. Nutrient cycles are discussed in Chapter 37 and Modules 37.15 through 37.19 and are important for understanding ecosystems.

    E. Two major processes are at work in an ecosystem and are illustrated in Figure 1.2:

        1. The recycling of chemical nutrient in an ecosystem.

        2. The flow of energy through the ecosystem.

    F. Chemicals or molecules that are recycled in an ecosystem include carbon dioxide, oxygen, water, and various other minerals. Energy is not recycled but passes through an ecosystem. It enters as sunlight and leaves as heat.

Module 1.3 Cells are the structural and functional units of life.

    A. Cells are the basic unit of life that can perform all functions necessary for life. A cell can:

        1. Regulate its internal environment.

        2. Take in and use energy.

        3. Respond to its local environment.

        4. Develop and maintain its complex organization.

        5. Divide to form new cells.

    B. An important theme of biology is the **emergent property** that states life is dependent on the organizational levels of a cell. More aptly put, "the whole is greater than the sum of its parts." The combination of the parts that form a more complex organization, regardless if it is a cell or a community, is called a **system.** The challenge to biologists is to understand the systems of biology.

    C. All organisms are composed of cells. There are two basic types of cells: **prokaryotes** and **eukaryotes** (Figure 1.3). Prokaryotes are smaller and less complex than eukaryotes, and we commonly call them bacteria. Eukaryotes are generally larger and more complex than prokaryotes. The complexity arises from the use of organelles to compartmentalize functions within eukaryotic cells.

    D. Irrespective of the differences between prokaryotes and eukaryotes, they do have common characteristics. For example, all cells use DNA as the genetic material.
    Preview: An introduction to the cell and the differences between prokaryotic and eukaryotic cells is presented in Chapter 4.

II. Evolution, Unity, and Diversity

Module 1.4 The unity of life: All forms of life have common features.

A. Life is diverse, but there are common themes that all living things exhibit.
Preview: When viewed under a microscope, all cells look very similar (Chapter 4).

B. Genetic information within all cells is DNA (Figure 1.4A). Variations within the sequence of DNA determine the diversity we see among organisms. However, because all organisms use DNA, a gene from one species can be inserted into a different species, and the gene will still be functional. The insertion of the human gene for insulin into a bacterial cell is a perfect example.
Preview: DNA is composed of nucleotides that contain the genetic information of all cells (Chapter 3; Module 3.16).

C. Other common properties of organisms are presented below.
1. *Order:* All living things have complex organization (Figure 1.4B).
2. *Regulation:* Organisms regulate their internal environment (Figure 1.4C).
3. *Growth and development:* Genes control the pattern of growth and development.
4. *Energy use:* Energy is taken in and transformed to a stable, useable from.
5. *Response to the environment:* All organisms respond to their environment (Figure 1.4D).
6. *Reproduction:* Organisms reproduce their own kind (Figure 1.4E).
7. *Evolution:* Reproduction fosters change over time.

D. You might want to focus on one group of organisms to emphasize the point that at each level of biological organization, there is similarity and diversity. For example, have the students describe the characteristics of a bird, and then ask them to name as many birds as they can.

Module 1.5 The diversity of life can be arranged into three domains.

A. Biologists look at life both vertically, as in Figure 1.1, and horizontally. There is a stunning array of different **species** that inhabit or once inhabited the Earth. *Species* is the term used for one type of organism (e.g., *Homo sapiens* or *Pelecanus occidentalis*).

B. Making sense of the diverse life forms in the world, or even in a complex environment such as a tropical rain forest, can be overwhelming. To organize and simplify the process, we need a system for categorizing these living things. The process of placing organisms into groups and giving them names is called **taxonomy.**

C. A classification system used up until the past decade placed all organisms into five **kingdoms.** This taxonomic scheme has been replaced with the **domain** system of classification, which enables biologists to group organisms using classical and molecular taxonomy (structure and function, and DNA and RNA sequence analysis).

D. The three domains can be divided into two groups: cells without a nucleus (prokaryotes) and cells with a nucleus (eukaryotes). Taxonomists are still debating the number of kingdoms within the three domains.
Preview: The differences between prokaryotes and eukaryotes are discussed in greater detail in Chapter 4.

E. **Domain Bacteria** includes unicellular prokaryotes that lack a nucleus (Figure 1.5A).

F. **Domain Archaea** includes unicellular prokaryotes (Figure 1.5B). As will be discussed in Chapter 16, this domain has characteristics of both Eukarya and Bacteria.
Preview: Differences between the Bacteria and Archaea are highlighted in Module 16.8.

G. **Domain Eukarya** includes unicellular and multicellular eukaryotes. A group of organisms called protists are shown in Figure 1.5C. This group is extremely diverse and will be divided into several kingdoms (some day). This group includes algae and protozoa.

H. The other three kingdoms included in the domain Eukarya are kingdom Plantae (multicellular photosynthetic autotrophs with ridged cell walls made of cellulose; Figure 1.5C), kingdom Fungi (mostly decomposers: molds, yeast, and mushrooms; Figure 1.5C), and kingdom Animalia (multicellular heterotrophs, cells without a cell wall; Figure 1.5C). *Preview:* The three-domain system is discussed further in Module 15.10.

Module 1.6 Evolution explains the unity and diversity of life.

Preview: This module previews Unit III, especially Chapter 13.

A. Darwin's book on evolution presented two important concepts.

1. Species evolved from ancestors, and there was modification in the process or, as Darwin stated, "descent with modification."

2. **Natural selection** occurs as heritable variations are exposed to environmental factors that favor the reproductive success of some individuals over others.

B. The synthesis of the idea for natural selection was inferred by Darwin from two observable features of life.

1. **Individual variation:** individuals in a population have variable inheritable traits.

2. **Unequal reproductive success:** a population of a species will overproduce offspring, and not all will survive and reproduce due to competition.

C. From these two observations, Darwin proposed the idea of **"Unequal reproductive success."** Those individuals with the most suitable traits for the current environmental conditions will survive and reproduce, passing on those traits to their offspring.

D. The product of natural selection is **adaptation,** the collection of favorable modifications in a population over time.

E. A simplified example of natural selection is presented in Figure 1.6B. Light gray beetles are favored by birds and are eaten, removing them from the beetle population before they can reproduce, which leaves the dark beetles to pass their traits on to future generations.

F. Evolution explains why organisms are adapted to their environments. A pangolin and killer whale are good examples of animals with many visible adaptations to a particular environment (Figure 1.6C).

III. The Process of Science

Module 1.7 Scientists use two main approaches to learn about nature.

A. Science is a way of knowing. The word science is derived from the Latin word for "to know." There are no absolute truths in science, and all that we understand about nature comes from our ability to observe the world around us. Scientists do not "believe" in something. Instead scientists have levels of confidence in explanations for natural phenomena.

B. Two approaches are commonly used by scientists to understand nature.

1. **Discovery science** is the process of gathering data by verifiable observations and measurements to explain natural phenomena. Pelicans diving into water to capture their prey or the sequence of human DNA are mere observations. From many careful observations, a process of inductive reasoning can lead to important conclusions such as the cell is the basic unit of life.

2. **Hypothesis-driven science** is conclusions drawn from the observations taken during "discovery science," which lead the inquisitive scientist to ask more questions. Why do pelicans dive so fiercely into the water when seeking fish, or what is the function of the DNA sequence?

C. What is a **hypothesis?** A hypothesis is a tentative or educated guess at an answer to a problem or question that is being asked. A good hypothesis makes predictions that can be tested. Part of the process of hypothesis-based science uses deductive reasoning, which flows from a general premise to a specific premise. The important aspect of this process is that the deduction can be tested.

Module 1.8 With hypothesis-based science, we pose and test hypotheses.

A. The five steps of the scientific method are listed below with a brief explanation of each step.

1. Observations come from others or results of earlier tests.

2. Questions are asked about unclear aspects of the observations: How? Why? When?

3. Hypotheses are tentative explanations of a phenomenon phrased in such a way as to be testable.

4. Predictions are logical, testable outcomes of the hypotheses developed by the use of deductive reasoning. Predictions take the form of if (statement of hypothesis) is true, then (predictions).

5. Tests of prediction are performed to determine if the predictions are supported (fail to falsify) or falsified.

   Preview: In addition to Module 1.8, other good examples of the application of the process of science to a problem can be found in, but are not limited to, Modules 36.7 (evolution shapes life histories), 37.20 (studies at Hubbard Brook), and Chapter 35 (Lorenz's and Tinbergen's studies on animal behavior).

B. Case studies illustrate the scientific process.

1. *A Case Study from Everyday Life:* The flashlight is a common household item that can be used to clearly demonstrate the scientific process. "How do you figure out how to fix it?" (Figure 1.8A).

2. *A Case Study of Hypothesis-Based Science:* The biological case study of the coral snake (Figure 1.8B) versus the king snake (Figure 1.8C) demonstrates the use of the scientific method. This experiment answers the question regarding the ring pattern of the king snake and the behavior of predators toward attacking coral snakes and king snakes (Figures 1.8D and E).

C. Two important qualities of the hypothesis-based science are illustrated in the flashlight example.

1. A hypothesis must be testable.

2. A hypothesis must be falsifiable.

   A hypothesis becomes credible when repeated attempts to disprove it fail.

IV. Biology and Everyday Life

Module 1.9 Connection: Biology is connected to our lives in many ways.

A. Biology in the news has an enormous impact on our everyday lives (Figure 1.9). Some examples of biology in the news are endangered species, genetically modified crops, global warming, water and air pollution, cloning of embryos, nutrition controversies, emerging diseases, and medical advances.

   Preview: These environmental concerns are discussed in more detail in Chapter 38.

B. **Technology** is the practical application of scientific knowledge and discovery. Scientists speak of discoveries, while engineers speak of inventions. Scientists and engineers benefit from the work and success of each other.

Class Activities

1. Illustrate how the process of science is applied in everyday life, even if only on a subconscious level. For example, ask the students what they do if, when they flip a light switch, the light does not go on, or what they do if their car will not start. Have them relate their activities to the process of science.

2. Divide the class into small groups. Have each group choose an organism and then decide which adaptations make it uniquely suitable for surviving in the habitat in which it is found. (For example, some dogs tend to bark quite a bit. Why? How is this an adaptation for surviving in the dog environment?) Have them explain how each of these adaptations is an anatomical/physiological solution to a particular environmental challenge. Because evolution is bound by historical constraints, for each of these adaptations, ask each group if they can think of a more efficient/elegant anatomical/physiological solution to the environmental challenge.

3. In small lecture or discussion sections, have students bring in current newspaper clippings on what they perceive to be a biological issue. (Virtually every newspaper every day will have something on medicine, ecology, biodiversity, pollution, nutrition, and countless other biological topics.) During lecture, have the class categorize each article according to its scientific validity. Have the students consider questions such as: the type of scientific approach that each article reports on—is it discovery science? hypothesis-driven science? Is the sample size of the study/studies mentioned? Is the sponsor of the science mentioned—e.g., did a company sponsor a study that concludes that its product does something wonderful? What could students do if they wanted to find out more about the topic? Where could they find scientifically valid information?

Transparency Acetates

Figure 1.1	Life's hierarchy of organization
Figure 1.2	The web of interactions in an ecosystem
Figure 1.3	Comparison of prokaryotic and eukaryotic cells
Figure 1.4A	One chain of a DNA molecule, its message written in the order of the four building blocks labeled A, T, C, and G
Figure 1.8A	The hypothesis-driven scientific method (Layer 1)
Figure 1.8A	The hypothesis-driven scientific method (Layer 2)
Figure 1.8A	The hypothesis-driven scientific method (Layer 3)
Figure 1.8E	Results of mimicry experiment

Reviewing the Concepts, page 13: DNA

Reviewing the Concepts, page 13: Evolution and natural selection

Connecting the Concepts, page 13: Some of biology's major concerns

Applying the Concepts, page 14: Graph of experiment results

Media

See the beginning of this book for a complete description of all media available for instructors and students. Animations and videos are available in the Campbell Image Presentation Library. Media Activities and Thinking as a Scientist investigations are available on the student CD-ROM and website.

Animations and Videos	Module Number
Sea Horse Video	1.6

Activities and Thinking as a Scientist	Module Number
Web/CD Activity 1A: *The Levels of Life Card Game*	1.1
Web/CD Activity 1B: *Classification Schemes*	1.5
Web/CD Thinking as a Scientist: *How Do Environmental Changes Affect a Population?*	1.6
Web/CD Thinking as a Scientist: *The Process of Science: How Does Acid Precipitation Affect Trees?*	1.8

CHAPTER 2

The Chemical Basis of Life

Teaching Objectives

Introduction Explain how the rattlebox moth uses and transfers defensive substances throughout its life cycle.

Elements, Atoms, and Molecules

2.1 Define matter, an element, and a trace element.
2.2 Explain how and why iron, iodine, and fluoride are added to the human diet.
2.3 Define a compound and explain how compounds in living organisms are different from compounds in nonbiological materials.
2.4 Describe the structure of an atom.
2.4 Define the atomic number and mass number of an atom.
2.4 Define an isotope and explain what makes some isotopes radioactive.
2.5 Explain why radioactive isotopes are important to biologists.
2.6 Explain how the electron configuration of an atom influences its chemical behavior.
2.7–2.10 Distinguish among nonpolar covalent bonds, polar covalent bonds, ionic bonds, and hydrogen bonds, noting their relative strengths and how and where they form.

Water's Life-Supporting Properties

2.11–2.14 Describe the special properties of water that make it vital to living systems. Explain how these properties are related to hydrogen bonding.
2.11 Define and distinguish between cohesion and surface tension.
2.12 Define and distinguish between heat and temperature.
2.14 Define a solute, a solvent, and a solution.
2.15 Explain how acids and bases directly or indirectly affect the hydrogen ion concentration of a solution.
2.15 Explain the basis for the pH scale.
2.15 Explain how buffers work.
2.16 Describe the causes of acid precipitation, and explain how it adversely affects the fitness of the environment.

Chemical Reactions

2.17 Define a chemical reaction, and distinguish between the reactants and products.

Key Terms

acid	base	covalent bond
acid precipitation	buffers	double bond
aqueous solution	chemical bond	electron
atom	chemical reaction	electron shell
atomic mass	cohesion	electronegativity
atomic number	compound	element

heat	nonpolar	salt
hydrogen bond	nucleus	solute
ion	pH scale	solution
ionic bond	polar covalent bond	solvent
isotopes	polar molecule	surface tension
mass number	product	temperature
matter	proton	trace element
molecule	radioactive isotope	
neutron	reactants	

Word Roots

co- = together; **-valent** = strength (*covalent bond:* an attraction between atoms that share one or more pairs of outer-shell electrons)

electro- = electricity (*electronegativity:* the tendency for an atom to pull electrons toward itself)

hydro- = water; **-philos** = loving; **-phobos** = fearing (*hydrophilic:* having an affinity for water; *hydrophobic:* having an aversion to water)

iso- = equal (*isotope:* an element having the same number of protons and electrons but a different number of neutrons)

neutr- = neither (*neutron:* a subatomic particle with a neutral electrical charge)

pro- = before (*proton:* a subatomic particle with a single positive electrical charge)

Lecture Outline

Introduction *Nature's Chemical Language*

    A. Chemicals play an important role in all organisms, whether controlling the function of the body, enticing a mate to reproduce, or scaring away a potential predator.

    B. Much has been learned about the role of these chemicals and how they control body function, behavior, ecosystems, and the process of evolution.

    C. This unit starts with atoms and goes up through the levels of the cell, explaining the basic chemical reactions of importance. The first chapter focuses on atoms and molecules of the cell.

I. Elements, Atoms, and Molecules

    Module 2.1 Living organisms are composed of about 25 chemical **elements.**

        A. Use of a holistic approach or reductionism requires understanding two basic principles: The preceding level builds upon each successive level of a hierarchy, and with each move upward new properties emerge that were not evident at the lower level.
        Review: This hierarchical organization is first discussed in Module 1.1.

        B. Elements are the basic chemical units that cannot be broken apart by typical chemical processes.

        C. There are 92 naturally occurring elements. Be sure to mention that "atom" is the name for an elemental unit.

D. Approximately 25 elements are required by living organisms. Four (oxygen, carbon, hydrogen, and nitrogen) are particularly abundant, making up 96.3% of the human body.

Module 2.2 Trace elements are common additives to food and water.

A. **Trace elements** are important for proper function, particularly as catalysts and enzyme cofactors.

B. An example given in the text refers to the importance of the element iodine. Discuss the amount needed each day (0.15 mg) compared to the recommended calcium intake each day (1,000 mg). Also discuss the disease related to iodine deficiencies.

Module 2.3 Elements can combine to form compounds.

A. **Compounds** contain two or more atoms in a fixed ratio.

B. Different combinations of atoms determine the unique properties of each compound. *NOTE:* At this point in your discussion, it might be useful to explain that our knowledge about chemistry is the result of several hundred years' worth of direct and indirect observations of the behavior of matter. Also explain that conventions used to show atoms and molecules convey various types of information. They don't show atoms and molecules the way they really are.

Module 2.4 Atoms consist of protons, neutrons, and electrons.

A. **Protons** and **neutrons** occupy the central region of an **atom** (the atomic **nucleus**), and **electrons** occupy the region surrounding this central area.

B. Neutrons have a mass of 1 and a charge of 0; protons have a mass of 1 and a charge of $+1$; electrons have an effective mass of 0 (1/2,000 of a proton) and a charge of -1.

C. Atoms of the same element always have the name number of protons. This **atomic number** defines each element's unique properties.
NOTE: Refer to a periodic table of the elements during your discussion for a wealth of interesting information on atomic structure.

D. The number of protons plus the number of neutrons determines each element's **atomic mass** or **mass number** (sometimes referred to as the atomic weight).

E. Atoms with the same atomic number but different atomic masses (different number of neutrons) are called **isotopes.**

F. If an isotope is unstable (radioactive), it changes to a stable form by releasing radioactive particles and energy.

Module 2.5 Connection: Radioactive isotopes can help or harm us.

A. Isotopes of the same element behave the same way chemically. Therefore, organisms are indiscriminate as to the isotopes they use.

B. **Radioactive isotopes** can function as "markers" or tracers for their nonradioactive counterparts. Researchers use radioactive markers to study the fate of elements and molecules in living systems (see Module 7.3 for an example).

C. Radioactive elements are also used in diagnostic medical procedures. The release of the radioactive decay is monitored by sophisticated instruments and assists in the diagnosis of diseases such as cancer and kidney failure. Radiation can also be used as a treatment. (Cancer patients receive radiation to kill the cancer cells, and hyperthyroid patients receive radioactive iodine to reduce the activity of the thyroid gland.)

D. Long-term exposure or exposure to high-energy radiation can cause diseases such as cancer. Organisms can develop cancer by exposure to radioactive material if the exposure is long term. For example, radon contamination in a house causes lung cancer. Radioactive exposure from the explosion of the nuclear reactor in Chernobyl, Ukraine, caused an increase in cancer as well as the death of 30 people in weeks.

Module 2.6 Electron arrangement determines the chemical properties of an atom.

A. The properties of elements emerge from the subatomic parts. The chemical reactivity of an atom depends on the number of electrons in the outer **electron shell** of the atom (Figure 2.6).

B. Atoms react to form molecules. Reactions involve sharing or transferring outer electrons.

C. *Preview:* Molecules play many roles in living organisms: energy storage and a means to transfer stored energy for doing work, structural components, control of activity, communication between cells and/or whole organisms, and a means of information storage and retrieval (Chapter 3).

D. There are two major **chemical bonds** used by elements to build compounds: covalent bonds and ionic bonds.
NOTE: In each of the following bond types, two rules are satisfied: (1) the resulting compound is electrically neutral, and (2) outer electron orbits are filled. The total energy available in a system determines which type will form and be maintained. H_2 is a covalent molecule, and NaCl is an ionic molecule.

Module 2.7 Ionic bonds are attractions between ions of opposite charge.

A. **Ions** are atoms that have lost or gained electrons from or to their outer shell. When an atom loses an electron, it becomes a positive ion (cation). When an atom gains an electron, it becomes a negative ion (anion).

B. Two or more ions can associate with one another to form a molecular bond due to the attraction of opposite charges that result from the transfer of electrons.

C. A good example is sodium chloride (Figure 2.7A, B). Sodium gives up one electron to chlorine, making the Na^+ a cation and the Cl^- an anion.

Module 2.8 Covalent bonds join atoms into molecules through electron sharing.

A. Each atom in a **molecule** composed of **covalent bonds** shares electrons in its outer shell with the other atom(s) in the molecule.

B. *Examples:* H_2, O_2, CH_4, and H_2O (Figure 2.8). Other larger examples: Figures 3.1, 3.2, and 3.4B.

Preview: The ability of carbon to form up to four covalent bonds and the impact this fact has on life are discussed in Module 3.1.

C. Hydrogen bonds are the third type and are discussed below.

Module 2.9 Unequal electron sharing creates polar molecules.

A. In nonpolar molecules (H_2, O_2, CH_4), covalent bonds are balanced because the electrons (and their negative charges) are equally shared by the atoms in the molecule.

B. In **polar molecules** (H_2O), the electrons around the atoms are not equally shared because the different atoms have different attractions for electrons. This results in one part of the molecule being slightly positive (usually where the hydrogen atoms are) and another part being slightly negative. The oxygen in water is slightly positive, and the two hydrogen atoms are slightly negative.

Module 2.10 Hydrogen bonds are weak bonds important in the chemistry of life.

A. The attraction of these slightly positive and negative charges between different molecules (or different parts of the same molecule in some cases) results in weak hydrogen bonds. Hydrogen from a water molecule binds weakly with the oxygen atom of another water molecule (Figure 2.10A).

B. **Hydrogen bonding** occurs in other biologically important compounds such as proteins and DNA. The saying "There is strength in numbers" applies to hydrogen bonds. Hydrogen bonds are weak, but they are numerous and hold molecules together.
Preview: For example, the secondary structure of a protein (α-helices and β-pleated sheets) is maintained by hydrogen bonds **(Module 3.14).**

II. Water's Life-Supporting Properties

Module 2.11 Hydrogen bonds make liquid water cohesive.

A. **Cohesion** is the tendency of water molecules to stick together.

B. Cohesion between water molecules allows them to form drops and be transported through the tissues of plants.

C. **Surface tension** results from the cohesion of water molecules to each other so that a small aquatic insect such as a water strider can walk across the top of a pond without sinking.
Preview: Transpiration (Module 32.3) is an example of how living systems take advantage of these characteristics of water.

Module 2.12 Water's hydrogen bonds moderate **temperature.**

A. Breaking hydrogen bonds requires a large amount of energy; therefore, as water is heated, it takes a large amount of energy to observe an increase in the temperature of the water. The temperature of water rises more slowly when heated than does the temperature of nonpolar liquids because water has so many hydrogen bonds.

B. The opposite is true of water as it cools; formation of hydrogen bonds causes the temperature of water to lower more slowly when cooled because heat is released as the hydrogen bonds are formed.

Module 2.13 Ice is less dense than liquid water (Figure 2.13).

A. Hydrogen bonds in ice result in an extremely stable, three-dimensional structure.

B. A given volume of ice has fewer water molecules than an equal volume of liquid water and is therefore less dense.

Module 2.14 Water is the solvent of life.

A. A **solution** is a homogeneous mixture of a liquid **solvent** and one or more **solutes** (solid or liquid compounds that dissolve in the solvent).

B. Because water is a polar molecule, it readily forms solutions with a wide variety of other polar compounds (for example, sugar) and with the charged ions of ionic compounds such as sodium chloride.

Module 2.15 The chemistry of life is sensitive to **acidic** and **basic** conditions (Figure 2.15).

    A. Another property of **aqueous solutions** important to living things is the pH (potential hydrogen) of the solution (a measure of acidity or basicity).

    B. pH expresses the tendency of water to ionize, dissociating into OH^- (hydroxide ions) and H^+ (hydrogen ions, actually, H_3O^+).

    C. Biological pH ranges from 1 (stomach acid, high concentration of H^+) to 9 (seawater, low concentration of H^+).

    D. A pH of 7 = neutral, $[H^+] = [OH^-]$; lower pH = acid, increased $[H^+]$; higher pH = basic, increased $[OH^-]$.

    E. Biological fluids contain **buffers,** substances that resist changes in pH by reacting with, and neutralizing, H^+ or OH^- ions.

Module 2.16 Connection: **Acid precipitation** threatens the environment.

    A. Compounds of sulfur and nitrogen are part of air pollutants released from the combustion of fossil fuels. These compounds react with atmospheric water to form acidic compounds (sulfuric and nitric acid).

    B. Low pH associated with acid rain can be harmful to organisms adapted to neutral pH.

    C. Acid rains definitely harm aquatic environments and likely cause various imbalances in terrestrial environments such as forests.
Preview: Module 36.18 discusses the impact of acid precipitation on a deciduous forest ecosystem (the Hubbard Brook studies).

    D. The capacity to withstand changes in pH (buffering) is naturally a characteristic of some areas (for example, limestone buffers acid rain).

    E. In recent decades, in the United States, Canada, and Europe, levels of acid precipitation have declined.

III. Chemical Reactions

Module 2.17 Chemical reactions change the composition of matter.

    A. Behavior of atoms and molecules is determined by the structure of the subatomic particles, particularly the electron configuration.

    B. The general form of a **chemical reaction** is:

        Reactants $\rightarrow$ Products.

    The **reactants** are the starting material, and the **products** are the result.
For example, $2\,H_2 + O_2 \rightarrow 2\,H_2O$. Notice that the number of atoms is the same on each side of the equation.

    C. Chemical reactions can be either catabolic or anabolic (as seen above in the synthesis of water). The example of a catabolic reaction is the splitting of β-carotene in two to make vitamin A.

Class Activities

1.   Emphasize the unique properties of water: its moderating influence on body temperature can be illustrated by comparing rather moderate coastal environments and their rather narrow temperature ranges with inland environments and their relatively wider temperature ranges. Ask what might have been the

impact on the evolution of life if ice were not less dense than water. What would happen to life currently in lakes if ice sank? Ask why things get wet (water is sticky because of its polar nature). Pour a beaker full of water until it nearly overflows the brim; ask why it does not overflow. Ask how, if hydrogen bonds are weak, can there be a column of water several hundred feet high, as in a Sequoia.

2. The activities of enzymes are sensitive to changes in pH. Have students consider the consequences of this as it relates to their own physiology. For example, salivary amylase works in the slightly acidic environment of the mouth but is denatured in the highly acidic environment of the stomach. Material that passes from the stomach to the small intestine must be neutralized so that enzymes found in the small intestine may function properly.

3. The text (Module 2.16) discusses the effects of acid precipitation on aquatic and forest ecosystems. Ask your students to consider how acid precipitation may affect other ecosystems. How might acid precipitation directly affect human health? Can/will/does acid precipitation have an effect on structures made of concrete? metal? plastic?

Transparency Acetates

Table 2.1	Chemical composition of the human body
Figure 2.4A	Helium atom
Figure 2.4B	Carbon atom (combined with Figure 2.4A)
Table 2.4	Isotopes of carbon
Figure 2.6	Atoms of four elements most common in living matter, all with incomplete outer electron shells
Figure 2.7A	Formation of an ionic bond, producing sodium chloride
Figure 2.7B	A crystal of sodium chloride
Table 2.8	Alternative ways to represent molecules
Figure 2.9	A water molecule
Figure 2.10A	Hydrogen bonds between water molecules
Figure 2.13	Water molecule arrangement in ice versus water
Figure 2.14	A crystal of salt (NaCl) dissolving in water
Figure 2.15	The pH scale
Figure 2.17A	Breaking and making of bonds in a chemical reaction
Figure 2.17B	Chemical reaction converting beta-carotene to vitamin A

Reviewing the Concepts, page 30: An atom

Connecting the Concepts, page 30: Elements, atoms, and molecules

Applying the Concepts, page 31: Fluorine and potassium atoms

Media

See the beginning of this book for a complete description of all media available for instructors and students. Animations and videos are available in the Campbell Image Presentation Library. Media Activities and Thinking as a Scientist investigations are available on the student CD-ROM and website.

Animations and Videos	Module Number
Ionic Bonds Animation	2.7
Covalent Bonds Animation	2.8
Water Structure Animation	2.11
Cohesion of Water Animation	2.11

Activities and Thinking as a Scientist	Module Number
Web/CD Activity 2A: *The Levels of Life Card Game*	2.1
Web/CD Thinking as a Scientist: *Connection: How Are Space Rocks Analyzed for Signs of Life?*	2.1
Web/CD Activity 2B: *Structure of the Atomic Nucleus*	2.4
Web/CD Activity 2C: *Electron Arrangement*	2.6
Web/CD Activity 2D: *Build an Atom*	2.6
Web/CD Activity 2E: *Ionic Bonds*	2.7
Web/CD Activity 2F: *Covalent Bonds*	2.8
Web/CD Activity 2G: *Nonpolar and Polar Molecules*	2.9
Web/CD Activity 2H: *Water's Polarity and Hydrogen Bonding*	2.10
Web/CD Activity 2I: *Cohesion of Water*	2.11
Web/CD Activity 2J: *Acids, Bases, and pH*	2.15
Web/CD Thinking as a Scientist: *Connection: How Does Acid Precipitation Affect Trees?*	2.16

CHAPTER 3

The Molecules of Cells

Teaching Objectives

Introduction Explain why lactose intolerance is now considered to be the norm. Also explain why lactose tolerance might have evolved in people of European descent.

Introduction to Organic Compounds
3.1 Explain why carbon is unparalleled in its ability to form large, diverse molecules.
3.1 Define organic compounds, hydrocarbons, a carbon skeleton, and an isomer.
3.2 Describe the properties of and distinguish among the five functional groups of organic molecules.
3.3 List the four classes of macromolecules, explain the relationship between monomers and polymers, and compare the processes of dehydration synthesis and hydrolysis.

Carbohydrates
3.4–3.7 Describe the structures, functions, properties, and types of carbohydrate molecules.

Lipids
3.8–3.10 Describe the structures, functions, properties, and types of lipid molecules.
3.10 Describe the health risks associated with the use of anabolic steroids.

Proteins
3.11–3.14 Describe the structures, functions, properties, and types of proteins.
3.15 Describe the major achievements of Linus Pauling.

Nucleic Acids
3.16 Compare the structures and functions of DNA and RNA.

Key Terms

alpha helix	denaturation	hydrophilic
amines	deoxyribonucleic acid	hydrophobic
amino acids	(DNA)	hydroxyl group
amino group	disaccharide	isomers
anabolic steroids	double helix	lipids
carbohydrate	enzymes	macromolecules
carbon skeleton	fat	monomers
carbonyl group	functional groups	monosaccharides
carboxyl group	genes	nitrogenous base
carboxylic acids	glycogen	nucleic acid
cellulose	hydrocarbons	nucleotides
dehydration reaction	hydrolysis	organic compounds

peptide bond	primary structure	steroids
phosphate group	protein	tertiary structure
phospholipids	quaternary structure	triglyceride
pleated sheet	ribonucleic acid (RNA)	unsaturated
polymers	saturated	waxes
polypeptide	secondary structure	
polysaccharides	starch	

Word Roots

carb- = coal (*carboxyl group:* a functional group present in organic acids, consisting of a carbon atom double-bonded to an oxygen atom)

di- = two (*disaccharide:* two monosaccharides joined together)

glyco- = sweet (*glycogen:* a polysaccharide sugar used to store energy in animals)

hydro- = water (*hydrocarbon:* an organic molecule consisting only of carbon and hydrogen)

iso- = equal (*isomer:* one of several organic compounds with the same molecular formula but different structures and therefore different properties)

macro- = large (*macromolecule:* a large molecule)

mono- = single; **-sacchar** = sugar (*monosaccharide:* simplest type of sugar)

poly- = many (*polysaccharide:* many monosaccharides joined together)

tri- = three (*triacylglycerol:* three fatty acids linked to one glycerol molecule)

Lecture Outline

Introduction *Got Lactose?*

  A. The central topic of this chapter is how smaller molecular units are assembled into larger ones.

  B. There are four large molecules discussed in this chapter: carbohydrates, lipids, proteins, and nucleic acids.

  C. Failure to make the correct molecules can lead to abnormalities at the cellular, tissue, organ, or organismal level as illustrated in the essay on lactose intolerance.

I. Introduction to Organic Compounds

  Module 3.1 Life's molecular diversity is based on the properties of carbon.

  A. **Organic compounds** contain at least one carbon atom (Figure 3.1).

  B. Carbon has 4 electrons in the outer shell; therefore carbon has a strong tendency to fill the shell to 8 by forming covalent bonds with other atoms, particularly hydrogen, oxygen, and nitrogen. The 4 electrons in the outermost shell of carbon allow it to form complex structures (e.g., long, branched chains, ring structures). This is a major reason carbon is the structural backbone of organic compounds. A compound composed only of carbon and hydrogen is called a **hydrocarbon,** which is generally nonpolar. A series of covalently attached carbons in a molecule form the backbone, or **carbon skeleton.** *Review:* Covalent bonds (**Module 2.8**).

NOTE: At this point you might want to ask the class if any of them have ever seen the episode of the original Star Trek in which the Horta, a silicon-based life form, appeared. Ask if silicon-based life makes chemical sense.

C. Point out the double bond in Figure 3.1, explaining that it represents 4 shared electrons. *NOTE:* Although the topic is not introduced here, you might mention that triple bonds—which occur in molecular nitrogen, among other places—are represented by three lines (6 shared electrons).

D. The way bonding occurs among atoms in molecules determines the overall shape of the molecule.

E. **Isomers** are molecules with the same numbers of each atom but with different structural arrangements of the atoms.

Module 3.2 Functional groups help determine the properties of organic compounds.

A. **Functional groups** are generally attached to or part of the carbon skeleton of different molecules and exhibit predictable chemical properties.

B. Functional groups are the atoms of an organic compound directly participating in chemical reactions. The sex hormones testosterone and estradiol illustrate the power of functional groups (Figure 3.2).

C. Figure 3.2 illustrates five functional groups important to life, discussing a few of the examples.

D. All of these functional groups have polar characteristics. Therefore, most of the molecules on which they are found are polar molecules.

Module 3.3 Cells make a huge number of large molecules from a small set of small molecules.

A. **Monomers** are the fundamental molecular unit. **Polymers** are **macromolecules** made by linking many of the same kind of fundamental units.

B. *Types of reactions (note that water is involved in both; Figure 3.3A, B):* **dehydration reaction**—molecules synthesized by loss of a water molecule between reacting monomers, the most common way organic polymers are synthesized; **hydrolysis**— literally, "breaking apart with water"—the most common way organic polymers are degraded.

C. The study of molecular reactions in living systems is a broad topic that will be a theme throughout the course. The two reactions reviewed in this module are ones involved in the formation of molecular structures introduced in the remaining modules.

D. Lactose intolerance results from the inability to hydrolyze lactose due to the absence of the enzyme lactase, thus illustrating the need to be able to perform the correct chemical reactions.

E. *Preview:* Chapter 4 will discuss the cellular framework on which and in which molecular reactions occur.

F. *Preview:* Chapters 5–7 discuss metabolism, i.e., cellular reactions involving energy uptake, storage, and release.

II. Carbohydrates

Module 3.4 Monosaccharides are the simplest carbohydrates.

NOTE: The word "carbohydrate" indicates that these compounds are made of carbon (carbo, C) and water (hydrate, H_2O). This is reiterated in the general formula $(CH_2O)_n$ for monosaccharides.

A. Show examples of the isomers glucose and fructose (Figure 3.4B).

B. The suffix "-ose" indicates that the molecule is a sugar.

C. In solution, many monosaccharides form ring-shaped molecules (Figure 3.4C).

D. *Preview:* The basic roles of simple sugars are as fuel to do work, as raw material for carbon backbones, and as the monomers from which disaccharides and polysaccharides are synthesized.

Module 3.5 Cells link two single sugars to form disaccharides.

A. Two monosaccharides are put together to form a **disaccharide** via a glycosidic bond (Figure 3.5). Combining two glucose molecules with the removal of water makes maltose.

B. Disaccharide formation is an example of a dehydration reaction (Module 3.3).

C. The most common disaccharide is sucrose (table sugar), which is composed of glucose and fructose.

Module 3.6 Connection: How sweet is sweet?

A. There are five taste receptors on the tongue: bitter, salty, sour, sweet, and umami (tastes like chicken!).

B. Humans perceive a sweet taste when a chemical binds to the sweet receptor on the tongue. The chemical can be a sugar or other chemicals such as aspartame.

C. The stronger the binding by a chemical to the sweet receptor, the sweeter the chemical is perceived to be. Fructose is considered 4 times sweeter than sucrose.

D. *Preview:* The discussion in this module continues with additional material on nutrition in **Chapter 21.**

E. Some artificial sweeteners bind to other receptors like bitter, thus the familiar bitter aftertaste.

Module 3.7 Polysaccharides are long chains of sugar units.

A. Different organisms use monosaccharides, such as glucose, to build several different polymers or **polysaccharides: starch, glycogen,** and **cellulose** (Figure 3.7).
NOTE: Hydrogen atoms and functional groups are not shown in the figure. The hydroxyls functional groups render carbohydrates hydrophilic.

B. Each of these molecules is synthesized by dehydration synthesis, but there are subtle differences in the covalent bonds that lead to different overall structures and functions. *Review:* Covalent bonds **(Module 2.8).**

C. Starch is used for long-term energy storage only in plants. Starch molecules are helical and may be either unbranched or branched. Animals can hydrolyze this polymer to obtain glucose.
NOTE: The unbranched form of starch is called amylose. The branched form is called amylopectin. Starches rich in amylopectin retain water and are often used in frozen foods. This can also be used to illustrate the convention used for naming enzymes—the starch amylose is broken down by the enzyme amylase.

D. Glycogen has the same kind of bond between monomers as starch, but it is highly branched. Glycogen also is used for long-term energy storage, but only in animals. Animals can hydrolyze this polymer to obtain glucose.

E. Cellulose has a different kind of bond between monomers, forming linear polymers that are cross-linked by hydrogen bonds with other linear chains. Cellulose is the principal structural molecule in the cell walls of plants and algae. Animals cannot hydrolyze this polymer to obtain glucose without the help of intestinal bacteria (only certain bacteria, protozoa, and fungi can hydrolyze cellulose); therefore, it is referred to as fiber.

III. Lipids

Module 3.8 Fats are lipids that are mostly energy-storage molecules.

A. In lipids, carbon and hydrogen predominate; there is very little oxygen, which makes them more or less **hydrophobic.** General molecular formula for fatty acid: $(CH_2)_n$.

B. Diverse types of lipids have different roles, including energy storage and structural and metabolic functions.

C. **Fats** are polymers of fatty acids (usually three) and one glycerol molecule, formed by dehydration reactions, and are called triglycerides or triacylglycerides (Figure 3.8B, C). Fats are tremendous sources of energy and can store approximately 2 times the equivalent of polysaccharides.

D. **Saturated** fatty acids have no double bonds between carbons (the carbons are "saturated" with hydrogen atoms). The molecular backbones are flexible and tend to ball up into tight globules. Saturated fats, such as butter and lard, are solid at room temperature.

E. **Unsaturated** fats may include several double bonds between carbons. This causes the molecules to be less flexible, and they do not pack into solid globules. Unsaturated fats, such as olive oil and corn oil, are liquid at room temperature.

F. Most plant fats are unsaturated, whereas animal fats are richer in saturated fats. *Preview:* There are two types of unsaturated fats (Chapter 21). Polyunsaturated fats include the essential fatty acids. Monounsaturated fats (in moderation), contrary to the general reputation of "fat," have cardiovascular benefits. Omega fats in fish are a good example of a healthful fat.
NOTE: By "hydrogenating" unsaturated oils, the double bonds are removed and the molecules become more solid at room temperature. These structurally modified (trans) fats are as detrimental as their naturally saturated counterparts in leading to atherosclerotic plaques.

Module 3.9 Phospholipids, waxes, and steroids are lipids with a variety of functions.

A. **Phospholipids** are a major component of cell membranes. They have two fatty acid molecules (instead of three) and a phosphate group.

B. **Waxes** are effective hydrophobic coatings formed by many organisms (insects, plants, and humans) to ward off water. They consist of a single fatty acid linked to an alcohol.

C. **Steroids** are lipids with backbones bent into rings. Cholesterol is an important steroid formed by animals (Figure 3.9; notice that the diagram omits carbons and hydrogens at each intersection in the rings and shows just the backbone shape). Among other things, cholesterol is the precursor to bile acids that function in the digestion of fats and is the starting material for the synthesis of female and male sex hormones (see Figure 3.2).
NOTE: Despite its reputation, cholesterol plays many vital roles in the body.

    D. *Preview:* The structural roles of phospholipid-containing membranes are introduced in Chapter 4, on cell structure; their molecular structure and function are discussed in Chapter 5, with other topics relating to cellular work. Like fats, they are polymers of fatty acids and glycerol, but they include a negatively charged PO_4 group in place of one fatty acid. This gives them the unique property of having a hydrophobic "tail" and a hydrophilic "head."

Module 3.10 Connection: Anabolic steroids and related substances pose health risks.

    A. **Anabolic steroids** are synthetic and natural variants of the male hormone testosterone, which, among other roles, causes the buildup of muscle and bone mass during puberty in men.

       NOTE: Since college-age body builders may be tempted to use steroids, you might want to point out some of the medical problems associated with such use, including problems such as testicular atrophy, liver cancer, cardiovascular disease, breast development in males, masculinization of females, and antisocial behavior (steroid rage).

IV. Proteins

Module 3.11 Proteins are essential to the structures and activities of life.

    A. **Proteins** are constructed from monomers called amino acids.

    B. The structure of the protein determines its function.

    C. The seven major classes of protein are:
      1. Structural: hair, cell cytoskeleton
      2. Contractile: as part of muscle and other motile cells, produce movement
      3. Storage: sources of amino acids, such as egg white
      4. Defense: antibodies, membrane proteins, complement proteins
      5. Transport: hemoglobin, membrane proteins
      6. Signaling: hormones, membrane proteins
      7. **Enzymatic:** regulate the speed of a biochemical reaction much like a chemical catalyst is used to speed up a reaction.

       NOTE: Refer back to the opening essay and the use of the enzyme lactase to hydrolyze lactose.

Module 3.12 Proteins are made from amino acids linked by peptide bonds.

    A. **Amino acids** are characterized by having an alpha carbon atom covalently bonded to one hydrogen, one amino group (NH_2), one carboxyl group (COOH), and one functional group symbolized by an R (Figure 3.12A).
      Review: Covalent bonds (**Module 2.8**).

    B. Each naturally occurring amino acid has one of 20 functional groups (Figure 3.12B), which determines the chemical characteristics of each amino acid.

    C. Amino acids are grouped into two categories based upon the characteristics of the R groups. The two categories are hydrophilic (polar neutral or charged) and hydrophobic (nonpolar). **See Appendix 2 for a complete list.**

    D. Organisms use amino acids as the monomer to build polypeptides by dehydration reactions. The bond between each amino acid is called a **peptide bond** (Figure 3.12C).

    E. The peptide bond can be broken by hydrolysis, to release free amino acids.
      NOTE: Add a reverse arrow and a water molecule to Figure 3.12C and label it "Hydrolysis."

F. **Polypeptides** are from several to more than a thousand amino acids long, and the specific sequence determines the function of the protein (a polypeptide with more than 20 amino acids is classified as a protein). To illustrate the enormous number of proteins, compare the 20 amino acids used to make proteins to the 26 letters of the alphabet for words.

Module 3.13 A protein's specific shape determines its function.

A. Long polypeptide chains include numerous and various amino acids.

B. The final structure of a protein, and thus its potential role, depends on the way these long, linear molecules fold.

C. Each sequence of amino acids spontaneously folds in a different way (Figure 3.13A). The folding creates grooves that function as binding sites for other molecules (Figure 3.13B).

D. Changes in heat, ionic strength, or salinity can cause proteins to unfold and lose their functionality (this is called **denaturation**).

E. The four levels of structure are shown in the protein transthyretin in Figures 3.14A, B, C, and D.
   NOTE: At each level in the diagrams, details are hidden to show the essential structure added at that level.

Module 3.14 A protein's shape depends on four levels of structure.

A. Transthyretin is found in blood and is important in the transport of a thyroid hormone and vitamin A.

B. Three-letter abbreviations represent amino acids; each amino acid is in a precise order in the chain (Figure 3.14A).

C. In transthyretin, there are four polypeptide chains, each with 127 amino acids.

D. Changes in the **primary structure** of a protein (the amino acid sequence) can affect its overall structure and, thus, its ability to function. Sickle cell disease is an excellent example of a single amino acid defect.

E. **Secondary structure** is a result of hydrogen bond formation occurring between amino (—NH) and carboxyl (—C=O) groups of amino acids in sequence along each polypeptide chain.
   Review: Hydrogen bonds **(Module 2.10).**

F. Depending on where the groups are relative to one another, the secondary structure takes the shape of an **alpha helix** or a **pleated sheet** (Figure 3.14B).

G. The R groups usually do not play a role in secondary structure and are not diagrammed.
   NOTE: Diagramming the secondary structures of proteins uses cylinders, flat arrows, and lines to represent helical regions, beta pleated sheets, and nonhydrogen-bonded regions (also called random coils), respectively.

H. **Tertiary structure,** which is the overall shape of the polypeptide, results from the clustering of hydrophobic and hydrophilic R groups and bond formation (hydrogen and ionic) between certain R groups along the coils and pleats (Figure 3.14C). An important and often overlooked covalent bond that maintains tertiary structure is the disulfide bond that forms between two Cysteine amino acids.

    I. In transthyretin, the tertiary shape is essentially globular, not fibrous like spider silk. The globular arrangement promotes hydrophilic amino acids to interact with the aqueous environment and forces the hydrophobic amino acids toward the center of the protein, sequestered from the water.

    J. Many (but not all) proteins consist of more than one polypeptide chain (also known as, subunits) and have **quaternary structure.**

    K. Transthyretin consists of four chains, each identical (Figure 3.14D). Other proteins might have all chains different or be additionally complexed with other atoms or molecules. Another good example of a protein with quaternary structure is hemoglobin: 4 subunits (2 + 2) and 4 heme prosthetic groups.
NOTE: Quaternary bonding is largely by polar and hydrophobic interaction.

Module 3.15 Talking About Science: Linus Pauling contributed to our understanding of the chemistry of life.

    A. Dr. Pauling felt that there was value in reductionism when studying biology in an attempt to answer questions about whole organisms.

    B. He was the first to describe the coiled and pleated-sheet secondary structure of protein and the first to describe the structure of hemoglobin and the abnormal form found in the red blood cells of those with sickle-cell disease.

    C. Later in his life, Pauling was most noted for his work on the role of vitamin C in maintaining health, which has not been substantiated.

    D. Pauling also had a lifelong interest in the biology of aging.

    E. As are many scientists, Pauling was politically active, being an advocate for a ban on the testing of nuclear weapons.

V. Nucleic Acids

Module 3.16 Nucleic acids are information-rich polymers of nucleotides.

    A. There are two types of **nucleic acids: deoxyribonucleic acid (DNA)** and **ribonucleic acid (RNA).** Nucleotides are complex molecules composed of three functional parts (Figure 3.16A, B): **phosphate group,** five-carbon sugar (deoxyribose in DNA, ribose in RNA), and **nitrogenous base.**

    B. There are five basic types of nitrogenous bases: A, T, G, and C in DNA and A, U, G, and C in RNA (Figure 10.2B, C).
NOTE: DNA nucleotide sequences encode the information required for production of the primary structure of proteins; such sequences are called **genes (Modules 10.7 and 10.8).**

    C. Nucleotide monomers join by dehydration reaction between the nucleotide parts (phosphate to sugar) to form polynucleotides with a linear structure of sugar-phosphate repeats (Figures 3.16A, B; Figure 10.2A).

    D. Hydrogen bonding between **nitrogenous bases** (A to T and G to C) causes the final structure of the nucleic acid.
Preview: The mechanisms by which these structures determine gene expression are discussed in Chapters 10 and 11.

    E. In DNA, two linear chains are held together in an antiparallel **double helix** (Figure 3.16C).

    F. In RNA, one linear chain may be wrapped around itself in places, forming one of three types of RNA: transfer RNA (tRNA), ribosomal RNA (rRNA), or messenger RNA (mRNA). See Chapter 10 for structural details.

Class Activities

1. Present your students with hydrocarbons of various lengths and hydrogen content. Ask them to see how many different isomers they can construct from these hydrocarbons. Point out to your class how the *cis* versus *trans* position of hydrogens relates to the hydrogenation of fatty acids.

2. To show that the polysaccharide starch is composed of smaller sugars, pass out grains of wheat, and have students chew on them for 5–10 minutes. As they chew, explain how the hydrolysis of plant starch produces the disaccharide maltose, which is noticeably sweet. Also point out that this only occurs in the presence of the right environment, including the enzyme salivary amylase (take this opportunity to illustrate the "ase" convention of naming enzymes: The starch amylose is broken down by the enzyme amylase) and the proper pH. The exact chemical role of this enzyme need not be introduced at this point. In larger classes, you might want to restrict this activity to discussion groups.

3. On a per gram basis, sugar alcohols are not as sweet as sucrose, yet sufficient amounts are used to achieve a comparable degree of sweetness in gums and candies that are labeled as being "dietetic" and "sugarless." Ask students what might account for the apparent contradiction.

    You might want to point out to your students that sugars are not the only compounds that are perceived as being sweet. For example, proteins known as thaumatins are 2,000 times sweeter than sucrose.

4. Ask your students to consider, based on what they have learned in this chapter, the role of fever as a mechanism for restoring homeostasis.

Transparency Acetates

Figure 3.1	Variations in carbon skeletons
Table 3.2	Some common functional groups
Figure 3.2	Differences in the functional groups of male and female sex hormones (carbons and their attached hydrogens omitted)
Figure 3.3A	Building a polymer chain
Figure 3.3B	Breaking a polymer chain
Figure 3.4B	Structures of glucose and fructose
Figure 3.4C	Three representations of the ring form of glucose
Figure 3.5	Disaccharide formation
Table 3.6	Sweetness scale
Figure 3.7	Polysaccharides
Figure 3.8B	A dehydration reaction linking a fatty acid to glycerol
Figure 3.8C	A fat molecule
Figure 3.9	Cholesterol, a steroid
Figure 3.12A	General structure of an amino acid
Figure 3.12B	Examples of amino acids
Figure 3.12C	Peptide bond formation
Page 44	Collagen
Figure 3.14A–D	Protein structure (Layer 1)
Figure 3.14A–D	Protein structure (Layer 2)

Figure 3.14A–D   Protein structure (Layer 3)

Figure 3.14A–D   Protein structure (Layer 4)

Figure 3.16A   A nucleotide

Figure 3.16B   Part of a polynucleotide

Figure 3.16C   DNA double helix

Reviewing the Concepts, page 48: Polymers

Connecting the Concepts, page 48: A carbon molecule

Connecting the Concepts, page 48: Classes of macromolecules and their monomers

Testing your Knowledge, page 49: Sucrose

Testing your Knowledge, page 49: An organic molecule

Applying the Concepts, page 49: Effectiveness of two enzymes at various temperatures

Media

See the beginning of this book for a complete description of all media available for instructors and students. Animations and videos are available in the Campbell Image Presentation Library. Media Activities and Thinking as a Scientist investigations are available on the student CD-ROM and website.

Animations and Videos	Module Number
Isomers, Step 1 Animation	3.1
Isomers, Step 2 Animation	3.1
Isomers, Step 3 Animation	3.1
Macromolecules Animation	3.3
Disaccharides Animation	3.5
Polysaccharides Animation	3.7
Lipids Animation	3.8
Contractile Proteins Animation	3.11
Defensive Proteins Animation	3.11
Enzymes Animation	3.11
Signal Proteins Animation	3.11
Storage Proteins Animation	3.11
Structural Proteins Animation	3.11
Transport Proteins Animation	3.11
Sensory Proteins Animation	3.11
Gene Regulatory Proteins Animation	3.11
Protein Structure Introduction Animation	3.14
Primary Protein Structure Animation	3.15
Secondary Protein Structure Animation	3.16
Tertiary Protein Structure Animation	3.17
Quaternary Protein Structure Animation	3.18

Activities and Thinking as a Scientist   Module Number

CHAPTER 4

A Tour of the Cell

Teaching Objectives

Introduction Explain why art is so important to an understanding of biology.

Introduction to the Cell

4.1 Compare the designs of and images produced by a light microscope, a scanning electron microscope, and a transmission electron microscope. Distinguish between magnification and resolving power.

4.1 Define cell theory and briefly describe the discoveries that led to its development.

4.2 Explain why there are upper and lower limits to cell size.

4.3–4.4 Distinguish between the structures of prokaryotic and eukaryotic cells.

4.4 Explain why compartmentalization is important in eukaryotic cells.

4.4 Compare the structures of plant and animal cells. Note the function of each cell part.

Organelles of the Endomembrane System

4.5–4.10, 4.12–4.13 Describe the structure and functions of the nucleus, endomembrane system, smooth and rough endoplasmic reticulums, Golgi apparatus, lysosomes, and vacuoles.

4.11 Explain how impaired lysosomal function can cause the symptoms of storage diseases.

Energy-Converting Organelles

4.14–4.15 Compare the structures and functions of chloroplasts and mitochondria.

The Cytoskeleton and Related Structures

4.16 Compare the structures and functions of microfilaments, intermediate filaments, and microtubules.

4.17 Explain how the structure of cilia and flagella relate to their functions.

Cell Surfaces and Junctions

4.18 Compare the structures and functions of cell surfaces and intercellular junctions of plant and animal cells.

Functional Categories of Organelles

4.19 Describe the four functional categories of eukaryotic organelles, noting which organelles are in each group.

4.19 Describe the three fundamental features of all life forms on our planet.

Key Terms

anchoring junctions
basal body
capsule
cell theory
cell wall
cellular metabolism
central vacuole
centrioles
chloroplasts
chromatin
chromosomes
cilia
cristae
cytoplasm
cytoskeleton
electron microscope (EM)
endomembrane system
endoplasmic reticulum (ER)
eukaryotic cells
extracellular matrix
flagella

gap junctions
glycoprotein
Golgi apparatus
granum
intermediate filaments
intermembrane space
light microscope (LM)
lysosome
magnification
microfilaments
micrographs
microtubules
mitochondria
mitochondrial matrix
nuclear envelope
nucleoid region
nucleolus
nucleus
organelles
pili
plasma membrane

plasmodesmata
prokaryotic cells
prokaryotic flagella
resolution
ribosomes
rough endoplasmic
   reticulum
rough ER
scanning electron
   microscope (SEM)
secretory protein
smooth endoplasmic
   reticulum
smooth ER
stroma
tight junctions
transmission electron
   microscope (TEM)
transport vesicle
vacuoles
vesicles

Word Roots

chloro- = green (*chloroplast:* the site of photosynthesis in plants and eukaryotic algae)

endo- = inner (*endomembrane system:* the system of membranes within a cell that include the nuclear envelope, endoplasmic reticulum, Golgi apparatus, lysosomes, vacuoles, and the plasma membrane)

extra- = outside (*extracellular matrix:* the substance in which animal tissue cells are embedded)

flagell- = whip (*flagellum:* a long whiplike cellular appendage that moves cells)

glyco- = sweet (*glycoprotein:* a protein covalently bonded to a carbohydrate)

lyso- = loosen (*lysosome:* a membrane-bounded sac of hydrolytic enzymes that a cell uses to digest macromolecules)

micro- = small; **-tubul** = a little pipe (*microtubule:* a hollow rod of tubulin protein in the cytoplasm of almost all eukaryotic cells)

nucle- = nucleus; **-oid** = like (*nucleoid:* the region where the genetic material is concentrated in prokaryotic cells)

plasm- = molded; **-desma** = a band or bond (*plasmodesmata:* an open channel in a plant cell wall)

pro- = before; **karyo-** = nucleus (*prokaryotic cell:* a cell that has no nucleus)

trans- = across; **-port** = a harbor (*transport vesicle:* a membranous compartment used to enclose and transport materials from one part of a cell to another)

vacu- = empty (*vacuole:* sac that buds from the ER, Golgi, or plasma membrane)

Lecture Outline

Introduction *The Art of Looking at Cells*

    A. The use of art to help illustrate difficult concepts being discussed has a long tradition in biology.

    B. *Review:* All organisms are composed of cells (**Module 1.3**).

    C. Cells are at a scale just below what humans can visibly perceive, but with a microscope, we can plainly see that all living things contain cells.

    D. The focus of this chapter is on the structure and function of the cell and the **organelles** that are found inside the cell.

I. Introduction to the Cell

Module 4.1 Microscopes provide windows to the world of the cell.

    A. Images formed by microscopes represent the object "under" the microscope. A picture of a microscopic image is called a micrograph.

    B. Magnification: the number of times larger the image appears than the true size of the object.

    C. Resolution: clarity of the image (resolving power; the ability to distinguish two objects as separate).

    D. Five types of microscopes that produced the images in the text form images in different ways. Each of these microscopes has advantages relative to the others, and a range of scales at which it functions best.

    E. **Light microscopes (LM)** bend the light coming through an object. The bent light rays form larger images in the viewer's eyes (Figure 4.1A). Well-resolved LM images are limited to 1,000 to 2,000 times larger than life size. The LM is particularly good for looking at living cells and cells and tissues that have been stained (Figure 4.1B). *NOTE:* Review the units of measure used in science that can be found in the table and in **Appendix 1.**

    F. **Electron microscopes (EM)** use electrons to visualize an object and can magnify images 100 times more than LM. **Scanning electron microscopes (SEM)** compose images on a TV screen, from electrons that bounce off the surfaces of the object. SEM images are usually about 10,000–20,000 times larger than life size. The SEM is particularly good for showing organismal and cellular surfaces under high magnification (Figure 4.1C).

    G. **Transmission electron microscopes (TEM)** compose images on camera film, from electrons that have traveled through very thin slices of the object and have been bent by magnetic lenses. TEM images are usually about 100,000–200,000 times larger than life size. The TEM is particularly useful for showing the internal structures of cells (Figure 4.1D).

    H. Modifications to LM have enhanced the imaging process. Two important advancements in LM are the differential interference-contrast and the confocal microscope (Figures 4.1E and F). The former is good for live specimens, while the latter uses fluorescence and lasers to visualize cellular details.

Module 4.2 Most cells are microscopic.

    A. *Review:* the scales of life (compare with Figure 1.1) (Figure 4.2A).

    B. Bacteria are the smallest cells (approximately 0.2 μm) and are at the lower limits of LM.

    C. Bird eggs are very large, mostly composed of food reserves.

D. Most plant and animal cells are in the range of 10 to 100 μm in diameter.

E. Large cells have a smaller ratio of surface area to volume than small cells (Figure 4.2B). The key to this discussion is the comparison of the surface to volume.

F. This fact imposes the upper limit on cell size (actually, cell volume) because materials have to flow across the surface to get to the inside. Larger cells require correspondingly greater surface area, which they do not have.

G. The small size of cells is limited by the total size of all the molecules required for cellular activity (DNA, ribosomes, life-process-governing proteins, etc.).

Module 4.3 Prokaryotic cells are structurally simpler than eukaryotic cells.

A. All living organisms can be separated into two categories base on cell type, **prokaryotic cells** and **eukaryotic cells** (Figure 4.3A). Common features of all cells are a **plasma membrane,** DNA, and **ribosomes.** The two groups of prokaryotic cells are the Bacteria and the Archaea.
Preview: The Archaea are more closely related to eukaryotes than they are to the Bacteria (Module 15.14).

B. Prokaryotic cells are usually relatively small (1–10 μm in length).

C. Prokaryotic cells lack a nucleus: DNA is in direct contact with cytoplasm and is coiled into a **nucleoid region** (Figure 4.3B). Eukaryotic cells have a true membrane-bound nucleus.

D. **Cytoplasm** includes ribosomes (protein factories) suspended in a semi-fluid.

E. Prokaryotic cells are otherwise composed of a bounding plasma membrane, complex outer **cell wall** (a rigid container, often with a sticky outer coat called a **capsule**), **pili,** and, sometimes, **flagella.**
Preview: The classification and evolution of the prokaryotes are discussed in Module 15.14 and Modules 16.7–16.10.

Module 4.4 Eukaryotic cells are partitioned into functional compartments.

A. Eukaryotic cells are usually relatively larger (10–100 μm or more) in diameter.

B. These cells are internally complex, with **organelles** of two types: membranous and nonmembranous.

C. Membranous organelles found in eukaryotic cells include the nucleus, endoplasmic reticulum, Golgi apparatus, mitochondria, lysosomes, and peroxisomes.

D. Nonmembranous organelles found in eukaryotic cells include ribosomes, microtubules, centrioles, flagella, and the cytoskeleton.

E. Organelles serve two major functions, to compartmentalize **cellular metabolism** and to increase the membrane surface area for membrane-bound biochemical reactions.

F. Animal cells are bounded by the plasma membrane alone, often have flagella, and lack a cell wall (Figure 4.4A).

G. Plant cells are bounded by both a plasma membrane and a rigid cell wall composed of cellulose (Figure 4.4B). In addition, plant cells usually have a central vacuole and chloroplasts, lack centrioles, and usually lack lysosomes and flagella.

H. Cells of eukaryotes in other kingdoms vary in structure and components (protists: Figures 4.12B, 16.20A–D, 16.23A, B; fungi: Figures 17.15A–C).

I. *Preview:* Membranes play an important role in defining many cellular structures. Introduce the phospholipid bilayer and the protein mosaic model of membrane structure, reminding students that a thorough discussion of the structure and function of membranes will come in Chapter 5 (Figure 5.12).

II. Organelles of the Endomembrane System

Module 4.5 The nucleus is the cell's genetic control center.

  A. The **nuclear envelope** is a double membrane, perforated with pores through which material can pass into and out of the **nucleus,** which separates this organelle from the cytoplasm (Figure 4.5).

  B. DNA can be seen as strands of chromatin dispersed inside the nucleus. Each strand of chromatin constitutes a **chromosome.** Prior to cell division, DNA is duplicated (see Module 10.4 and 10.5).

  C. During cell division, chromosomes coil up and become visible through a light microscope.

  D. The **nucleolus,** also within the nucleus, is composed of chromatin, RNA, and protein. The function of nucleoli is the manufacture of ribosomes.

  E. Besides the storage of heritable material, the nucleus synthesizes messenger RNA that leaves the cell and directs the synthesis of proteins at ribosomes.

Module 4.6 Overview: Many cell organelles are connected through the endomembrane system.

  A. An extensive system of membranous organelles, referred to as the **endomembrane system,** work together in the synthesis, storage, and export of molecules (see Figures 4.10A and 4.13).

  B. Each of these organelles is bounded by a single membrane. Some are in the form of flattened sacs; some are rounded sacs; and some are tube-shaped.

  C. The major function of the endomembrane system is to divide the cell into separate compartments.

Module 4.7 Smooth endoplasmic reticulum has a variety of functions.

  A. The **smooth endoplasmic reticulum,** or **smooth ER,** is a series of interconnected tubes that lacks surface ribosomes (Figure 4.7).

  B. One job of smooth ER is to synthesize lipids.

  C. In other forms of smooth ER, enzymes help process materials as they are transported from one place to another. An example of this function is the detoxification of drugs by smooth ER in liver cells.

  D. A third function of smooth ER is the storage of calcium ions that are required for muscle contraction.
  NOTE: You may need to review the concept of enzymes as proteins functioning as biological catalysts (**Module 3.11**).

Module 4.8 Rough endoplasmic reticulum makes membrane and proteins.

  A. **Rough endoplasmic reticulum (rough ER)** is composed of flattened sacs that often extend throughout the entire cytoplasm (Figure 4.7). The rough ER has three functions: synthesis, modification, and packaging of proteins.

  B. Ribosomes on rough ER make proteins, some of which are incorporated into the membrane. Other proteins are packaged in membranous sacs that bud off the rough ER and are transported to the Golgi apparatus (Figure 4.8).

Module 4.9 The Golgi apparatus finishes, sorts, and ships cell products.

   A. Transport vesicles from the ER fuse on one end of a **Golgi apparatus** to form flattened sacs (Figure 4.9).

   B. These sacs move through the stack like a pile of pancakes added at one end and eaten from the other. Molecular processing occurs in the sacs as they move through the Golgi.

   C. At the far end, modified molecules are released in transport vesicles.

Module 4.10 Lysosomes are digestive compartments within a cell.

   A. **Lysosomes** are one kind of vesicle produced at the far end of the Golgi (Figure 4.10A).

   B. Lysosome vesicles contain hydrolytic enzymes that break down the contents of other vesicles, damaged organelles, or bacteria with which they fuse (Figures 4.10B and C). Lysosomes are the recycling center for the cell.

Module 4.11 Connection: Abnormal lysosomes can cause fatal diseases.

   A. Lysosomal storage diseases result from an inherited lack of one or more hydrolytic enzymes from lysosomes.

   B. In Pompe's disease, lysosomes lack glycogen-digesting enzyme, damaging the muscle and liver. In Tay-Sachs disease, lysosomes lack lipid-digesting enzymes, which damages the nervous system.

Module 4.12 Vacuoles function in the general maintenance of the cell.

   A. **Vacuole** is the general term given to other membrane-bounded sacs.

   B. Plants have **central vacuoles** that function in storage, play roles in plant cell growth, maintain turgor pressure, and may function as large lysosomes (Figures 4.12A and 4.4B). The vacuoles may also contain pigments or poisons.

   C. Contractile vacuoles in cells of freshwater protists (both protozoa and algae) function in water balance (Figure 4.12B).

Module 4.13 A review of the endomembrane system.

   A. Discuss the structural connections between the various organelles in this system. The red arrows show the functional connections (Figure 4.13).

   B. Vesicles can fuse with the plasma membrane and deliver the content to the extracellular environment without the content actually crossing the plasma membrane.

III. Energy-Converting Organelles

Module 4.14 Chloroplasts convert solar energy to chemical energy.

   A. **Chloroplasts** are found in most cells of plants and in cells of photosynthetic protists (algae) (Figure 4.14).

   B. Chloroplasts are double-membrane-bounded.

   C. Chloroplasts are the site of photosynthesis.

   D. The structure of the organelle fits its function. As we will see, the capturing of light and electron energizing occur on the **granum** (plural, grana), and chemical reactions that form food-storage molecules occur in the **stroma.**

   E. *Preview:* Photosynthesis is covered in detail in Chapter 7, and the origin of chloroplasts is discussed in Module 16.18.

Module 4.15 Mitochondria harvest chemical energy from food.

    A. **Mitochondria** are found in all cells of eukaryotes, except a few anaerobic protozoans (Figure 4.15).

    B. Mitochondria are double-membrane-bounded organelles with two membrane spaces, the **intermembrane space** and the **mitochondrial matrix.**

    C. Mitochondria are the site of cellular respiration, the conversion of glucose to ATP.

    D. The structure of the organelle fits its function. As we will see, the ATP-generating electron transport system is embedded in the inner membrane **(cristae),** and chemical reactions occur in compartments between membranes.

    E. *Preview:* Cellular respiration is covered in detail in Chapter 6, and the origin of mitochondria is discussed in Module 16.18.

IV. The Cytoskeleton and Related Structures

Module 4.16 The cell's internal skeleton helps organize its structure and activities.

    A. The organelles discussed up to this point, particularly the endomembrane system, provide cells with some support.

    B. The cytoskeleton adds to this support, plays a role in cell movement, and may have a role in cell signaling (Figure 4.17A).

    C. The cytoskeleton is a three-dimensional meshwork of fibers: **microfilaments, intermediate filaments,** and **microtubules** (Figure 4.16).

    D. Microfilaments are solid rods composed of globular proteins. They participate in cell movement, including muscle contraction (discussed more in Chapter 30).

    E. Intermediate filaments are ropelike strands of fibrous proteins. These structures are tension bearing and anchor some organelles.
       NOTE: The cytoskeletal fibers of anchoring junctions are intermediate filaments (Module 4.18).

    F. Microtubules are hollow tubes composed of globular proteins. Microtubules guide the movement of organelles through the cell and are the basis of ciliary and flagellar movement.

Module 4.17 Cilia and flagella move when microtubules bend.

    A. Although **cilium** and **flagellum** are similar in structure, they were named prior to understanding that the internal structures are similar. Cilia are short and numerous, while flagella are long and fewer (Figures 4.17A and B).

    B. In both cases, these nonmembranous organelles are minute, tubular extensions of the plasma membrane that surround a complex arrangement of microtubules (Figure 4.17C).

    C. Cilia and flagella function to move whole cells (for example, sperm) or to move materials across the surface of a cell (for example, respiratory tract cells).

    D. The underlying structure consists of nine microtubule doublets arranged in a cylinder around a central pair of microtubules. At the base within the cell body **(basal body),** the structure is slightly different (Figure 4.17C).

    E. Various types of whipping movements of a whole flagellum or cilium occur when the microtubule doublets move relative to neighboring doublets. The connecting dynein arms apply the force driven by the energy released from ATP.

    F. *Preview:* Basal bodies are in the cytoplasm below these external extensions. They are identical in cross section to **centrioles,** which function in cell division (Figure 4.4A, Module 8.6, and Figure 8.6).

V. Cell Surfaces and Junctions

Module 4.18 Cell surfaces protect, support, and join cells.

    A. Prokaryotic cells and eukaryotic cells of many protists function independently of one another and relate directly to the outside environment.

    B. In multicellular plants, cell walls protect and support individual cells and join neighboring cells into interconnected and coordinated groups (tissues) (Figure 4.18A). *Preview:* Plant cells and tissues (Module 31.5).

    C. Plant cell walls are multilayered and are composed of various mixtures of polysaccharides and proteins. The dominant polysaccharide in plant cells is cellulose. Lignin is a sugar-based molecule that adds rigidity and resists degradation.

    D. **Plasmodesmata** are channels through the cell walls connecting the cytoplasm of adjacent plant cells (Figure 4.18A).

    E. In multicellular animals, cells secrete and are embedded in sticky layers of glycoproteins, the **extracellular matrix,** which can protect and support the cell as well as regulate cell activity (Figure 4.18B).

    F. In animal tissues, cells are joined by several types of junctions. **Tight junctions** provide leak-proof barriers (for example, intestinal cells). **Anchoring junctions** join cells to each other or to the extracellular matrix but allow passage of materials along the spaces between cells or cells attached to an extracellular matrix (common in tissues that stretch such as skin). **Gap junctions** provide channels between cells for the movement of small molecules (for example, ion flow in cardiac muscle).
Preview: Epithelial tissue is attached to the underlying extracellular matrix by cell junctions **(Module 20.4).**
NOTE: Provide examples of the importance of these cell junctions for the human body. For example: the role of tight junctions in the gastrointestinal tract, the role of anchoring junctions in keeping skin cells attached to each other and to the body (mention epidermolysis bullosa, a disease in which there is an inherited defect in anchoring junctions; ask what the result would be), and the role of communicating junctions in cardiac muscle contraction.

VI. Functional Categories of Organelles

Module 4.19 Eukaryotic organelles comprise four functional categories.

    A. Manufacture: synthesis of macromolecules and transport within the cell.

    B. Breakdown: elimination and recycling of cellular materials.

    C. Energy processing: conversion of energy from one form to another.

    D. Support, movement, and communication: maintenance of cell shape, anchorage and movement of organelles, and relationships with extracellular environments.

    E. There are structural similarities within each of the four categories that underlie their function.

    F. All four categories work together as an integrated team, producing the emergent properties at the cellular level.

    G. There are three common features shared by all life forms: (1) Cell enclosed by a membrane that controls the internal environment, (2) DNA is the heritable material, and (3) perform metabolic processes.

Class Activities

1. As time and resources permit, present views of living cells doing dynamic things. Protozoans, algae in pond water, and cheek cells are good examples of dynamic cells as opposed to the dead, stained, static cells students usually see.

2. After giving your cell tour lectures and reviewing the various cell organelles and their functions, show students a few previously unseen illustrations of cells of various types. Let the students describe and name the dominant organelles they observe. Continue this activity as you proceed through the course, to help add some depth to the understanding of tissue and cell types in animals, plants, and other organisms.

3. Ask students to consider how chloroplast (Module 4.14) and mitochondrial (Module 4.15) structure reflect their prokaryotic origins.

4. Ask your students to make correlations between organelle function and analogous organ function. Also, analogies can be made between relationships among organelles and those of the components of a factory.

Transparency Acetates

Table 4.1	Measurement Equivalents
Figure 4.2A	The sizes of cells and related objects
Figure 4.2B	Effect of cell size on surface area
Figure 4.3B	A prokaryotic cell
Figure 4.4A	An animal cell
Figure 4.4B	A plant cell
Figure 4.5	The nucleus and rough endoplasmic reticulum
Figure 4.7	Smooth and rough endoplasmic reticulum
Figure 4.8	Synthesis and packaging of a secretory protein by the rough ER
Figure 4.9	The Golgi apparatus
Figure 4.10A	Lysosome formation and functions (Layer 1)
Figure 4.10A	Lysosome formation and functions (Layer 2)
Figure 4.10A	Lysosome formation and functions (Layer 3)
Figure 4.10B	Lysosomes in a white blood cell
Figure 4.12A	Central vacuole in a plant cell
Figure 4.12B	Contractile vacuoles in *Paramecium* (combined with Figure 4.12A)
Figure 4.13	Connections among the organelles of the endomembrane system
Figure 4.14	The chloroplast
Figure 4.15	The mitochondrion
Figure 4.16	Fibers of the cytoskeleton
Figure 4.17C	Structure of a eukaryotic flagellum or cilium
Figure 4.18A	Plant cell walls and cell junctions
Figure 4.18B	Animal cell surfaces and cell junctions
Table 4.19	Eukaryotic organelles and their functions

Connecting the Concepts, page 68: Structures of an animal cell

Media

See the beginning of this book for a complete description of all media available for instructors and students. Animations and videos are available in the Campbell Image Presentation Library. Media Activities and Thinking as a Scientist investigations are available on the student CD-ROM and website.

Animations and Videos	Module Number
Cytoplasmic Streaming Video	4.2
Lysosome Formation Animation	4.10
Paramecium Vacuole Video	4.12
Endomembrane System Animation	4.13
Paramecium Cilia Video	4.17
Cilia and Flagella Animation	4.17
Anchoring Junctions Animation	4.18
Gap Communicating Junctions Animation	4.18
Tight Junctions Animation	4.18

Activities and Thinking as a Scientist	Module Number
Web/CD Activity 4A: *Metric System Review*	4.1
Web/CD Thinking as a Scientist: *Connection: What Is the Size and Scale of Our World?*	4.2
Web/CD Activity 4B: *Prokaryotic Cell Structure and Function*	4.3
Web/CD Activity 4C: *Comparing Prokaryotic and Eukaryotic Cells*	4.4
Web/CD Activity 4D: *Build an Animal Cell and a Plant Cell*	4.4
Web/CD Activity 4E: *Overview of Protein Synthesis*	4.8
Web/CD Activity 4F: *The Endomembrane System*	4.13
Web/CD Activity 4G: *Build a Chloroplast and a Mitochondrion*	4.15
Web/CD Activity 4H: *Cilia and Flagella*	4.17
Web/CD Activity 4I: *Cell Junctions*	4.18
Web/CD Activity 4J: *Review: Animal Cell Structure and Function*	4.19
Web/CD Activity 4K: *Review: Plant Cell Structure and Function*	4.19
Web/CD Thinking as a Scientist: *Connection: How Are Space Rocks Analyzed for Signs of Life?*	4.19

CHAPTER 5

The Working Cell

Teaching Objectives

Introduction   Describe how and where fireflies produce light.

Energy and the Cell

5.1   Define and compare kinetic energy, potential energy, chemical energy, and heat.

5.2   Define the first and second laws of thermodynamics. Explain how these laws of thermodynamics guide energy transformations.

5.3   Define and compare endergonic and exergonic reactions. Explain how cells use cellular respiration and energy coupling to survive.

5.4   Explain how ATP functions as an energy shuttle.

How Enzymes Function

5.5   Explain how enzymes speed up chemical reactions.

5.6   Describe the structure of an enzyme-substrate interaction.

5.7   Explain how the cellular environment affects enzyme activity.

5.8   Explain how competitive and noncompetitive inhibitors alter an enzyme's activity.

5.8   Describe the process of feedback inhibition.

5.9   Explain how certain poisons, pesticides, and drugs inhibit enzymes.

Membrane Structure and Function

5.10   Explain how membranes help organize the chemical activities of a cell.

5.11   Relate the structure of phospholipid molecules to the structure and properties of cell membranes.

5.12   Describe the fluid mosaic structure of cell membranes.

5.13   Describe the diverse functions of membrane proteins.

5.14   Define diffusion and describe the process of passive transport.

5.15   Explain how transport proteins facilitate diffusion.

5.16   Explain how osmosis can be considered to be the diffusion of water across a membrane.

5.17   Distinguish among hypertonic, hypotonic, and isotonic solutions.

5.17   Explain how plant and animal cells change when placed into hypertonic or hypotonic solutions.

5.15, 5.18   Compare the processes of facilitated diffusion and active transport.

5.19   Distinguish among exocytosis, endocytosis, phagocytosis, pinocytosis, and receptor-mediated endocytosis.

5.20   Describe the cause of hypercholesterolemia.

5.21   Describe the central role of chloroplasts and mitochondria in harvesting energy and making it available for cellular work.

Key Terms

active site	exergonic reaction	phagocytosis
active transport	exocytosis	phosphorylation
ATP	facilitated diffusion	pinocytosis
cellular metabolism	feedback inhibition	plasmolysis
cellular respiration	first law of thermodynamics	potential energy
chemical energy	fluid mosaic	receptor-mediated
coenzyme	heat	endocytosis
cofactors	hypercholesterolemia	receptors
competitive inhibitor	hypertonic	second law of
concentration gradient	hypotonic	thermodynamics
endergonic reactions	induced fit	selective permeability
endocytosis	isotonic	signal transduction
energy	kinetic energy	substrate
energy coupling	noncompetitive inhibitor	thermodynamics
energy of activation (E_A)	osmoregulation	tonicity
entropy	osmosis	
enzyme	passive transport	

Word Roots

endo- = within (*endergonic reaction:* a reaction that absorbs free energy from its surroundings)

endo- = inner; **cyto-** = cell (*endocytosis:* the movement of materials into a cell. Cell-eating.)

ex- = out (*exergonic reaction:* a reaction that proceeds with a net release of free energy)

hyper- = exceeding; **-tonus** = tension (*hypertonic:* a solution with a higher concentration of solutes)

hypo- = lower (*hypotonic:* a solution with a lower concentration of solutes)

Lecture Outline

Introduction *Cool "Fires" Attract Mates and Meals*

    A. Characteristics of organisms (the light of a firefly, the red pigments of a New England autumn, the trumpeting of an elk, the rank odor of mildew in a damp closet) are all the products of chemical reactions that occur in organisms and their cells.

    B. Organisms carry out chemical reactions for the purpose of energy transformation. In fact, all reactions involve some energy transformation.

    C. This chapter covers several topics involved in how cells actually perform work: energy, enzymes, and membranes.
    Preview: Some reactions are simply required for biosynthesis (for example, the digestion of food into smaller parts, the formation of pigments, or the release of smelly waste products). Biosynthesis is discussed further in **Module 6.15.**

I. Energy and the Cell

Module 5.1 Energy is the capacity to perform work.

A. **Energy** can only be described and measured by how it affects matter. Energy is defined as the capacity to perform work. There are two forms of energy.

B. **Kinetic energy** is the energy of motion (Figure 5.1A). **Heat** (or thermal energy) is the kinetic energy associated with randomly moving molecules. The energy in light is another form of kinetic energy (talk about capturing energy from light during photosynthesis).

C. **Potential energy** is the stored capacity to perform work as a result of location or structure (Figure 5.1B). The most important form of potential energy in living things is the potential energy stored in the arrangement of atoms in molecules (structure). This is called **chemical energy.** The cell can convert the chemical energy (potential energy in the bonds) to kinetic energy and perform work.
NOTE: Some everyday examples help clarify these early definitions, such as Figure 5.1C and diagrams of water flowing downhill, dammed up, and flowing through a turbine or over a waterwheel.

Module 5.2 Two laws govern energy transformations.

A. **Thermodynamics** is the study of energy transformation that occurs in matter.
Preview: As discussed in Module 36.8, there is a limit to the length of a food chain. These limits are the direct result of the laws of thermodynamics.

B. **First law of thermodynamics** (energy conservation). The total amount of energy in the universe is constant; this energy can be transferred or transformed but neither created nor destroyed. Discuss the light bulb in the classroom that converts the electricity to light energy (and some heat, which is explained in the second law).

C. **Second law of thermodynamics** (entropy or disorder increases). Every energy change results in increased disorder, or increased entropy (when looking at the state of the energy throughout the system studied). As energy is converted from one form to another, unusable energy is lost to the surrounding environment in the form of heat (Figure 5.2A). Remind the students that this is why our body temperature is at 37°C and why we must sweat to stay cool when we work or play hard.

D. Biological systems function in much the same way; although some chemical energy may be channeled into useful work (protein synthesis), there is always an increase in disorder (Figure 5.2B).

Module 5.3 Chemical reactions either store or release energy.

A. **Endergonic reactions** require an input of energy equal to the difference in the potential energy of the reactants and products (Figure 5.3A).

B. *Preview:* Photosynthesis (Chapter 7) is an important process that is endergonic, using the energy of sunlight to form organic compounds.

C. **Exergonic reactions** result in an output of energy equal to the difference in the potential energy of the reactants and products (Figure 5.3B).

D. Burning and **cellular respiration** are both exergonic processes by which the chemical energy of the reactants is released to form energy-poor products. For example, in the case of burning wood, this happens rapidly with much "waste" of the chemical energy in the form of heat and light. In cellular respiration, glucose is oxidized (burned) to carbon dioxide and water with the production of ATP and heat.

Preview: Cellular respiration (Chapter 6) is an important biological process that releases the potential energy of fuel molecules (carbohydrates, lipids, proteins) slowly, to form some energy-poor reactants, and, most important, to convert the chemical energy of fuel molecules into smaller, usable amounts of chemical energy in the form of ATP (Module 5.4).

E. **Cellular metabolism** is the sum total of all the endergonic and exergonic reactions in cells.

F. **Energy coupling** is the combination of an endergonic reaction with an exergonic reaction to obtain the desired products for the cell.

Module 5.4 ATP shuttles chemical energy and drives cellular work.

A. Most endergonic cellular reactions require small amounts of energy, rather than the large amounts of energy available in food storage molecules.

B. Even a single glucose molecule contains too much energy. It's like a $100 bill: it's easier to work with some tens or fives.

C. Adenosine triphosphate (ATP) is the energy-rich (spendable) small molecule for cellular reactions. It transfers usable amounts of energy from exergonic, food energy–releasing reactions to the endergonic reactions where cell work is done. ATP is composed of three negatively charged phosphates, one ribose, and one adenine (Figure 5.4A).

D. Various covalent bonds link the atoms in the parts of ATP, but the terminal bonds connecting the outer two phosphate parts are energy rich and easily broken by hydrolysis.

E. The hydrolysis of ATP to release some of its chemical energy is an exergonic reaction (Figure 5.4A). When ATP gives up its energy, it forms ADP and an energy shuttle, the phosphate group.

F. The phosphate group is one of the reactants and the energy source for an endergonic reaction. This energizing process is known as **phosphorylation.** The products of the reaction hold chemical energy and are ready to do cellular work. Cellular work can be divided into three types: chemical (protein synthesis), mechanical (muscle contraction), and transport movement of molecule across membranes (see Module 5.18 and Figure 5.4B).

G. ATP regeneration is the reverse process. Endergonic reactions involved in cellular respiration phosphorylate (and energize) ADP in dehydration synthesis.

H. ATP is constantly being regenerated and used in a cycle involving endergonic dehydration synthesis and exergonic hydrolysis (Figure 5.4C).

II. How Enzymes Function

Module 5.5 Enzymes speed up the cell's chemical reactions by lowering energy barriers.

A. **Enzymes** are large protein molecules that function as biological catalysts. A catalyst is a chemical that speeds up the reaction without itself being consumed (Figures 5.5A and B). Ask the students if there are other ways to speed up chemical reactions (heat).

B. The **energy of activation** is the amount of energy, an "energy barrier," that must be put into an exergonic reaction before the reaction will proceed (analogy of the Mexican jumping beans, Figure 5.5A; energy of activation, Figure 5.5B).

Module 5.6 A specific enzyme catalyzes each cellular reaction.

A. The reactant in an enzyme-catalyzed reaction is the **substrate.**

B. One part of the enzyme binds to the substrate at the **active site,** holding the substrate in a specific position that facilitates the reaction. The interaction of the substrate with enzyme at the active site causes a conformational change of the enzyme referred to as an **induced fit** and promotes the chemical reaction (Figure 5.6).

NOTE: Enzyme names end in -ase and are often named after their substrates. For example, the enzyme that catalyzes the hydrolysis of sucrose is sucrase. Ask the students if they know anyone who can't drink milk (lactose intolerance and lactase deficiency).

C. At the end of the reaction, the substrate changes into the product and is released, and the enzyme is unchanged.

Module 5.7 The cellular environment affects enzyme activity.

A. Factors such as temperature, pH, salt concentration, and the presence of **cofactors** often affect the way enzymes work.

Preview: Magnesium (Mg^{2+}) is a cofactor that is essential for the proper functioning of chlorophyll (Module 32.6).

B. Organic cofactors are called **coenzymes.**

Preview: Vitamins are coenzymes (Chapter 21, Module 21.17).

Module 5.8 Enzyme inhibitors block enzyme action.

A. Inhibitors work by binding with the active site (**competitive inhibitors**) or some other site (**noncompetitive inhibitors**) on the enzyme, thus affecting the enzyme's ability to bind with the substrate (Figure 5.8).

B. Feedback inhibition is a type of inhibition whereby enzyme activity is blocked by a product of the reaction catalyzed by the enzyme.

NOTE: Negative feedback mechanisms are of major importance in the regulation of biological systems. A very clear example of this is seen in the regulation of female and male reproductive systems (Chapter 27).

Module 5.9 Connection: Many poisons, pesticides, and drugs are enzyme inhibitors.

A. For example, cyanide inhibits the production of ATP during respiration and the nerve gas sarin inhibits the enzyme acetylcholinesterase.

B. The pesticide malathion also inhibits the enzyme acetylcholinesterase but is used at doses too low to be harmful to humans.

C. The antibiotic penicillin interferes with an enzyme that helps build bacterial cell walls.

D. Pain killers such as aspirin and ibuprofen inhibit the enzyme used to induce pain. Other therapeutic drugs used to combat HIV and cancer are also enzyme inhibitors.

III. Membrane Structure and Function

Module 5.10 Membranes organize the chemical activities of cells.

A. Membranes separate cells from the outside environments, including, in multicellular organisms, the environment in other cells that perform different functions.

B. Membranes control the passage of molecules from one side of the membrane to the other.

C. In eukaryotes, membranes partition function into organelles.

D. Membranes provide reaction surfaces, and organize enzymes and their substrates.

Preview: The electron transport chain and chemiosmosis (**Figures 6.6, 6.10,** and **7.9**).

E. Membranes are **selectively permeable,** which means some substances can pass through a membrane more easily than other substances. Compare ethanol (as a fixative) to glucose.

F. Membrane thickness cannot be seen in sections under the light microscope. Membranes can be resolved in TEM micrographs (Figure 5.10).

Module 5.11 Membrane phospholipids form a bilayer.

A. Phospholipids are like fats, with two nonpolar fatty acid "tails" that are hydrophobic and one polar phosphate "head" attached to the glycerol that is hydrophilic (Figure 5.11A).

B. In water, thousands of individual molecules form a stable bilayer, aiming their polar heads out, toward the water, and their nonpolar tails in, away from the water (Figure 5.11B).

C. The hydrophobic interior of this bilayer offers an effective barrier to the flow of most hydrophilic molecules but allows the passage of hydrophobic molecules.

Module 5.12 The membrane is a fluid mosaic of phospholipids and proteins.

A. It is a mosaic because the proteins form a "tiled pattern" in the "grout ground" of the phospholipid bilayer (Figure 5.12).

B. It is fluid (like salad oil) because the individual molecules are more or less free to move about laterally.

C. The two sides of the membrane usually incorporate different sets of proteins and lipids: glycoproteins and glycolipids.

D. Some proteins extend through both sides of the bilayer and bind to the cytoskeleton and/or the extracellular matrix.
    NOTE: Cholesterol is a common constituent of animal cell membranes and stabilizes membrane fluidity at different temperatures (Figure 5.12). So cholesterol is not always "bad."

Module 5.13 Proteins make the membrane a mosaic of function.

A. Identification tags: particularly glycoproteins (and nonprotein-containing glycolipids) (Figure 5.12).

B. Enzymes: catalyzing intracellular and extracellular reactions (Figure 5.13A).

C. **Receptors:** triggering cell activity when a messenger molecule attaches (e.g., signal transduction; Figure 5.13B).
    Preview: **Signal transduction** is a message-transfer process that causes the cell to respond to the external message that bound to the receptor (**Module 11.14).**

D. Cell junctions: either attachments to other cells or the internal cytoskeleton.

E. Transporters: of hydrophilic molecules (Figure 5.13C).

Module 5.14 Passive transport is diffusion across a membrane.

A. **Diffusion** is the tendency for particles of any kind to spread out spontaneously from an area of high concentration to an area of low concentration.
    NOTE: A **concentration gradient** is a form of potential energy. The movement of the molecules is kinetic energy.

B. **Passive transport** across membranes occurs (as diffusion does everywhere) when a molecule diffuses down a concentration gradient. At equilibrium, molecules continue to diffuse back and forth, but there is no net change in concentration anywhere (Figure 5.14A).

C. Different molecules diffuse independently of one another (Figure 5.14B).

D. Passive transport is an extremely important way for small molecules to get into and out of cells. For example, O_2 moves into red blood cells and CO_2 moves out of these cells by this process in the lungs. The reverse process takes place in the tissue because the concentration gradients have reversed.

Module 5.15 Transport proteins facilitate diffusion across membranes (Figure 5.15).

A. **Facilitated diffusion** occurs when a pored protein, spanning the membrane bilayer, allows a solute to diffuse down a concentration gradient.

B. The cell does not expend energy.

C. The rate of facilitated diffusion depends on the number of such transport proteins, in addition to the strength of the concentration gradient.

D. Water is a polar molecule and, therefore, needs the assistance of transport proteins when crossing membranes. A good example of this is the aquaporins (water transport proteins) in the collecting ducts of the kidneys.

Module 5.16 Osmosis is the diffusion of water across a membrane.

A. If a membrane that is permeable to water but not to a solute separates an area of high solute concentration (hypertonic) from an area of low solute concentration (hypotonic), the water diffuses by **osmosis** to the hypertonic area until the concentration of each solute is the same on both sides of the membrane.
   NOTE: Osmosis can cause a physical force to be applied to the hypertonic solution. In the case shown in Figure 5.16, this osmotic force raises the level of the solution on the right against the force of gravity, until the weight difference in levels equals the osmotic force.

B. The direction of osmosis is determined only by the difference in total solute concentrations.

C. Two solutions equal in solute concentrations are isotonic to each other; therefore, osmosis does not occur.

D. However, even in isotonic solutions separated by a selectively permeable membrane, water molecules are moving in both directions at equal rates.

Module 5.17 Water balance between cells and their surroundings is crucial to organisms.

A. Cell membranes act as selectively permeable membranes between the cell contents and its surroundings (Figure 5.17). The propensity of a cell to gain or lose water with its surroundings is referred to as **tonicity.**

B. If a plant or animal cell is **isotonic** with its surroundings, no osmosis occurs, and the cells do not change. However, plant cells in such environments are flaccid or wilted, lacking the turgor that helps support some plant tissues.

C. An animal cell in a **hypotonic** solution will gain water and pop (lyse). A plant cell in a hypotonic solution will become turgid, as the cell wall counters the osmotic force of water moving in.

D. An animal cell in a **hypertonic** solution will lose water and shrivel (crenate). A plant cell in a hypertonic solution will lose water past the cell membrane but not the cell wall, resulting in the plasma membrane pulling away from the inside of the cell wall and the cell as a whole losing turgor. This process is called **plasmolysis.**
   Preview: The control of water balance, **osmoregulation,** is discussed in **Module 25.4.**

Module 5.18 Cells expend energy for active transport.

A. **Active transport** involves the assistance of a transport protein when moving a solute against a concentration gradient (Figure 5.18, steps 1–4).

B. Energy expenditure in the form of ATP-mediated phosphorylation is required to help the protein change its structure and, thus, move the solute molecule.
Preview: A very important example of a coupled active transport system is the Na^+-K^+ pump, which functions in nerve impulse transmission (**Modules 28.4** and **28.5**).

Module 5.19 Exocytosis and endocytosis transport large molecules.

A. In **exocytosis,** membrane-bounded vesicles containing large molecules fuse with the plasma membrane and release their contents outside the cell (Figure 5.19A).

B. In **endocytosis,** the plasma membrane surrounds materials outside the cell, closes around the materials, and forms membrane-bounded vesicles containing the materials (Figure 5.19B).

C. Three important types of endocytosis are **phagocytosis** ("cell eating"), **pinocytosis** ("cell drinking"), and **receptor-mediated endocytosis** (very specific) (Figure 5.19C).

Module 5.20 Connection: Faulty membranes can overload the blood with cholesterol (Figure 5.20).

A. Cholesterol is carried in the blood by low-density lipoprotein (LDL) particles.

B. In people with normal cholesterol metabolism, excess LDL-bound cholesterol in the blood is eliminated by receptor-mediated endocytosis by liver cells.

C. In people with a genetic condition that results in increased levels of cholesterol (hypercholesterolemia), fewer or no such receptor sites exist, and the people accumulate LDL-bound cholesterol. These people are at high risk for developing heart disease.
Preview: The genetics of this disease is discussed in **Module 9.12.** As discussed in **Module 21.24,** hypercholesterolemia can also be a result of lifestyle.

Module 5.21 Chloroplasts and mitochondria make energy available for cellular work.

A. The subjects of this chapter (energy, enzymes, and membranes) are important parts of the functioning of these two organelles and the processes they carry out (photosynthesis and cellular respiration).

B. Photosynthesis and cellular respiration are linked.

C. Solar energy is used by chloroplasts to build energy-rich molecules in endergonic reactions.
Preview: Photosynthesis is discussed in Chapter 7.

D. The energy-rich molecules release their energy to form ATP in mitochondria.
Preview: Cellular respiration is discussed in Chapter 6.

E. The chemicals involved as the reactants in chloroplasts are the products in mitochondria, and vice versa.

Class Activities

1. To demonstrate osmosis, take a limp piece of celery and place it in cold water (a hypotonic solution); the water will move into the celery by osmosis, and the resulting turgor pressure will stiffen the celery.

2. Have your students consider why, since they shower and bathe in hypotonic solutions, they do not fill with water and explode.

3. See if your students can relate their understanding of the material covered in this class to the childhood cruelty of putting salt on slugs.

4. Though osmoregulation will be discussed in a later chapter (Chapter 25), see if your students can think of mechanisms that would permit plants and animals to survive in either a hypertonic (saltwater) or a hypotonic (freshwater) environment.

Transparency Acetates

Figure 5.2B	Energy transformations in a cell
Figure 5.3A	Endergonic reaction
Figure 5.3B	Exergonic reaction
Figure 5.4A	ATP structure and hydrolysis
Figure 5.4B	How ATP powers cellular work
Figure 5.4C	The ATP cycle
Figure 5.5A	Jumping-bean analogy for energy of activation (E_A) and the role of enzymes
Figure 5.5B	The effect of an enzyme on E_A
Figure 5.6	The catalytic cycle of an enzyme
Figure 5.8	How inhibitors interfere with substrate binding
Figure 5.11A	Phospholipid molecule
Figure 5.11B	Phospholipid bilayer
Figure 5.12	The plasma membrane and extracellular matrix of an animal cell
Figure 5.13A–C	Enzyme activity, signal transduction, transport
Figure 5.14A	Passive transport of one type of molecule
Figure 5.14B	Passive transport of two types of molecules (combined with Figure 5.14A)
Figure 5.15	Transport protein providing a pore for solute passage
Figure 5.16	Osmosis
Figure 5.17	How animal and plant cells behave in different solutions
Figure 5.18	Active transport of two solutes across a membrane
Figure 5.19A	Exocytosis
Figure 5.19B	Endocytosis (combined with Figure 5.19A)
Figure 5.20	A cell using receptor-mediated endocytosis to take up an LDL

Connecting the Concepts, page 86: The catalytic cycle of an enzyme

Connecting the Concepts, page 87: Molecules cross cell membranes

Media

See the beginning of this book for a complete description of all media available for instructors and students. Animations and videos are available in the Campbell Image Presentation Library. Media Activities and Thinking as a Scientist investigations are available on the student CD-ROM and website.

Animations and Videos	Module Number
Energy Concepts Animation	5.1
How Enzymes Work Animation	5.6
Membrane Structure Animation	5.11
Receptor Proteins Animation	5.13
Diffusion Animation	5.14
Osmosis Animation	5.15
Plasmolysis Video	5.17
Turgid *Elodea* Video	5.17
Active Transport Animation	5.18
Exocytosis and Endocytosis Introduction Animation	5.19
Exocytosis Animation	5.19
Phagocytosis Animation	5.19
Pinocytosis Animation	5.19
Receptor-Mediated Endocytosis Animation	5.19

Activities and Thinking as a Scientist	Module Number
Web/CD Activity 5A: *Energy Transformations*	5.2
Web/CD Activity 5B: *Chemical Reactions and ATP*	5.3
Web/CD Activity 5C: *The Structure of ATP*	5.4
Web/CD Activity 5D: *How Enzymes Work*	5.6
Web/CD Thinking as a Scientist: *How Is the Rate of Enzyme Catalysis Measured?*	5.7
Biology Labs On-Line: *How Enzymes Work*	5.8
Web/CD Activity 5E: *Membrane Structure*	5.12
Web/CD Activity 5F: *Signal Transduction*	5.13
Web/CD Activity 5G: *Selective Permeability of Membranes*	5.13
Web/CD Thinking as a Scientist: *How Do Cells Communicate with Each Other?*	5.13
Web/CD Activity 5H: *Diffusion*	5.14
Web/CD Activity 5I: *Facilitated Diffusion*	5.15
Web/CD Activity 5J: *Osmosis and Water Balance in Cells*	5.17
Web/CD Thinking as a Scientist: *How Does Osmosis Affect Cells?*	5.17
Web/CD Activity 5K: *Active Transport*	5.18
Web/CD Activity 5L: *Exocytosis and Endocytosis*	5.19
Web/CD Activity 5M: *Build a Chemical Cycling System*	5.21

CHAPTER 6

How Cells Harvest Chemical Energy

Teaching Objectives

Introduction   Compare the structure and functions of slow and fast muscle fibers. Explain why some people seem to be natural sprinters.

Introduction to Cellular Respiration

6.1   Compare the processes and locations of cellular respiration and photosynthesis. Explain how you rely on energy from the sun.

6.2   Define and compare the processes of breathing and cellular respiration.

6.3   Describe the overall chemical equation for cellular respiration. Compare the efficiency of this process in cells to the efficiency of a gasoline automobile engine.

6.4   Explain how the human body uses its daily supply of ATP.

6.5   Explain how the energy in a glucose molecule is released during cellular respiration.

6.5   Explain how redox reactions are used in cellular respiration.

6.5   Describe the roles of dehydrogenase, NAD^+, and the electron transport chain in cellular respiration.

Stages of Cellular Respiration and Fermentation

6.6   List the cellular regions where glycolysis, the citric acid cycle, and oxidative phosphorylation occur. Note whether substrate-level phosphorylation or chemiosmosis occur at each of these sites.

6.7–6.12   Compare the reactants, products, and energy yield of the three stages of cellular respiration.

6.11   Explain how rotenone, oligomycin, and uncouplers interrupt critical events in cellular respiration.

6.13   Compare the reactants, products, and energy yield of alcohol and lactic acid fermentation. Distinguish between strict anaerobes and facultative anaerobes.

Interconnections Between Molecular Breakdown and Synthesis

6.14   Explain how polysaccharides, fats, and proteins are broken down to yield ATP. Explain why a gram of fat yields more ATP than a gram of starch or protein.

6.15   Explain how food molecules are used in biosynthesis.

6.16   Describe the fundamental relationship between respiration and photosynthesis.

Key Terms

acetyl CoA (acetyl coenzyme A)	dehydrogenase	oxidation
alcohol fermentation	electron transport chain	oxidative phosphorylation
ATP synthases	facultative anaerobe	redox reaction
cellular respiration	glycolysis	reduction
chemiosmosis	intermediates	strict anaerobe
citric acid cycle	lactic acid fermentation	substrate-level phosphorylation
	NAD^+	

Word Roots

glyco- = sweet; **-lysis** = split (*glycolysis:* the splitting of glucose into pyruvate)

Lecture Outline

Introduction *How Is a Marathoner Different from a Sprinter?*

    A. *Review:* The definition of metabolism and what it entails (Chapter 5).

    B. Harvesting chemical energy from food molecules is one side of a cycle that, in eukaryotes, often involves mitochondria and chloroplasts (Module 5.21).

    C. Muscles in our legs are of two types: slow-twitch and fast-twitch. The difference between the muscle types is determined by the type of work they do and the type of metabolic processes they perform. Sprinters have proportionally more fast-twitch muscle, while distance runners have a larger portion of slow-twitch muscle.

    D. Slow-twitch muscles metabolize glucose in the presence of O_2 (aerobic respiration), producing large amounts of ATP, and can, therefore, work for a long period of time. Fast-twitch muscles metabolize glucose in the absence of O_2 (anaerobic), producing very little ATP, and, therefore, can work for only a short amount of time, albeit furiously.

    E. This chapter covers the various metabolic pathways by which energy is released from food molecules, particularly glucose, in the presence (**cellular respiration**) and absence of oxygen.

I. Introduction to Cellular Respiration

Module 6.1 Photosynthesis and respiration provide energy for life.

    A. All living organisms require energy to maintain homeostasis, to move and reproduce. The ultimate source of energy is the sun.

    B. Plants, algae, and photosynthetic bacteria and protists perform photosynthesis (the conversion of CO_2 and H_2O into O_2 and glucose). Stored energy from glucose can be released and transferred to ATP.

    C. Molecules are cycled through an ecosystem, but the flow of energy is one-way (Figure 6.1).

Module 6.2 Breathing supplies oxygen to our cells and removes carbon dioxide.

    A. The oxygen needed to burn food by the process of cellular respiration is outside the bodies of organisms and is obtained by breathing (respiration).

    B. ATP is needed by cells to perform work.

    C. Mitochondria use O_2 in the process of cellular respiration.

    D. The muscular, respiratory, and circulatory systems combine forces to bring reactants (food molecules and O_2) to cells and remove waste products (CO_2 and H_2O) from cells in an effort to make ATP (Figure 6.2).

Module 6.3 Cellular respiration banks energy in ATP molecules.

    A. Overall equation:

$$C_6H_{12}O_6 + 6\,O_2 \rightarrow 6\,CO_2 + 6\,H_2O + \text{energy in the form of ATP and heat (Figure 6.3)}.$$

B. *Review:* The second law of thermodynamics. Remind students that the wasted energy is lost to each system as random kinetic energy (heat).

C. Compare the efficiency of the overall process in cells (about 40%) to the efficiency of energy use by an automobile (about 25%).

Module 6.4 Connection: The human body uses energy from ATP for all its activities.

A. Energy is used for body maintenance, for example, breathing, digesting food, temperature regulation, and blood circulation.

B. Voluntary activities require additional energy input and use calories at a faster rate than simple body maintenance (Table 6.4).

C. A general estimate for an adult human of average weight for both types of energy expenditure is 2,200 kcal per day.

Module 6.5 Cells tap energy from electrons "falling" from organic fuels to oxygen.

A. One glucose molecule contains more energy than a cell needs to use for a single job.

B. Discuss the rearrangements that have occurred in the locations of bonds in the reactants and products of cellular respiration.

C. Describe the strong electronegative attraction that oxygen has for electrons (Module 2.8).

D. Compare the burning of a cube of sugar, which releases light and heat, to the use of sugar by a cell. The former is fast and uncontrolled, while the latter is slow and controlled (stepwise).

E. The movement of hydrogens represents transfer of electrons (Figure 6.5A).
Review: The coupling of the release of energy from ATP, an exergonic reaction, to provide energy to drive endergonic reactions is discussed in Module 5.4.

F. The paired reactions at each step in the transfer of energy are known as **redox** (reduction-oxidation) **reactions.**

G. **Oxidation** reactions involve electron loss and are the exergonic half (Figure 6.5A, top half).

H. **Reduction** reactions involve electron gain and are the endergonic half (Figure 6.5A, bottom half).
NOTE: A mnemonic for this is LEO-GER: Loss of Electrons, Oxidation; Gain of Electrons, Reduction.

I. At each step in the breakdown of glucose, small redox reactions occur involving an enzyme, **dehydrogenase,** and its coenzyme, NAD^+, that function as an electron shuttle.

J. During each step, the breakdown portion (glucose being stripped of its electrons) is oxidized while the NAD^+ is reduced, forming NADH.

K. At the beginning of a different set of reactions, all the NADH generated as above gives up its energetic electrons and NAD^1 is regenerated (Figure 6.5B).

L. These energetic electrons then pass from molecule to molecule in an "energy cascade," or **electron transport chain.** Each molecule is temporarily reduced by the oxidation of the previous molecule and, in turn, is oxidized when it reduces the next.
NOTE: This gradual release of energy can be analogized to a Slinky going down a flight of steps one step at a time.

M. The ultimate electron acceptor in this part of the overall process is oxygen.

N. During the cascade, small amounts of energy are released, which can build ATP.

II. Stages of Cellular Respiration and Fermentation

Module 6.6 Overview: Respiration occurs in three main stages.

A. Summarizing and previewing the overall process, cellular respiration is composed of three major steps:

1. **Glycolysis** occurs in the cytoplasm and converts glucose to two molecules of pyruvate.

2. The **citric acid Cycle** occurs in the mitochondrial matrix and finishes the breakdown of pyruvate to CO_2, providing electrons for the 3rd stage.

3. **Oxidative phosphorylation** occurs on the inner mitochondrial membrane and is a major site of ATP synthesis.

B. These three parts are interconnected, as shown in Figure 6.6, which also shows the location of ATP synthesis. A major function of cellular respiration is the synthesis of ATP for cellular work.

C. ATP synthesis can occur by two mechanisms:

1. **Substrate-level phosphorylation:** the addition of a phosphate to ADP from an intermediate of glycolysis or the citric acid cycle (see Module 6.7).

2. Oxidative Phosphorylation: electrons from the electron transport chain generate a chemiosmotic gradient that can drive the synthesis of ATP.

D. **Chemiosmosis** was first described by Peter Mitchell as a mechanism to synthesize ATP. The electron transport chain generates a chemical gradient when H^+ cross the mitochondrial membrane. The enzyme **ATP synthase** then uses the flux of H^+ back to the mitochondrial matrix to drive the synthesis of ATP (see Module 6.10 for more details).

Module 6.7 Glycolysis harvests chemical energy by oxidizing glucose to pyruvic acid.

A. This process occurs in the cytoplasm.

B. Overall there are nine chemical steps, the net result of which is to split one six-carbon sugar molecule into two three-carbon pyruvic acid molecules (Figure 6.7A).

C. Each of the nine intermediate steps involves a separate enzyme (Figure 6.7C).

D. In addition to glucose, ADP, phosphate, and NAD^+ are required as reactants. ATP is also required for the generation of **intermediates** such as glucose-6-phosphate. Conversely, ATP can be generated from intermediates in the process described in the previous module (substrate-level phosphorylation; Figure 6.7B).

E. Glycolysis can be broken into two phases: Steps 1–4 are preparatory and require ATP input (Figure 6.7C; "preparatory phase"); Steps 5–9 are energy releasing, producing ATP and NADH (Figure 6.9B; "energy payoff phase").

F. Net energy production for glycolysis: 2 ATP (immediately usable for cellular work) and 2 NADH molecules for each glucose molecule entering the process.

Module 6.8 Pyruvic acid is chemically groomed for the citric acid cycle.

A. This process occurs in the mitochondrial matrix (the fluid within the inner mitochondrial membrane) (Figure 6.8).

1. Pyruvate is oxidized, reducing NAD^+ to NADH (off to the electron transport chain).

2. Pyruvate is stripped of a carbon, releasing CO_2.

3. Pyruvate is complexed with coenzyme A, resulting in the molecule acetyl coenzyme A (**acetyl CoA**), the high-energy (but not as high as glucose) fuel for the citric acid cycle.

B. Net energy production for this step: 2 NADH molecules per glucose molecule entering the process.

Module 6.9 The citric acid cycle completes the oxidation of organic fuel, generating many NADH and $FADH_2$ molecules.

A. This process occurs in the mitochondrial matrix.

B. Overall there are five chemical steps, the net result of which is to disassemble one two-carbon acetyl CoA into two CO_2 molecules while reducing one FAD molecule and three NAD^+ molecules (Figure 6.9A).

C. Each of the five intermediate steps involves a separate enzyme (Figure 6.9B).

D. In addition to acetyl CoA, ADP, phosphate, NAD^+, FAD (another energy shuttle molecule), and oxaloacetic acid are required as reactants.

E. The five intermediate reactions regenerate oxaloacetic acid. This molecule is required at the beginning, and thus the cycle can start again.

F. Coenzyme A is released at the first step and goes back to groom more pyruvic acid.

G. Net energy production for the citric acid cycle: 2 ATP (immediately usable), 6 NADH (not immediately usable), and 2 $FADH_2$ (not immediately usable) for each glucose molecule entering the whole cellular respiration process.
   NOTE: The total number of energy-rich molecules generated from the oxidation of glucose is 4 ATP, 10 NADH and 2 $FADH_2$.

Module 6.10 Most ATP production occurs by oxidation phosphorylation.

A. The electron transport chain is a series of protein complexes built into the cristae (inner mitochondrial membrane) (Figure 6.10).

B. Each protein in the chain oscillates between reduced and oxidized states as the energetic electrons from NADH and $FADH_2$ pass through their region.

C. As redox occurs, H^+ are actively transported from inside the cristae to the intermembrane space.

D. The resulting H^+ ions' gradient drives the production of ATP in the matrix, as the H^+ ions are transported through the ATP synthase.

E. The name "oxidative phosphorylation" comes from the redox reactions of the electron transport chain and the phosphorylation of ATP that is driven by the H^+ gradient.

F. These ATP molecules are produced only if O_2 is available as the terminal electron acceptor.

Module 6.11 Connection: Certain poisons interrupt critical events in cellular respiration (Figure 6.13).

A. Rotenone (a plant product commonly used to kill fish and insect pests), cyanide, and carbon monoxide block various parts of the electron transport chain.
   Preview: Biological magnification can be a consequence of the use of such biocides (Module 38.3).

B. The antifungal agent oligomycin blocks passage of hydrogen ions through the ATP synthases molecule.

C. "Uncouplers," such as dinitrophenol, cause the cristae to leak H^1 ions so that the H^+ ions' gradient is not maintained, and chemiosmosis cannot occur.

Module 6.12 Review: Each molecule of glucose yields many molecules of ATP.

  A. Glycolysis in cytoplasm yields some ATP in the absence of O_2 but mostly prepares for further steps in the mitochondria that require O_2.

  B. The citric acid cycle in the mitochondrial matrix yields some ATP directly but strips out CO_2, producing energy shuttles.

  C. The electron transport chain produces copious amounts of ATP, but only in the presence of O_2.

  D. Three ATP are produced for each NADH and 2 ATP are produced for each $FADH_2$ introduced into the electron transport chain.

  E. However, these are maximums. In some cells, ATP is required to shuttle NADH from the cytoplasm into the mitochondrion. Thus, the estimate of the total yield of ATP generated by the aerobic respiration of glucose has a theoretical maximum of 38 (Figure 6.12).
  NOTE: This is a good time to discuss the meaning behind the diagrammatic representations of metabolism and how the processes are studied. Reactions proceed from one "pool" of a compound to the next, depending on concentration gradients and the presence of the correct enzymes. The reactions are all happening in many places at the same time. Research into these pathways involves the introduction of radioactive isotope-labeled reactants followed by the recovery of the labeled products (Modules 2.5 and 7.3).

Module 6.13 Fermentation is an anaerobic alternative to cellular respiration.

  A. Fermentation refers to energy-releasing molecular rearrangements in the absence of oxygen. In the two cases reviewed in this module, the role of fermentation is to recharge NAD^+ so that glycolysis can continue to proceed in the absence of O_2. In addition, products are produced that are reduced and still energy rich.
  NOTE: You might want to tell the story of the individual who never drank alcohol and yet got drunk whenever he ate. What happened is that outpouchings in his intestines (an anaerobic environment) contained yeast that produced ethanol by fermentation whenever he ate. A fun way to finish this story is to ask the students to picture him getting arrested for driving under the influence of food.

  B. **Lactic acid fermentation,** characteristic of many organisms including animals and bacteria, results in one three-carbon lactic acid molecule. Although the accumulation of lactic acid causes muscle fatigue in animals, it is less toxic than alcohol and can be removed from the affected cells and detoxified by the liver with the Cori cycle (Figure 6.13A).

  C. **Alcoholic fermentation,** characteristic of some yeasts and bacteria, results in one two-carbon ethanol. This product is toxic, and high concentrations will ultimately kill the cells that produce it (Figure 6.13B).
  NOTE: Different strains of yeast are killed by concentrations of up to 20%.

  D. Organisms that can live only in environments that lack oxygen are known as **strict anaerobes.** These organisms lack the necessary molecular and cellular equipment with which to carry out cellular respiration.
  NOTE: Since aerobic photosynthesis evolved earlier than aerobic respiration, the oxygen that was produced was a toxin.

  E. Organisms that can live in environments lacking or containing oxygen are known as **facultative anaerobes.** The production of beer and wine uses the facultative anaerobe's ability to grow in the absence of O_2 and produce ethanol as a byproduct (Figure 6.13C).

III. Interconnections Between Molecular Breakdown and Synthesis

Module 6.14 Cells use many kinds of organic molecules as fuel for cellular respiration.

A. Free glucose is not the most common source of fuel in most animal diets, including the human diet. Each of the basic food types can be used as a source of energy (Figure 6.14).

B. Carbohydrates (polysaccharides and sugars) are usually hydrolyzed by digestive enzymes (or liver enzymes) to glucose, which enters glycolysis.

C. Proteins must first be digested to their constituent amino acids. The amino acids are then transformed into various compounds, which enter the middle of glycolysis or the citric acid cycle. Toxic parts of amino acids are stripped off and eliminated in urine (urea) or used to synthesize other compounds.

D. Fats contain almost twice as much energy per unit weight as carbohydrates. They must first be digested to glycerol and free fatty acids. Glycerol enters in the middle of glycolysis, and the free fatty acids are converted into multiple copies of acetyl CoA and enter the citric acid cycle.

E. *Preview:* Human nutrition and the fate, following digestion, of many of the types of basic foods introduced here (and in the next module) are the subjects of Chapter 21.

Module 6.15 Food molecules provide raw materials for biosynthesis.

A. Cells and organisms obtain some raw materials directly from the digestion of the macromolecules in food (Figure 6.15).

B. The processes that produce new molecules often appear to be the reverse of processes that break down the same class of molecules. However, there are differences in the details, as discussed in Module 6.14.

C. ATP is required in biosynthetic pathways and produced by degradative pathways.

Module 6.16 The fuel for respiration ultimately comes from photosynthesis.

A. Cells of all living things can harvest molecular energy by either cellular respiration or fermentation (Figure 6.16).

B. The ability to convert light energy into stored molecular energy is a process limited to plants (photosynthesis, the subject of Chapter 7).

Class Activities

1. The production of CO_2 as a by-product of cellular respiration can be demonstrated by using a straw to blow bubbles into a pH indicator solution. CO_2 will make the solution acidic.

2. When looking at food labels, all fats are treated as though they contain the same number of calories. Ask your students if, based on what they learned about the structure of fats in Chapter 3 and cellular respiration in this chapter, this is strictly true. Recall that fats are energy-rich molecules because they contain many hydrogens; however, fats vary in the number of fatty acids they contain as well as in the length and degree of saturation of these fatty acids.

Transparency Acetates

Media

See the beginning of this book for a complete description of all media available for instructors and students. Animations and videos are available in the Campbell Image Presentation Library. Media Activities and Thinking as a Scientist investigations are available on the student CD-ROM and website.

Animations and Videos	Module Number
Glycolysis Animation	6.7
Citric Acid Cycle Animation	6.8
Electron Transport Animation	6.10
Fermentation Animation	6.13

Activities and Thinking as a Scientist	Module Number
Web/CD Activity 6A: *Glycolysis*	6.7
Web/CD Activity 6B: *The Citric Acid Cycle*	6.9
Web/CD Activity 6C: *Electron Transport and Chemiosmosis*	6.10
Web/CD Activity 6D: *Overview of Cellular Respiration*	6.12
Web/CD Activity 6E: *Fermentation*	6.13
Web/CD Thinking as a Scientist: *How Is the Rate of Cellular Respiration Measured?*	6.12
Biology Labs On-Line: *Stages of Cellular Respiration and Fermentation*	6.12

Photosynthesis: Using Light to Make Food

Teaching Objectives

Introduction Explain how plants can be used as a renewable energy source. Explain why this is better than burning fossil fuels.

An Overview of Photosynthesis

7.1 Define the terms autotrophs, photoautotrophs, and producers.

7.2 Describe the structure of chloroplasts and their location in a leaf. Identify specifically where most light energy is converted to chemical energy.

7.3 Explain how plants produce oxygen. Describe the experiments that revealed the source of the oxygen produced during photosynthesis.

7.4 Describe the role of redox reactions in photosynthesis and cellular respiration.

7.5 Compare the reactants and products of the light reactions and the Calvin cycle. Explain how the term photosynthesis relates to these reactions.

The Light Reactions: Converting Solar Energy to Chemical Energy

7.6 Describe the properties and functions of the different photosynthetic pigments.

7.7 Explain how photosystems capture solar energy.

7.8–7.9 Explain how the electron transport chain and chemiosmosis generate ATP, NADPH, and oxygen in the light reactions.

7.9 Compare photophosphorylation and oxidative phosphorylation.

The Calvin Cycle: Converting CO_2 to Sugars

7.10 Describe the reactants and products of the Calvin cycle. Explain why this cycle is dependent upon the light reactions.

Photosynthesis Reviewed and Extended

7.11 Review the overall process of the light reactions and the Calvin cycle, noting the products, reactants, and locations of each major step.

7.12 Compare the mechanisms that C_3, C_4, and CAM plants use to obtain carbon dioxide. Note examples of plants that use each of these systems.

Photosynthesis, Solar Radiation, and Earth's Atmosphere

7.13 Describe the greenhouse effect and explain how deforestation and the use of fossil fuels affect this phenomenon.

7.14 Explain how the ozone layer forms, how human activities have damaged it, and the consequences of the destruction of the ozone layer.

Key Terms

autotrophs	grana	photosynthesis
C_3 plants	greenhouse effect	photosystem
C_4 plants	light reactions	producers
Calvin cycle	mesophyll	reaction center
CAM plants	photoautotrophs	stomata
carbon fixation	photon	stroma
electromagnetic energy	photophosphorylation	thylakoids
global warming	photorespiration	wavelength

Word Roots

auto- = self; **-troph** = food (*autotroph:* an organism that obtains organic food molecules without eating other organisms)

meso- = middle (*mesophyll:* the green tissue in the middle, inside of a leaf)

photo- = light (*photosystem:* cluster of pigment molecules)

Lecture Outline

Introduction *Plant Power*

    A. As the world population continues to increase and the demand for energy grows, more fossil fuel will be burned. Burning fossil fuel increases the greenhouse gases that are polluting the atmosphere.

    B. Review the overall equation for photosynthesis, and note that it is the reverse of cellular respiration (figure at top of left page).

$$6CO_2 + 6H_2O \xrightarrow[\text{Energy}]{\text{Light}} C_6H_{12}O_6 + 6O_2$$

    C. Growing willow trees as a source of renewable energy is currently an area of research into alternative fuels. Willow trees grow fast; are capable of sprouting, which reduces the need to replant; and generate more BTUs than other types of wood.

I. An Overview of Photosynthesis

Module 7.1 Autotrophs are the producers of the biosphere.

    A. **Autotroph** means "self-feeder," and the term is applied to any organism that makes its own food without eating, decomposing, or absorbing other organisms or organic molecules.

    B. Autotrophs produce the biosphere's food supply (Module 37.11).

    C. **Producers** include plants, algae, some prokaryotes, and certain protists (Figures 7.1A–D). Producers that use light energy are referred to as photoautotrophs. *NOTE:* We will return to the term producer in our discussion of community ecology and the flow of energy among different kinds of organisms (Chapter 36).

Module 7.2 Photosynthesis occurs in chloroplasts.

Review: Figures 4.4B and 4.14 for plant cell and chloroplast structure.

A. This is true for all photosynthetic organisms except prokaryotes, and it is true for all green parts of plants.
   NOTE: It is also true for the not-quite-so-green parts of other photosynthetic eukaryotes.

B. In most plants, the leaves and, specifically, **mesophyll** cells are the dominant photosynthetic locations (Figure 7.2).

C. Other structures in leaves provide entries and exits for the reactants and products of the process: CO_2 and O_2 diffuse through **stomata;** H_2O moves through veins from the roots.

D. Within the **stroma** of chloroplasts, carbon dioxide is built up into sugars.

E. The green pigment that absorbs light energy is chlorophyll, which is located in **thylakoid** membranes (stacks of thylakoids are called **grana**) within the chloroplasts.
   NOTE: Ask students to note the parallels between photosynthesis and cellular respiration, particularly in the types of underlying processes and the locations in which these processes occur, but be careful not to confuse the two sequences.

Module 7.3 Plants produce O_2 gas by splitting water.

A. Experiments in the 1950s tested the early hypothesis of Ingenhousz that the oxygen given off in photosynthesis came from the reactant CO_2 (Figure 7.3A). Two experiments used ^{18}O-labeled reactants as tracers (see Modules 2.4 and 2.5; Figure 7.3B).
   NOTE: The splitting of water in photosynthesis is the major source of O_2 in the atmosphere.

B. A plant given $C^{18}O_2$ did not give off $^{18}O_2$.

C. A plant given $H_2^{18}O$ did give off $^{18}O_2$.

D. Additional experiments have confirmed where other atoms in the products come from (Figure 7.3C).
   NOTE: In Figures 7.3B and C, the overall equation for photosynthesis is written a bit differently, showing that water is both a reactant and a product. It takes 2 water molecules to get enough oxygen atoms to make 1 oxygen molecule. Since 6 molecules of oxygen are generated for each molecule of glucose formed, 12 water molecules are needed and some new water is formed at the end, with oxygen coming from the CO_2 and hydrogens from the original water molecules.

Module 7.4 Photosynthesis is a redox process, as is cellular respiration.

A. When H_2O molecules are split, yielding O_2, the water molecules are oxidized, giving up their electrons (and H^+ ions) (Figure 7.4A).

B. At the same time, CO_2 molecules are reduced to glucose as electrons and H^+ ions are added to them.

C. Compare this to the reverse overall reaction in cellular respiration (Module 6.5), where glucose is oxidized and oxygen is reduced (Figure 7.4B).

D. In photosynthesis, the electrons travel "uphill" from the water to the glucose, adding the light energy captured by chlorophyll (endergonic reactions).

E. In cellular respiration, the electrons travel "downhill" from the glucose to the water, giving up their energy to ATP (exergonic reactions).

Module 7.5 Overview: Photosynthesis occurs in two stages linked by ATP and NADPH.

   A. **Light reactions:** steps that convert light energy to chemical energy and produce O_2 gas as a waste product. These reactions occur in the thylakoid membranes and produce chemical energy shuttles in the form of ATP and energized electron shuttles in the form of NADPH. Light is required for these steps (Figure 7.5).
   NOTE: O_2 is produced as a waste product. When aerobic photosynthesis evolved, oxygen was and still is for certain organisms a toxin (see Module 6.13).

   B. **Calvin cycle:** a cyclical series of steps that assembles glucose from CO_2 molecules. These reactions occur in the stroma (the fluid outside the thylakoids but inside the inner chloroplast membrane) and use the energy and electrons from ATP and NADPH respectively in **"carbon fixation."** Light is not directly required, but because production of the shuttles (ATP and NADPH) requires light, the Calvin cycle steps usually occur during daytime (Figure 7.5).

II. The Light Reactions: Converting Solar Energy to Chemical Energy

Module 7.6 Visible radiation drives the light reactions.

   A. Light is a type of energy called radiation, or **electromagnetic energy,** which travels in rhythmic waves. The distance between the crest of each wave can be measured and is called a **wavelength.**

   B. Only a small fraction of electromagnetic radiation can be perceived by organisms. Humans perceive visible light of different wavelengths as different colors (Figure 7.6A).

   C. The full electromagnetic spectrum includes radio waves, which have long wavelengths, to gamma rays, which have very short wavelengths. The shorter the wavelength, the higher the energy. The energy in ultraviolet (UV) light is high enough to cause damage to proteins and nucleic acids, which can lead to cancer.

   D. During the light reactions, a leaf absorbs some light wavelengths (blue-violet and red-orange) and not others (what we see is reflected as green light) (Figure 7.6B).

   E. A variety of pigments are involved in absorbing light of different wavelengths (in plants, chlorophyll a, chlorophyll b, and carotenoids).

   F. In plants, only chlorophyll a participates directly in the light reactions. The other pigments function to broaden the range of energy absorbed and convey this additional trapped energy to the chlorophyll a.

   G. While some carotenoids absorb light energy that will be used in photosynthesis, other carotenoids protect chlorophyll from the damaging effects of excessive light energy.
   NOTE: Carotenoids are vitamin A precursors (Modules 21.8 and 2.17).

   H. In addition to behaving as waves, light also behaves as discrete packets of energy called **photons.** Each pigment is capable of absorbing light of a specific wavelength based upon the energy of the photon.

Module 7.7 Photosystems capture solar power.

   A. When a pigment absorbs a photon, the energy of one of the pigment's electrons is raised to an excited, unstable state. It returns to the unexcited (ground) state and releases the energy as heat.
   NOTE: The molecular structure of chlorophyll a is perfectly suited as a light trapper, containing many double bonds that expose many electron clouds to the passing radiation.

   B. In some cases, if the pigment is isolated from its surrounding molecular environment, the excited electron will lose its energy, return to the normal level, and emit heat or light (fluorescence). For instance, chlorophyll a fluoresces red (Figures 7.7A and B).

C. In contrast, in intact chloroplasts, the excited electrons are passed (the chlorophyll at the reaction center is oxidized) to a neighboring molecule, the primary electron acceptor (reduction).

D. Within the thylakoid membranes, many pigment molecules (200–300) are grouped with associated proteins into an antenna assembly, but only a single chlorophyll a molecule acts as the reaction center (Figure 7.7C).

E. Two **photosystems** (antenna assembly, 1 **reaction center,** and 1 primary electron acceptor) have been identified, which differ in the wavelengths of peak light absorption: the chlorophyll a in photosystem I absorbs light at 700 nm and is called P700, while photosystem II absorbs light at 680 nm and is called P680.
NOTE: If you look at Figures 4.15 and 7.2, you will see that the thylakoid membrane is continuous. The different grana are connected by thylakoid membranes called stroma lamellae. The stroma lamellae mainly bear PS I, the grana mainly PS II.

Module 7.8 In the light reactions, electron transport chains generate ATP and NADPH.

A. The kinetic energy of light is absorbed.

B. The absorbed energy excites electrons.

C. The excited electrons are passed along an electron transport chain in a series of redox reactions.

D. The energy released by these redox reactions is used to generate ATP and NADPH.

E. The production of NADPH requires 2 electrons. Photosystem I obtains these electrons from photosystem II. Photosystem II gets its electrons from the splitting of water, a process that also produces 2 H^+ and $\frac{1}{2}$ O_2 (Figure 7.8A).

F. Use the mechanical diagram to help explain the process of electron flow through the two photosystems (Figure 7.8B)
NOTE: There is evidence that manganese cations (Mn^{++}) are directly involved in the splitting of H_2O.

Module 7.9 Chemiosmosis powers ATP synthesis in the light reactions.

A. The energy released from the electron transport chain is used to pump H^+ ions (formed when water was split) from the stroma across the thylakoid membrane to the interior of the thylakoids. This creates a concentration gradient across the thylakoid membrane (Figure 7.9).
Review: (Modules 5.1 and 5.14) Concentration gradients are a form of kinetic energy.

B. ATP synthase provides a port through which the H^+ ions can diffuse (potential energy) back into the stroma, releasing energy that is used to phosphorylate ADP to ATP.

C. This process, by which light provides energy for the chemiosmotic production of ATP, is known as **photophosphorylation.**

D. This process is very similar to chemiosmosis in mitochondria (Module 6.10).

E. A comparison of oxidative phosphorylation between mitochondria and chloroplast reveals several differences.
Example: Mitochondrial energy source is organic molecules (chloroplast and light), use O_2 as the final electron acceptor (chloroplast and $NADP^+$), and generate ATP and H_2C (chloroplast, ATP, and NADPH).

III. The Calvin Cycle: Converting CO_2 to Sugars

Module 7.10 ATP and NADPH power sugar synthesis in the Calvin cycle.

A. The net result of the Calvin cycle is the synthesis of a phosphorylated, three-carbon molecule, glyceraldehydes-3-phosphate (G3P) from three carbon dioxide molecules (from the air). The energy and electrons are provided by ATP and NADPH from the light reactions (Figure 7.10A).

B. Each CO_2 molecule is added to a five-carbon intermediate (RuBP, for ribulose bisphosphate) catalyzed by the enzyme RuBP carboxylase (rubisco) (Figure 7.10B).

C. A number of rearrangements of molecules occur in many steps, some involving the use of energy from ATP, some oxidizing the NADPH (the reactants in these being reduced at the same time).

D. The last step of the cycle is the regeneration of the RuBP. The reactions involve considerable rearrangements of structure; all are proceeding at once, and since the steps ultimately regenerate one of the starting reactants, they can be regarded as occurring in a cycle.

E. It takes three molecules of CO_2, entering the cycle one at a time, for every G3P produced.

F. G3P can be used to make glucose or other organic compounds.

G. The Calvin cycle takes place in the chloroplast stroma. The process is summarized in 4 steps:
   1. Carbon fixation
   2. Reduction
   3. Release of one molecule of G3P
   4. Regeneration of RuBP

IV. Photosynthesis Reviewed and Extended

Module 7.11 Review: Photosynthesis uses light energy to make food molecules.

A. Photosynthesis is a two-part process—the trapping of energy (the light reaction) and then using that energy to produce sugar molecules in the Calvin cycle (Figure 7.11).

B. Sugar molecules a plant produces are the plant's own food supply, expended during cellular respiration.

C. Plants use sugars as building blocks for other organic compounds, including cellulose.

D. Plants, and other photosynthesizers, are the ultimate source of food for almost all other organisms.

Module 7.12 C_4 and CAM plants have special adaptations that save water.

A. Plants that use only the Calvin cycle to fix carbon are known as **C_3 plants.**

B. During water shortages, C_3 plants try to conserve water by closing their leaf pores. Since new CO_2 is not able to enter the plant, oxygen rather than CO_2 is fixed to RuBP by rubisco. This is called **photorespiration,** and it yields no sugar molecules and produces no ATP.

C. **C_4 plants** have special adaptations that conserve water and prevent photorespiration (Figure 7.12-left). These adaptations involve producing four-carbon compounds in separate cells with a special enzyme. During hot, dry weather the stomata are closed and the CO_2 concentration is much lower than the O_2 concentration. To counteract the low CO_2 levels, the Calvin cycle is maintained by using the four-carbon compounds, which are broken down to release CO_2 to complete the Calvin cycle. C_4 metabolism is found in corn, sorghum, and sugarcane.

D. **CAM** (crassulacean acid metabolism) **plants** form CO_2 into four-carbon compounds with another special enzyme at night, when temperatures are lower, humidity higher, and CO_2 more available (Figure 7.12-right). During the day, the four-carbon compounds are released to the Calvin cycle. CAM is found in several different types of succulent plants, such as cacti, pineapples, and jade plants.

V. Photosynthesis, Solar Radiation, and Earth's Atmosphere

Module 7.13 Photosynthesis could moderate global warming.

A. Radiant energy from the sun is trapped in a greenhouse that can then be used to grow plants when the weather is too cold to grow them outside (Figure 7.13A).

B. In the atmosphere, CO_2, water vapor, and methane retain heat from the Earth that would otherwise radiate back into space. This is the basis for the **greenhouse effect** (Figure 7.13B).

C. Burning fossil fuels (oil, coal, and gas) and wood releases excess CO_2, which may be causing **global warming.** There has been a 30% increase in atmospheric CO_2 content since the start of the industrial revolution.
Preview: The greenhouse effect is revisited in Chapter 38 (Module 38.5).

D. Photosynthesizers are a natural CO_2 sink and can moderate the effect of fossil fuels burning. However, a decrease in the world's forest has paralleled the increase in global warming.

E. The use of energy plantations may hold the key to a future with less CO_2 and reduced global warming.

Module 7.14 Talking About Science: Mario Molina talks about the Earth's protective ozone layer.
Preview: Module 38.4.

A. In the atmosphere, O_2 is converted into O_3 (ozone) by high-energy solar radiation. Atmospheric ozone is also destroyed by compounds that are natural components of the atmosphere.

B. The ozone layer shields the surface of the Earth from UV radiation. UV radiation is damaging to life. For example, it can cause cancer in humans and damage crops.

C. Chlorofluorocarbons (CFCs) are human-made chemicals that were used as refrigerants, as propellants, and in other industrial processes. CFCs deplete ozone, and this results in increased UV radiation reaching the Earth's surface.

D. CFC production has been banned in developed countries and will be phased out of use in developing countries. However, CFCs are very stable and are expected to remain in the atmosphere, damaging the ozone layer. Molina predicts that the ozone layer will not recover until the middle of the next century. Since the ban on CFC usage began in 1996, there has been a steady decline in CFC production.

E. Molina points out that the long-term environmental and economic costs of not dealing with environmental issues are greater than the short-term costs of dealing with these issues.

Class Activities

1. With a prism, demonstrate the spectrum of wavelengths in visible light.

2. Set up a demonstration using paper or thin-layer chromatography to separate the pigments in a leaf. The visual spread of pigments supports the multipigment makeup of photosystems, a fact that is not immediately apparent.

3.   If the facilities are available, demonstrate some of the controlling factors in photosynthesis, using *Elodea* (or other aquatic plants available from aquarium supply stores). Set this up several hours before lecture. Trap the *Elodea* and its emitted oxygen bubbles in inverted, water-filled test tubes. One experimental setup could contain boiled water (to remove the CO_2). Use an unfiltered bright light, several different cellophane filters, and aluminum foil around different test tubes to show the efficiency of photosynthesis at different wavelengths. A glowing splint thrust into the gas will demonstrate its chemical makeup. In introducing these experiments, be sure to discuss experimental procedure, including the use of controls.

4.   Ask students to describe the parallels between photosynthesis and cellular respiration, particularly in the types of underlying processes and the locations in which these processes occur.

5.   Other than the obvious, a greenhouse, ask your class if they can think of any situations that are analogous to the greenhouse effect. The one that always comes to mind is how the interior of a car can get hot on a sunny day even if it is not particularly hot outside.

6.   How might a full-blown greenhouse effect affect the particular location of your school? Will your location end up under water? become a desert? Perhaps the greenhouse effect will improve the climate of your region. Which countries would suffer the most/least from greenhouse conditions? Have your students contrast the United States with low-lying nations such as Bangladesh and island nations such as Great Britain.

Transparency Acetates

Chapter 7 Introduction, page 108: The summary equation for photosynthesis

Figure 7.2	The location and structure of chloroplasts
Figure 7.3B	Experiments tracking the oxygen atoms in photosynthesis
Figure 7.3C	Fates of all the atoms in photosynthesis
Figure 7.4A	Photosynthesis (uses light energy)
Figure 7.4B	Cellular respiration (releases chemical energy)
Figure 7.5	An overview of photosynthesis (Layer 1)
Figure 7.5	An overview of photosynthesis (Layer 2)
Figure 7.5	An overview of photosynthesis (Layer 3)
Figure 7.6A	The electromagnetic spectrum and the wavelengths of visible light
Figure 7.6B	The interaction of light with a chloroplast
Figure 7.7B	Light-excited chlorophyll in isolation
Figure 7.7C	Light-excited chlorophyll embedded in a photosystem
Figure 7.8A	Electron flow in the light reactions of photosynthesis
Figure 7.8B	A mechanical analogy of the light reactions
Figure 7.9	The production of ATP by chemiosmosis in photosynthesis
Figure 7.10A	An overview of the Calvin cycle
Figure 7.10B	Details of the Calvin cycle (Layer 1)
Figure 7.10B	Details of the Calvin cycle (Layer 2)
Figure 7.10B	Details of the Calvin cycle (Layer 3)
Figure 7.11	A summary of the chemical processes of photosynthesis
Figure 7.12	Comparison of photosynthesis in C_4 and CAM plants

Figure 7.13B CO_2 in the atmosphere and global warming

Figure 7.14B   The ozone hole in the Southern Hemisphere, spring 2000

Reviewing the Concepts, page 123: The two stages of photosynthesis

Connecting the Concepts, page 123: Chemiosmotic synthesis of ATP in mitochondria and chloroplasts

Connecting the Concepts, page 124: Photosynthesis

Media

See the beginning of this book for a complete description of all media available for instructors and students. Animations and videos are available in the Campbell Image Presentation Library. Media Activities and Thinking as a Scientist investigations are available on the student CD-ROM and web site.

Animations and Videos	Module Number
Light Reactions Animation	7.9
Calvin Cycle Animation	7.10

Activities and Thinking as a Scientist	Module Number
Web/CD Activity 7A: *The Sites of Photosynthesis*	7.2
Web/CD Activity 7B: *Overview of Photosynthesis*	7.5
Web/CD Activity 7C: *Light Energy and Pigments*	7.6
Web/CD Thinking as a Scientist: *How Does Paper Chromatography Separate Plant Pigments?*	7.6
Web/CD Activity 7D: *The Light Reactions*	7.9
Web/CD Activity 7E: *The Calvin Cycle*	7.10
Web/CD Thinking as a Scientist: *How Is the Rate of Photosynthesis Measured?*	7.11
Biology Labs On-Line: *Photosynthesis Reviewed and Extended*	7.11
Web/CD Activity 7F: *Photosynthesis in Dry Climates*	7.12

CHAPTER 8

The Cellular Basis of Reproduction and Inheritance

Teaching Objectives

Introduction Compare sexual and asexual reproduction. Explain how asexual reproduction can be used to save a species from extinction.

Connections Between Cell Division and Reproduction

8.1 Compare the relationship between a parent and its offspring resulting from asexual versus sexual reproduction.

8.2 Explain why cell division is essential for eukaryotic and prokaryotic life.

8.3 Explain how daughter prokaryotic chromosomes are separated from each other during binary fission.

The Eukaryotic Cell Cycle and Mitosis

8.3–8.4 Compare the structure of prokaryotic and eukaryotic chromosomes.

8.5 Describe the stages and significance of the cell cycle.

8.6 List the phases of mitosis, and describe the events characteristic of each phase. Recognize the phases of mitosis from diagrams and micrographs.

8.7 Compare cytokinesis in animals and plants.

8.8–8.9 Explain how anchorage, cell density, and growth factors control the cell cycle.

8.10 Explain how cancerous cells are different from healthy cells. Distinguish between benign and malignant tumors, and explain the strategies behind some common cancer treatments.

8.11 Describe the functions of mitosis.

Meiosis and Crossing Over

8.12 Explain how chromosomes are paired. Distinguish between autosomes and sex chromosomes.

8.13 Distinguish between (a) somatic cells and gametes and (b) diploid cells and haploid cells.

8.14 List the phases of meiosis I and meiosis II, and describe the events characteristic of each phase. Recognize the phases of meiosis from diagrams or micrographs.

8.15 Describe key differences between mitosis and meiosis. Explain how the result of meiosis differs from the result of mitosis.

8.16–8.18 Explain how crossing over during prophase I of meiosis, independent orientation of chromosomes at metaphase I, and random fertilization contribute to genetic variation in sexually reproducing organisms.

Alterations of Chromosome Number and Structure

8.19 Explain how and why karyotyping is performed.

8.20 Describe the causes and symptoms of Down syndrome.

8.21 Define nondisjunction, explain how it can occur, and describe what can result.

8.22 Describe the consequences of abnormal numbers of sex chromosomes.

8.23 Describe the main types of chromosomal changes. Explain why cancer is not usually inherited.

Key Terms

anaphase	deletion	meiosis
anchorage dependence	density-dependent inhibition	metaphase
asexual reproduction	diploid cell	metastasis
autosomes	Down syndrome	mitosis
benign tumor	duplication	mitotic phase (M phase)
binary fission	fertilization	mitotic spindle
cancer cells	gametes	nondisjunction
carcinomas	genetic recombination	prometaphase
cell cycle	genome	prophase
cell cycle control system	growth factor	sarcomas
cell division	haploid cell	sex chromosomes
cell plate	homologous chromosomes	sexual reproduction
centromere	interphase	sister chromatids
centrosomes	inversion	somatic cell
chiasma	karyotype	telophase
chromatin	leukemias	translocation
chromosomes	life cycle	trisomy 21
cleavage furrow	locus	tumor
crossing over	lymphomas	zygote
cytokinesis	malignant tumor	

Word Roots

ana- = up, throughout, again (*anaphase:* the mitotic stage in which the chromatids of each chromosome have separated and the daughter chromosomes are moving to the poles of the cell)

auto- = self (*autosome:* the chromosomes that do not determine gender)

bi- = two (*binary fission:* a type of cell division in which a cell divides in half)

centro- = the center; **-mere** = a part (*centromere:* the narrow "waist" of a condensed chromosome)

chiasm- = marked crosswise (*chiasma:* the X-shaped microscopically visible region representing homologous chromosomes that have exchanged genetic material through crossing over during meiosis)

chroma- = colored (*chromatin:* DNA and the various associated proteins that form eukaryotic chromosomes)

cyto- = cell; **-kinet** = move (*cytokinesis:* division of the cytoplasm)

di- = two (*diploid:* cells that contain two homologous sets of chromosomes)

fertil- = fruitful (*fertilization:* process of fusion of a haploid sperm and a haploid egg cell)

gamet- = a wife or husband (*gamete:* a haploid egg or sperm cell)

gen- = produce (*genome:* a cell's endowment of DNA)

haplo- = single (*haploid:* cells that contain only one chromosome of each homologous pair)

inter- = between (*interphase:* time when a cell metabolizes and performs its various functions)

karyo- = nucleus (*karyotype:* a display of the chromosomes of a cell)

meio- = less (*meiosis:* a variation of cell division which yields daughter cells with half as many chromosomes as the parent cell)

meta- = between (*metaphase:* the mitotic stage in which the chromosomes are aligned in the middle of the cell, at the metaphase plate)

soma- = body (*somatic:* body cells with 46 chromosomes in humans)

Lecture Outline

Introduction *Rain Forest Rescue*

    A. Introduce the general topics of reproduction, genetics, and inheritance, perhaps tracing the pedagogical development of the chapters in this unit.

    B. A **life cycle** is the sequence of life forms (and the processes forming them) from one generation to the next. A life cycle can be divided into two phases:
Stage 1: development, from a fertilized egg to an adult
Stage 2: reproduction, formation of new individuals from preexisting ones, which occurs through **fertilization** of an egg with a sperm.

    C. **Sexual reproduction** involves passing traits from two parents to the next generation.

    D. **Asexual reproduction** involves passing traits from only one parent to the next generation.

    E. A complete set of the heritable material in a cell is called a **genome.** Most cells contain two complete sets. Cells involved in sexual reproduction carry only one set.
NOTE: There are two conflicting events in the whole life cycle progression: How, during reproduction, are faithful copies of organisms assured? How, during development, are subtle changes to the cells of a multicellular organism introduced?

I. Connections Between Cell Division and Reproduction

  Module 8.1 Like begets like, more or less.

    A. This is strictly true only for organisms reproducing asexually.

    B. Single-celled organisms, like amoebas, can reproduce asexually by dividing in two. Each daughter cell receives an identical copy of the parent's genes (Figure 8.1A). Genes are contained in the **chromosomes,** which are composed of DNA.

    C. For multicellular organisms (and many single-celled organisms), the offspring are not genetically identical to the parents, but each is a unique combination of the traits of both parents (Figure 8.1B).

    D. Breeders of domestic plants and animals manipulate sexual reproduction by selecting offspring that exhibit certain desired traits. In doing so, the breeders reduce the variability of the breed's population of individuals.
NOTE: You might want to discuss the ethics of selective breeding as well as the impact of reduced variability on a population's survivorship. For example, some species have reduced genetic variability due to being pushed to the verge of extinction by human behaviors, as discussed in the opening essay.
Preview: Observations of the work of breeders were part of the data Charles Darwin used in developing the theory of natural selection (Module 13.2).

Module 8.2 Cells arise only from preexisting cells.

    A. This principle was formulated in 1858 by German physician Rudolf Virchow.

    B. Cell reproduction is called **cell division.**

    C. Cell division has two major roles. It enables a fertilized egg to develop through various embryonic stages, for an embryo to develop into an adult organism and to replace cells that have died from normal use or injury. It ensures the continuity from generation to generation; it is the basis of both asexual reproduction and sperm and egg formation in sexual reproduction.

Module 8.3 Prokaryotes reproduce by binary fission.

    A. Genes of most prokaryotes are carried on a circular DNA molecule. Prokaryotic chromosomes are simpler than eukaryotic chromosomes.

    B. Packaging is minimal: The DNA is complexed with a few proteins and attached to the plasma membrane at one point.

    C. Most of the DNA lies non-membrane-bounded in a region of the cell called the nucleoid.

    D. **Binary fission** is the type of cell division that prokaryotic cells use for reproduction (Figure 8.3A). Prior to dividing, an exact copy of the chromosome is made. This is no small task even though the single chromosome of a prokaryotic cell is much smaller than a eukaryotic cell chromosome. As the new chromosome is synthesized, it moves to the opposite side of the cell. During the duplication process, the cell elongates. Finally, the plasma membrane and new cell wall "pinch" through the cell (Figure 8.3B), separating the two chromosomes into two new, genetically identical cells.
      Preview: Fission in sea anemones is discussed in Module 27.1.

II. The Eukaryotic Cell Cycle and Mitosis

Module 8.4 The large, complex chromosomes of eukaryotes duplicate with each cell division.

    A. Whereas a typical bacterium might have 3,000 genes, human cells, for example, have approximately 35,000 genes.

    B. The majority of these genes are organized into several separate, linear chromosomes that are found inside the nucleus.

    C. The DNA in eukaryotic chromosomes is complexed with protein and together are called chromatin. This complex packaging organizes and allows expression of much greater numbers of genes (Chapter 11).
      Review: Module 4.5.

    D. During the process of cell division, chromatin condenses and the chromosomes become visible under the light microscope (Figure 8.4A).

    E. In multicellular plants and animals, the body cells (somatic cells) contain twice the number of chromosomes as the sex cells. Humans have 46 chromosomes in their somatic cells and 23 chromosomes in their sex cells. Different species may have different numbers of chromosomes.

    F. The DNA molecule in each chromosome is copied prior to the chromosomes' becoming visible.

    G. As the chromosomes become visible, each is seen to be composed of two identical **sister chromatids,** attached at the **centromere** (Figure 8.4B).

H. It is the sister chromatids that are parceled out to the daughter cells (the chromatids are then referred to as chromosomes). Each new cell gets a complete set of identical chromosomes (Figure 8.4C).

Module 8.5 The cell cycle multiplies cells.

NOTE: The result of this process (more or less) is two daughter cells that are genetically identical to each other and to their parental cell.

A. Most cells in growing, and fully grown organisms divide on a regular basis (once an hour, once a day), although some have stopped dividing. This process allows new cells to replace worn-out or damaged cells.

B. Such dividing cells undergo a cycle, a sequence of steps that is repeated from the time of one division to the time of the next, called the **cell cycle** (Figure 8.5).

C. **Interphase** represents 90% or more of the total cycle time and is divided into G_1, S, and G_2 subphases.

D. During G_1, the cell increases its supply of proteins and organelles and grows in size.

E. During S, DNA synthesis (replication) occurs.

F. During G_2, the cell continues to prepare for the actual division, increasing the supply of other proteins, particularly those used in the process.

G. Cell division itself is called the mitotic phase (the M phase, it excludes interphase) and involves two subprocesses, mitosis (nuclear division) and cytokinesis (cytoplasmic division). Ask your students what would happen if mitosis occurred without cytokinesis.

H. The overall result is two daughter cells, each with identical sets of chromosomes.

I. Mitosis is very accurate. In experiments with yeast, one error occurs every 100,000 divisions.
Preview: The molecular mechanism by which DNA is copied prior to mitosis is discussed in Modules 10.4 and 10.5.

Module 8.6 Cell division is a continuum of dynamic changes.

NOTE: If possible, show a video or film clip of the process. Stress the dynamic, repeating, and continuous nature of mitosis, pointing out that biologists divide the overall process into what appear to be five natural phases, to make it easier to follow.

A. Interphase: duplication of the genetic material ends when chromosomes begin to become visible (Figure 8.6).

B. **Prophase** (the first stage of mitosis): The mitotic spindle is forming, emerging from two **centrosomes** (also known as microtubule-organizing centers [MTOCs]). Centrosomes migrate to opposite ends of the cell.

C. **Prometaphase:** This stage ends when the chromatins have completely coiled into chromosomes; nucleoli and nuclear membrane disperse. The **mitotic spindle** provides a scaffold for the movement of chromosomes and attaches to chromosomes at their kinetochore.
Review: The mitotic spindle is made of microtubules (Module 4.16).

D. **Metaphase:** The spindle is fully formed; chromosomes are aligned single file with centromeres on the metaphase plate (the plane that cuts the spindle's equator).

E. **Anaphase:** Chromosomes separate from the centromere, dividing to arrive at poles.
NOTE: The concept that a single chromosome can consist of a single chromatid or two chromatids and that when two chromatids separate they are then independent

chromosomes can be confusing. The way to determine the number of chromosomes a cell contains is to count the centromeres.

F. **Telophase** is the reverse of prophase: Cell elongation continues, a nuclear envelope forms around chromosomes, chromosomes uncoil, and nucleoli reappear.

G. Cytokinesis: the division of the cytoplasm. This usually, but not always, accompanies telophase.

Module 8.7 Cytokinesis differs for plant and animal cells.

NOTE: The cells of advanced plants do not have centrioles (Figure 8.4A).

A. In animals, a ring of microfilaments contracts around the periphery of the cell, forming a **cleavage furrow** that eventually cleaves the cytoplasm (Figure 8.7A). Microfilaments are composed of the same proteins responsible for muscle contraction, namely myosin and actin (see Module 30.8).

B. In plants, vesicles containing cell wall material collect in the center of the cell then gradually fuse, from the inside out, forming a **cell plate** that gradually develops into a new wall between the two new cells. The membranes surrounding the vesicles fuse to form the new parts of the plasma membrane (Figure 8.7B).
NOTE: For the plant, the process of cytokinesis must accommodate the cell wall.

Module 8.8 Anchorage, cell density, and chemical growth factors affect cell division.

A. To grow and develop, or replenish and repair tissues, multicellular plants and animals must control when and where cell divisions take place.

B. Most animal and plant cells will not divide unless they are in contact with a solid surface; this is known as **anchorage dependence.**

C. Laboratory studies show that cells usually stop dividing when a single layer is formed and the cells touch each other (Figure 8.8A). This **density-dependent inhibition** of cell growth is controlled by the depletion of **growth factor** proteins in masses of crowded cells (Figure 8.8B). Growth factors are proteins secreted by cells that stimulate growth of other cells in close proximity.

Module 8.9 Growth factors signal the cell cycle control system.

A. The **cell cycle control system** regulates the events of the cell cycle. Three major checkpoints exist (Figure 8.9A):

1. At G_1 of interphase
2. At G_2 of interphase
3. At the M phase

B. If, at these checkpoints, a growth factor (go-ahead signal) is released, the cell cycle will continue. If a growth factor is not released, the cell cycle will stop (Figure 8.9B). The signals are transmitted within the cell by signal transduction (see Figure 5.13B).
Preview: This regulation is a type of signal transduction (Modules 11.14 and 5.13).

C. Nerve and muscle cells are nondividing cells stuck at the G_1 checkpoint and have exited the cell cycle. These cells are now in the **G_0 phase.**

Module 8.10 Connection: Growing out of control, cancer cells produce malignant tumors.

NOTE: Cancer is a general term for many diseases in multicellular animals and plants involving uncontrolled cell division with the resultant tumor metastasizing (Figure 8.10). Breast cancer is illustrated in this figure. For females at age 90 there is a 1-in-8 lifetime risk of breast cancer—the risk of dying of cardiovascular disease is much greater.

Preview: Lifestyle and cancer are discussed in Modules 11.20 and 21.24.

A. **Cancer cells** are nonresponsive to cell cycle control system, divide unchecked, and can invade other tissues. The process of cancer spreading from the original site to other sites in the body via the blood is called **metastasis**.

B. Cells that evade destruction by the immune system and develop into a mass are called a **tumor.** If the tumor spreads, it is referred to as a **malignant tumor.** This is in contrast to a **benign tumor,** which does not spread (metastasize).

   NOTE: This is not to say that a benign tumor cannot cause death.

   NOTE: When someone dies of cancer, they rarely die as a result of the primary tumor; it is usually the metastases that kill them.

C. Cancers are named according to the tissue or organ of origin.

   1. **Carcinomas:** epithelial cancers

   2. **Sarcomas:** supportive (connective) tissue cancers

   3. **Leukemias** and **Lymphomas:** cancers of the blood-forming tissues

D. Usually, cancer cells do not exhibit density-dependent inhibition.

E. Some cancer cells divide even in the absence of growth factors.

F. Some cancer cells actually continually synthesize factors that keep them dividing. Thus, unlike normal mammalian cells (in culture), there is no limit to the number of times cancer cells can divide (they are immortal).

G. Radiation and chemotherapy are two treatments for cancer. Radiation disrupts the process of cell division by damaging the DNA. Cancerous cells appear to have lost the ability to repair damaged DNA. Because cancer cells divide more often than most normal cells, they are more likely to be affected by radiation, which damages the DNA. Chemotherapy involves drugs that, like radiation, disrupt cell division. Some of these drugs—for example, Taxol—target the mitotic spindle.

H. Side effects from chemotherapy treatment result from damage to normal cells.

Module 8.11 Review of the function of mitosis: Growth, cell replacement, and asexual reproduction.

A. Mitosis and cytokinesis (cell division) are used to add more cells to growing tissue (Figure 8.11A).

B. Cell division is also used to replace dead or damaged tissue (Figure 8.11B).

C. Cell division can be used in asexual reproduction, producing genetically identical offspring (Figure 8.11C).

III. Meiosis and Crossing Over

Module 8.12 Chromosomes are matched in homologous pairs.

A. In diploid organisms, **somatic cells** (nonsex cells) have pairs of **homologous chromosomes.** Homologous chromosomes share shape and genetic loci (singular, **locus;** location of a particular gene on a chromosome), and carry genes controlling the same inherited characteristics (Figure 8.12).

B. Each of the homologues is inherited from a separate parent.
NOTE: The sets are combined in the first cell following fertilization and passed down together from cell to cell during growth and development by mitosis.

C. In humans, 22 pairs, found in males and females, are **autosomes.** Two other chromosomes are **sex chromosomes.**

D. In mammalian females, there are two X chromosomes; in male mammals, there is an X and a Y chromosome.
Preview: Sex chromosomes, sex determination, and sex chromosome anomalies are discussed further in Modules 8.22, 9.21, 9.22, and 9.23.

Module 8.13 Gametes have a single set of chromosomes.

A. Adult animals have somatic cells with two sets of homologues (**diploid cell,** 2*n*).

B. Sex cells (**gametes,** eggs and sperm) have one set of homologues (**haploid cell,** *n*). These cells are produced by meiosis.

C. Sexual life cycles involve the alternation between a diploid phase and a haploid phase (Figure 8.13).

D. The fusion of haploid gametes in the process of fertilization results in the formation of a diploid **zygote.**

Module 8.14 Meiosis reduces the chromosome number from diploid to haploid.

A. An understanding of the cell cycle is needed for an understanding of meiosis.

B. **Meiosis** is a type of cell division that produces haploid gametes in diploid organisms.

C. Like mitosis, meiosis is preceded by a single duplication of the chromosomes.

D. The overall result of meiosis is four daughter cells, each with half the number of chromosomes (haploid).

E. Again, the process is dynamic but may stop at certain phases for long periods of time.

F. The process includes two consecutive divisions (meiosis I and meiosis II).

G. The halving of the chromosome number occurs in meiosis I (Figure 8.14). The result is two haploid cells, with each chromosome consisting of two chromatids.

H. Sister chromatids separate in meiosis II (Figure 8.14).

I. The result is four haploid cells.
Preview: Gamete formation by meiosis is discussed in Module 27.4.

Module 8.15 Review: A comparison of mitosis and meiosis.

A. The cell diagrammed has four chromosomes, two homologous pairs (Figure 8.15).

B. All the events unique to meiosis occur in meiosis I. In prophase I, homologous chromosomes pair to form a tetrad, and crossing over occurs between homologous chromatids.
NOTE: This results in the formation of unique genetic combinations (Module 8.16).

C. Meiosis II is virtually identical to mitosis (except the cells are haploid).

D. Mitosis results in two daughter cells, each with the same chromosomes as the parent cell. Mitosis can happen in diploid or haploid cells.

E. Meiosis results in four daughter cells (or, at least, nuclei), each with half the number of chromosomes as the parent cell. Meiosis happens only in diploid cells.

Module 8.16 Independent orientation of chromosomes in meiosis and random fertilization lead to varied offspring.

    A. During prophase I of meiosis, each homologue pairs up with its "other." During this process, X and Y chromosomes behave as a homologous pair (Figure 8.16).
    NOTE: This pairing of homologues is called synapsis.

    B. When they separate at anaphase I, maternally and paternally inherited homologues move to one pole or the other independently of other pairs.
    Preview: This is the basis of Mendel's Laws (Modules 9.3, 9.5, and 9.7).

    C. Given n chromosomes, there are 2^n ways that different combinations of the half-pairs can move to one pole.

    D. In humans, there are 2^{23} combinations (8 million) of combining an individual's maternally inherited and paternally inherited homologues.

    E. Combining gametes into zygotes suggests that there are $2^{23} \rightarrow 2^{23}$ combinations (64 trillion) in the zygote (but see the next two modules).
    Preview: The consequences of the large amount of genetic variation generated by sexual reproduction are contrasted with the lower levels of genetic variation associated with asexual reproduction in Module 27.1.

Module 8.17 Homologous chromosomes carry different versions of genes.

    A. Simplified examples: coat color and eye color in mice.

    B. *C* (agouti = brown) and *c* (white) for different versions of the coat-color gene and *E* (black) and *e* (pink) for different eye-color genes (Figure 8.17A).

    C. In this example, with the information up to this point, there would be two possible outcomes for the genes on the two chromosomes in a gamete (2^1) (Figure 8.17B).

Module 8.18 Crossing over further increases genetic variability.

    A. **Crossing over** is a genetic rearrangement between two homologues (sister chromatid exchange). The site of crossing over is called a **chiasma** (Figure 8.18A).

    B. This happens between chromatids within tetrads, as homologues pair up during synapsis (prophase I).

    C. Crossing over produces new combinations of genes (**genetic recombination**) (Figure 8.18B).

    D. Because crossing over can occur several times in variable locations among thousands of genes in each tetrad, the possibilities are much greater than calculated above. Essentially, two individual parents could never produce identical offspring from two separate fertilizations.
    NOTE: It is for this reason that, with the exception of identical twins (and the like), everyone is a unique genetic entity never seen before and never to be seen again. However, with the successful cloning of mammals, the possibility of identical organisms is possible, though not probable.
    Preview: The mechanisms discussed here that result in new genetic combinations, meiosis and fertilization, do not occur in bacteria. However, there are several processes in which bacteria engage that result in the production of new genetic combinations (Modules 10.22 and 10.23).

IV. Alterations of Chromosome Number and Structure

Module 8.19 A karyotype is a photographic inventory of an individual's chromosomes.

   A. Blood samples are cultured for several days under conditions that promote cell division of white blood cells (Figure 8.19).
   NOTE: Red blood cells lack nuclei and do not divide.

   B. The culture is treated with a chemical that stops cell division at metaphase.

   C. White blood cells are separated, stained, and squashed in an effort to spread out the chromosomes.

   D. The individual chromosomes in a photograph are cut out and rearranged by number. The ordered display of chromosomes is called a **karyotype** (Figure 8.19 insert of normal human male).

   E. From this the genetic sex of an individual can be determined and abnormalities in chromosomal structure and number can be detected.

Module 8.20 Connection: An extra copy of chromosome 21 causes Down syndrome.

   A. In most cases, human offspring that develop from zygotes with an incorrect number of chromosomes abort spontaneously.

   B. **Trisomy 21** is the most common chromosome-number abnormality, with 3 copies of chromosome 21, occurring in about 1 out of 700 births (Figure 8.20A).

   C. **Down syndrome** (common name for trisomy 21) includes a wide variety of physical, mental, and disease-susceptibility features (Figure 8.20B).

   D. The incidence of Down syndrome increases with the age of the mother (Figure 8.20C).
   NOTE: The age of the father is also correlated with an increased incidence of Down syndrome.

Module 8.21 Accidents during meiosis can alter chromosome number.

   Review: Meiosis (Module 8.14).

   A. **Nondisjunction** is the failure of chromosome pairs to separate during either meiosis I or meiosis II (Figures 8.21A and B).

   B. Fertilization of an egg resulting from nondisjunction with a normal sperm results in a zygote with an abnormal chromosome number (Figure 8.21C).

   C. The explanation for the increased incidence of trisomy 21 among older women is not entirely clear but probably involves the length of time a woman's developing eggs are in meiosis. Meiosis begins in all eggs before the woman is born, and finishes as each egg matures in the monthly cycle following puberty. Eggs of older women have been "within" meiosis longer.

Module 8.22 Connection: Abnormal numbers of sex chromosomes do not usually affect survival.

   A. Unusual numbers of sex chromosomes upset the genetic balance less than do unusual numbers of autosomes, perhaps because the Y chromosome carries fewer genes, and extra X chromosomes are inactivated as Barr bodies in females.
   Preview: X-chromosome inactivation is discussed in Module 11.5.

    B. Abnormalities in sex chromosome number result in individuals with a variety of different characteristics, some more seriously affecting fertility or intelligence than others (Table 8.22).

    C. The greater the number of X chromosomes (beyond 2), the more likely is (and the greater the severity of) mental retardation.

    D. These sex chromosome abnormalities illustrate the crucial role of the Y chromosome in determining a person's sex. A single Y is enough to produce "maleness," even in combination with a number of Xs (Klinefelter's syndrome), whereas the lack of a Y (Turner's syndrome) results in "femaleness" (Figures 8.22A and B).

Module 8.23 Alterations of chromosome structure can cause birth defects and cancer.

    A. Deletions, duplications, and inversions occur within one chromosome (Figure 8.23A).

        1. **Deletion:** loss of a fragment of chromosome

        2. **Duplication:** addition of a fragment to sister chromatid

        3. **Inversion:** reattachment of a fragment in reverse order

    B. Inversions are less likely to produce harmful effects than deletions or duplications because all the chromosome's genes are still present.

    C. Duplications, if they result in the duplication of an oncogene in somatic cells, may increase the incidence of cancer.

    D. **Translocation** involves the transfer of a chromosome fragment between nonhomologous chromosomes (Figure 8.23B).

    E. Translocations may or may not be harmful. One type of translocation is observed in Down syndrome, where a portion of one chromosome 21 is missing and has attached elsewhere.

    F. Chromosomal changes in somatic cells may increase the risk of cancer (Figure 8.23C). *Preview:* The genetic basis of cancer is discussed in more detail in Modules 11.16–11.20.

Class Activities

1. Show a video or film clip that illustrates the dynamic development of the early, few-cell to larval stages of a tadpole or echinoderm as a basis from which to start this lecture. Time-lapse movies of mitosis are also valuable for stressing the dynamic nature of this process. Be sure to describe any change in the time frame used in the films. Ask students to watch for points at which there are natural hesitations in the flow of activity, or events that might be used to divide the process into phases. Then go over the process with figures from the text, pointing out the fact that biologists have divided up the process into what appear to be natural phases, to make it easier to follow.

2. Sets of interconnected plastic beads can be used to demonstrate the behavior of chromosomes during both the cell cycle and meiosis.

3. Give your students photographs that they can use to construct karyotypes. See if they can use these karyotypes to diagnose the sex of an individual as well as chromosomal abnormalities.

Transparency Acetates

Figure 8.3A	Binary fission of a prokaryotic cell
Figure 8.4B	Electron micrograph of a duplicated chromosome
Figure 8.4C	Chromosome duplication and distribution (combined with Figure 8.4B)
Figure 8.5	The eukaryotic cell cycle
Figure 8.6	The stages of cell division (Part 1)
Figure 8.6	The stages of cell division (Part 2)
Figure 8.7A	Cleavage of an animal cell
Figure 8.7B	Cell plate formation in a plant cell
Figure 8.8A	An experiment demonstrating density-dependent inhibition, using animal cells grown in culture
Figure 8.8B	An experiment demonstrating the effect of growth factors on the division of cultured animal cells
Figure 8.9A	Mechanical model for the cell cycle control system
Figure 8.9B	How a growth factor signals the cell cycle control system
Figure 8.10	Growth and metastasis of a malignant (cancerous) tumor of the breast
Figure 8.12	A homologous pair of chromosomes
Figure 8.13	The human life cycle
Figure 8.14	The stages of meiosis (Part 1)
Figure 8.14	The stages of meiosis (Part 2)
Figure 8.15	Comparison of mitosis and meiosis
Figure 8.16	Results of the independent orientation of chromosomes at metaphase I
Figure 8.17A	Differing genetic information on homologous chromosomes
Page 142	Distinguishing the homologous pair of chromosomes from sister chromatids
Figure 8.18A	Chiasmata
Figure 8.18B	How crossing over leads to genetic recombination
Figure 8.19	Preparation of a karyotype from a blood sample (Layer 1)
Figure 8.19	Preparation of a karyotype from a blood sample (Layer 2)
Figure 8.19	Preparation of a karyotype from a blood sample (Layer 3)
Figure 8.19	Preparation of a karyotype from a blood sample (Layer 4)
Figure 8.20C	Maternal age and incidence of Down syndrome
Figure 8.21A	Nondisjunction in meiosis I
Figure 8.21B	Nondisjunction in meiosis II
Figure 8.21C	Fertilization after nondisjunction in the mother
Figure 8.22A	A man with Klinefelter syndrome (XXY)
Figure 8.22B	A woman with Turner syndrome (XO)
Table 8.22	Abnormalities of sex chromosome number in humans
Figure 8.23A	Alterations of chromosome structure involving one chromosome or a homologous pair
Figure 8.23B	Chromosome translocation between nonhomologous chromosomes
Figure 8.23C	The translocation associated with chronic myelogenous leukemia

Media

See the beginning of this book for a complete description of all media available for instructors and students. Animations and videos are available in the Campbell Image Presentation Library. Media Activities and Thinking as a Scientist investigations are available on the student CD-ROM and website.

Animations and Videos	Module Number
Mitosis Overview Animation	8.6
Late Interphase Animation	8.6
Prophase Animation	8.6
Prometaphase Animation	8.6
Metaphase Animation	8.6
Anaphase Animation	8.6
Telophase Animation	8.6
Cytokinesis Animation	8.6
Mitosis and Cytokinesis Animation	8.6
Animal Mitosis (time-lapse) Video	8.7
Hydra Budding Video	8.11
Interphase I Animation	8.14
Prophase I Animation	8.14
Metaphase I Animation	8.14
Anaphase I Animation	8.14
Telophase I & Cytokinesis Animation	8.14
Meiosis II & Cytokinesis Animation	8.14
Crossing Over Animation	8.18

Activities and Thinking as a Scientist	Module Number
Web/CD Activity 8A *The Cell Cycle*	8.5
Web/CD Thinking as a Scientist *How Much Time Do Cells Spend in Each Phase of Mitosis?*	8.6
Web/CD Activity 8B *Mitosis and Cytokinesis Animation*	8.7
Web/CD Activity 8C *Mitosis and Cytokinesis Video*	8.7
Web/CD Activity 8D *Asexual and Sexual Life Cycles*	8.13
Web/CD Activity 8E *Meiosis Animation*	8.15
Web/CD Activity 8F *Origins of Genetic Variation*	8.18
Web/CD Thinking as a Scientist *How Is Crossing Over Measured in the Fungus* Sordaria?	8.18

CHAPTER 9

Patterns of Inheritance

Teaching Objectives

Introduction Explain how dog genetics can provide insight into human inheritance.

Mendel's Laws

9.1 Describe the pangenesis theory and blending hypothesis. Explain why both ideas are now rejected.

9.2 Explain why Mendel's decision to work with peas was a good choice. Define and distinguish among true-breeding organisms, hybrids, the P generation, the F_1 generation, and the F_2 generation.

9.3 Define and distinguish between the following pairs of terms: genotype versus phenotype, dominant allele versus recessive allele, and heterozygous versus homozygous. Also define a monohybrid cross and a Punnett square.

9.3 Explain how Mendel's law of segregation describes the inheritance of a single characteristic.

9.4 Describe the genetic relationship between homologous chromosomes.

9.5 Explain how Mendel's law of independent assortment applies to a dihybrid cross. Illustrate this law with examples from Labrador retrievers and Mendel's work with peas.

9.6 Explain how a testcross is performed to determine the genotype of an organism.

9.7 Explain how and when the rule of multiplication and the rule of addition should be used to determine the probability of an event. Explain why Mendel was wise to use large sample sizes in his studies.

9.8 Explain how family pedigrees can help determine the inheritance of many human traits.

9.9 Explain how recessive and dominant disorders are inherited. Provide examples of each.

9.10 Compare the health risks, advantages, and disadvantages of the following forms of fetal testing: amniocentesis, chorionic villus sampling, and ultrasound imaging. Describe the ethical dilemmas created by advances in biotechnology.

Variations on Mendel's Laws

9.11–9.15 Describe the inheritance patterns of incomplete dominance, multiple alleles, pleiotropy, and polygenic inheritance.

9.16 Explain why human skin coloration is not sufficiently explained by polygenic inheritance.

9.17 Describe the limits, benefits, and ethical challenges of genetic testing.

The Chromosomal Basis of Inheritance

9.18 Define the chromosome theory of inheritance. Explain the chromosomal basis of the laws of segregation and independent assortment.

9.19 Explain how linked genes are inherited differently from nonlinked genes.

9.20 Describe T. H. Morgan's studies of crossing over.

9.21 Explain how Sturtevant created gene maps.

Sex Chromosomes and Sex-Linked Genes

9.22 Explain how sex is genetically determined in humans and the significance of the *SRY* gene. Compare the sex determination system in humans to those in fruit flies, grasshoppers, birds, and bees.

9.23–9.24 Describe the patterns of sex-linked inheritance, noting examples in fruit flies and humans.

Key Terms

ABO blood group
achondroplasia
alleles
amniocentesis
carriers
chorionic villus sampling (CVS)
chromosome theory of inheritance
codominant
complete dominance
cross
cross-fertilization
cystic fibrosis
dihybrid cross
dominant allele
Duchenne muscular dystrophy

F_1 generation
F_2 generation
genetics
genotype
hemophilia
heterozygous
homozygous
Huntington's disease
hybrids
inbreeding
incomplete dominance
law of independent assortment
law of segregation
linked genes
monohybrid cross
P generation
pedigree

phenotype
pleiotropy
polygenic inheritance
Punnett square
recessive allele
recombination frequency
red-green color blindness
rule of addition
rule of multiplication
self-fertilize
sex chromosomes
sex-linked gene
testcross
true-breeding
ultrasound imaging

Word Roots

-centesis = a puncture (*amniocentesis:* a technique for determining genetic abnormalities in a fetus by the presence of certain chemicals or defective fetal cells in the amniotic fluid, obtained by aspiration from a needle inserted into the uterus)

co- = together (*codominance:* phenotype in which both dominant alleles are expressed in the heterozygote)

di- = two (*dihybrid cross:* a breeding experiment in which parental varieties differing in two traits are mated)

pleio- = more (*pleiotropy:* when a single gene impacts more than one characteristic)

poly- = many; **gen-** = produce (*polygenic:* an additive effect of two or more gene loci on a single phenotypic character)

Lecture Outline

Introduction *Purebreds and Mutts—A Difference of Heredity*

    A. Close observations of breeding organisms and their offspring (Labrador puppies) show patterns in the inheritance of characteristics that can be predicted (chapter opening photo). However, inheritance patterns can be rather unpredictable, as indicated in the photo of the mongrel pups (chapter-opening photo).

    B. Behavior can be partially explained by **genetics** (the science of heredity), but the environment in which an organism lives also influences behavior.

    C. We will see that patterns of inheritance can be explained by the behavior of chromosomes during meiosis and fertilization.

I. Mendel's Laws

Module 9.1 The science of genetics has ancient roots.

    A. The ancient Greeks believed in pangenesis, the idea that particles governing the inheritance of each characteristic collect in eggs and sperm and are passed on to the next generation.

    B. But many, including Aristotle, realized there were problems with this idea: The potential to produce characteristics is inherited, not pieces of the characteristics themselves. The development or activity of other cells does not change reproductive cells.

    C. Based on artificial breeding, nineteenth-century observers believed in the "blending" hypothesis, in which characteristics from both parents blend in the offspring.

    D. *Preview:* Plant and animal breeders provide data not only for hypotheses concerning inheritance, but this information also greatly influenced the ideas of Charles Darwin and Alfred Wallace, at about the same time (Module 13.1).

Module 9.2 Experimental genetics began in an abbey garden.

    A. Mendel was university trained in precise experimental technique (Figure 9.2A). He studied peas because they offered advantages over other organisms. Peas grow easily, have relatively short life spans (one year), have numerous and distinct characteristics (Figure 9.2D), and the mating of individuals can be controlled so the parentage of offspring can be known for certain.
        NOTE: This is a place to talk about the fact that good biological experimentation often results from the choice of suitable study organisms that enable the experimenter to focus on particular questions.

    B. Mendel's paper, published in 1866, argued that there are discrete, heritable factors (what we call genes) transmitted from generation to generation.

    C. Mendel could intentionally have a flower **self-fertilize** by covering it with a bag, or he could allow **cross-fertilization** between two different plants by dusting the carpels of one with the pollen of another (Figure 9.2C).
        NOTE: The life history of flowering plants, for our purposes here, is similar to that of most animals, with male and female gamete–producing organs found in flowers (Figure 9.2B).

    D. By continuous self-fertilization for many generations, Mendel developed true-breeding varieties of plants (continued to show a characteristic when self-fertilized) for each of the characteristics he followed. He found seven characteristics, each of which came in two distinct forms (Figure 9.2D).

E. Mendel then performed an experiment that produced **hybrids** (offspring from two different varieties) by performing a **cross** (cross-fertilization) of plants with two different traits. For example, peas with purple flowers and those with white flowers were crossed.

F. In these experiments, the true-breeding parents are the **P generation** (P for parental), their hybrid offspring is the F_1 **generation** (F for filial, Latin for *son*), and the offspring of mating two F_1 individuals is the F_2 **generation** (second filial).

Module 9.3 Mendel's law of segregation describes the inheritance of a single characteristic.

Review: Point out that the law of segregation is a reflection of the events of meiosis (Module 8.14).

A. **Law of segregation:** Pairs of genes segregate (separate) during gamete formation; the fusion of gametes at fertilization pairs genes once again.

B. Mendel conducted a **monohybrid cross** with flower color (Figure 9.3A). The results of this experiment were as follows: out of 929 F_2 offspring, 705 were purple, and 224 were white, a ratio of 3:1.
   NOTE: The proportions are not exactly ¾ and ¼ because mating involves probabilities. See below.

C. Mendel observed that each of the seven characteristics exhibited the same inheritance pattern.

D. Mendel developed four hypotheses:
   1. There are alternative forms of genes, the units that determine heritable characteristics. These alternative forms are called **alleles.**
   2. For each inherited characteristic, an organism has two genes, one from each parent. They may be the same allele (**homozygous)** or different alleles (**heterozygous).**
   3. When the two alleles are different, the one that is fully expressed is said to be the **dominant allele,** and the one that is not noticeably expressed is said to be the **recessive allele.**
   4. A sperm or egg carries only one allele for each characteristic because the allele pairs segregate from each other during gamete production. This is called the **law of segregation** (see anaphase I and anaphase II; Module 8.14).

E. Conventions for alleles: *P*, the dominant (purple) allele, and *p*, the recessive (white) allele. P generation: *PP* × *pp*; their gametes: *P* and *p*; F_1 generation: *Pp* (Figure 9.3B).

F. The **Punnett square** is used to keep track of the gametes (two sides of the square) and offspring (cells within the square) (Figure 9.3B).

G. Homozygous dominant (*PP*), homozygous recessive (*pp*), and heterozygous (*Pp*) refer to the **genotype** (the nature of the genes as inferred from observations and knowledge of how the system works). The **phenotype** is what we see (expressed traits).

Module 9.4 Homologous chromosomes bear the two alleles for each characteristic.

A. *Review:* Homologous pairs (Module 8.12).

B. Although Mendel knew nothing about chromosomes, our knowledge of chromosome arrangements (in homologous pairs) strongly supports the law of segregation.

C. Alleles of a gene reside at the same locus on homologous chromosomes (Figure 9.4).
   NOTE: One of the chromosomes illustrated was inherited from the female parent, the other from the male parent.

Module 9.5 The law of independent assortment is revealed by tracking two characteristics at once.

Review: Point out that the law of independent assortment is a reflection of the events of meiosis (Module 8.14).

A. **Law of independent assortment:** Each pair of alleles segregates independently from the other pairs during gamete formation.

B. **Dihybrid cross:** Breed two true-breeding strains, each exhibiting one of the two forms of two characteristics (in the example used, round yellow-seeded plants [*RRYY*]) and wrinkled green-seeded plants [*rryy*]). Hybridize these two strains as the P generation, resulting in hybrid offspring (F_1: *RrYy*). Then allow the F_1 to self-fertilize (*RrYy* $\times$ *RrYy*). *NOTE:* Each of these individuals produces the same four gametes: *RY, Ry, rY,* and *ry.* Taking one gamete from each individual means that there are 4^2, or 16, possible gametic combinations.

C. Two hypotheses arise form this experiment: The characteristics are inherited either dependently or independently of each other (Figure 9.5A).

D. Results: The F_1 generation exhibits only the dominant phenotype (this is expected). The F_2 generation exhibits a phenotypic ratio of 9:3:3:1 (round yellow: round green: wrinkled yellow: wrinkled green).
NOTE: $9 + 3 + 3 + 1 = 16$, the same as the number of possible gametic combinations. That the phenotypic ratio adds up to the number of possible gametic combinations serves as a check of the results of a cross.

E. Use a Punnett square to analyze these results, with the sides of the square representing the male and female gametes possible if alleles of two characteristics segregate independently. Notice that the genotypes that produce the same phenotype are not all the same (Figure 9.5A).

F. Fur color and vision defects (PRA) in Labradors follow this pattern of assortment if pure strains of black Labs and chocolate Labs are used as the P generation. *B* allele = black fur; *b* allele = brown fur; *N* allele = normal vision; *n* allele = blind (see Figure 9.5B). If two Labs of genotype *BbNn* are bred, the phenotypic ratio will follow the expected ratio from the example with peas, 9:3:3:1. Four dogs will be blind; one of which is a chocolate Lab (*bbnn*).

Module 9.6 Geneticists use the testcross to determine unknown genotypes.

A. A **testcross** involves crossing an unknown genotype expressing the dominant phenotype with the recessive phenotype (by necessity, homozygous).

B. Each of two possible genotypes (homozygous or heterozygous) gives a different phenotypic ratio in the F_1 generation. Homozygous dominant gives all dominant. Heterozygous gives half recessive, half dominant (Figure 9.6).
NOTE: This technique uses phenotypic results to determine genotypes.

Module 9.7 Mendel's laws reflect the rules of probability.

A. Events that follow probability rules are independent events; that is, one such event does not influence the outcome of a later such event. If you flip a coin four times and get four heads, the probability for tails on the next flip is still ½.

B. The probability of two events occurring together is the product of the probabilities of the two events occurring apart (the **rule of multiplication**).

C.   Thus, when studying how the alleles of two (or more) genes that segregate independently behave, use the probabilities of how they behave individually.
NOTE: The probability of a recessive phenotype occurring in a monohybrid cross is 1 out of 4 ($\frac{1}{4}$). The probability of two recessives occurring together in a dihybrid cross is $\frac{1}{4} \times \frac{1}{4}$, or 1 out of 16 (recall $9 + 3 + 3 + 1 = 16$). In a trihybrid cross, as mentioned, the probability of a triple recessive is 1 out of 64 (or $\frac{1}{4} \times \frac{1}{4} \times \frac{1}{4} = \frac{1}{64}$).

D.   If there is more than one way an outcome can occur, these probabilities must be added, as in the case of determining the chances for heterozygous mixtures (the **rule of addition**).

Module 9.8 Connection: Genetic traits in humans can be tracked through family pedigrees.

A.   Point out the commonly used, symbolic conventions on the **pedigree** chart (family tree), showing the appearance of congenital deafness in a Martha's Vineyard family (Figure 9.8).

B.   By applying Mendel's laws, one can deduce the information on the chart from the pattern of phenotypes.

C.   Assuming that Jonathan Lambert inherited his deafness from his parents, the only explanation is that his deafness is caused by a recessive allele because neither of his parents was deaf. Because some of his children were deaf, his wife, Elizabeth Eddy, must have been a **carrier** (possess the heterozygous genotype and express the dominant phenotype). From this it follows that all their hearing children were carriers.

D.   This final deduction shows the power of applying Mendelian laws to pedigrees and how to make predictions.
NOTE: Since the pattern in the pedigree is not tied to gender. the gene for congenital deafness is not sex-linked.

Module 9.9 Connection: Many inherited disorders in humans are controlled by a single gene.

A.   There are thousands of known genetic traits that are attributable to a single gene locus and show simple Mendelian patterns of inheritance (Table 9.9).

B.   Many human characteristics are thought to be determined by simple dominant-recessive inheritance, and sometimes the ratio of dominant-to-recessive phenotype exhibits a Mendelian ratio (Figure 9.9A).

C.   **Recessive Disorders:** Most disorders are caused by recessive alleles and vary in the severity of the expressed trait.
NOTE: The terms *dominant* and *recessive* refer only to whether or not a characteristic is expressed in the heterozygous state, not to whether it is the most common.

D.   The vast majority of people afflicted with recessive disorders are born to normal, heterozygous parents (Figure 9.9A).
NOTE: It is really only the distribution of phenotypes in the offspring of one couple of known phenotype or genotype that will follow Mendelian laws.

E.   **Cystic fibrosis** is the most common lethal genetic disease in the United States.

F.   Most genetic diseases of this sort are not evenly distributed across all racial and cultural groups because of the prior and existing reproductive isolation of various populations.

G.   Laws forbidding **inbreeding** (mating with close relatives) may have arisen from observations that such marriages more often resulted in miscarriages, stillbirths, and birth defects. On the other hand, there is a debate over this issue because seriously detrimental alleles would likely be eliminated from populations when expressed in the homozygous embryo, and there are societies where inbreeding occurs without detrimental results.

H. **Dominant Disorders:** Some disorders are caused by dominant alleles. These disorders vary in how deadly they are. Some are nonlethal handicaps, some are lethal in the homozygous condition, and some are intermediate in severity.

I. **Achondroplasia,** a type of dwarfism, is lethal in the homozygous condition; individuals who express the trait are heterozygous.

J. Other conditions attributable to dominant alleles are lethal only in older adults, so the allele can be passed to children before it is realized that the parent has the condition. A prime example of this type of dominant disorder is **Huntington's disease.**

K. With practice, the laws and techniques outlined above can be used to determine many interesting things about the genotypes of individuals. This information, in turn, can be used to predict future characteristics in offspring.

Preview: In large populations, the prevalence of dominant and recessive characteristics may depend on whether one or the other allele confers advantages or disadvantages on those who have it. Population genetics will be discussed in Chapter 13.

Module 9.10 Connection: New technologies can provide insight into one's genetic legacy.

A. Circumstances may lead a couple to seek medical advice and counseling prior to conception, during a pregnancy, or after birth of a child. There are several methods that can be used to assist in the process.

B. **Identifying carriers:** Tests can be performed that can identify if a person is a carrier of a particular recessive allele that can cause disease. Carriers of recessive alleles such as Tay-Sachs disease, sickle-cell disease, and cystic fibrosis can be identified.

C. **Fetal testing:** During the pregnancy, several techniques can be used.

1. **Amniocentesis** involves taking a sample of the amniotic fluid that bathes the fetus, at 14–20 weeks. This fluid contains living fetal cells (from the skin and the mouth cavity) and can be karyotyped. Some chemical tests can be performed on the fluid itself (Figure 9.10A, left).

2. **Chorionic villus sampling (CVS)** involves removing tissue from the fetal side of the placenta nurturing a fetus, at 8–10 weeks. These cells are rapidly dividing and can be immediately karyotyped. Some biochemical tests can be performed (Figure 9.10A, right). CVS has the added advantage of speed over amniocentesis; however, both carry a slight risk of complications to the mother and/or the fetus (1% and 2%, respectively).

3. Analysis of the mother's blood can detect abnormal levels of certain hormones (HCG and estriol) or proteins produced by the fetus (alpha-fetoprotein). Abnormal levels may indicate that the fetus has Down syndrome or a neural tube defect. All three tests are often used as a triple screening regimen.

D. **Fetal imaging:**

1. **Ultrasound imaging** of the fetus provides a noninvasive view inside the womb (Figure 9.10B).

2. Fetoscopy provides a more direct view of the fetus through a needle-thin viewing scope inserted into the uterus. Fetoscopy, like CVS and amniocentesis, carries a small risk and is reserved for situations with higher probabilities of disorders (for example, older parents or situations where genetic counseling has uncovered a higher risk).

E. **Newborn screening:** State laws mandate the routine screening of all infants for the genetic disorder called PKU (phenylketonuria). If left untreated, the baby will develop mental retardation. If caught early, the child will most likely develop normally.

F. **Ethical considerations:** Ethical issues and questions abound.

1. Will all parties maintain confidentiality during and after genetic counseling? If not, will insurance coverage be compromised, will couples be stigmatized, and will misinformed people mistake carrier for contagious disease?

2. If fetal testing suggests that there is a problem that cannot be helped by routine surgery or other therapy, the difficult choice must be made between terminating a pregnancy by abortion and carrying a defective baby to term.

II. Variations on Mendel's Laws

Module 9.11 The relationship of genotype to phenotype is rarely simple.

A. The inheritance of many characteristics among all eukaryotes follows the laws that Mendel discovered.
NOTE: Discussing these laws first has allowed us to focus on the conventions and basic functioning of the system that underlies inheritance patterns.

B. However, most characteristics are inherited in ways that follow more complex patterns.

C. Before looking at the chromosomal explanation of Mendel's law of independent assortment, we will look at four such complex patterns: incomplete dominance, multiple alleles at a gene locus, pleiotropy, and polygenic inheritance.

D. These patterns are extensions of Mendel's laws, not exceptions to them.

Module 9.12 Incomplete dominance results in intermediate phenotypes.

A. **Complete dominance** was illustrated in the work done by Mendel. The flowers were always purple or white. **Incomplete dominance** describes the situation where one allele is not completely dominant in the heterozygote; the heterozygote usually exhibits characteristics intermediate between both homozygous conditions.

B. Snapdragon color is a good example of how this works. Note that the possibilities of each genotype are the same as in a case of complete dominance, but the phenotypic ratios are different (Figure 9.12A).

C. Another example is the inheritance of alleles that relate to hypercholesterolemia. Normal individuals (*HH*) have normal amounts of LDL receptor proteins; while diseased (*hh*) individuals (rare in the population, about 1 in 1 million) have no receptors and five times the amount of blood cholesterol. *Hh* individuals (1 in 500) have half the number of receptors and twice the amount of blood cholesterol (Figure 9.12B).
Preview: Lifestyle can also lead to hypercholesterolemia (Module 21.20).
Preview: In this last example, the relative numbers of each phenotype in the population depend on the manner in which genes are inherited in populations, the subject of Chapter 13.

Module 9.13 Many genes have more than two alleles in the population.

A. The **ABO blood groups** in humans follow this pattern, in which individuals can have two alleles from a set of three possible alleles.

B. These blood-type alleles code for two carbohydrates (or the absence of either carbohydrate) on the surface of red blood cells (a total of three alleles). There are six possible genotypes and four possible phenotypes.

C. When blood is transfused, recipients develop antibodies (discussed further in Chapter 24) for the types of carbohydrate on the donor red blood cells that the recipients lack.

D. Type O (universal donor, a misnomer) has neither carbohydrate and can receive no other type. Type AB (universal recipient, also a misnomer) has both carbohydrates and should receive no other type. Type A has carbohydrate A and can receive A or O. Type B has carbohydrate B and can receive B or O (Figure 9.13). The AB blood type is an example of **codominance;** both alleles are expressed in the heterozygous individual. Remember that codominance is not the same as incomplete dominance (the expression of one intermediate trait).

Module 9.14 A single gene may affect many phenotypic characteristics.

A. **Pleiotropy** is the common situation in which a gene influences multiple characteristics.

B. An example is the inheritance of an allele that encodes for an abnormal hemoglobin and, in the homozygous condition, causes sickle-cell disease.
Preview: The allelic variant that is responsible for sickle-cell disease is discussed in Module 10.16.

C. The sickle shape of the red blood cells confers a whole suite of symptoms on homozygous individuals, attributable to three underlying difficulties resulting from the abnormal cell shape (Figure 9.14).

D. The normal and abnormal alleles are another good example of codominance, so heterozygous individuals (carriers) can exhibit some symptoms, although normally they are healthy.

E. The incidence of the allele is relatively high in individuals of African descent (one in 10 African-Americans is heterozygous), because sickle-cell carriers are somewhat protected from malaria, a protozoan-caused disease prevalent in tropical regions.
Preview: This is an example of the action of natural selection (Chapter 13).

Module 9.15 A single characteristic may be influenced by many genes.

A. **Polygenic inheritance** is the additive effect of two or more genes on a single phenotypic characteristic.

B. Skin pigmentation is just such a phenotypic character whose underlying genetics has not been completely determined. Figure 9.16 is hypothetical, showing the phenotypic outcome of mixtures of three genes for skin color, each with two alleles coding for "additive units," which produce the overall characteristic. *AABBCC* would be a very-dark-skinned person while *aabbcc* would be a very-light-skinned person. Because the effect of the genes is additive, a person with the genotype *AABbcc* would have the same skin color as a person with the genotype *AaBbCc*. In reality, the human skin has even more variations than illustrated here.
NOTE: Point out to your students how much easier it is to solve genetic problems such as these using probabilities instead of Punnett squares.

Module 9.16 The environment affects many characteristics.

A. The example of skin color in Module 9.15 is a gross underexaggeration of the range of skin color in humans. The bell-shaped curve in Figure 9.15 would more accurately represent the range of skin color. However, because of environmental influences, no degree of characterization of genes will fully explain the range of skin color in humans.

B. Many characteristics are a result of the combination of genetic and environmental influences. This statement holds true for organisms besides humans. An oak tree is genetically locked into being an oak, but the leaf size, shape, and shades of green are influenced by the exposure to the wind and sun.

C. The old and hotly contested debate of "nature versus nurture" still rages. There are some traits that are undeniably determined by the genes that we inherit (for example, ABO blood group). But are all phenotypes determined by the genotype? Consider red blood cell count and altitude.

D. A good example of environmental influence is illustrated by identical twins that are easily distinguished. It is important to remember that environmental influences are not passed on the next generation.

Module 9.17 Genetic testing can detect disease-causing alleles.

A. The field of genetic testing (also known as genetic screening) has expanded dramatically in the past decade.

B. Diagnostic testing is used to confirm or rule out the existence of a genetic disorder. This procedure can be used on the unborn (prenatal testing) as well as after birth (particularly adults). This type of testing is designed to identify a person predisposed to certain disorders such as colon cancer or breast cancer (BRCA1 or BRCA2).

C. Ethical, moral, and medical issues are being raised by the increased use of genetic testing. Insurability of persons with detected genetic disorders is also an issue of concern (see breast cancer researcher, Mary Claire King, Module 11.19).

III. The Chromosomal Basis of Inheritance

Module 9.18 Chromosome behavior accounts for Mendel's laws.

A. While the existence and behavior of chromosomes was not appreciated by Mendel himself, the significance of his work was understood later, in the late 1800s and early 1900s. Out of this understanding came the **chromosome theory of inheritance.** The theory states that genes occupy specific loci on chromosomes, and it is the chromosomes that undergo segregation and independent assortment during meiosis.

B. We have already seen that the fact that there are homologous pairs of chromosomes accounts for the law of segregation.

C. The fact that there are several sets of homologous pairs of chromosomes accounts for the law of independent assortment. Figure 9.18 illustrates Mendel's laws.
NOTE: Mendel's seven garden pea characteristics all sorted independently of each other because the genes governing each characteristic are all on separate chromosomes.

Module 9.19 Genes on the same chromosome tend to be inherited together.

A. **Linked genes** are located close together on the same chromosome.

B. The inheritance of such genes does not follow the pattern described by the law of independent assortment because the two genes are normally inherited together on adjoining portions of the same chromosome.

C. The phenotypic ratios of such dihybrid crosses approach that of a monohybrid cross (3:1), rather than the typical pattern of the dihybrid cross (9:3:3:1) (Figure 9.19).

Module 9.20 Crossing over produces new combinations of alleles.

A. Homologous chromosomes will undergo crossing over during meiosis and produce new combinations of alleles (review Module 8.18).

B. Figure 9.20A illustrates the process of crossing over between two linked genes and the production of four different gamete genotypes.

    C. Early examples of recombination were demonstrated in fruit flies (Figure 9.20B) by embryologist T. H. Morgan and colleagues in the early 1900s.

    D. The percentage of recombinant offspring is called the **recombination frequency** (Figure 9.20C).

Module 9.21 Geneticists use crossover data to map genes.

    A. The study of fruit-fly genetics resulted in considerable additional understanding of genetic laws. Fruit flies have many phenotypic characters, are easily raised and bred in captivity, and have a short life cycle. In addition, they have only four chromosomes (simplifying the situation), and these chromosomes can be easily visualized in nondividing cells in the salivary glands.
    NOTE: This is another example of the use of an experimental organism that lends itself to study.

    B. A. H. Sturtevant, one of Morgan's colleagues (both seen in Figure 9.21A), developed a technique of using crossover data to map the locations of genes on chromosomes on which they were linked.

    C. Sturtevant assumed that the rate of recombination was proportional to the distance between two genes on a chromosome (Figure 9.21B) and this information could be used to construct a genetic map (Figure 9.21C).

IV. Sex Chromosomes and Sex-Linked Genes

Module 9.22 Chromosomes determine sex in many species.

    A. **Sex chromosome** are the genes (commonly designated X and Y) present in many animals, including fruit flies and humans, which determine the sex of the individual.

    B. Sex chromosomes in humans are nonidentical members of a homologous pair. In humans, XX individuals are female, and XY are male (Figure 9.22A).

    C. A crucial role in the human sex determination is played by the *SRY* (sex-determining region of the Y chromosome) gene. This gene initiates the development of testes. An individual who does not have a functioning *SRY* gene develops ovaries.

    D. In other species, other patterns of sex chromosomes exist (Figures 9.22B and C). For example, fish, butterflies, and birds use the egg to determine the sex of the offspring, and the sex chromosomes are designated with W and Z. The eggs are either W or Z, and males have the genotype ZZ, while females are genotype ZW.

    E. In some species, chromosome number rather than chromosome type determines sex (Figure 9.22D). In some invertebrates, diploid individuals are female and haploid are male.
    NOTE: In sea turtles, for example, the temperature at which the fertilized eggs are incubated determines sea turtles' sex.

    F. Plants that produce both eggs and sperm are said to be monoecious. Animals that produce both eggs and sperm are hermaphroditic. The chromosome complement for all individuals in such species will be the same.

Module 9.23 Sex-linked genes exhibit a unique pattern of inheritance.

    A. Sex chromosomes contain genes specifying sex and other genes for characteristics unrelated to sex. These genes are said to be **sex-linked genes.**

    B. Because of linkage and location, the inheritance of these characteristics follows peculiar patterns.

C. Examples are presented using eye color in fruit flies (X-linked recessive for white eyes; Figure 9.23A). Depending on the genotypes of the parents, three patterns emerge:

1. Female $X^R X^R$ × Male $X^r Y$: All offspring with red eyes regardless of the sex of the individuals (Figure 9.23B).
2. Female $X^R X^r$ × Male $X^R Y$: All females with red eyes, half the males with red eyes and the other half with white eyes (Figure 9.23C).
3. Female $X^R X^r$ × Male $X^r Y$: An even number of each type regardless of the sex (Figure 9.23D).

D. In humans, most sex-linked characteristics result from genes on the X chromosome. *Preview:* Thus, mostly males are affected (Module 9.24).

NOTE: Other sex-related patterns of inheritance include sex-influenced genes, sex-limited genes, genome imprinting, and mitochondrial inheritance. Pattern baldness is an example of a sex-influenced trait; the allele for pattern baldness behaves as a recessive in females and a dominant in males (its expression requires sufficient testosterone). A sex-limited gene is one that can be expressed in only one sex or the other; for example, some testicular tumors are the result of inheriting a particular allelic variant (obviously, testicular tumors cannot be expressed in females). In genome imprinting the same DNA sequence is expressed differently based on whether it was inherited from the female or male parent. For example, if an individual is missing a particular segment of paternal chromosome 15, the result is Prader-Willi syndrome; if the same segment is missing from maternal chromosome 15, the result is Angelman syndrome. Mitochondrial genes are all inherited from the female parent.

Module 9.24 Connection: Sex-linked disorders affect mostly males.

A. Examples of such characteristics are red-green color blindness, a type of muscular dystrophy, and hemophilia.

B. Because the male has only one X chromosome, his recessive X-linked characteristic will always be exhibited.

C. Most known sex-linked traits are caused by genes (alleles) on the X chromosome.

D. When these traits are recessive (most are), males express them because they have only one X. Females who have the allele are normally carriers and will exhibit the condition only if they are homozygous.

E. Males cannot pass sex-linked traits to sons (who get a Y from their father).

F. **Red-green color blindness** is a complex of sex-linked disorders, each of which is caused by an allele on the X chromosome. The result is considerable variation in the changes in color perception (Figure 9.24A).

G. **Hemophilia** is a sex-linked trait with a particularly well-studied history because of its incidence among the intermarrying royal families of Europe (Figure 9.24B).

NOTE: Hemophilia contributed to the Russian revolution of 1917. Rasputin gained influence over Czar Nicholas II and Czarina Alexandra by his apparent ability to control hemophilic episodes experienced by their son, Alexis.

H. **Duchenne muscular dystrophy** (DMD) is a severe disease that causes progressive loss and weakening of muscle tissue and has been traced to a particular nucleotide sequence.

NOTE: A functional version of the protein dystrophin is missing in individuals with DMD. Dystrophin is found in the plasma membrane (sarcolemma) of muscle fibers (Modules 20.6, 30.7, and 30.8). It appears that the result of not having a functional version of dystrophin is an increase in calcium ion levels in the sarcoplasm (cytoplasm of a muscle fiber). The excess calcium ions appear ultimately to lead to degeneration of the muscle fiber.

Class Activities

1. Remind students that most of the details covered in this chapter can be deduced by observation of patterns of inheritance across generations. Make an accounting of the ratios of some simple, Mendelian characteristics among your class (earlobes, mid-digital hair, tongue curling, etc.). You may want to see if it is possible to determine the genotypes of students for these characteristics by comparing how they express the characteristic with how each of their parents expresses that characteristic. Examine the distribution of phenotypes such as those illustrated in Figure 9.8A in your class by asking for a show of hands. You may want to explain that the class represents a "freely interbreeding" population in which the 3:1 ratio of dominant-to-recessive phenotypes is maintained only if there is no relative advantage of one characteristic over the other. However, since any class is a small sample size and there is no control over the parents of those in the class, it is unlikely that the class ratio will be 3:1 for any of these traits. Point out to the class how the dominant character is not always the most common character. This demonstration ties in with the process of science as discussed in Chapter 1 and helps preview population genetics (Chapter 13).

2. Ask your students which events of meiosis allow for the application of the rule of multiplication and the rule of addition.

3. See if, based on their phenotype and the phenotypes of their parents and other relatives for a particular trait, students can use a family pedigree to determine their genotype and the genotypes of their relatives for that trait.

Transparency Acetates

Figure 9.2B	Anatomy of a garden pea flower
Figure 9.2C	Mendel's technique for cross-fertilization of pea plants
Figure 9.2D	The seven pea characteristics studied by Mendel
Figure 9.3A	Crosses tracking one characteristic (flower color)
Figure 9.3B	Explanation of the crosses in Figure 9.3A
Figure 9.4	Homologous chromosomes
Figure 9.5A	Two hypotheses for segregation in a dihybrid cross
Figure 9.5B	Independent assortment of two genes in the Labrador retriever
Figure 9.6	Using a testcross to determine genotype
Figure 9.7	Segregation and fertilization as chance events
Figure 9.8B	Pedigree showing inheritance of deafness in a family from Martha's Vineyard
Figure 9.9A	Offspring produced by parents who are both carriers for a recessive disorder
Table 9.9	Some autosomal disorders in humans
Figure 9.10A	Testing a fetus for genetic disorders
Figure 9.12A	Incomplete dominance in snapdragon color
Figure 9.12B	Incomplete dominance in human hypercholesterolemia
Figure 9.13	Multiple alleles for the ABO blood groups
Figure 9.14	Sickle-cell disease, multiple effects of a single human gene
Figure 9.15	A model for polygenic inheritance of skin color
Figure 9.18	The chromosomal basis of Mendel's principles (Layer 1)
Figure 9.18	The chromosomal basis of Mendel's principles (Layer 2)

Media

See the beginning of this book for a complete description of all media available for instructors and students. Animations and videos are available in the Campbell Image Presentation Library. Media Activities and Thinking as a Scientist investigations are available on the student CD-ROM and website.

Animations and Videos	Module Number
Ultrasound of Human Fetus 1 Video	9.10
Ultrasound of Human Fetus 2 Video	9.10

Activities and Thinking as a Scientist	Module Number
Web/CD Activity 9A: *Monohybrid Cross*	9.3
Web/CD Activity 9B: *Dihybrid Cross*	9.6
Web/CD Activity 9C: *Gregor's Garden*	9.7
Web/CD Activity 9D: *Incomplete Dominance*	9.12
Web/CD Activity 9E: *Linked Genes and Crossing Over*	9.21
Web/CD Activity 9F: *Sex-Linked Genes*	9.23
Web/CD Thinking as a Scientist: *How Is the Chi-Square Test Used in Genetic Analysis?*	9.23
Biology Labs On-Line: *Sex Chromosomes and Sex-Linked Genes*	9.23

CHAPTER 10

Molecular Biology of the Gene

Teaching Objectives

Introduction: Explain how a herpesvirus invades a cell and forces the cell to reproduce the virus.

The Structure of the Genetic Material

10.1 Describe the experiments of Griffith, Avery, and Hershey and Chase, which demonstrated that DNA is the genetic material.

10.2–10.3 Compare the structure of DNA and RNA.

DNA Replication

10.4 Explain how the structure of DNA facilitates its replication.

10.5 Describe the process of DNA replication.

The Flow of Genetic Information from DNA to RNA to Protein

10.6 Describe the locations, reactants, and products of transcription and translation.

10.7–10.8 Explain how the "languages" of DNA and RNA are used to produce polypeptides.

10.9 Explain how RNA is produced.

10.10 Explain how eukaryotic RNA is processed before leaving the nucleus.

10.11 Explain how tRNA functions in the process of translation.

10.12 Describe the structure and function of ribosomes.

10.13 Explain how translation begins.

10.14 Describe the step-by-step process by which amino acids are added to a growing polypeptide chain.

10.15 Diagram the overall process of transcription and translation.

10.16 Describe the major types of mutations and their possible consequences.

Microbial Genetics

10.17 Compare the lytic and lysogenic reproductive cycles of a phage.

10.18 Compare the structures and reproductive cycles of an enveloped RNA virus and the herpesvirus.

10.19 Describe the common characteristics of plant viruses.

10.20 Explain why RNA viruses tend to have an unusually high rate of mutation.

10.20 Describe three ways that new disease-causing viruses evolve.

10.21 Explain how the AIDS virus enters a host cell and reproduces.

10.22 Define and compare the processes of transformation, transduction, and conjugation.

10.23 Describe the roles of bacterial F factors. Define a plasmid, and explain why R plasmids pose serious human health problems.

Key Terms

A site	introns	reverse transcriptase
adenine (S)	lysogenic cycle	ribosomal RNA (rRNA)
AIDS	lytic cycle	RNA polymerase
anticodon	messenger RNA (mRNA)	RNA splicing
bacteriophages	molecular biology	semiconservative model
capsid	mutagen	start codon
codon recognition	mutagenesis	stop codon
codons	mutation	sugar-phosphate
conjugation	nucleotides	backbone
cytosine (C)	P site	terminator
DNA ligase	peptide bond formation	thymine (T)
DNA polymerases	phages	transcription
double helix	plasmid	transduction
emerging viruses	polynucleotide	transfer RNA (tRNA)
exons	promoter	transformation
F factor	prophage	translation
genetic code	R plasmids	translocation
guanine (G)	reading frame	triplet code
HIV	retroviruses	uracil (U)

Word Roots

liga- = bound or tied (*DNA ligase:* a linking enzyme for DNA replication)

Lecture Outline

Introduction *Saboteurs Inside Our Cells*

   A. The chromosome theory of inheritance set the historical and structural stage for the development of a molecular understanding of the gene.

   B. Many of the basics of molecular biology began to be understood by studying viruses and the mechanism used by viruses to gain control over DNA replication and the transcriptional and translational machinery of a cell.

   1. *Review:* Are viruses living things? Recall some of the characteristics of life that viruses do not exhibit, particularly cellular structure and metabolism (Module 1.1).

   2. Viruses are composed of a protein coat and internal DNA (or RNA), and they depend on the metabolism of their host to make more viral particles (Figure 10.1C).

   3. Viruses infect all living things.

   4. Experimental systems using phages (bacterial viruses or bacteriophages) were a logical choice for early experiments on the **molecular biology** of the gene. Phages are simple, with simple genes infecting relatively simple and easily manipulated bacteria.

   C. This chapter focuses on the structure of DNA, how it is replicated, and the process of protein synthesis through transcription and translation.

I. The Structure of the Genetic Material

Module 10.1 Experiments showed that DNA is the genetic material.

A. DNA is commonly referred to by grade-school children and routinely manipulated by scientists. The identification of the structure and function of DNA as the heritable material was, however, not an easy task. The debate at the turn of the 20th century was over what the material of heredity was, protein or DNA.

B. In 1928, Griffith showed that some substance (he did not know what) conveyed traits (pathogenicity) from heat-killed bacteria to living bacteria without the trait.

C. Evidence gathered during the 1930s and 1940s showed it was DNA rather than protein (both complex macromolecules found in chromosomes) that was the genetic material.

D. In 1952, Hershey and Chase, using a virus called T2, showed that it was the DNA in the virus that infected the bacterial cell. Viruses of this type are called **bacteriophages** (**phages** for short).

E. The structure of a T2 phage is very simple, consisting of a protein coat and a DNA core (Figure 10.1A).

F. Hershey and Chase devised a simple experiment using T2 phage and demonstrated that the radioactive isotope of sulfur (found only in proteins) was not transferred into new viral particles, whereas the radioactive isotope of phosphorus (found only in DNA) was transferred (Figure 10.1B).

G. The reproductive cycle (also known as the lytic cycle) of a T2 phage results in the production of multiple copies of the T2 phage and the death of the infected bacterial cell (Figure 10.1C).

Module 10.2 DNA and RNA are polymers of nucleotides.

A. *Review:* The polymeric nature of DNA and RNA **polynucleotides** (Module 3.16 and Figures 3.16A, B, and C).

B. Focus on the chemical structure of the three components of each monomer **nucleotide:** an acidic phosphate group; deoxyribose, a five-carbon sugar; and nitrogenous bases (Figure 10.2A). The **sugar-phosphate backbone** holds the nitrogenous bases in place.

C. Mention the presence of a ribose sugar, rather than a deoxyribose sugar, in RNA (Figure 10.2C).

D. Briefly discuss the structural similarities and differences among the four nitrogenous bases (**thymine T, cytosine C, adenine A,** and **guanine G**) that occur in DNA and the one, **uracil (U),** that occurs instead of thymine in RNA, noting their commonly used abbreviations (Figures 10.2B and C).

E. Note the structural similarities between DNA and RNA molecules. The only differences are the ribose sugar and the use of uracil in RNA (Figure 10.2D).

Module 10.3 DNA is a double-stranded helix.

A. Below are some of the data that went into the Watson-Crick DNA model (Figure 10.3B).

1. The chemical structure of DNA, including that of the component structures

2. Wilkins and Franklin's X-ray crystallographs (from which one can deduce helical form and width and repeating length of the helix) (Figure 10.3A)

3. Chargaff's chemical analysis showing that the amounts of A and T, and G and C, were always equal

4. Previous knowledge that the ratios of A + T to G + C varied from species to species

B. The model that fit all the observations was a **double helix** (a twisted rope ladder) with sugar backbones on the outside and hydrogen-bonded nitrogenous bases on the inside (Figures 10.3C and D).

C. G always bonds with C, and A always bonds with T, but there are no restrictions on the linear sequence of nucleotides along the length of the helix.
NOTE: While not overtly stated in the accompanying text, Figure 10.3D illustrates that it is the combination of one purine and one pyrimidine that accounts for the known width of the double helix. This figure also illustrates that adenine and thymine are joined by two hydrogen bonds and guanine and cytosine are joined by three hydrogen bonds.

D. Two strands of the double helix run in opposite directions.
NOTE: The strands are antiparallel.

E. The Watson-Crick model was proposed in a short paper in 1953 and almost immediately led to proposed mechanisms about DNA function.
NOTE: The story of American James Watson's and his English colleague Francis Crick's discovery of the structure of DNA includes many aspects of great scientific discoveries: making the necessary observations, careful thought as to what the observations mean, insightful formulation of a hypothesis (model) based on the analysis of the observations, and being in the right place at the right time. There is also some controversy about the manner in which some of the story unfolded.

II. DNA Replication

Module 10.4 DNA replication depends on specific base pairing.

A. The nature of the reproductive process, and of the cell cycle involved in it, requires that complete and faithful copies of DNA be produced (replicated).

B. Watson and Crick stated in their original paper that their model suggested a copying mechanism.

C. The mechanism proposed and confirmed by the end of the 1950s involved each half of the double helix functioning as a template upon which a new, missing half is built (Figure 10.4A).

D. Each new double helix consists of one old and one new strand; thus, the mechanism of replication is **semiconservative.**

E. The actual mechanism involves a complex arrangement of molecular players, the help of enzymes, and some geometric contortions including untwisting of the parent helix and retwisting the daughter helices (Figure 10.4B).
NOTE: Ask your students what life (if any) would be like on Earth if DNA replication were mistake free.

Module 10.5 DNA replication: A closer look.

A. DNA replication in eukaryotes occurs simultaneously at many sites (replication bubbles) on a double helix. This allows DNA replication to occur in a shorter period of time than replication from a single origin would allow (as it occurs in prokaryotes) (Figure 10.5A).

B. **DNA polymerases** can attach nucleotides only to the 3' end of a growing daughter strand. Thus, replication always proceeds in the 5' to 3' direction.

C. Within the replication bubbles, one daughter strand is synthesized continuously while the other daughter strand must be synthesized in short pieces, which are then joined together by a separate DNA polymerase and **DNA ligase** (Figure 10.5C).
NOTE: These short pieces of DNA are called Okazaki fragments.

D. Despite its speed (50–500 pairs per second), replication is very accurate, with approximately one mistaken nucleotide pair in a billion.

E. DNA polymerases and DNA ligase also proofread the new daughter strands.

F. This replication process assures that daughter cells will carry the same genetic information as each other and as the parental cell.

III. The Flow of Genetic Information from DNA to RNA to Protein

Module 10.6 The DNA genotype is expressed as proteins, which provide the molecular basis for phenotypic traits.

A. *Review:* The roles that proteins play in organisms (Module 3.11).

B. The proteins an organism can make (with a variety of functions) are illustrated by the molecular basis of phenotypic traits.

C. The molecular basis of genotype is now recognized to be DNA. There is an intermediate molecule (RNA) that carries the information from the DNA to the process that synthesizes proteins. The flow of genetic information is illustrated in Figure 10.6A.

D. This flow is now known to occur in two stages: **transcription** of the genetic code in the nucleus to an RNA molecule, and **translation** of the RNA message in the cytoplasm (Figure 10.6A).

E. The one gene–one enzyme hypothesis was formulated in the 1940s by Beadle and Tatum, who were studying nutritional mutants of the mold Neurospora. They found that genetic mutants lacked single enzymes needed to complete metabolic pathways (Figure 10.6B).

F. This idea was soon extended to include all proteins (adding a variety of structural types) and later restricted to individual polypeptides (because some proteins are composed of several distinct polypeptide chains). For example, hemoglobin has four polypeptides made from two genes. It is now referred to as the one gene–one polypeptide hypothesis.

Module 10.7 Genetic information written in codons is translated into amino acid sequences.

A. The flow of genetic information can be summarized in the following way: DNA to RNA to polypeptide (protein).

B. The nucleotide monomers represent letters in an alphabet that can form words in a language. Each word codes for one amino acid in a polypeptide.

C. There are four letters (A, T, G, and C) and 20 amino acids. One-letter words would create 4 distinct words. Two-letter words would create a vocabulary of 16 words (4 × 4). Three-letter words would create a vocabulary of 64 words (4 × 4 × 4). The **triplet code** of bases is the three-letter code on RNA, which determines the amino acid sequence on a polypeptide.
Review: Recall the discussion of probability in Module 9.7.

D. Triplets of bases are the smallest words of uniform length that can specify all the amino acids. These triplets are known as **codons.**

Module 10.8 The genetic code is the Rosetta stone of life.

A. The first codon was deciphered by Nirenberg in 1961.

B. Nirenberg added polyuracil (an artificially made RNA polynucleotide) to a mixture containing ribosomes and other cell fractions required for translation. The polypeptide polyphenylalanine was produced, which indicated UUU was the codon for phenylalanine.

C. The code was completely known by the end of the 1960s. It shows redundancy but no ambiguity (Figure 10.8A).

D. Make a polypeptide using an arbitrary sequence of bases and the information provided in the chart in Figure 10.8A (see Figure 10.8B as an example).

E. The code is virtually the same for all organisms. Thus, bacterial cells can translate the genetic messages of human cells, and vice versa. This provides evidence to the relatedness of all life and suggests that the genetic code was established early in the history of life.
Preview: Recombinant DNA techniques enable biologists to transfer genes of one organism to another and have them expressed (Chapter 12 and Modules 10.22 and 23).

Module 10.9 Transcription produces genetic messages in the form of RNA.

A. In transcription, one strand of DNA serves as a template for the new RNA strand.

B. **RNA polymerase** constructs the RNA strand during transcription (Figure 10.9A).

C. RNA synthesis is a multistep process (Figure 10.9B):

1. Transcription is initiated from one strand of the DNA, as indicated by a **promoter region** (the site at which RNA polymerase attaches); the DNA unwinds.

2. RNA synthesis and elongation occur.

3. Finally, the mRNA sequence is terminated when the process reaches a special **terminator** region of the DNA.
NOTE: Transcription means copying a message into a new medium.
Preview: The regulation of this process is discussed in Chapter 11.

D. Two other types of RNA (ribosomal RNA, or rRNA, and transfer RNA, or tRNA) play a role in translation and are transcribed by this process.

Module 10.10 Eukaryotic RNA is processed before leaving the nucleus.

A. RNA that encodes an amino acid sequence is called **messenger RNA (mRNA).**

B. In prokaryotes, transcription and translation both occur in the cytoplasm.

C. In eukaryotes, a completed mRNA molecule leaves the nucleus, and the message is translated in the cytoplasm. Review Module 10.6 (Figure 10.6A).

D. Prior to leaving the nucleus, however, RNA is modified in a process called **RNA splicing.** The regions of DNA that are not used in the production of protein (**introns**) must be removed, leaving only the **exons.** Exons are ligated, and the ends of the modified RNA molecule have additional nucleotides (tail and cap) added in an effort to assist exiting the nucleus, reduce enzymatic attack once in the cytoplasm, and promote binding to the ribosome (Figure 10.10).

E. Splicing can occur with the help of a variety of proteins, or RNA can self-splice. The process of splicing offers the mechanism of multiple polypeptides from one gene.

F. The players in the translation process include ribosomes, tRNA molecules, enzymes, protein factors, and sources of cellular energy.
NOTE: Translation means rewording a message into a new language. The new language in this case is the linear sequence of amino acids in polypeptides.

Module 10.11 Transfer RNA molecules serve as interpreters during translation.

A. Amino acids that are to be joined in correct sequence cannot recognize the codons on the mRNA.

B. Transfer RNA molecules (tRNA), one or more for each type of amino acid, match the right amino acid to the correct codon (Figures 10.11A and B).

C. Each tRNA contains a region (the **anticodon**) that recognizes and binds to the correct codon for its amino acid on the mRNA.

D. The right tRNA for each amino acid and its amino acid are temporarily joined by the aid of a specific enzyme (at least one for each tRNA–amino acid complex) via the expenditure of one ATP molecule (Figure 10.11C). The amino acid is not shown in the figure due to its small size.

Module 10.12 Ribosomes build polypeptides.

A. Ribosomes are composed of **ribosomal RNA (rRNA)** and protein, arranged in two subunits (Figure 10.12A).

B. The shape of ribosomes provides a platform on which protein synthesis can take place. There are locations for the mRNA, and two tRNA–amino acid complex binding sites (Figures 10.12B and C).

C. The difference between prokaryotic and eukaryotic ribosomes, though small, is exploited with antibiotics such as tetracycline and streptomycin.

Module 10.13 An initiation codon marks the start of an mRNA message.

A. Translation can be divided into the same three phases as transcription: initiation, elongation, and termination.

B. An mRNA molecule is longer than the genetic message it contains. It contains a starting nucleotide sequence that helps in the initiation phase and an ending sequence that helps in the termination phase (Figures 10.13A and B part 1 and Figure 10.15 part 5).

C. Initiation is a two-step process.
   1. The initial sequence helps bind the mRNA to the small ribosomal subunit; a specific **start codon** (AUG) binds with an initiator tRNA anticodon (UAC) carrying the amino acid methionine (Figure 10.13B part 1).
   2. The large ribosome binds to the small subunit as the initiator tRNA fits into the **P site** on the large subunit (Figure 10.13B part 2). The other amino acid binding site, referred to as the **A site,** is empty and ready for the next tRNA–amino acid complex.

Module 10.14 Elongation adds amino acids to the polypeptide chain until a stop codon terminates translation.

A. Elongation involves three steps (Figure 10.14).
   1. **Codon recognition:** The anticodon of an incoming tRNA–amino acid complex binds with the codon at the ribosome's A site.
   2. **Peptide bond formation:** A polypeptide bond is formed between the growing polypeptide (attached to the tRNA at the P site) and the new amino acid.
   3. **Translocation:** The P site tRNA leaves the complex, and the A site tRNA–polypeptide chain complex moves to the P site.

B. An enzyme within the ribosome structure catalyzes the formation of the polypeptide bond.

C. Elongation continues until a special **stop codon** (UAA, UAG, or UGA) causes termination of the process. The finished polypeptide is released, and the ribosome splits into its two subunits.

Module 10.15 Review: The flow of genetic information in the cell is DNA → RNA → protein.

   A. Figure 10.15 is a summary of the five stages of transcription and translation.

   B. The synthesis of a strand of mRNA complementary to a DNA template is transcription (stage 1; DNA to mRNA).

   C. The conversion of the information encoded within a strand of mRNA into a polypeptide is translation (stages 2 through 5; mRNA to protein).

   D. *Review:* Following their synthesis, several polypeptides may come together to form a protein with quaternary structure. Levels of protein structure are discussed in Module 3.14.

Module 10.16 Mutations can change the meaning of genes.

   A. Many differences in inherited traits in humans have been traced to their molecular deviation.

   B. A change in the nucleotide sequence of DNA is known as a **mutation.**

   C. Certain substitutions of one nucleotide base for another will lead to mutations, resulting in the replacement of one amino acid for another in a polypeptide sequence (Figure 10.16A). Base substitutions usually cause a gene to produce an abnormal product (sickle hemoglobin), or they result in no change if the new codon still codes for the same amino acid.

   D. A base substitution is known to account for the type of hemoglobin produced by the sickle-cell allele (Module 9.14).

   E. Base substitutions rarely lead to improved or changed genes that may enhance the success of the individual in which they occur. These types of mutations provide the genetic variability that may lead to the evolution of new species (Chapter 13) (Figure 10.16B).

   F. The addition or subtraction of nucleotides may result in a shift of the three-base **reading frame;** all codons past the affected one are likely to code for different amino acids (Figure 10.16B). The profound differences that are produced will almost always result in a nonfunctional polypeptide.

   G. The addition or deletion of a nucleotide can also change a reading frame codon into a stop codon, which terminates the translation process resulting in a shortened nonfunctional polypeptide.

   H. **Mutagenesis** can occur spontaneously or because of physical (UV radiation) or chemical **mutagens.**
       Preview: Such mutagenesis may result in cancer (Modules 11.16–11.20).

IV. Microbial Genetics

Module 10.17 Viral DNA may become part of the host chromosome.

   A. Viruses depend on their host cells for the replication, transcription, and translation of their nucleic acid. In some respects a virus is like a box filled with nucleic acid. The box portion of a virus is called a **capsid,** and the capsid is at times enclosed by a membrane envelope.

   B. Some bacteriophages are known to replicate in two ways (Figure 10.17).

   C. In the **lytic cycle,** a phage immediately directs the host cell to replicate the viral nucleic acid, transcribes and translates its protein-coding genes, assembles new viruses, and causes host cell lysis, releasing the reproduced phages.

D. In the **lysogenic cycle,** a phage's DNA is inserted into the host cell DNA by recombination and becomes a **prophage.** This DNA sequence is replicated with the host cell's DNA over many generations. Finally, some environmental cue directs the prophage to switch to the lytic cycle. Such prophages may cause the host bacterial cell to act differently than if the prophage were not there. Diphtheria, botulism, and scarlet fever are a direct result of prophage gene expression in bacterial cells.

Module 10.18 Connection: Many viruses cause disease in animals.

A. Viruses have a great variety of infectious cycles in eukaryotes. Those that infect plants or animals can cause disease.
NOTE: Organisms from all kingdoms have viruses that infect their cells.

B. In one type (enveloped RNA virus, such as the virus that causes mumps), the viral genes are in the form of RNA, which functions as a template to make complementary RNA. Complementary RNA functions either as mRNA to direct virus protein synthesis directly or as a template from which more viral RNA is made. Newly assembled viral particles leave the cell by enveloping themselves in host plasma membrane (Figure 10.18B).

C. Other viruses of eukaryotes, such as the herpesviruses that cause chickenpox, shingles, mononucleosis, cold sores, and genital herpes, reproduce inside the host cell's nucleus and can insert as a provirus in the host DNA, much like a prophage in the lysogenic cycle.
NOTE: Viruses that cause cold sores and genital herpes are different strains of the herpesviruses.

D. *Preview:* Animals defend against viruses through their immune systems. Vaccines, which induce the immune system's delayed responses to viral coat molecules, offer a possible defense against future viral infection (Chapter 24).

E. Antibiotic drugs used to treat bacterial infections cannot be used to treat viral infections. Viruses are not alive; therefore, viruses cannot be killed!

Module 10.19 Connection: Plant viruses are serious agricultural pests.

A. Most plant viruses are RNA viruses (Figure 10.19).

B. Insects, farmers, and gardeners may all spread plant viruses.

C. Infected plants may pass viruses to their offspring.

D. There are no cures for most viral diseases of plants. Research has focused on prevention and the selective breeding of resistant varieties.

Module 10.20 Connection: Emerging viruses threaten human health.

A. HIV, the virus that causes AIDS, is an example of an **emerging virus,** as are Ebola (Figure 10.20A) and hantavirus (Figure 10.20B).

B. Other recently identified viruses are the SARS virus, the West Nile virus, and a new flu virus in China that comes from birds.

C. Mutation of existing viruses is the major source of new viral diseases. High rates of mutation, particularly of RNA viruses, also accounts for the difficulty the immune system has in dealing with viruses.
Preview: This high mutation rate plays a major role in the difficulty of developing treatments and vaccines for HIV (Module 24.18).

D. The reasons for the rapid spread of viruses are intriguing areas of research. AIDS went unnoticed for many years. Then changes in technology and social behavior promoted the rapid spread around the world.

Module 10.21 The AIDS virus makes DNA on an RNA template.

A. The virus that causes **AIDS** (acquired immune deficiency syndrome) is human immunodeficiency virus, or **HIV** (Figure 10.21A).

B. HIV particles are enveloped, like those that cause mumps. Although they carry genes in the form of RNA, these genes are expressed by being first transcribed back to DNA with an enzyme called **reverse transcriptase,** at which time they enter the host cell's chromosomes as a provirus and remain unexpressed for several years. HIV finally becomes active by using the host cell's machinery to reassemble new viruses, much like a DNA virus (Figure 10.21B). Viruses that use reverse transcriptase are called retroviruses because they reverse the usual order of DNA to RNA.
Preview: Reverse transcriptase as a tool of biotechnology is discussed in Module 12.5.

C. *Preview:* HIV infects cells involved in the human immune system and is discussed in greater detail in Module 24.12.

Module 10.22 Bacteria can transfer DNA in three ways.

A. *Review:* In sexually reproducing organisms, new genetic combinations are the result of meiosis and fertilization (Chapter 8). Review the process of bacterial reproduction binary fission in Module 8.3. The mechanisms discussed in this module are the ways that bacteria produce new genetic combinations.

B. *Review:* Studies by Griffith showed nonpneumonia-causing strains of Pneumococcus becoming disease-causing in a culture medium that previously contained the disease-causing strain (Module 10.1).

C. **Transformation** is the taking up of DNA from the nonliving environment around a bacterium (Figure 12.1A). Transformation caused the results Griffith observed.

D. **Transduction** is the transfer of bacterial genes from one bacterium to another by a phage (Figure 12.1B).

E. **Conjugation** is the process by which two bacteria mate (Figure 12.1C). Conjugation is initiated by "male" cells (gene donors) that recognize "female" cells (gene recipients) by means of the male sex pili. After the initial male-female recognition, a cytoplasmic bridge forms between two cells. Replicated DNA from the male passes through this bridge to the female.

F. In all three mechanisms, the new DNA is integrated into the existing DNA in the recipient by a crossover-like event that replaces part of the existing DNA (Figure 12.1D).

G. These mechanisms are not reproductive. Sexual reproduction does not occur in bacteria, unlike the situation in plants and animals.

Module 10.23 Bacterial plasmids can serve as carriers for gene transfer.

A. The **F** (fertility) **factor** is a portion of *E. coli* DNA that carries genes for making sex pili and other requirements for conjugation.

B. The F factor may be integrated into the main bacterial DNA, or it may exist as a separate, circular DNA fragment, a **plasmid,** that is free in the cytoplasm. Plasmids replicate separately from the main DNA.

C. If the F factor is integrated into the donor's main DNA, replication begins. The replicated length of DNA is transferred from the donor to the recipient but usually breaks before the remaining F factor is transferred. Thus, the recipient does not receive the F-factor genes, and it and its descendants remain female (Figure 12.2A).

D. If the F factor exists as a separate plasmid, it replicates into a linear DNA molecule that is entirely transferred to the recipient. The recipient and all its descendants become male (Figure 12.2B).

E. When extra genes are transferred, the plasmid is acting as a vector.

F. Plasmids that carry genes other than those needed for conjugation are called vectors. For example, **R plasmids** are a class of plasmids that carry genes for antibiotic resistance. The widespread use of antibiotics in medicine and agriculture has tended to kill bacteria that lack R plasmids and favor those bacteria that have R plasmids.
NOTE: The ease of transmission of plasmid DNA has been implicated in the rapid transfer of DNA among bacteria, even between different species. Transfers such as these are partly responsible for the spread of multidrug-resistant bacteria, particularly Mycobacterium tuberculosis (natural selection; Modules 13.4, 13.5, and 13.22).

G. As will be seen later in the chapter, plasmids have important places among the techniques of genetic engineers.

Class Activities

1. Initiate a class discussion of how human behaviors have promoted the spread of emerging viruses. Be sure that your students understand how the spread of emerging viruses, bacteria, and parasites can be related to global climatic patterns.

Transparency Acetates

Figure 10.1A   Phage T2
Figure 10.1B   The Hershey-Chase experiment
Figure 10.1C   Phage reproductive cycle
Figure 10.2A   DNA polynucleotide
Figure 10.2B   Nitrogenous bases of DNA
Figure 10.2C   An RNA nucleotide
Figure 10.2D   Part of an RNA polynucleotide
Figure 10.3C   A rope-ladder model for the double helix
Figure 10.3D   Three representations of DNA
Figure 10.4A   A template model for DNA replication
Figure 10.4B   Untwisting and replication of DNA
Figure 10.5A   Multiple "bubbles" in replicating DNA
Figure 10.5B   The opposite orientations of DNA strands
Figure 10.5C   How daughter DNA strands are synthesized
Figure 10.6A   Flow of genetic information in a eukaryotic cell
Figure 10.7   Transcription and translation of codons
Figure 10.8A   Dictionary of the genetic code (RNA codons)
Figure 10.8B   Deciphering the genetic information in DNA
Figure 10.9A   A close-up view of transcription
Figure 10.9B   Transcription of a gene

Figure 10.10   The production of eukaryotic mRNA

Figure 10.11A   The structure of tRNA

Figure 10.11B   A simplified model of tRNA

Figure 10.12A   The true shape of a functioning ribosome

Figure 10.12B   Binding sites of a ribosome

Figure 10.12C   A ribosome with occupied binding sites

Figure 10.13A   A molecule of mRNA

Figure 10.13B   The initiation of translation

Figure 10.14   Polypeptide elongation

Figure 10.15   Summary of transcription and translation

Figure 10.16A   The molecular basis of sickle-cell disease

Figure 10.16B   Types of mutations and their effects

Figure 10.17   Two types of phage reproductive cycles (Layer 1)

Figure 10.17   Two types of phage reproductive cycles (Layer 2)

Figure 10.18A   An influenza virus

Figure 10.18B   The reproductive cycle of an enveloped virus

Figure 10.19   Tobacco mosaic disease (mottling of leaves) and the structure of the virus (right)

Figure 10.21A   A model of HIV structure

Figure 10.21B   The behavior of HIV nucleic acid in a host cell

Figure 10.22A   Transformation

Figure 10.22B   Transduction

Figure 10.22C   Conjugation

Figure 10.22D   Integration of donated DNA into the recipient cell's chromosome

Figure 10.23A   Transfer of chromosomal DNA by an integrated F factor

Figure 10.23B   Transfer of an F-factor plasmid

Reviewing the Concepts, page 206: DNA structure

Reviewing the Concepts, page 206: Translation

Connecting the Concepts, page 207: The flow of genetic information through the cell

---

Media

See the beginning of this book for a complete description of all media available for instructors and students. Animations and videos are available in the Campbell Image Presentation Library. Media Activities and Thinking as a Scientist investigations are available on the student CD-ROM and web site.

Animations and Videos	Module Number
Phage T2 Reproductive Cycle Animation	10.1
Hershey-Chase Experiment Animation	10.1
DNA and RNA Structure Animation	10.2
DNA Structure	10.3
DNA Replication Overview Animation	10.4
DNA Replication Animation	10.5
Leading Strand Animation	10.5

Activities and Thinking as a Scientist   Module Number

CHAPTER 11

The Control of Gene Expression

Teaching Objectives

Introduction Explain how cloning can be used to help protect endangered species. Describe the risks and limits of cloning animals.

Gene Regulation

11.1 Describe and compare the regulatory mechanisms of the *lac* operon, *trp* operon, and operons using activators.

11.2 Explain how selective gene expression yields a variety of cell types in multicellular eukaryotes.

11.3 Describe examples of dedifferentiation followed by redifferentiation in plant and animal cells.

11.4 Explain how DNA is packaged into chromosomes. Explain how packing influences gene expression.

11.5 Explain how the tortoiseshell pattern of a cat is formed.

11.6 Explain how eukaryotic gene expression is controlled, and compare it to gene control in prokaryotes.

11.7 Describe the process and significance of alternative DNA splicing.

11.8 Explain how mRNA breakdown, initiation of translation, protein activation, and protein breakdown can each regulate gene expression.

11.9 Explain how the control of gene expression in eukaryotic cells is analogous to the control of water moving through the series of pipes that carry water from your local water supply to a faucet in your home.

Animal Cloning

11.10 Describe and compare the processes of reproductive cloning and therapeutic cloning.

11.11 Describe the potential uses of reproductive cloning of nonhuman mammals.

11.12 Compare the sources and properties of embryonic stem cells and adult stem cells.

The Genetic Control of Embryonic Development

11.13 Describe generally the cascade of events that occur during fruit fly development. In particular, note the role of homeotic genes.

11.14 Describe the roles of cell-to-cell signaling and signal-transduction pathways in development.

11.15 Explain why it appears that the early versions of homeobox genes arose very early in the history of life.

The Genetic Basis of Cancer

11.16 Explain how viruses, proto-oncogenes, and tumor-suppressor genes can each contribute to cancer.

11.17 Explain how mutations in *ras* or *p53* proteins can lead to cancer.

11.18 Describe the main events in the development of colon cancer.

11.19 Describe the recent discoveries associated with the genetic basis of familial breast cancer.

11.20 Describe factors that can increase or decrease your risk of developing cancer.

Key Terms

activators	histones	regeneration
adult stem cells	homeoboxes	regulatory gene
alternative RNA splicing	homeotic gene	repressor
carcinogens	nuclear transplantation	reproductive cloning
clone	nucleosome	signal transduction pathway
differentiation	oncogene	silencers
embryonic stem cells	operator	therapeutic cloning
(ES cells)	operon	transcription factors
enhancers	promoter	tumor-suppressor genes
gene expression	proto-oncogene	X chromosome inactivation

Word Roots

trans- = across (*signal-transduction pathway:* the process by which a signal on a cell's surface is converted into a specific cellular response inside the cell)

Lecture Outline

Introduction *To Clone or Not to Clone*

    A. A **clone** is a genetically identical organism, which originated from a somatic cell nucleus of another organism. All the a

    B. There are a multitude of problems associated with cloning an organism, including rapid onset of "old age" and age-related illnesses of the cloned organism.

    C. Ethical and evolutionary issues are being raised with the ability to clone to curb the extinction of endangered species.

    D. This chapter describes the control of gene expression in prokaryotes and eukaryotes, methods and applications of animal cloning, the connections between embryonic development and gene regulation, and the genetic basis of cancer.

I. Gene Regulation

    Module 11.1 Proteins interacting with DNA turn prokaryotic genes on or off in response to environmental changes.

    A. The process of turning on or turning off a gene is called gene regulation. Gene regulation or control allows an organism to respond quickly to changes in the environment. The flow of information from gene to protein is called **gene expression.**

    B. This model of gene control was first proposed as a hypothesis in 1961 by Jacob and Monod, for the control of lactose utilization enzymes in *E. coli* (Figure 11.1A).
    NOTE: Much experimental evidence has since confirmed the existence of this and other operons in many bacteria.

C. Important features of the model: An **operon** consists of several DNA sequences coding for different enzymes, all involved in the same cellular process. Expression of the operon is controlled as a unit. Other DNA sequences in and near the operon control the operon's expression. The presence or absence of the enzyme's substrate turns on or off the controls.

D. Operon expression normally starts with RNA polymerase binding at the **promoter** region (the first nongene region of the operon), moving along and transcribing each gene in the operon.

E. When the *lac* operon is "turned off," a **regulatory gene** is transcribed and translated into a **repressor** protein. The repressor protein binds with the **operator** region of the operon, repressing the transcription of the genes further along the operon (Figure 11.1B). Operators are located between the promoter and the utilization-genes for translation.

F. When the *lac* operon is "turned on," the regulatory gene continues to be transcribed and translated into repressor, but the presence of substrate (lactose) interferes with the binding of the repressor to the operator. This permits the expression of the remainder of the operon. Expression continues until the substrate is used up. Then the repressor is free to repress the operator, and the operon turns off as above (Figure 11.1B).

G. The *lac* operon is repressed when lactose is absent and transcribed when lactose is present.

H. Another operon, the *trp* operon, is transcribed when tryptophan is absent and repressed when tryptophan is present. The enzymes expressed by the *trp* operon help synthesize tryptophan (Figure 11.1C). Both the *trp* operon and the *lac* operon are repressor-controlled operons.

I. A third type of operon uses **activators** rather than repressors. Activators are proteins produced by the regulatory genes. The activator proteins bond to DNA and make it easier for RNA polymerase to bind to the promoter region of an operon.

Module 11.2 Differentiation yields a variety of cell types, each expressing a different combination of genes.

A. Producing eukaryotic organelles and regulating their functions require a much more complex network of gene control.

B. In multicellular eukaryotes, there is the added complexity of regulating what kinds of cells are produced when and where.

C. Muscle, pancreas, and blood cells (and other cell types) of a single animal all are derived by repeated cell divisions and **differentiation** from the zygote. Differentiation of cells is a result of turning on and off genes.

D. The structure of each cell type is visibly different, reflecting its function (Figure 11.2).

E. The patterns of gene expression for the cell types in the figure illustrates the role gene expression has in the structure and function of cells. All cells listed have the enzymes for glycolysis, but only red blood cells have hemoglobin.

Module 11.3 Differentiated cells may retain all of their genetic potential.

A. Experimental evidence supports the retention of all of a multicellular organism's DNA in each of its differentiated cells, in most cases.

B. F. C. Steward and his students were the first to demonstrate that fully differentiated plant cells retained the information to grow an entirely new plant (Figure 11.3).

C. Animals can undergo the process of regeneration (the replacement of a lost part) as demonstrated when a salamander regrows a lost leg. The process requires the dedifferentiation of cells, cell division, and then redifferentiation.

Module 11.4 DNA packing in eukaryotic chromosomes helps regulate gene expression.

A. The total DNA in a human cell's 46 chromosomes would stretch 3 meters.
NOTE: This amount of DNA is packed in cell nuclei as small as 5 mm in diameter, a reduction factor of almost 1 million!

B. All the DNA fits because of elaborate packing: DNA wrapping around histones and other proteins into **nucleosomes,** coiling, supercoiling, and additional folding into chromosomes (Figure 11.4).
NOTE: During interphase, chromosomes of most cells are more loosely packed than the metaphase chromosome shown in Figure 11.4. Heterochromatin in the nucleus is not expressed, while euchromatin is expressed.

C. DNA packing prevents gene expression, most likely by preventing transcription.

Module 11.5 In female mammals, one X chromosome is inactive in each cell.

A. An interesting known example of the role of DNA packing in the control of expression is **X chromosome inactivation** in the cells of female animals. Certain cell lines have one or the other X chromosome (inherited from the individual's mother or father) inactivated; thus, there can be a random mosaic of expression of these two X chromosomes.

B. The tortoiseshell cat is a wonderful example of this phenomenon (Figure 11.5). The gene for fur color is on the X chromosome, which is randomly expressed as one allele is turned off and the other is turned on, resulting in a patchwork effect of coat color.

Module 11.6 Complex assemblies of proteins control eukaryotic transcription.

A. In both prokaryotes and eukaryotes, gene regulation is based on the regulation of transcription. However, whereas prokaryotes combine several regulated genes into one operon, eukaryotes apparently tend to regulate individual genes. Thus, in eukaryotes there are many more regulatory proteins involved and a greater degree of complex interactions than in prokaryotes.

B. Activation appears to be of greater importance in the regulation of eukaryotic gene expression than is repression. **Transcription factors** (of which activators are an example) interact with enhancer sites (a DNA sequence) in regulating the binding of RNA polymerase to a gene's promoter (Figure 11.6).

C. The binding of activators to **enhancers** initiates transcription. Unlike the operators in prokaryotes, enhancers in eukaryotes are usually some distance away from the gene they regulate and can be on either side of the gene.

D. Repressor proteins interact with nucleotide sequences called **silencers.** Repressor proteins bind to the silencer and inhibit the start of transcription.

E. Eukaryotes do not have operons, and related genes are often found scattered about the genome. Regulation of functionally related genes seems to be dependent on their association with a specific enhancer(s). Multiple copies of transcription factors bind simultaneously with all the enhancers of a gene group, prompting coordinated gene expression.

Module 11.7 Eukaryotic RNA may be spliced in more than one way.

    A. Introns have been shown to function in gene regulation. RNA splicing may regulate the movement of mRNA from the nucleus to the cytoplasm. **Alternative RNA splicing** provides a cell with several possible products from one gene region (Figure 11.7). A good example of this is the sex determination of the fruit fly. The pattern of RNA splicing of the same gene determines the sex of the fly. Approximately 100 examples of alternative splicing have been identified in the human genome.

    B. Finally, it has been suggested that introns make genes longer, thereby increasing the possibility of crossovers between exons, and providing another mechanism for increasing genetic diversity.
    Review: Crossing over (Module 8.18).

Module 11.8 Translation and later stages of gene expression are also subject to regulation.

    A. In addition to the regulation of transcription and posttranscriptional modification, gene expression can be regulated at the level of mRNA degradation, translation initiation, protein activation, and protein breakdown.

    B. Breakdown of mRNA: The lifetimes of mRNA molecules vary, controlling the amount of protein translated from a single transcription and posttranscriptional processing event. In nonmammalian vertebrates, red blood cells lose their nuclei but not their ribosomes and mRNAs, which can continue to translate into hemoglobin for a month or more.

    C. Initiation of translation: Some inhibitory control of the process of translation is known, such as the inhibitory action of a protein found in red blood cells when heme subunits are not available.

    D. Protein activation: Posttranslational control mechanisms in eukaryotes often involve cutting polypeptides into smaller, active final products (Figure 11.8).

    E. Protein breakdown: Another posttranslational control affects how fast protein products are degraded.

Module 11.9 Review: Multiple mechanisms regulate gene expression in eukaryotes.

    A. In multicellular eukaryotes, the control mechanisms of gene expression are varied and complex (Figure 11.9).

    B. Cellular differentiation of eukaryotic cells depends on turning on and off genes in the proper sequence. Each cell retains all the genetic material necessary to clone a new organism.

II. Animal Cloning

Module 11.10 Nuclear transplantation can be used to clone animals.

    A. The process of animal cloning, referred to as **nuclear transplantation,** uses the nucleus of a somatic cell and places it into a surrogate egg devoid of its nucleus.

    B. If the result of the cloning process culminates in the live birth of an organism, it is called **reproductive cloning.**

    C. **Embryonic stem (ES) cells** come from the blastocyst. These cells can be used to produce any type of cell, provided the proper conditions exist. **Therapeutic cloning** is performed with ES cells.

Module 11.11 Connection: Reproductive cloning has valuable applications, but human reproductive cloning raises ethical issues.

    A. Cloning mammals presents an advantage that previously was not available to researchers. Now geneticists can investigate the effects of a single gene or group of genes.

    B. Scientists in the agriculture industry are using cloning technology to breed genetically identical stock with desired traits. The pharmaceutical industry is experimenting with animals that could produce drugs that can be used in treating a variety of diseases, for example cystic fibrosis.

    C. Figure 11.11 shows piglets that were cloned as a source of organ transplants. Severe tissue rejection has been reduced and possibly eliminated through genetically engineered pigs that have been cloned.

    D. The first human embryo clone was reported in 2001 by the biotechnology company ACT. This was quickly followed by the announcement by a South Korean research team of a human clone developing to the blastocyst stage.

    E. Two issues are raised when performing cloning of any type, but particularly human clones.

        1. Is it really practical and cost effective?

        2. Is it morally the right thing to do?

Module 11.12 Connection: Therapeutic cloning can produce stem cells with great medical potential.

    A. Embryonic stem (ES) cells can divide indefinitely under the right laboratory conditions and, when stimulated, give rise to a wide variety of cell types (Figure 11.12). The hope of medical scientists is to some day be able to grow any tissue and even organs in the lab that can be used to treat patients in need of such therapy.

    B. An alternative with less controversy surrounding the research is the use of **adult stem cells.** Many adult tissues have stem cells that can give rise to selected cell types. This avenue of research has promise and is currently under investigation with some degree of success. The controversy over ES cells versus adult stem cells still continues with no apparent resolution in the near future.

III. The Genetic Control of Embryonic Development

Module 11.13 Cascades of gene expression and cell-to-cell signaling direct the development of an animal.

    NOTE: An example of these cascades can be seen in the determination of which end of a fruit-fly egg cell will become the head and which end will become the tail. These events occur within the ovaries of the mother fly and involve the following series of events (Figure 11.13B).

    A. Early studies on fruit flies led to work that revolutionized the concepts of development and gene expression. Figure 11.13A illustrates how improper cell-to-cell signaling can cause mutations in an organism.

    B. The egg cell produces (by gene activation) a protein that signals the adjacent follicle cells.

    C. These follicle cells are stimulated (in gene activation) to produce proteins that provide feedback to the egg cell.

    D. As a result, the new fly's head-to-tail axis is determined by a specific mRNA located at one end of the cell.

E. After fertilization, repeated mitosis results in the development of the embryo from the zygote. Translation of the head mRNA results in the production of a protein concentration gradient from head to tail. This protein concentration gradient corresponds to a gradient of gene expression.

F. This gradient of gene expression results in the development of the fly's body segments.

G. The cascade continues as this gradient of gene expression results in further differentiation and specialization of the body segments.

H. The master control genes that regulate these major features of the body plan (body segments and the body parts that develop at each segment) are called **homeotic genes.**

I. Homeotic genes are master controls that function during embryonic development in animals to determine the developmental fates of different groups of cells destined to become different tissues.
Preview: Embryonic development is discussed in detail in Modules 27.9–27.15.

J. The improper functioning of homeotic genes can lead to bizarre changes in morphology (Figure 11.13A).

Module 11.14 Signal transduction pathways convert messages received at the cell surface to responses within the cell.

A. As shown in Module 11.13, the gene expression of one cell can affect the gene expression of other cells. This is the result of **signal transduction pathways.**
Review: Signal transduction plays a major role in the regulation of the cell cycle (Module 8.9).
Preview: The importance of signal transduction pathways is also shown in the discussions of cancer (Module 11.16) and control systems (Chapters 26 and 33).

B. The main components of a signal transduction pathway are shown in Figure 11.14 and are listed below.
  1. The signaling cell secretes signal molecules.
  2. The signal molecules bind to receptors on the target cell's plasma membrane.
  3. This results in a cascade of events.
  4. That leads to the activation of a specific transcription factor.
  5. The transcription factor activates a specific gene.
  6. This results in the expression of the protein for which the gene codes.

Module 11.15 Key developmental genes are very ancient.

A. Virtually every homeotic gene found in fruit flies contains a common 180-nucleotide sequence. Very similar sequences have been found in virtually all eukaryotic organisms studied and even some prokaryotes.

B. These organisms range from unicellular organisms such as yeast to plants, earthworms, frogs, chickens, mice, and humans.
NOTE: This is evidence for the common origin of life and is relevant to the material in Module 1.5 (Unity in Diversity).

C. These nucleotide sequences, called **homeoboxes,** translate into a small polypeptide sequence that binds to specific DNA sequences and thereby regulates their expression. See Figure 11.15 for a comparison of the fruit fly and mouse homeotic genes.

III. The Genetic Basis of Cancer

Module 11.16 Cancer results from mutations in genes that control cell division.

Preview: Table 11.20 lists the incidence of several types of cancer.

A. In all its forms, cancer is a disease of gene expression.
Preview: Diet influences cancer risk (Module 21.24).

B. Viruses can cause cancer by inserting cancer-causing genes (**oncogenes**) into the host genome.
Review: Modules 10.17–10.19 and 10.21 discuss how viruses insert genes into a host's genome.

C. A normal gene with the potential to become an oncogene is called a **proto-oncogene.** Proto-oncogenes usually code for proteins that stimulate cell division or affect growth-factor synthesis or function. There are three ways to change a proto-oncogene into an oncogene, which can lead to cancer (Figure 11.16A).

1. A mutation that results in a failure to regulate the production of these proteins will result in the conversion of a proto-oncogene into an oncogene.

2. Formation of multiple copies of a proto-oncogene will result in the conversion to an oncogene.

3. Relocation of a proto-oncogene to an alternate location under new controls will result in the conversion to an oncogene.

D. Most cancers occur in somatic cells; thus, they are not inherited.

E. Mutations in **tumor-suppressor genes,** genes whose products inhibit cell division, also contribute to uncontrolled cell division and tumor formation (Figure 11.16B).

Module 11.17 Oncogene proteins and faulty tumor-suppressor proteins can interfere with normal signal-transduction pathways.

Review: Regulation of the cell cycle (Module 8.10) and signal-transduction pathways (Module 11.14).

A. In response to a growth factor, a signal-transduction pathway can act to stimulate cell division (Figure 11.17A). In response to a growth-inhibiting factor, a signal-transduction pathway can act to inhibit cell division (Figure 11.17B).

B. A mutation in a proto-oncogene may produce an oncogene that may produce a hyperactive version of a protein that stimulates cell division, even in the absence of growth factor. Moreover, abnormal amounts or versions of growth factor, transcription factor, and so on, could all result in the abnormal excess production of proteins that stimulate cell division.

C. Faulty tumor-suppressor genes produce faulty tumor-suppressor proteins that may fail to inhibit cell division.

D. Figures 11.17A and B illustrate two different types of gene mutations (*ras* and *p53*) that have been implicated in 30% and 50% of all cancers, respectively.

Module 11.18 Multiple genetic changes underlie the development of cancer.

A. More than one somatic mutation is required to produce a significant cancer (Figure 11.18B). An example of this is the development of colon cancer.

B. Colon cancer first appears as an unusually high rate of cell division occurring in apparently normal cells. Next, a benign tumor (polyp) appears, followed by the development of this benign tumor into a malignant tumor (Figure 11.18A).

C. Underlying these changes are changes at the DNA level (that are passed on to daughter cells in the cell cycle) to proto-oncogenes and tumor-suppressor genes (including tumor-suppressor genes that code for proteins involved in the repair of damaged DNA). That several mutations are required explains why some cancers can take a long time to develop.

Module 11.19 Talking about Science: Mary-Claire King discusses mutations that cause breast cancer.

A. Dr. King, currently a professor at the University of Washington, has spent 25 years studying the genetic basis of breast cancer (Figure 11.19).

B. Breast cancer strikes 1 out of every 10 American women in her lifetime.
NOTE: At the populational level, the risk of cardiovascular disease is greater. However, an individual's risk will vary with genetics and lifestyle (Module 11.18).

C. Most breast cancer does not appear to have a heritable basis.

D. However, the study of familial cases of breast cancer may provide insight into the underpinnings of nonhereditary breast cancer.

E. King and her colleagues have succeeded in identifying a gene on chromosome 17, *BRCA1,* that is mutated in many families with a history of familial breast cancer.

F. The presence of a mutated *BRCA1* gene greatly increases a woman's risk of developing breast and ovarian cancer.

G. There is evidence that the normal version of *BRCA1* is a tumor-suppressor gene, but the exact function of the protein produced from *BRCA1* is not known.

H. In addition to *BRCA1,* another gene, *BRCA2,* has also been linked to an increased risk of familial breast cancer.

I. The discovery of these genes allows for genetic testing of women to determine their risk for breast and ovarian cancer. Unfortunately, current treatment for the prevention of these cancers is radical. There is also the question of how insurance companies will deal with people with known genetic predisposition.

Module 11.20 Avoiding carcinogens can reduce the risk of cancer.
NOTE: There is much evidence that the tendency to get certain cancers is hereditary (Module 11.19).
Review: The cellular basis of cancer is discussed earlier in this chapter and in Module 8.23.

A. Cancer-causing agents (other than viruses) are called **carcinogens.**

B. Mutagenic chemicals cause mutations. In general, mutagens are carcinogens. Two significant mutagens are X-rays and UV radiation.
NOTE: Almost inevitably there will be a student in the class who goes to a tanning salon. Damage to the skin by exposure to UV radiation results in a tan. UV radiation is a mutagen that greatly increases the risk of skin cancer, and the younger the age at which the exposure occurs, the greater the risk. Depletion of the ozone layer increases the amount of UV radiation that reaches the Earth's surface.

C. The largest group of carcinogens are mutagenic chemical compounds. Substances from tobacco are known to cause more cases and types of cancer than any other single agent (Table 11.20).

D. Exposure to carcinogens is addictive, so long-term exposure to these agents is more likely to cause cancer.

E. Tissues in which cells have a high rate of cell division are more likely to become cancerous.

F. Many factors that expose a person to cancer-causing agents involve voluntary behaviors. But other voluntary behaviors, such as choosing to reduce the animal fat and include more fiber, certain vitamins, and certain phytochemicals (compounds found in plants) in one's diet, can lower the risk.
    Preview: Diet can influence cancer risk (Module 21.24).

Class Activities

1. Link gene regulation to the students' development from a single undifferentiated cell (the zygote) through all the stages of their lives; relate this to embryonic development (Chapter 27).

2. This is a good time to remind your students that science does not operate in a vacuum, that scientists need to be aware of the social impact of their work. The Bush administration has placed limits on stem cell research. This is the time to initiate a discussion of whether the government has the right to do so, of the ethics of stem cell research, and the ethics of using stem cells for the treatment of diseases.

3. When discussing changes in lifestyle to reduce the risk of cancer (i.e., stop smoking, stop using tanning beds), you may also want to take this opportunity to link this topic to the environmental concepts discussed in Chapter 38 by discussing the effect of ozone depletion (Module 7.14) on skin cancer rates.

Transparency Acetates

Figure 11.1B	The *lac* operon
Figure 11.1C	Two types of repressor-controlled operons
Figure 11.3A	Growth of a carrot plant from a differentiated root cell
Figure 11.4	DNA packing in a eukaryotic chromosome
Figure 11.5	Tortoiseshell pattern on a cat, a result of X chromosome inactivation
Figure 11.6	A model for the turning on of a eukaryotic gene
Figure 11.7	Production of two different mRNAs from the same gene
Figure 11.8	Protein activation: The role of polypeptide cleavage in producing the active insulin protein
Figure 11.9	The gene expression "pipeline" in a eukaryotic cell
Figure 11.10	Nuclear transplantation for cloning
Figure 11.12	Differentiation of stem cells in culture
Figure 11.13B	Key steps in the early development of head-tail polarity in a fruit fly
Figure 11.14	A signal transduction pathway that turns on a gene (Layer 1)
Figure 11.14	A signal transduction pathway that turns on a gene (Layer 2)
Figure 11.14	A signal transduction pathway that turns on a gene (Layer 3)
Figure 11.14	A signal transduction pathway that turns on a gene (Layer 4)
Figure 11.15	Comparison of fruit fly and mouse homeotic genes

Media

See the beginning of this book for a complete description of all media available for instructors and students. Animations and videos are available in the Campbell Image Presentation Library. Media Activities and Thinking as a Scientist investigations are available on the student CD-ROM and web site.

Animations and Videos	Module Number
DNA Packing Animation	11.4
Turning on a Gene Animation	11.6
Control of Translation Animation	11.8
Protein Processing Animation	11.10
Development of Head-Tail Axis in Fruit Fly Animation	11.13
Overview of Cell Signaling Animation	11.14
Signal-Transduction Pathway Animation	11.14

Activities and Thinking as a Scientist	Module Number
Web/CD Activity 11A: *The* lac *Operon in* E. coli	11.1
Web/CD Thinking as a Scientist: *How Do You Design a Gene Expression System?*	11.6
Web/CD Activity 11B: *Gene Regulation in Eukaryotes*	11.8
Web/CD Activity 11C: *Review: Gene Regulation in Eukaryotes*	11.9
Web/CD Activity 11D: *Development of Head-Tail Polarity*	11.13
Web/CD Thinking as a Scientist: *How Can the "Head" Gene Be Regulated to Alter Development?*	11.13
Web/CD Activity 11E: *Signal Transduction Pathway*	11.19
Web/CD Activity 11F: *Connection: Causes of Cancer*	11.19

CHAPTER 12

DNA Technology and Genomics

Teaching Objectives

Introduction   Explain how DNA evidence was first used to solve two horrible crimes.

Bacterial Plasmids and Gene Cloning

12.1   Explain how plasmids are used in gene cloning.

12.2   Explain how restriction enzymes are used to "cut and paste" DNA into plasmids.

12.3   Describe the process used to produce many copies of a desired human gene.

12.4   Explain how plasmids and phages can be used to construct genomic libraries.

12.5   Explain how a cDNA library is constructed and how it is different from genomic libraries constructed using plasmids or phages.

12.6   Explain why different organisms are used to mass produce proteins.

12.7   Explain how DNA technology has helped to produce insulin, growth hormone, and vaccines.

Restriction Fragment Analysis and DNA Fingerprinting

12.8   Explain how a nucleic acid probe can be used to identify clones carrying specific genes.

12.9   Explain how DNA microarrays make it easy to determine exactly what genes are active in any particular cell at a certain time.

12.10   Explain how gel electrophoresis is used to sort DNA and proteins.

12.11   Explain how restriction fragment analysis is used to detect differences in DNA sequences.

12.12   Explain how DNA fingerprinting is used to make identifications and answer questions about family relationships.

12.13   Describe the recent efforts and potential of human gene therapy. Discuss the ethical issues that these techniques present.

12.14   Explain how the polymerase chain reaction works. Describe the circumstances where it is best used, and list examples of its application.

Genomics

12.15   Describe the three overlapping stages of the Human Genome Project. Explain why it is important to sequence the genomes of humans and other organisms.

12.16   Describe the structure and possible functions of the noncoding sections of the human genome. Note the current estimate of the number of human genes and explain how human complexity can come from such a low number.

12.17   Describe the extent to which the genomes of nonhuman organisms have been mapped. Explain why this work is significant, and describe some of the recent findings from these efforts.

Genetically Modified Organisms

12.18   Explain how genetically modified organisms are transforming agriculture.

12.19   Describe the risks posed in the creation and culturing of GM organisms and the safeguards that have been developed to minimize risks.

12.20   Describe the significance of the human genome project and some of its surprising results.

Key Terms

biotechnology	genetically modified (GM) organisms	repetitive DNA
clone		restriction enzymes
complementary DNA (cDNA)	genomic library	restriction fragment length polymorphisms (RFLPs)
DNA fingerprinting	genomics	restriction fragments
DNA ligase	Human Genome Project (HGP)	restriction site
DNA microarray	nucleic acid probe	reverse transcriptase
DNA technology	PCR	telomeres
forensic science	plasmids	Ti plasmid
gel electrophoresis	polymerase chain reaction	transgenic organism
gene cloning	proteomics	transposons
gene therapy	recombinant DNA	vaccine
genetic engineering	recombinant DNA technology	vector
genetic marker		

Lecture Outline

Introduction *DNA and Crime Scene Investigations*

    A. DNA fingerprinting can distinguish one person's DNA from any other (except twins) and is a forensic technique used to solve crimes.

    B. The first case to use DNA fingerprinting technology was a double murder in England back in 1983 and 1986. Alec Jeffreys of Leicester University developed the first DNA fingerprinting identification system and was asked by police to assist in solving the crime.

    C. Since that first crime was solved, the use of **DNA technology** has revolutionized the field of forensics, the science of legal investigation. Other areas of science have also benefited including genomics, agriculture, and even history. Of particular interest is the Human Genome Project whose goal is the map of the entire human genome.

I. Bacterial Plasmids and Gene Cloning

    Module 12.1 Plasmids are used to customize bacteria: An overview.

    A. Figure 12.1 presents a simplified version of how one can use **recombinant DNA technology** (combing genes from different sources) to replicate a gene.

    B. **Plasmids** are small, circular, self-replicating pieces of DNA isolated from a bacterium. A gene can be inserted into a plasmid then added to a bacterium for replication, a process called **gene cloning.**

    C. The five steps for gene cloning are as follows:

       1. Isolate plasmid from bacterium.

       2. Isolate gene of interest from another cell.

       3. Insert gene of interest into plasmid (now called a **recombinant DNA**).

       4. Bacterial cell takes up plasmid containing gene of interest through a process called transformation (see Module 10.22).

       5. Bacterial cell divides along with the plasmid and forms a **clone** of cells (genetically identical cells).

D. The bacteria are grown in culture to produce many copies of the isolated gene of interest (the gene is cloned) or its protein product.

E. **Genetic engineering** (the direct manipulation of genes) uses the cloning technique described above for practical purposes.

F. Genetic engineering has promoted the development of an industry called **biotechnology,** which manipulates organisms or their components to make products for human use. Examples of such products are human insulin and human growth hormone.

Module 12.2 Enzymes are used to "cut and paste" DNA.

A. **Restriction enzymes** were first discovered in bacteria in the late 1960s.

B. In nature, bacteria use restriction enzymes to cut up intruder DNA from phages and from other organisms into nonfunctional pieces. The bacteria first chemically modify their own DNA so it will not be cut.

C. Several hundred restriction enzymes and about 100 recognition sequences have been discovered.

D. DNA from two sources is cut by the same restriction enzyme. These enzymes are cut at a specific restriction-enzyme recognition sequence called a **restriction site** (usually a palindrome). The result is a **restriction fragment** containing a double-stranded sequence of DNA with single-stranded "sticky ends" (Figure 12.2).

E. DNA fragments may pair at their sticky ends via hydrogen bonds. This pairing is temporary, but **DNA ligase** (pasting enzyme) can make it permanent. The result of this is the formation of **recombinant DNA.**
   Review: DNA ligase is normally used in DNA replication (Module 10.5).

Module 12.3 Genes can be cloned in recombinant plasmids: A closer look.

A. The example in Figure 12.3 uses a hypothetical situation where human gene V is cloned.
   1. Isolate plasmid from bacterium and from another cell.
   2. Cut both plasmid and DNA with same restriction enzyme.
   3. Mix cut plasmid and restriction fragment to allow bonding of sticky ends.
   4. Add DNA ligase to seal bonds.
   5. Place recombinant plasmid in bacterium by transformation.
   6. Clone bacterium with recombinant plasmid.

B. The procedure described in this module is a "shotgun" approach since the specific gene isn't targeted.

C. The complete set of genes from the original cell contained in many plasmids and housed in clones of bacterial cells is called a **genomic library.**

Module 12.4 Cloned genes can be stored in genomic libraries.

A. Using a shotgun approach to do this, scientists cut up all the DNA from a cell into thousands of fragments, each of which carries one or a few genes of unknown identity (one or more fragments will carry the gene of interest).

B. These fragments are temporarily stored in a **genomic library** of plasmids in separate bacterial cells (plasmid library), or in separate phage clones (phage library) (Figure 12.4).

Module 12.5 Reverse transcriptase helps make genes for cloning.

   A. A problem with cloning and bacterial synthesis of eukaryotic gene products is that bacterial genes do not contain introns.

   B. Special enzymes called **reverse transcriptases** are found in retroviruses. These enzymes make DNA from viral genome RNA (Module 10.21).
   NOTE: An example of such a retrovirus is HIV.

   C. Genes that are expressed can be isolated by using mRNA that has already had its introns spliced out. When reverse transcriptase is mixed with this mRNA, single-stranded DNA is produced. Double-stranded DNA is synthesized with the enzyme DNA polymerase (Figure 12.5).

   D. These DNA fragments (called **complementary DNA** or **cDNA**) are again temporarily stored in plasmid or phage libraries called cDNA libraries.

   E. The cDNA sequences (which have no introns) are shorter and easier to manipulate than the complete unmodified gene sequence.

Module 12.6 Connection: Recombinant cells and organisms can mass-produce gene products.

   A. Bacteria are the host of choice for making large amounts of eukaryotic gene products because bacteria are simple and can be grown rapidly and cheaply (Table 12.6).

   B. The single-celled fungus *Saccharomyces cerevisiae* (bread and wine yeast) is one of the simplest eukaryotes that can be grown rapidly and cheaply. Yeast also has plasmids that can be used as vectors. In some cases, yeast does a better job than bacteria in expressing eukaryotic genes.

   C. Some products are best made by mammalian cells. The genes of interest are often cloned in bacterial plasmids first then introduced to the final host.

   D. Among these mammalian cell products are monoclonal antibodies, which are glycoproteins used widely in research on cellular structures and functions. The sugar chain part of monoclonal antibodies can be added to the protein part only under the control of the eukaryotic gene expression system.

   E. The use of whole animals to mass produce a protein of interest has been explored by pharmaceutical companies. Figure 12.6 shows sheep that produce milk containing a gene for a blood protein that may be a treatment for cystic fibrosis.

   F. *Preview:* Module 24.12 offers a more in-depth discussion of monoclonal antibodies.

Module 12.7 Connection: DNA technology is changing the pharmaceutical industry and medicine.

   A. **Therapeutic Hormones:** Human insulin (Figure 12.7A) and human growth hormone were two of the first commercially produced recombinant DNA products.

   B. **Diagnosis and Treatment of Disease:** DNA technology is currently being used to identify people with HIV; through the use of gene expression profiles, people will be informed of potential diseases prior to the appearance of symptoms.

   C. **Vaccines:** Harmless or derivative variants of proteins produced on the surfaces of pathogens can stimulate a person's immune system. Exposing a person to the **vaccine** (usually by injection) primes the person's immune system to recognize and destroy the pathogen upon subsequent infection. Vaccines are particularly important in the defense against many viral diseases such as Hepatitis B (Figure 12.7B).
   NOTE: Normally, vaccines are made using natural mutant forms of pathogens or proteins extracted from the pathogens.

D. Recombinant DNA techniques can be used to make vaccines in many ways: mass production of vaccine proteins; assembling artificial mutant pathogens; and adding proteins from several pathogens to the coat of the natural mutant smallpox virus, which was previously used to successfully eradicate smallpox.

II. Restriction Fragment Analysis and DNA Fingerprinting

Module 12.8 Nucleic acid probes identify clones carrying specific genes.

A. If some of the bacterial clones in the genomic library actually produce the product expressed by the gene of interest, testing the cell or the medium in which they are growing for the product can isolate the right clone.

B. If this cannot be done, scientists use radioactive- (or fluorescent-) labeled single-stranded **nucleic acid probes** that pair with selected regions of the gene of interest. The cells or phages in the genomic library that bind the radioactive label contain the gene in question (Figure 12.8).

C. The complementary **probes** can be assembled artificially if some DNA sequence in the gene of interest or the amino acid sequence of the target protein (and hence a corresponding sequence of nucleotides) is known.

D. A genomic library made by the shotgun approach can be screened rather quickly for a gene of interest using the DNA probe technique. Once the clone has been identified, the gene and the product can be mass produced by culturing the bacterial colony that contained the gene.

Module 12.9 Connection: DNA microarrays test for the expression of many genes at once.

A. **DNA microarrays** are an extension of the procedure presented in Module 12.8, a micro-method for the rapid identification of multiple genes expressed by a cell.

B. Figure 12.9 illustrates the procedure and the result of a DNA microarray assay. Fluorescence correlates with gene expression. The technique is presented below.
   1. Isolate mRNA.
   2. Make cDNA from mRNA using reverse transcriptase.
   3. Apply cDNA (single-stranded) to wells.
   4. cDNA binds to corresponding gene, and unbound cDNA is rinsed away.

C. This technique has many potential applications, including but not limited to:
   1. Gene activation in healthy or diseased tissues.
   2. Response of tissues to drug therapy.
   3. Gene analysis for an individual to determine the risk of certain diseases in an effort to reduce risk factors.

Module 12.10 Gel electrophoresis sorts DNA molecules by size.

A. **Gel electrophoresis** sorts proteins and nucleic acids on the basis of their size and/or charge. DNA is negatively charged (phosphates groups) and will migrate toward the positive electrode.

B. Longer macromolecules move through the gel more slowly than do shorter macromolecules. The result of this differential rate of movement is a pattern of bands on the gel, each band consisting of macromolecules of one particular size (Figure 12.10).

Module 12.11 Restriction fragment length polymorphisms can be used to detect differences in DNA sequences.

A. Nucleotide sequences of all but identical twins are different.

B. Extracted DNA from a person's cells can be cut up into a set of fragments by exposing the DNA to a series of different restriction enzymes (Figure 12.11A; recall Module 12.2).

C. Differences in DNA sequences on homologous chromosomes produce sets of **restriction fragments** that differ in length and number between different, nonidentical-twin individuals. The differences in restriction fragments produced by this technique are called **restriction fragment length polymorphism** (**RFLPs,** pronounced "rif-lips").

D. These DNA fragments are of different lengths and will migrate different distances in an electrophoretic gel (Figure 12.11B).

E. A **genetic marker** is any DNA sequence whose inheritance can be tracked. It may or may not be a gene or a sequence within a gene (Figure 12.11C).

F. Restriction fragment analysis was used to enable workers studying Huntington's disease to find a genetic marker closely associated with the HD gene.

G. Once the genetic marker is known for a particular disease, restriction fragment analysis can be used to test for it.

Module 12.12 Connection: DNA technology is used in courts of law.

A. DNA technology is used extensively in **forensic science** (the science of legal investigation).

B. An individual's band pattern from RFLP analysis is called a **DNA fingerprint.** Like traditional fingerprints, DNA fingerprints are unique.

C. DNA fingerprinting uses RFLP analysis to identify small amounts of DNA from body fluids or tissue.

D. DNA lasts in the environment much longer than proteins. DNA can be extracted from as few 1,000 cells.

E. In criminal investigations, restriction fragments are compared with those of other sources (Figures 12.12A and B).

F. Increasingly, repetitive DNA sequences are being used for DNA fingerprinting. These sequences are regions of repetitive DNA that vary in length among individuals.

G. The technology of DNA fingerprinting has been shown to be very reliable. The chance that two people have the same DNA fingerprint is approximately one out of 100,000 to one billion depending on the number of restriction enzymes and which genetic materials are used.

Module 12.13 Connection: Gene therapy may someday help treat a variety of diseases.

A. **Gene therapy,** the alteration of an afflicted person's genes, holds much as yet unrealized promise.

B. In certain cases where a disorder is due to a single gene, it is possible to replace defective genes with normal genes.

C. An example is a trial procedure that should cure individuals with an autosomal recessive allele that causes defective functioning of the immune system and is usually fatal. Bone marrow stem cells, which are essential for blood cell formation, are removed. By means of a retrovirus, the defective gene is replaced with the normal one. The recombinant cells are cloned in culture and reintroduced in the individual, after the natural bone marrow cells have all been killed (Figure 12.13).

D. To date, most gene therapy trials have been unsuccessful, and little scientific evidence supports the use to cure diseases. Questions related to the safety and ethical uses of gene therapy are being raised.

E. The expense of these techniques raises ethical questions concerning who can have access to these therapies. Further ethical questions are raised concerning the use of gene therapy, not for treatment of disease but for enhancement of physical ability and appearance as well as intelligence. The ultimate question is, What are the potential implications of genetic engineering, particularly of sex cells, on humans? Might an allele that is harmful in the current environment be essential to survival in a future environment?

Module 12.14 The PCR method is used to amplify DNA sequences.

NOTE: Tools such as RFLP, PCR, and DNA sequencing have also been used in conservation biology. For example, are populations of an endangered species actually members of the same species (in which case they can be interbred) or are they distinct species?

A. The **polymerase chain reaction (PCR)** is a technique for copying a single DNA sequence many times. The DNA need not be in large quantities or very pure.

B. A mixture of the DNA, DNA polymerase, and nucleotide monomers will continue to replicate, forming a geometrically increasing number of copies (Figure 12.14).

C. The key to PCR is the heat-resistant form of DNA polymerase that was discovered in hot springs. Unlike most enzymes that denature at high temperatures, this DNA polymerase is stable during the high-temperature step in each cycle.

D. This technique has revolutionized DNA work because sequences can now be obtained from extremely small samples. Prehistoric DNA from a number of sites has been cloned into partial genomes using PCR. Tiny amounts of body fluids can now be used from crime scenes because of PCR.

III. Genomics

Module 12.15 Connections: The Human Genome Project is an ambitious application of DNA technology.

A. An internationally government-funded group of scientists began to sequence the human genome starting in 1990. The undertaking was dubbed the **Human Genome Project (HGP).** There are three major stages involved in mapping the human genome.

B. *Genetic (linkage) mapping:* This involves constructing a map of more than 5,000 genetic markers that act as a set of references for other work.

C. *Physical mapping:* The number of base pairs between the markers from step one is determined by cutting the DNA with restriction enzymes, cloning them, determining the overlaps, and determining the order of the fragments in the chromosomes.

D. *DNA sequencing:* This is the process that elucidated the exact order of the nucleotide pairs in each fragment and, hence, each chromosome (Figure 12.15).

E. A former government scientist (J. Craig Venter) decided to use the shotgun approach and founded the company Celera Genomics. Going directly to step 3, random fragments of DNA were sequenced. Due to this approach and stiff competition, 90% of the human genome was completed by February 2001.

F. The project has (and already is providing) huge potential benefits. It has allowed insight into embryonic development and evolution, and identification of genes that cause genetic disorders and genes that are partly implicated in more common diseases such as cancer, heart disease, diabetes, schizophrenia, alcoholism, and Alzheimer's disease. Literally hundreds of disease-associated genes have been found because of this project.

G. DNA sequences are available on the Internet.

Module 12.16 Most of the human genome does not consist of genes.

A. The most startling piece of data from the project is the relatively small number of genes that are present in the human genome—only 1 1/2 to 2 times the number in the fruit fly.

B. The human genome probably has only approximately 25,000 to 30,000 genes (that is, 15 to 20 times the number of genes).

C. Approximately 97% of the human genome is noncoding, consisting of sequences such as promoters and enhancers.

D. The DNA found between genes mainly consists of **repetitive DNA.** Loss of repetitive DNA at the ends of chromosomes **(telomeres)** leads to cell death. Abnormally long repeats may play a role in cancer cell immortality.

E. Longer sequences of repetitive DNA (hundreds of nucleotides long) are found scattered about the genome. Little is known about the functions of these regions of DNA; however, most of them appear to be associated with **transposons** (jumping genes). Transposons can move or be copied from one location to another and land in the middle of a gene, causing disruption.

Module 12.17 Connection: The science of genomics compares whole genomes.

A. Approximately 150 species have had their genome sequenced as of 2004 (Table 12.17). Most have been prokaryotes, and about 20 have been eukaryotes. The first eukaryote to have its genome sequenced was *Saccharomyces cerevisiae* (Baker's yeast), and *Caenorhabditis elegans* was the first multicellular organism to have its genome sequenced.

B. Sequence data of many organisms helps scientists interpret the data from the HGP. For example, if a gene in humans is found to be similar to a gene in yeast and the function of the yeast gene is already known, much can be inferred about the human gene.

C. **Genomics** is the study of an entire genome or a comparison between genomes. Genomic studies provide insight into questions such as the organization of genomes, regulation of gene expression, growth and development, and evolution.

D. The next endeavor for scientists to undertake is determining the function of all the proteins produced by the genes of a species. This is called **proteomics.** There are many more proteins in humans than can be accounted for by genes. It is the proteins that do the bulk of the work for a cell.

E. Large catalogs of genes and proteins will/are being established, which will enable scientists to study life on a more global perspective.

IV. **Genetically Modified Organisms**

Module 12.18 Genetically modified organisms are transforming agriculture.

A. **Genetically modified (GM) organisms** are being developed by agricultural scientists using DNA technology in an effort to improve plants and animals. Some examples currently in use are plants that ripen slowly and resist spoilage.

B. The bacterium *Agrobacterium tumefaciens,* which is pathogenic to a number of plant hosts, is used to transfer genes between plants, in recombined form with the bacterium's **Ti plasmid.** The resulting **transgenic** plant cells are cloned in culture and grown into adult plants (Figure 12.18A). These recombinant plants contain foreign DNA and are called **transgenic organisms.**
    NOTE: This process can be done much more rapidly than by depending on a full season for natural breeding to produce hybrids, and genes can be transferred between unrelated plants.

C. Many transgenic plants that are currently in field trials have received genes for herbicide resistance. Other plants are being engineered to be resistant to pathogens and pest insects. The hope is that this will reduce the need for the application of chemical insecticides.
    NOTE: Unless care is taken, the evolution of weeds, pathogens, and pest insects that can get around these barriers is inevitable (*Preview:* Chapter 13, especially Module 13.18).

D. The nutritional value of genetically modified plants has been improved through DNA technology. A good example of this is golden rice (Figure 12.18B). This GM rice has had a gene inserted that promotes the production of β-carotene, the precursor to vitamin A used in sight. Therefore people who depend on rice as a major portion of their diet will no longer be deficient in vitamin A and the occurrences of blindness will decrease.

E. Transgenic animals are also being developed. The process starts with unfertilized eggs, which are removed from the host. The eggs are fertilized *in vitro,* and the gene of interest is injected directly into the fertilized egg. The eggs are placed in a surrogate mother, and if the gene is incorporated into the egg, the animal born is a transgenic animal.

F. The goals are the same as traditional breeding programs—improved wool, more and leaner meat—but the process is more flexible. For example, transgenic chickens are being engineered to produce pharmaceutical products (see Module 12.6).

Module 12.19 Could GM organisms harm human health or the environment?

A. Scientists in the United States and in other countries have developed safety guidelines to minimize the risks involved in genetic engineering (Figure 12.19A).

B. The guidelines designate laboratory safety procedures for various types of experiments, including procedures normally used to protect scientists who study natural pathogens.

C. The guidelines also specify the kinds of microorganisms that can be used, often requiring that the recipient organisms be genetically altered so that they cannot live outside the laboratory.
    NOTE: Certain kinds of experiments are forbidden or strictly regulated, such as working with human cancer genes or genes of extremely virulent pathogens.

D. A multinational agreement was negotiated in 2000 requiring that all GM food products shipped to other countries be identified, which would allow the receiving country to decide if the GM products posed a health or environmental risk.

E. Concern has been expressed by certain organizations over cross-pollination of wild plants with GM plants, which may lead to "superweeds" that will be difficult to control (Figure 12.19B).

F. Technological advances involve risk taking; therefore, better decisions can be made when sound scientific evidence is used in the decision process rather than basing decisions on fear or blind optimism.

Module 12.20 Genomics researcher Eric Lander discusses the Human Genome Project.

A. Dr. Eric Lander taught economics at Harvard Business School before entering the field of biology and participating in the Human Genome Project (HGP). He founded the Broad Institute of MIT and Harvard, which uses genomics to develop new methods to investigate and treat diseases.

B. The results of HGP will provide researchers the opportunity to examine the human genome from a "big picture" approach rather than from a single gene or at the component level. Prior to the HGP, textbooks estimated the number of genes in the human genome to be 100,000. Since then, the number of genes is estimated at 25,000 (and falling).

C. Lander sees the results of the HGP as a springboard for the next generation of researchers to revolutionize the field of evolutionary biology.

Class Activities

1. I am sure you are familiar with OMIM (home page of Online Mendelian Inheritance in Man [http://www3.ncbi.nlm.nih.gov/Omim/]). Have each of your students choose a trait/disease of theirs or of their family's and use OMIM to find out what is known about the genetics of the trait/disease.

2. Class discussion can also focus on the ethical issues of the use of these techniques on humans. Should parents be allowed to genetically engineer a child to be a star athlete? a genius? Would this be acceptable as long as the gametes are left alone? Should gametes be engineered so that a disease such as Huntington's is eliminated? What about the future? A gene that is harmful in the present environment may be of benefit in a different environment.

3. Further class discussion can focus on whether or not the anticipated results of the Human Genome Project justify the expense. Have the students gather information on a genetic characteristic or disorder from Human Genome Internet sites (for example: To Know Ourselves: The U.S. Department of Energy and the Human Genome Project [http://www.ornl.gov/hgmis/publicat/tko/index.html]).

Transparency Acetates

Figure 12.1	An overview of gene cloning (Layer 1)
Figure 12.1	An overview of gene cloning (Layer 2)
Figure 12.1	An overview of gene cloning (Layer 3)
Figure 12.2	Creating recombinant DNA using a restriction enzyme and DNA ligase
Figure 12.3	Cloning a gene in a bacterial plasmid (Layer 1)
Figure 12.3	Cloning a gene in a bacterial plasmid (Layer 2)
Figure 12.3	Cloning a gene in a bacterial plasmid (Layer 3)
Figure 12.4	Genomic libraries
Figure 12.5	Making an intron-lacking gene from eukaryotic mRNA
Table 12.6	Some protein products of recombinant DNA technology
Figure 12.8	How a DNA probe tags a gene by base pairing
Figure 12.9	DNA microarray
Figure 12.10	Gel electrophoresis of DNA

Figure 12.11A   Restriction site differences between two homologous samples of DNA

Figure 12.11B   Gel electrophoresis of restriction fragments

Figure 12.11C   The use of restriction fragment analysis to detect a harmful allele (Layer 1)

Figure 12.11C   The use of restriction fragment analysis to detect a harmful allele (Layer 2)

Figure 12.11C   The use of restriction fragment analysis to detect a harmful allele (Layer 3)

Figure 12.13   One type of gene therapy procedure

Figure 12.14   DNA amplification by PCR

Table 12.17   Some important completed genomes

Figure 12.18A   Using the Ti plasmid as a vector for genetically engineering plants

Reviewing the Concepts, page 250: Genomic libraries

Reviewing the Concepts, page 250: Gel electrophoresis can sort DNA molecules by size

Connecting the Concepts, page 250: A DNA technology-based investigation of a drop of blood

---

Media

See the beginning of this book for a complete description of all media available for instructors and students. Animations and videos are available in the Campbell Image Presentation Library. Media Activities and Thinking as a Scientist investigations are available on the student CD-ROM and website.

Animations and Videos	Module Number
Restriction Enzymes Animation	12.2
Cloning a Gene Animation	12.3
Biotechnology Lab Video	12.11

Activities and Thinking as a Scientist	Module Number
Web/CD Thinking as a Scientist: *How Can Antibiotic-Resistant Plasmids Transform* E. coli?	12.3
Web/CD Activity 12A: *Restriction Enzymes*	12.2
Web/CD Activity 12B: *Cloning a Gene in Bacteria*	12.3
Web/CD Activity 12C: *Gel Electrophoresis of DNA*	12.10
Web/CD Thinking as a Scientist: *How Can Gel Electrophoresis Be Used to Analyze DNA?*	12.10
Web/CD Activity 12D: *Analyzing DNA Fragments Using Gel Electrophoresis*	12.11
Biology Labs On-Line: *Bacteria as Tools for Manipulating DNA*	12.11
Web/CD Activity 12E: *Connection: DNA Fingerprinting*	12.12
Web/CD Activity 12F: *The Human Genome Project: Human Chromosome 17*	12.15
Web/CD Activity 12G: *Connection: Applications of DNA Technology*	12.18
Web/CD Activity 12H: *Connection: DNA Technology and Golden Rice*	12.19

CHAPTER 13

How Populations Evolve

Teaching Objectives

Introduction   Describe five adaptations that help blue-footed boobies survive.

Darwin's Theory of Evolution

13.1   Briefly describe the history of evolutionary thought.

13.1   Explain how Darwin's voyage on the *Beagle* influenced his thinking.

13.1   Describe the ideas and events that resulted in Darwin's 1859 book.

13.2   Explain how the work of Thomas Malthus and the process of artificial selection influenced Darwin's development of the idea of natural selection.

13.2   Describe Darwin's assumptions in developing the concept of natural selection.

13.3   Explain how fossils form, noting examples of each process.

13.3   Explain how the fossil record provides some of the strongest evidence of evolution.

13.4   Explain how biogeography, comparative anatomy, comparative embryology, and molecular biology document evolution.

13.5   Describe two examples of natural selection known to occur in nature. Note three key points about how natural selection works.

Population Genetics and the Modern Synthesis

13.6   Define the gene pool, a population, and a species.

13.6   Explain the significance of the modern evolutionary synthesis.

13.6   Explain how microevolution occurs.

13.7   Describe the five conditions required for Hardy-Weinberg equilibrium.

13.7–13.8   Explain the significance of Hardy-Weinberg equilibrium to natural populations and to public health science.

13.9   Define genetic drift and gene flow. Explain how the bottleneck effect and the founder effect influence microevolution.

13.10   Explain how genetic bottlenecks threaten the survival of certain species.

Variation and Natural Selection

13.11   Explain why only some variation is heritable. Explain how genetic variation is measured.

13.12   Explain how mutation and sexual recombination produce genetic variation.

13.13   Explain how antibiotic resistance has evolved.

13.14   Explain how genetic variation is maintained in populations.

13.14   Explain what is meant by neutral variation.

13.15   Define fitness. Explain how "survival of the fittest" can be misleading.

13.16   Describe the three general outcomes of natural selection.

13.17   Define and compare intrasexual selection and intersexual selection.

13.18   List four reasons natural selection cannot produce perfection.

Key Terms

artificial selection
balancing selection
biogeography
bottleneck effect
cline
comparative anatomy
comparative embryology
descent with modification
directional selection
disruptive selection
evolution
evolutionary adaptation
fitness
fossil record

fossils
founder effect
frequency-dependent
   selection
gene flow
gene pool
genetic drift
Hardy-Weinberg
   equilibrium
heterozygote advantage
homologous structures
homology
microevolution
modern synthesis

molecular biology
mutations
natural selection
neutral variation
paleontologists
polymorphic
population
population genetics
sexual dimorphism
species
stabilizing selection
strata
vestigial organs

Word Roots

bio- = life; **geo-** the Earth (*biogeography:* the study of the past and present distribution of species)

homo- = like, resembling (*homology:* similarity in characteristics resulting from a shared ancestry)

muta- = change (*mutation:* a change in the DNA of genes that ultimately creates genetic diversity)

paleo- = ancient (*paleontology:* the scientific study of fossils)

poly- = many; **morph-** = form (*polymorphism:* the coexistence of two or more distinct forms of individuals in the same population)

Lecture Outline

Introduction *Clown, Fool, or Simply Well Adapted?*

    A. *Review:* Evolution is the central theme of biology. Evolutionary adaptation is a universal characteristic of living things (see **Module 1.6**).
    NOTE: More than any other idea in biology, evolutionary theory serves to tie the discipline together. T. Dobzhansky: "Nothing in biology makes sense except in the light of evolution."

    B. If you look at any organism critically, you are first struck by the differences from other organisms.

       1. Further observation often reveals that an organism's features show some relationship to where the organism lives and what it does in its environment.

       2. The blue-footed booby has enormous webbed feet, an oil producing gland that keeps the booby afloat, a nostril that can close under water that prevents water from entering the lungs, a gland that secrets salt from consumed sea water, and a torpedo-like body—all adaptations that make life on the sea feasible.

I. Darwin's Theory of Evolution

Module 13.1 A sea voyage helped Darwin frame his theory of evolution.

A. Awareness of each organism's adaptations and how they fit the particular conditions of its environment helps us appreciate the natural world (Figure 13.1A).

B. Early Greek philosophers held various views. Anaximander (about 2,500 years ago) suggested that life arose in water and that simpler forms preceded more complex forms of life. On the other hand, Aristotle, who strongly influenced later thinkers, believed that species were fixed and did not evolve.

C. This latter view was advanced by the Judeo-Christian tradition that all species were created in a single act of creation about 6,000 years ago.

D. From his study with **fossils,** Buffon (mid-1700s) suggested that Earth was much older and raised the possibility that different species arose from common ancestors, although he later argued against this point.
NOTE: Buffon also believed in catastrophism: Following natural disasters, some species die off, while populations of others (already present in lower numbers) increase in numbers to become more dominant than they had been.

E. Lamarck (early 1800s) was the first to strongly support the idea of evolution, but he believed the mechanism for change was the inheritance of acquired characteristics.

F. Born in 1809, Darwin joined the crew of the surveying ship Beagle as a naturalist for a world-encircling voyage in 1831 (Figure 13.1B).

G. Comparisons of South American fossils with living species there and fossils elsewhere, and observations of organisms and their distributions on the Galápagos Islands, made particularly strong impressions on him.

H. Darwin was influenced by Lyell's Principles of Geology, in which he promoted the idea of continual, gradual, and consistent geological change.

I. After his return, Darwin began work on an essay to document his observations and his new theory of evolution.

J. In the mid-1850s, Wallace conceived essentially the same theory, based on his observations in Indonesia. He contacted Darwin, and presentations of both their works were made by Darwin's colleagues to the scientific community in 1858.

K. Darwin's On the Origin of Species by Means of Natural Selection was published in 1859 and contains a well-constructed argument for natural selection, backed by considerable evidence. He uses the phrase "descent with modification," which encapsulates the concept of evolution.

L. Darwin's view of evolution: The history of life is like a tree, with multiple branches occurring from the base of the trunk to the tips of the branches. Species on a given branch are more closely interrelated than related to species on other branches. Darwin perceived a unity among all species through a common ancestor.

Module 13.2 Darwin proposed natural selection as the mechanism of evolution.

Review: Evolution as an explanation for the unity and diversity of life was first discussed in **Module 1.6.**

A. Darwin observed that species tend to produce excessive numbers of offspring, that the expression of traits varies among the individuals of a population, and that many of these traits are heritable.

    B. English economist Thomas Malthus's essay discussed the inevitable human suffering resulting from populations growing faster than supplies of resources.

    C. Darwin had personal knowledge of and interest in **artificial selection** (Figures 13.2A and B) and compared the results of artificial selection to the variation seen among closely related species (Figure 13.2C).

    D. Two important points can be drawn from Darwin's theory of **natural selection:**

        1. Ancestral species gave rise to the diverse life forms by transfer of heritable traits to offspring that best promote reproduction. He called this "descent with modification."

        2. Over vast amounts of time, the gradual accumulation of changes in the characteristics among the individuals in a population occurs.

Module 13.3 The study of fossils provides strong evidence for evolution.

    A. Hard parts, such as skeletons and shells, remain after other organic matter has decomposed. Such parts fossilize easily (Figure 13.3A).

    B. Petrified fossils form by the slow mineralization of organic materials (Figure 13.3B).

    C. Fossilized molds of organisms form when a covered area decays and fills in with other sediment (Figure 13.3C).

    D. Dinosaur footprints are left behind in the mud and fossilized (Figure 13.3D)

    E. Some fossils, such as those of leaves, retain remnants of organic matter with molecular fragments that can be analyzed (Figure 13.2E).

    F. Organisms trapped in tree resin can be fossilized intact, within the fossilized amber, protected from decomposition by bacteria and fungi (Figure 13.2F).

    G. Other media have preserved organisms. The "Ice Man" found in 1991 was preserved in ice some 5,000 years ago (Figure 13.2G).

    H. The **fossil record** is an array of fossils appearing within the layers (**strata**) of sedimentary rocks. Sedimentary rocks form from accumulations of waterborne sediments. Sedimentary deposits occur in strata. Each layer contains fossils of organisms among the deposits, with younger strata on top of older strata (Figure 13.2H).

    I. The fossil record shows a historical sequence of organisms from the oldest known fossils, prokaryotes, dating from more than 3.5 billion years ago, through the subsequent appearance of eukaryotes, on through many intermediate steps to modern forms—a sequence that has an overall pattern of change from simple to more complex forms. *NOTE:* Such a sequence, whereby links are seen between extinct organisms and species alive today, is predicted by evolutionary theory (Figure 13.3I). One of the best-documented series is the evolution of modern horses.
Preview: The fossil record chronicles macroevolution (Module 15.1).

Module 13.4 A mass of other evidence reinforces the evolutionary view of life.

    A. **Biogeography** makes observations about the distribution of different but obviously related life forms around the world and in neighboring geographical regions. Island forms are most similar to forms found on the closest mainland, rather than those found on ecologically similar but more distant islands.

    B. **Comparative anatomy** of homologous structures (Figure 13.4A): for example, all mammals have the same basic limb structure. **Homology** among species indicates a common ancestor. **Vestigal organs** is another line of evidence of common ancestry.
Preview: Module 15.6.

    C. **Comparative embryology** shows that different organisms go through similar embryonic stages. For example, evidence that all vertebrates evolved from a common ancestor is that all have an embryonic stage in which gill pouches appear in the throat region (Figure 13.4B).
    NOTE: In addition to pharyngeal gill pouches, vertebrates, along with all chordates, also have in common the presence of, at some point in their life cycle, a notochord (a cartilaginous supporting rod), a dorsal hollow nerve cord (spinal cord), and a post-anal tail.

    D. **Molecular biology** demonstrates the universality of the genetic code (see **Module 10.8**), the conservation of amino acid sequences in proteins such as hemoglobin (Table 13.4), and the presence of very similar homeotic genes in very different species (see **Module 11.13**).

    E. Darwin's most daring hypothesis, that all living organisms are related, is supported by the findings from molecular biology studies.

Module 13.5 Connection: Scientists can observe natural selection in action.

    A. Two good examples of natural selection can be seen in the mantid. In both cases, new populations have resulted but not new species (Figure 13.5A).

    B. Natural selection is a work in progress and has been documented more than 100 times. A frightening case that is frequently repeated is the response of insects to insecticides. Those that have the predisposition for resistance will survive and pass on this trait (a gene) to their offspring (Figure 13.5B).
    Preview: The same concept will be discussed with bacteria and the resistance to antibiotic therapy **(Module 16.10).**

    C. These two examples illustrate that natural selection is an editing process, not a creative mechanism. They also show that natural selection is regional, timely, and can occur rapidly.

II. Population Genetics and the Modern Synthesis

Module 13.6 Populations are the units of evolution.

    A. A **population** is a group of individual organisms living in the same place at the same time.

    B. Evolution is measured as the change in frequency of a given characteristic within a population over a succession of generations.

    C. Darwin realized this, but he did not know about the genetic mechanisms.

    D. During the 1920s, **population genetics** was combined with Darwinian principles and Mendelian genetics into a comprehensive theory of evolution known as the **modern evolutionary synthesis.** This theory uses concepts from population genetics, paleontology, taxonomy, and biogeography. It concentrates on the population as the unit of evolution and natural selection's role in evolution.

    E. Central to this synthesis is the sexual species concept. A sexual species is a group of populations whose individuals have the potential to interbreed and produce fertile offspring. A given sexual species has an overall range, with concentrations of individuals in local populations.
    NOTE: This is the same as the biological species concept introduced in Chapter 14.
    Preview: Since the sexual (biological) species concept concerns actually or potentially interbreeding populations, it is difficult to apply it to the fossil record. Another species concept that is more readily applied to the fossil record is the evolutionary species concept.

F. Opportunities for breeding among populations of the same species vary, depending on the species and on the extent of isolation of the populations.
   Review: The basic concepts of Mendelian genetics (Chapter 9).

G. A population's **gene pool** consists of all the alleles in all the individuals making up the population.

H. Most gene loci are represented by two or more alleles across a population, and individuals (of most eukaryotes) carrying two alleles can be homozygous or heterozygous for the locus.

I. During **microevolution,** the relative frequencies of the alleles governing characteristics change. For example, those insects with a gene that confers resistance to an insecticide will outnumber those insects without this particular gene. Thus, the allele frequency for insecticide resistance will be higher in fields sprayed with insecticide than in untreated fields.

Module 13.7 The gene pool of a nonevolving population remains constant over the generations.

   NOTE: This example is entirely arbitrary and will work with any numbers. Have students verify this fact by trying other examples.

A. Use the example of a hypothetical population of 500 blue-footed boobies. Nonwebbed feet (*WW* or *Ww*) are dominant over webbed feet (*ww*), and a single gene (alleles *W* and *w*) governs the characteristic: 320 have *WW*, 160 have *Ww*, and 20 have *ww* genotypes (Figure 13.7A).

B. The **Hardy-Weinberg equation** shows that allele frequencies are stable in a population not undergoing microevolution: $p^2 + 2pq + q^2 = 1$. That is, the population is made up of: homozygous dominant genotypes (p^2) + heterozygous genotypes ($2pq$) + homozygous recessive genotypes (q^2). Also note that $p = 1 - q$.
   NOTE: If you have the patience, it may be worth the effort of taking your students through the derivation of the Hardy-Weinberg equation. Using the example given here: There are only two alleles of this particular gene, thus their frequencies must sum to 1 ($p + q = 1$). The probability of *WW* is $p \times p = p^2$; the probability of *ww* is $q \times q = q^2$; there are two ways of being heterozygous, *Ww* and *wW*; thus the frequency of the heterozygote is $2pq$. Continuing, many of your students will be familiar with the FOIL method from their math classes; have them apply it to the following: $p + q = 1$; since $1 \times 1 = 1$, $(p + q)(p + q) = 1$. FOILing this gives us $p^2 + 2pq + q^2 = 1$.

C. The frequencies of *WW*, *Ww*, and *ww* in the first generation are 0.64, 0.32, and 0.04. Since blue-footed boobies are diploid, there are 1,000 alleles in the population, and their frequencies are $p = 0.80$ *W* and $q = 0.20$ *w* (Figure 13.7B).

D. If random mating occurs between various members of this population, then the laws of probability will predict the genetic makeup of the next generation (see **Module 9.7**).

E. On average, the next generation will have $p \times p$ *WW* individuals (= 0.64), ($p \times q$) + ($q \times p$) *Ww* individuals ($2pq = 0.32$, since there are two ways to get *pq* in a zygote, depending on whether the *q* is in the sperm or in the egg), and $q \times q$ *ww* individuals (= 0.04) (Figure 13.7C). The allele frequencies remain the same.

F. Five conditions are required for Hardy-Weinberg equilibrium.
   1. The population is very large.
   2. The population is isolated (no migration of individuals, or gametes, into or out of the population).
      NOTE: No gene flow (**Module 13.9**).

3. Mutations do not alter the gene pool.
4. Mating is random.
5. All individuals are equal in reproductive success (no natural selection).
   NOTE: No fitness differences **(Modules 13.15 and 13.18).**

G. **Hardy-Weinberg equilibrium** rarely exists in natural populations (in this sense it can be viewed as a control, **Module 1.8**), but understanding the assumptions behind it gives us a basis for understanding how populations evolve.

Module 13.8 Connection: The Hardy-Weinberg equation is useful in public health science.

A. Estimating frequencies of harmful alleles among the population at large helps public health scientists assess and prioritize their efforts.

B. For example, if PKU occurs in one out of 10,000 babies ($q^2 = 0.0001$), then $q = 0.01$, $p = 0.99$, and $2pq$ (the frequency of carrier heterozygotes) $= 0.0198$.
   NOTE: This exercise can be used with any of the frequencies of genes from Table 9.9.

Module 13.9 In addition to natural selection, genetic drift and gene flow can contribute to evolution.

NOTE: Approach this by asking your students to identify situations that will violate the conditions listed in Module 13.8.

A. **Genetic drift** is a change in a gene pool of a small population due to chance. The effect of a loss of individuals from a population is much greater when there are fewer individuals. The **bottleneck effect** is genetic drift resulting from a disaster that reduces population size (such as the example of the elephant seals; Figures 13.9A and B). The **founder effect** is genetic drift resulting from colonization of a new area by a small number (even one) of individuals (likely important in the evolution of animals and plants on the Galápagos Islands).
   NOTE: Genetic drift is evolution by sampling error.

B. **Gene flow** is a gain or loss of alleles from a population due to immigration or emigration of individuals or gametes.

C. Nonrandom mating is more often the case, particularly among animals, where choice of mates is often an important part of behavior but does not change allele frequency and therefore does not affect microevolution.

D. Differential success in reproduction is probably always the case for natural populations. The resulting **natural selection** is the factor that is likely to result in adaptive changes to a gene pool.
   NOTE: Differential reproductive success is measured in terms of fitness differences (see **Module 13.15**).

E. The amount and kind of genetic variation in the population limit the degree of adaptation that can occur.

Module 13.10 Connection: Endangered species often have reduced variation.

A. This is becoming more of a problem as human activity (habitat destruction, the introduction of exotic [nonnative] species, unregulated hunting) endangers wild populations, particularly those that are already small.
   NOTE: The consequences of such human activity are discussed in **Chapter 38.**

B. These animals suffered bottlenecks due to disease, hunting, and drought. There is an extremely high degree of genetic uniformity—higher than some strains of highly inbred laboratory mice.

C. This high degree of homogeneity exhibited by cheetahs, coupled with loss of habitat, leaves the cheetah's future in the wild open to question.
   NOTE: Ask your students if cheetahs should be preserved by human intervention. Sooner or later species go extinct; perhaps it is the preservation, not the extinction, of the cheetah that will be due to human interference.

III. Variation and Natural Selection

Module 13.11 Variation is extensive in most populations.

A. Variation in a single characteristic can be caused by the effect of one or more genes or from the action of the environment inducing phenotypic change.

B. A population is **polymorphic** for a characteristic if two or more morphs (contrasting forms) are noticeably present; these may be visible or biochemical characteristics (Figure 13.11). Much of this variation can be attributed to polygenic inheritance.
   Review: Polygenic inheritance is discussed in Module 9.16.

C. Most populations exhibit geographic variation in the distribution of characteristics. This variation may show stratification, varying smoothly across the population. This type of variation is referred to as a **cline.**

D. Genetic variation can be measured in two ways: first, by determining the average percent of gene loci that are heterozygous (gene diversity) and second, by determining the nucleotide diversity of DNA sequences.

Module 13.12 Mutation and sexual recombination generate variation.

A. Mutation is the ultimate source of all variation facilitating evolution. Most mutations occur in body cells; only mutations in gametes can be passed to offspring.
   Review: Mutation (**Module 10.16**) and meiosis (especially **Modules 8.16, 8.17, and 8.18**).

B. Mutations normally are harmful if they affect the protein, but they may improve an organism's adaptation to an environment that is changing. Organisms with very short generation spans, like bacteria, can evolve rapidly by mutation alone.

C. Sexual recombination shuffles the mixture of alleles in diploid organisms. Independent assortment of homologous chromosomes, crossing over, and random fertilization of sperm and egg all play a role. Organisms that reproduce sexually tend to have longer life spans, and sexual recombination is necessary to increase the variation stemming from single mutations (Figure 13.12).

Module 13.13 Connection: The evolution of antibiotic resistance in bacteria is a serious public health concern.

A. Antibiotics were first developed in the 1930s and became standard medical practice for the prevention of infectious diseases during WWII.

B. Forces of evolution (natural selection) have accelerated the development of antibiotic-resistant strains of bacteria.
   Review: Antibiotic resistance is carried on plasmids that are easily transferred between bacterial cells (Module 12.2).

C. Overuse and misuse of antibiotics has contributed to the proliferation of antibiotic-resistant strains of bacteria.

D. Multidrug-resistant strains of the organism that causes tuberculosis (Mycobacterium tuberculosis) have appeared at alarming rates in the United States and are ravaging other parts of the world (Figure 13.13).

Module 13.14 Diploidy and balancing selection preserve variation.

A. An ancestral population is varied, with individuals having characteristics suited for many types of environments.

B. Over successive generations, those individuals with the characteristics best suited for the environment leave more offspring. These characteristics increase in the subsequent generations.

C. Those individuals with characteristics not suited for the environment leave fewer offspring. These characteristics decrease in subsequent generations.

D. The effects of recessive alleles are not often displayed in diploid organisms. Recessive alleles may be "hidden" from natural selection when they are found in combination with a dominant allele. Thus, variation is retained in a population subject to selection. *NOTE:* Since such variation is hidden, it takes many generations to eliminate (if they are eliminated at all) disadvantageous recessive alleles from a population. *Review:* Cystic fibrosis is only expressed in individuals who are homozygous recessive for this disorder **(Module 9.9)**.

E. **Balancing selection** occurs when natural selection maintains genetic variability by allowing two or more phenotypic forms in a population resulting in balanced polymorphism. **Heterozygote advantage** is a situation in which the heterozygote is favored over either homozygote. As a result, variation is maintained in the population. An example of this is the sickle-cell allele where one homozygote is susceptible to malaria, the other homozygote suffers from sickle-cell disease, and the heterozygote is resistant to malaria and normally does not suffer from sickle-cell disease **(Module 9.14)**.

F. A second mechanism that promotes balanced polymorphism is **frequency-dependent selection.** For example, if too many of one type (or morph) of organism is present in a population, that type will be selected against, reducing that type's total numbers.

G. Some characteristics showing neutral variation (such as human fingerprints) apparently provide no selective advantage (Figure 13.14).

H. The frequency of these characteristics may change as a result of genetic drift, but not by natural selection.

I. It is impossible to demonstrate that an allele brings no benefit to an organism, and it may be that some supposedly neutral variations provide benefits in some environments.

Module 13.15 The perpetuation of genes defines evolutionary fitness.

A. Emphasize that it is the survival of genes and the phenotypic traits expressed by the genes, not individual organisms, that are important. It is the genes that survive through the passage of time, not the individual organism(s), that are important.

B. Fitness is defined as the relative contribution that an individual makes to the gene pool of the next generation.

Module 13.16 Natural selection can alter variation in a population in three ways.

NOTE: The starting population is a continuum from very light- to very dark-colored deer mice (Figure 13.16).

A. **Stabilizing selection** tends to narrow the range in population variability toward some intermediate form. This occurs in relatively stable environments. *Preview:* An example of stabilizing selection is the birth weight of human babies, which tends to be in the 6.5- to 9-pound range (see **Module 27.17**).

B. **Directional selection** tends to move the modal (most common) form toward one of the extremes. This is most common during times of environmental change or when organisms find themselves in new habitats.

Preview: A good example of the effects of directional selection on life history patterns can be found in the discussion of guppies subject to different selective pressures (see **Module 36.7**).

C. Distributive selection occurs when environmental conditions are varied in a way that favors both extremes over the intermediate form.

Module 13.17 Sexual selection may produce sexual dimorphism.

A. **Sexual dimorphism** is illustrated by two examples of secondary sexual characteristics.

B. Competition between males for the privilege to mate with a female may depend on the strength of the male and his superior ability compared to other males (Figure 13.17A).

C. Other characteristics such as plumage in birds may actually be detrimental to the survival of the male due to increased risk of predators. The reward of mate selection due to a larger plumage than other males, however, may outweigh the potential risk factors (Figure 13.17B).

Module 13.18 Natural selection cannot fashion perfect organisms.

A. There are four reasons that account for imperfections in organisms in spite of natural selection:

1. Organisms are locked into historical constraints; nature doesn't start from scratch each time there is a need for change.

2. Adaptations are often compromises; some adaptations to change provide an advantage along with a disadvantage.

3. Chance and natural selection interact; nature's ways are not always in the best interest of the organism in question.

4. Selection can only edit existing variations; if an adaptation to change is needed and none is available in a population, that population may become extinct.

B. Natural selection operates on a "better than" basis, and it would be unreasonable to expect perfection from a process with such limitations.

Class Activities

1. As pointed out in Module 13.8, the Hardy-Weinberg equation plays a role in public health science. This role can be demonstrated by having students, working in groups, choose a health issue that has a genetic basis (e.g., PKU, cystic fibrosis, sickle-cell disease, Tay-Sachs, etc.) and see how it applies to public health planning in the community in which they live. The current and projected population size of the community must be considered when completing this exercise.

2. Point out that one of the major health care crises humans are facing is the development of antibiotic-resistant bacteria. Ask your students how many of them, when given prescription antibiotics, finish the entire prescription. There will, almost inevitably, be at least one student who does not. Point out how this contributes to the increase in the numbers of antibiotic-resistant strains of bacteria. Further, as discussed in Chapter 12, bacteria can exchange plasmids; thus, bacteria never exposed to a particular antibiotic can be resistant to that antibiotic as a result of plasmid exchange.

Transparency Acetates

Figure 13.1B   The voyage of the *Beagle* (1831–1836). The insets show a young Charles Darwin and his ship.

Figure 13.2B   Eight breeds of dogs (all members of the same species), the results of hundreds to thousands of years of artificial selection

Figure 13.2C   Five different species of canines, the results of thousands to millions of years of natural selection

Figure 13.3I   *Basilosaurus,* an extinct whale whose hind legs link living whales with their land-dwelling ancestors

Figure 13.4A   Homologous structures: Vertebrate forelimbs

Figure 13.3B   Evolutionary relationships between humans and five other vertebrates, based on hemoglobin comparisons

Table 13.4   Comparison of a protein in a different species

Figure 13.5B   Evolution of pesticide resistance in insect populations

Figure 13.7A   Imaginary blue-footed boobies, with and without foot webbing

Figure 13.7B   Gene pool of original population of boobies

Figure 13.7C   Gene pool of next generation of boobies

Figure 13.9A   The bottleneck effect

Figure 13.12   Shuffling alleles by sexual recombination

Figure 13.16   Three possible effects of natural selection on a phenotypic character (Layer 1)

Figure 13.16   Three possible effects of natural selection on a phenotypic character (Layer 2)

Figure 13.16   Three possible effects of natural selection on a phenotypic character (Layer 3)

Reviewing the Concepts, page 278: Natural selection—the mechanism of evolution

Reviewing the Concepts, page 278: Outcomes of selection

Connecting the Concepts, page 278: Causes of evolutionary change

Media

See the beginning of this book for a complete description of all media available for instructors and students. Animations and videos are available in the Campbell Image Presentation Library. Media Activities and Thinking as a Scientist investigations are available on the student CD-ROM and website.

Animations and Videos	Module Number
Galápagos Tortoise Video	13.1
Galápagos Islands Overview Video	13.1
Galápagos Marine Iguana Video	13.1
Galápagos Sea Lion Video	13.1
Grand Canyon Video	13.1
Causes of Microevolution Animation	13.9
Genetic Variation from Sexual Recombination Animation	13.12

Activities and Thinking as a Scientist	Module Number
Web/CD Activity 13A: *Darwin and the Galápagos Islands*	13.1
Web/CD Activity 13B: *The Voyage of the* Beagle: *Darwin's Trip Around the World*	13.1
Web/CD Thinking as a Scientist: *How Do Environmental Changes Affect a Population?*	13.2
Web/CD Activity 13C: *Reconstructing Forelimbs*	13.4
Biology Labs On-Line: *Darwin's Theory of Evolution*	13.5
Web/CD Thinking as a Scientist: *How Can Frequency of Alleles Be Calculated?*	13.7
Web/CD Activity 13D: *Causes of Microevolution*	13.9
Biology Labs On-Line: *Population Genetics and the Modern Synthesis*	13.10
Web/CD Activity 13E: *Genetic Variation from Sexual Recombination*	13.12
Web/CD Thinking as a Scientist: *Connection: What Are the Patterns of Antibiotic Resistance?*	13.13

CHAPTER 14

The Origin of Species

Teaching Objectives

Introduction Describe the specific problems of classifying mosquitoes in London and North America.

Concepts of Species

14.1 Define and distinguish between microevolution and macroevolution.

14.2 Compare the definitions, advantages, and disadvantages of the different species concepts.

14.3 Describe five types of prezygotic barriers and three types of postzygotic barriers that prevent populations belonging to closely related species from interbreeding.

Mechanisms of Speciation

14.4 Explain how geologic processes can fragment populations and lead to speciation.

14.5 Explain how reproductive barriers might evolve in isolated populations of animals. Refer to experiments on laboratory-raised fruit flies and to desert pool pupfish.

14.6 Explain how sympatric speciation can occur and how it typically happens in plants.

14.7 Explain why polyploidy is important to modern agriculture.

14.7 Explain how modern wheat evolved.

14.8 Define adaptive radiation, and explain why the Galápagos finches are a good example.

14.9 Describe the discoveries of Peter and Rosemary Grant working with Darwin's finches.

14.10 Compare the gradualism model and the punctuated equilibrium model of evolution. Explain which model is most consistent with the fossil record. Explain how the idea that species appear suddenly is misleading.

Macroevolution

14.11 Define an exaptation, and describe two examples in birds.

14.12 Explain how genes that program development are important in the evolution of life.

14.12 Define and describe examples of paedomorphosis.

14.13 Explain why evolutionary trends do not reflect directions or goals of evolution.

Key Terms

adaptive radiation	habitat isolation	phylogenetic species
allopatric speciation	hybrid breakdown	concept
behavioral isolation	hybrid inviability	polyploid
biological species concept	hybrid sterility	punctuated equilibrium
ecological species concept	macroevolution	reproductive barrier
evo-devo	mechanical isolation	speciation
exaptation	morphological species	sympatric speciation
gametic isolation	concept	taxonomy
gradualism model	paedomorphosis	temporal isolation

Word Roots

allo- = other; **-metron** = measure (*allometric growth:* the variation in the relative rates of growth of various parts of the body, which helps shape the organism)

sym- = together; **-patri** = father (*sympatric speciation:* a mode of speciation occurring as a result of a radical change in the genome that produces a reproductively isolated subpopulation in the midst of its parent population)

Lecture Outline

Introduction *Mosquito Mystery*

A. Microevolutionary changes, as discussed in Chapter 13, show us how populations change over time. When do we know that distinctly new species have evolved?

B. Critical to determining the limits of a species is understanding if two populations are truly reproductively isolated. For example, two populations of mosquitoes exist in London with very little overlap in their respective habitats.

1. The mosquitoes that live above ground hibernate during the winter and breed during the warm months of spring and summer.

2. The mosquitoes that live in the London Underground breed all year round.

3. When the two types of mosquitoes were brought together to breed, no offspring were produced. Thus, the mosquitoes are truly different species.
Preview: This is an example of speciation by temporal isolation (**Module 14.3**).

C. New evidence indicated that the two species did not diverge from one species but were already separate species and that Culvex molestus came from southern climates. The explanation became complicated upon examination of the mosquito in the United States. It appeared to be a hybrid of the two mosquito species in London. The U.S. mosquito was capable of transmitting the West Nile virus from birds to people and thus the rapid spread of the disease in the United States.

Module 14.1 The origin of species is the source of biological diversity.

A. Most of Darwin's book On the Origin of Species dealt with natural selection and adaptation to a particular environment (microevolution) and little on the explanation of how a new species actually emerges.

B. Speciation is the focal point of evolution, which leads to biodiversity.

C. **Macroevolution** refers to the development of novel adaptations that lead to defining properties of a large group of organisms (e.g., flowers on plants, legs on land vertebrates, and feathers on birds).

I. Concepts of Species

Module 14.2 What is a species?

A. **Taxonomy** is the science of naming and classifying organisms. These names are in the form of binomials, the forms first used by Linnaeus in the 1700s. The binomial for the human species is Homo sapiens.

B. A biological species is defined as a population or group of populations whose members have the potential to interbreed and produce fertile offspring.
    Review: This is the same as the sexual species concept introduced in **Module 13.6.**

C. Two different species can appear to be almost identical (for example, the mosquitoes in the opening essay or the western and eastern meadowlarks in Figure 14.1A).

D. A single species can exhibit considerable diversity of form (for example, humans, Figure 14.1B). But what defines a species is the ability to produce fertile offspring. This is called the **biological species concept.**

E. The mosquitoes in the opening essay could not produce any offspring, thus they are different species. Humans look very different, which is determined by our heritage. However, humans are one species because we can produce fertile offspring irrespective of our heritage.

F. The biological species concept cannot be applied to asexually reproducing organisms, nor can it be applied to the fossil record. In these cases, similarity of appearance, biochemical features, and the fossil record are used to distinguish among species.

G. Several other species concepts are presented in this module.
    1. **Morphological species concept:** Species are classified based on phenotypic traits (the appearance of the organism).
    2. **Ecological species concept:** Species are defined based upon their ecological niche.
    3. **Phylogenetic species concept:** Species are catalogued based on their evolutionary tree (genetic history) and molecular evidence from DNA sequence analysis.

Module 14.3 Reproductive barriers keep species separate.

A. Prezygotic barriers prevent mating or fertilization (Table 14.3).
    1. Differential timing of mating **(temporal isolation),** such as the mosquito example (opening essay), and as illustrated with the skunks in Figure 14.3A, or as is the case with many plants that reproduce at different times.
    2. Reproductive habitat differences **(habitat isolation),** such as the differences between two related species of toad.
    3. **Behavioral isolation** may involve differences in display (examples are the fireflies discussed in the opening essay of Chapter 5, the courtship ritual of the blue-footed boobies [Figure 14.3B]), or pheromones.
    4. **Mechanical isolation** concerns structural differences that prevent copulation or the transfer of gametes (e.g., the unique structure of some flowering plants insures proper pollination) (Figure 14.3C).
    5. **Gametic isolation** occurs when gametes fail to unite; such as different species of sea urchins all releasing their gametes into the oceans with only specific gametic pairings occurring.

B. Postzygotic barriers prevent the development of fertile adults (Table 14.3).
    1. **Hybrid inviability:** The hybrids do not live, as for example, when two different species of frog mate, but the hybrid does not survive.
    2. **Hybrid sterility:** The hybrids are not fertile, such as when a female horse and a male donkey mate to produce a sterile mule (Figure 14.3D).
    3. **Hybrid breakdown:** There is progressive weakening of successive generations of interbreeding hybrids. The first generation of hybrids is fertile, but with subsequent generations, hybrid fitness declines.

II. Mechanisms of Speciation

Module 14.4 Geographic isolation can lead to speciation.

A. **Allopatric speciation** involves changes in allele frequencies in two or more geographically isolated populations stemming from one initial population and is most likely in a small, isolated population.

B. Changes occur by microevolutionary processes (mutation, genetic drift, and natural selection).

C. Many factors can produce geographical isolation: mountain formation, deep canyons, the removal of land bridges between continents, or continental drift (Figure 14.4).

D. The effectiveness of barriers depends on how effective dispersal is in the organisms that might speciate and on the size of the population. Small populations are more likely to develop into a new species than are large populations. Large mammals may find it easy to cross mountain ranges, while a wide river may stop small mammals.

E. Geographical isolation does not necessarily lead to speciation. Speciation occurs only after barriers to reproduction are established.

Module 14.5 Reproductive barriers may evolve as populations diverge.

A. Reproductive barriers may result when populations are isolated and diverge due to environmental adaptations.

B. Diana Dodd tested this hypothesis using two populations of fruit flies (Figure 14.5A).

C. One population was fed maltose, and the other was fed starch. After several generations, the fruit flies were allowed to mingle and mate. Preferences were observed for mates raised on the same food. Thus, reproductive barriers were in the process of developing between these two populations of fruit flies.

D. Evolutionary biologists have identified species that have developed reproductive barriers as a result of geographic isolation. The mosquitoes of London and the antelope squirrels of the Grand Canyon are good examples. The unique species of pupfish in each isolated spring in Death Valley are thought to have evolved over a short time period as a result of geographic isolation (Figure 14.5B).

Module 14.6 New species can arise within the same geographic area as the parent species.

A. **Sympatric speciation** (speciation in the same geographic location) seems to be rare among animal species but has played an important role in plant evolution.

B. The most common type of sympatric speciation occurs when an accident during cell division (cells dividing by mitosis rather than by meiosis) results in an extra set of chromosomes **(polyploidy).**

C. Tetraploid plants can form by self-fertilization of diploid gametes in a flower where meiosis has not reduced the chromosome set (Figure 14.6A).

D. The plant that grows from the tetraploid zygote can reproduce by self-fertilization but cannot produce fertile offspring by mating with its diploid ancestors because these offspring would be triploid.

E. Sympatric speciation by polyploidy was first discovered in evening primroses by de Vries in the early 1900s (Figure 14.6B).

F. Most polyploid species are the result of the hybridization of two species with the resulting offspring being sterile. However, the polyploid hybrid may reproduce asexually. Or an error in mitosis or meiosis could produce viable gametes, resulting in a new species.

Module 14.7 Connection: Polyploid plants clothe and feed us.

    A. Scientists estimate that 25–50% of all plants are polyploid. Most commercially grown food and fiber plants are polyploid hybrids: oats, potatoes, bananas, peanuts, barley, plums, apples, sugarcane, coffee, wheat, and cotton.
       NOTE: It has been natural for humans to select, for practical purposes, the better strains (from a human perspective) from among the offspring of chance matings.

    B. The genetic diversity of polyploid hybrids is often advantageous.

    C. The recent evolutionary history of bread wheat (Triticum aestivum, Figure 14.7A) is believed to have occurred by a series of steps involving hybridization, a failure of meiosis, an additional hybridization, and nondisjunction (Figure 14.7B).

    D. Plant geneticists attempt to produce plant hybrids with special characteristics by exposing them to chemicals that induce errors in mitosis and meiosis.

Module 14.8 Adaptive radiation may occur in new or newly vacated habitats.

    Review: The case of the increased incidence of hereditary deafness on the island of Martha's Vineyard shows how allele frequencies can change over relatively short periods of time on an island **(Module 9.8).**

    A. The emergence of numerous species from a common ancestor in one diverse environment (such as the Galápagos) is known as adaptive radiation.

    B. Such islands must be close enough together or to the mainland to allow for occasional dispersion, but far enough apart to provide isolation most of the time.

    C. Darwin's finches (14 closely related species, distinguished by morphology and habitat) of the Galápagos island chain are excellent examples of the results of island speciation (Figures 14.8A and B).

Module 14.9 Talking About Science: Peter and Rosemary Grant study the evolution of Darwin's finches.

    A. Peter and Rosemary Grant first tested the hypothesis put forth by Darwin that the 14 finch species on the Galápagos Islands resulted from food adaptations through natural selection.

    B. The size and shape of the finch beak dictates the type of food that is consumed by the finch.

    C. On a rare occurrence, a male of one species mates with a female of another species, producing hybrids with intermediate beak sizes.

    D. During drought years, the hybrids die because they cannot compete with either of the parent species for food, thus maintaining divergent evolution of the finches.

Module 14.10 The tempo of speciation can appear steady or jumpy.

    A. In the **gradualism model,** populations isolated from the ancestral stock change slowly as their allele frequencies shift during adaptation by natural selection. Darwin's proposals incorporated this model (Figure 14.10).
       NOTE: In Figures 14.10A and B, the sizes of the arrows' bases represent the population sizes.

    B. Most of the fossil record does not support the gradualist model because most new species seem to appear suddenly in rock strata, without intermediary transitional forms.

C. In the **punctuated equilibrium** model, periods of rapid evolutionary change (punctuation) and speciation are interrupted by long periods of little or no detectable change (equilibrium or stasis) (Figure 14.10B).
NOTE: Using this definition, the amount of time considered a geological instant would vary with the age of the species.

D. Though once the subject of heated debate, most evolutionary biologists now see both models as having merit, even with some species evolving by a combination of these models. Current research is focused on the tempo of evolution.

III. Macroevolution

Module 14.11 Evolutionary novelties may arise in several ways.

A. Darwin's theory of gradual change can explain how intricate and subtle alterations of a structure can lead to evolution of species.

B. A good example of structural refinement over time is the eye (Figure 14.11). All eyes of molluscs are capable of discerning light from dark, yet the complexity varies greatly.

C. An **exaptation** is a feature that evolved in one context and was later adapted for another function. It is unlikely that feathers and light bones were developed initially for flight, but instead were adapted for flight once present.

Module 14.12 Genes that control development are important in evolution.

A. The convergence of two scientific disciplines into one has led to some interesting concepts. Evolutionary biology and developmental biology have merged into evo-devo, which looks at how slight genetic changes can be magnified into significant phenotypic changes. Changes in the genes that control development can have profound effects on the product (the adult).

B. **Paedomorphosis** is the retention of juvenile body features in the adult (Figure 14.12A). The adult axolotl (salamander) retains the external gills of its juvenile ancestors.

C. Paedomorphosis has been important in the evolution of humans and chimpanzees from a common ancestor. The large, paedomorphic human skull and the long period of time as a nonreproductive child (unique in humans) provide the human with more space for a larger brain and more time to learn from adults (Figure 14.12B).
Preview: Human evolution is discussed in detail in Chapter 19.

D. Evolutionary biologist Stephen Jay Gould contends that youthful characteristics in children elicit parental affection and care. He uses Mickey Mouse's early evolution as a cartoon character to illustrate this concept (Figure 14.12C).

Module 14.13 Evolutionary trends do not mean that evolution is goal directed.

A. Evolutionary trends show gradual, one-directional changes in morphology over long periods of evolutionary time, such as the increase in brain complexity among human ancestors and the increase in size and modification of the limbs seen in the lineage that gave rise to modern horses (Figure 14.13).

B. Unequal survival of new species can explain this apparent trend.

C. Unequal speciation with equal survival of all new species can also explain the data (see **Module 13.7**). Current debate exists over the relative importance of each of these mechanisms.

D. Evolutionary trends are not preordained or unchangeable. Such trends can stop or reverse.

Class Activities

1. Have your students consider the question of whether or not dogs and wolves are two different species (as they are currently classified) or if they are actually a single species.

Transparency Acetates

Figure 14.1   How speciation increases diversity

Table 14.3   Reproductive barriers between species

Figure 14.5A   Evolution of reproductive barriers in lab populations of fruit flies

Figure 14.6A   Sympatric speciation by polyploid formation

Figure 14.7B   The evolution of wheat

Figure 14.8B   Adaptive radiation on an island chain

Figure 14.10A   Gradualist model

Figure 14.10B   Punctuated equilibrium model (combined with Figure 14.10A)

Figure 14.11   A range of eye complexity among molluscs

Figure 14.12B   The "evolution" of Mickey Mouse

Figure 14.13   The branched evolution of horses

Reviewing the Concepts, page 296: Reproductive barriers

Connecting the Concepts, page 296: Speciation

Connecting the Concepts, page 296: Mechanisms of macroevolution

Media

See the beginning of this book for a complete description of all media available for instructors and students. Animations and videos are available in the Campbell Image Presentation Library. Media Activities and Thinking as a Scientist investigations are available on the student CD-ROM and website.

Animations and Videos	Module Number
A Scrolling Geologic Time Scale Animation	14.12

Activities and Thinking as a Scientist	Module Number
Web/CD Thinking as a Scientist: *How Do New Species Arise by Genetic Isolation?*	14.6
Web/CD Activity 14A: *Polyploid Plants*	14.7
Web/CD Activity 14B: *Exploring Speciation on Islands*	14.8
Web/CD Activity 14C: *Mechanisms of Macroevolution*	14.11
Web/CD Activity 14D: *Paedomorphosis: Morphing Chimps and Humans*	14.12

CHAPTER 15

Tracing Evolutionary History

Teaching Objectives

Introduction   Describe the current and historical understandings of the evolutionary relationships between dinosaurs and birds.

Macroevolution and Earth's History

15.1   Briefly describe the history of life on Earth, noting the major eras, when they occurred, and which types of life were most abundant. Describe the key events that occurred at the boundaries of eras.

15.2   Distinguish between the relative age and absolute age of a fossil. Explain how radiometric dating is used to determine the age of rocks and fossils and when carbon-14 and potassium-40 are most appropriately used.

15.3   Describe the process of continental drift, and explain its significance to the history of life on Earth.

15.4   Explain how mountains, volcanoes, and earthquakes are a consequence of plate tectonics.

15.5   Describe the causes, frequency, and consequences of mass extinctions over the past 600 million years.

Phylogeny and Systematics

15.6   Distinguish between homologous and analogous structures and homoplasies. Describe examples of each.

15.7   Explain the goals of systematics. List in order from most specific to most general, the progressively broader categories of classification used in systematics.

15.8   Describe the goals of phylogenetic systematics. Define the terms monophyletic, clade, derived character, primitive character, ingroup, outgroup, cladogram, and parsimony.

15.9   Explain how molecular biology is used as a tool in systematics. Describe examples used to study panda and human evolution. Explain why some studies use mitochondrial DNA and other studies use ribosomal DNA. Define a molecular clock.

15.10   Compare the five-kingdom and three-domain systems of classification.

Key Terms

analogy	domain	molecular clock
binomial	family	molecular systematics
clades	five-kingdom system	monophyletic
cladistics	genus	orders
cladogram	geologic record	out-group
classes	Gondwana	Pangaea
continental drift	in-group	parsimony
convergent evolution	kingdoms	phyla

phylogenetic trees   shared derived characters   taxon
phylogeny   shared primitive characters   three-domain system
plate tectonics   species
radiometric dating   systematics

Word Roots

clado- = branch (*cladogram:* a dichotomous phylogenetic tree that branches repeatedly)

mono- = one (*monophyletic:* pertaining to a taxon derived from a single ancestral species that gave rise to no species in any other taxa)

parsi- = few (*principle of parsimony:* the premise that a theory about nature should be the simplest explanation that is consistent with the facts)

phylo- = tribe; **-geny** = origin (*phylogeny:* the evolutionary history of a taxon)

Lecture Outline

Introduction *Are Birds Really Dinosaurs with Feathers?*

   A. Evolutionary biologists can learn much about the history of life on Earth from fossil records. John Ostrum raised the controversial question about the origin of birds and the relationship with dinosaurs as their predecessor.

   B. Through careful analysis of fossil records, Ostrum presented a convincing argument supporting the theory that birds are descendents of dinosaurs (*Archaeopteryx,* left page in text).

   C. More evidence was presented in support of Ostrum's theory with the new method of evaluating evolutionary relationships called cladistic analysis.

   D. The current hypothesis of the origin of birds from dinosaurs is now widely accepted.

   E. Now the debate by the evolutionary biologist is, "How did dinosaurs learn to fly?" There are two common scenarios.

      1. Feathered dinosaurs used their feathers to assist when capturing prey or escaping predators.

      2. They used them to glide to the ground from trees.

   F. The second scenario has gained favor, particularly in light of the most recent discovery of a fossil (*Microraptor,* right page in text) that dates back to 120 million years. This fossil is a feathered, four-winged gliding dinosaur.

I. Macroevolution and Earth's History

   Module 15.1 The fossil record chronicles macroevolution.

      Review: The fossil record (Module 13.2).

   A. Macroevolution, the main events in the evolutionary history of life on Earth, is determined by comparing the fossil records in strata representing various ages, from various parts of Earth's surface.

   B. Using the information gleaned from fossil sequences, a **geologic record** has been established by geologists. The geologic time scale is a standardized, hierarchical system of age categories (Table 15.1). Earth's history is divided into three eons: Archaean, Proterozoic, and Phanerozoic. Archaean and Proterozoic are grouped together into the Precambrian, which lasted approximately 4 billion years. The Phanerozoic covers approximately the past 550 million years.

C. The oldest fossils are of microorganisms from 3.5 billion years ago (bya) during the early Precambrian era. The oldest eukaryote fossils are from 2.2 bya and multicellular organism fossils are from 1.2 bya.

D. Late Precambrian fossils show that animal life had diversified by 600 million years ago (mya).

E. Early Paleozoic (542 mya) rocks bear fossils that gave rise to modern organisms, as well as fossils of extinct lineages.

F. By 400 mya, during the middle Paleozoic ("ancient animal") era, life had moved out of water and onto dry land.

G. The Mesozoic ("middle animal") era is the age of reptiles and cone-bearing plants. During this era, the first mammals, birds, and angiosperms appeared.

H. The Cenozoic ("recent animal") era began 65 mya and is the age of mammals and flowering plants.

I. *Homo sapiens* arose during the Pleistocene epoch (100,000 to 200,000 years ago). *Preview:* Human evolution is discussed in Chapter 19.

Module 15.2 The actual ages of rocks and fossils mark geologic time.

A. The record of fossils in rock strata chronicles the relative ages of life.

B. The actual ages of fossils can be obtained by **radiometric dating.** Radioactive isotopes "decay" at a known rate relative to other isotopes. For instance, half of an amount of ^{14}C decays to ^{12}C in 5,730 years. Measuring the relative amounts of the two isotopes in a sample (and comparing this ratio to the ratio known to have been in the original organism, that is, the ratio of ^{14}C to ^{12}C in the atmosphere) gives the actual age of the sample, with an error factor of about 10%. Elements with longer half-lives are used to date older fossils for example potassium-40 (^{40}K) has a half-life of 1.3 billion years.

Module 15.3 Continental drift has played a major role in macroevolution.

A. In 1912, Wegener proposed **continental drift** as a mechanism that accounts for the similarities of coastal outlines of present-day continents. The proposal was not accepted because geologists knew of no method that would cause continents to move.

B. Continents are the above-water parts of crustal plates that "float" on the underlying mantle. New crust is formed along ocean ridges, and old crust is destroyed at the leading margins of the plates (Figure 15.3A).

C. About 250 mya, the present continents were united as a single supercontinent called **Pangaea.** This must have made weather patterns and climate much different than they are now (Figure 15.3B).

D. In the early Mesozoic (180 mya), Pangaea began to break apart, first forming northern (Laurasia) and southern (Gondwana) landmasses. This process was completed 135 mya (Figure 15.3B).

E. About 65 mya, the beginnings of the modern continents could be seen (Figure 15.3B).

F. Continental drift is an ongoing process. For example, the ongoing collision in the Himalayan region is creating forces that are splitting the Indo-Australian plate, resulting in Australia moving independently of India.

G. Relative distributions of present-day life forms and their fossilized ancestors are explained by the proposed course of recent continental drift (Figures 15.3C and D). *NOTE:* The example your students will be most familiar with is the California earthquakes (Module 15.4).

Module 15.4 Connection: Tectonic trauma imperils local life.

A. The geologic processes that move Earth's crustal plates are called **plate tectonics.**

B. Earthquakes are the result of the movement of crustal plates (Figure 15.4A).

C. Volcanic eruptions occur along plate margins or mid-ocean ridges and can build mountains or islands, such as the Galápagos (Figure 15.4B), and can pose a threat to local populations (Figure 15.4C).

Module 15.5 Mass extinctions were followed by diversification of life-forms.

A. During the past 600 million years, there have been six mass extinction events. During these events, the extinction rate was massive, and two have been studied extensively.

B. A major extinction occurred at the end of the Permian period, coinciding with the formation of Pangaea. At this time, more than 96% of all species of marine animals went extinct. The cause of this mass extinction coincides with an exceptionally active volcanic period in present-day Siberia.
   NOTE: The ends of the major eras (Paleozoic and Mesozoic) discussed in Module 15.3 correspond to the major extinction events. The dividing lines between the periods correspond to other major changes in fossil assemblages.

C. At the end of the Cretaceous period (65 mya), many lineages of terrestrial plants and animals and about half the marine animals, became extinct.

D. Particularly noteworthy was the demise of the dinosaurs (within a span of less than 10 million years), which had dominated the land and air for 150 million years during the Mesozoic era.

E. Several, not necessarily mutually exclusive, explanations have been proposed to account for this change: an asteroid impact in what is now the Caribbean Sea (Figure 15.5), slow changes in climate due to continental drift, and massive volcanic activity in India during the late Cretaceous that contributed to cooling.

F. Mass extinction events are followed by huge increases in diversity as surviving organisms (apparently) exploit new environmental opportunities.

II. Phylogeny and Systematics

Module 15.6 Phylogenies are based on homologies in fossils and living organisms.

A. The evolutionary history of a group of organisms is called **phylogeny** (*phylon* is Greek for tribe, and *genesis* means origin).

B. **Systematics** is the analytical approach to the study of the diversity of life and the evolutionary relationships of organisms.

C. Fossil records, though incomplete, are reconstructed to gain insight into the phylogenic relationships of organisms.

D. Other approaches such as morphologic and molecular similarities are used to study phylogeny. Organisms that share structural similarities may have common ancestral backgrounds and, therefore, can be described as having homologous structures.

E. Organisms are not required to share common ancestors to have similar structures. In a process called **convergent evolution,** unrelated organisms can develop functionally and morphologically similar structures (Figure 15.6). Structural similarities of this type are referred to as **analogous** structures. Chance molecular similarities between two organisms that are not a result of common ancestry are called homoplasies.

Module 15.7 Systematics connects classification with evolutionary history.

A. Reconstructing phylogenies, assigning scientific names, and classifying the names are all aspects of the biological science of systematics.

B. Common names can be ambiguous because there are so many species and because different people use different names for the same species or the same name for different species. For example, crayfish (*Cambarus pocatus*) is also called a crawdad, stone crab, or mud bug. *Panulirus argus* is also called a crayfish but also goes by the names of spiny lobster, crawfish, rock lobster, and langouste. To add to the confusion, compare the following names: crayfish, jellyfish, and silverfish and note that none are fish.

C. Linnaeus devised the **binomial** form for a species' scientific name (**genus** name plus **specific epithet**—for example, *Felis catus*, the domestic cat) and a hierarchical system of progressively broader categories (Figure 15.7A).
NOTE: The species name is always italicized or underlined.

D. Systematics reflects the hierarchical nature of biology. The major levels of classification, from most to least inclusive, from a lesser degree of relatedness to a greater degree of relatedness, are **domain, kingdom, phylum, class, order, family, genus,** and **species.**
NOTE: A good mnemonic for this hierarchy is "Dear King Phillip Come Out For Goodness' Sake."

E. Ideally, the species **taxon** is based on a real group in nature (biological species), but all the other larger taxa are determined according to systematists' understanding of relationships between and among species.

F. Although identifying species often requires judgment calls, classifying species into higher taxa always does.

G. It has always been a goal of taxonomists to have their taxonomic systems reflect the evolutionary relationships and phylogeny of whatever groups are in the phylogenetic tree (Figure 15.7B).

Module 15.8 Cladograms are diagrams based on shared characters among species.

A. **Cladistics** is concerned only with the order of branching in phylogenetic lineages. Each branch on a **cladogram** represents the most recent ancestor common to all the taxa beyond that point. All the taxa above a branch share one or more homologous features. The result of this analysis should be **clades** (groupings) consisting of taxa that are **monophyletic** or from a "single tribe" (Figure 15.8A).

B. Homologous characters shared by a group of species and their common ancestor are called **shared primitive characters.** For example, the common ancestor of all vertebrates had five toes; therefore, the presence of five toes is a primitive character.

C. Homologous characters unique to each lineage are called **shared derived characters.** For example hair and mammary glands are derived characteristics that distinguish the mammalian lineage from other vertebrates.
NOTE: These shared derived characteristics are termed synapomorphies.

D. The comparison of an **in-group** with an **out-group** aids in the determination of whether a character is primitive or derived. The in-group consists of the taxa being analyzed. The out-group, while having a known relationship to the in-group, is not a member of the in-group. Characters shared by the in-group and out-group are considered shared primitive characters; characters unique to the in-group are considered shared derived characters.

E. Derived characteristics are used to identify branch points of a cladogram (the opposable thumb is a derived characteristic used to separate primates from other mammals).

F. Cladistics is particularly well suited for analysis of the similarities and differences of molecular data, which may be done entirely objectively and parsimoniously. **Parsimony** seeks the simplest explanation of observed data.

G. Cladistics has demonstrated that birds are a lineage of dinosaurs more closely related to crocodiles than are lizards and snakes (Figure 15.8B). This is the preferred classification of these groups that many biology textbooks (including this one) have adopted.

Module 15.9 Molecular biology is a powerful tool in systematics.

A. Molecular systematics uses DNA and RNA to compare relatedness and is a useful tool for tracing evolutionary history. The closer the nucleic acid sequences are between two organisms, the more likely that they share a common ancestor.

B. Bears and raccoons have long been recognized to be closely related mammals based on morphology, but such relationships can be clarified by analyzing DNA and proteins. This example is based on DNA and blood proteins. High amino acid or nucleotide sequence homology indicates similarities between species and recent divergence in the phylogenetic tree. Data suggest that lesser pandas may be more closely related to raccoons than to bears (Figure 15.9A).

C. Molecular trees can cover both long and short periods of time. rRNA comparisons are used for analyses that date back hundreds of millions of years, while mtRNA is used for more recent molecular analyses. We are more closely related to fungi than to green plants (Figure 15.9B).

D. Molecular comparisons using DNA pose challenges when homologous regions are aligned. DNA analysis is not difficult if the species being compared are closely related, differences may be only a few nucleotides. However, if the species are distantly related, the problem of DNA alignment requires computer-assisted analysis that seeks homologous regions; then alignments are made and homologies determined.

E. **Molecular clocks** can be used to accurately measure the rate change in nucleotide sequences over time. Comparisons of known divergent events and molecular sequence changes correlate closely over time. For example, an analysis of the fossil record of sharks and tuna compared to the genes of these species indicates that sharks and tuna diverged much further back in time than perhaps bats and dolphins. Molecular divergence has kept better track of time than have morphological changes.
   Review: Many molecular techniques are discussed in Chapter 12.

F. Based on the molecular evidence gathered from entire genomes, it has been determined that we are more closely related to the chimpanzee than to the gorilla (Figure 15.9C).

Module 15.10 Arranging life into kingdoms is a work in progress.

A. Linnaeus used a two-kingdom system to categorize life at the most inclusive level of classification.
   Review: The diversity of life can be arranged into three domains (Module 1.5).

B. In 1969, Whittaker proposed a **five-kingdom system** (Figure 15.10A): Monera (prokaryotes), Protista (unicellular eukaryotes), Plantae (multicellular eukaryotes, photosynthetic autotrophs with cell walls), Fungi (eukaryotic decomposers with cell walls), and Animalia (multicellular eukaryotes without cell walls, heterotrophs).

NOTE: The multicellular protists are highly variable in the degree to which their cells are cooperative/specialized. A sequence can be set up that reflects hypothesized intermediates from unicellularity to true multicellularity.

C. The Protista comprise a polyphyletic group that will be split into several kingdoms.

D. With the advent of molecular systematics and cladistics, the classification systems in current use will certainly undergo modifications.

E. This text uses the **three-domain system** (Figure 15.10B): Bacteria and Archaea are composed of the prokaryotes, and Eukarya are the eukaryotes.

F. *Preview:* As will be discussed in Module 16.8, Archaea are more closely related to Eukarya than they are to Bacteria.

Class Activities

1. Have the students imagine what the dominant life form might now be if the Cretaceous mass extinction had not taken place (Module 15.5). Would a dinosauran lineage have evolved humanlike intelligence? What might have happened to that insectivore lineage whose descendants evolved into modern humans?

2. Working in groups, have your students choose a species and consider how a particular structure might be an exaptation in the evolutionary future of that species.

3. Have your students consider the basis of distinguishing homology from analogy. For example, are the torpedo-shaped bodies of dolphins, sharks, and penguins homologous or analogous? the wings of birds, bats, and insects? the forelimbs of humans, bats, whales? Consider what evolutionary processes are responsible for the similarity of these structures.

Transparency Acetates

Figure 15.1	The geologic record
Figure 15.3A	Earth's crustal plates
Figure 15.3B	Continental drift
Figure 15.3D	Lungfish distribution, a result of continental drift
Figure 15.4A	The San Andreas fault (shown north of Los Angeles), a boundary between two crustal plates
Figure 15.5	The impact hypothesis for the Cretaceous mass extinction
Figure 15.7A	Heirarchical classification of the domestic cat
Figure 15.7B	The relationships between classification and phylogeny
Figure 15.8A	Constructing a cladogram
Figure 15.8B	A phylogenetic tree of reptiles
Figure 15.9A	A phylogenetic tree based on molecular data
Figure 15.9B	Phylogenetic tree of humans, plants, and fungi
Figure 15.9C	Phylogenetic tree of some hominoids
Figure 15.10A	The five-kingdom classification scheme
Figure 15.10B	The three-domain classification scheme

Reviewing the Concepts, page 311: Continental drift

Reviewing the Concepts, page 311: Cladistics

Reviewing the Concepts, page 311: Kingdoms and domains

Connecting the Concepts, page 311: Key ideas about systematics

Applying the Concepts, page 312: Cladogram

Media

See the beginning of this book for a complete description of all media available for instructors and students. Animations and videos are available in the Campbell Image Presentation Library. Media Activities and Thinking as a Scientist investigations are available on the student CD-ROM and website.

Animations and Videos	Module Number
Macroevolution Animation	15.1
Paedomorphosis Animation	15.1
Lava Flow Video	15.4
Volcanic Eruption Video	15.4
Classification Schemes Animation	15.10

Activities and Thinking as a Scientist	Module Number
Web/CD Activity 15A: *A Scrolling Geologic Record*	15.1
Web/CD Activity 15B: *Mechanisms of Macroevolution*	15.5
Web/CD Thinking as a Scientist: *How Is Phylogeny Determined Using Protein Comparisons?*	15.9
Web/CD Activity 15C: *Classification Schemes*	15.10

CHAPTER 16

The Origin and Evolution of Microbial Life: Prokaryotes and Protists

Teaching Objectives

Introduction   Describe the formation of stromatolites, and explain the significance of the organisms that produce them.

Early Earth and the Origin of Life

16.1   Describe the conditions under which the first life likely formed and the nature of those first living organisms.

16.2   Describe the timing and likely events that led to the origin of life on Earth.

16.3   Describe the experiments of Dr. Stanley Miller and their significance in understanding how life might have first evolved on Earth.

16.4   Explain the potential role of clay particles in the early evolution of life on Earth.

16.5   Describe the roles of RNA in the early evolution of life on Earth.

16.6   Describe the nature of the first cooperative associations of molecules enclosed by membranes.

Prokaryotes

16.7   Describe the evolutionary history and diverse roles of prokaryotic life.

16.8   Compare the characteristics of Bacteria and Archaea. Explain why biologists consider Archaea to be more closely related to eukaryotes than to bacteria.

16.9   Compare the different shapes of prokaryotes.

16.10   Describe the structures and functions of the diverse features of prokaryotes. Explain how these features have contributed to their success.

16.11   Describe the nutritional diversity of prokaryotes. Describe examples of metabolic cooperation within a species and between prokaryotic species.

16.12   Describe the diverse types of Archaea living in extreme and more moderate environments.

16.13   Distinguish between the subgroups of the domain Bacteria, noting the particular structure, special features, and habitats of each group.

16.14   Describe some of the diseases associated with bacteria. Distinguish between exotoxins and endotoxins, noting examples of each.

16.15   Describe the history of bioterrorism and the effectiveness of anthrax as a weapon.

16.16   Describe the important positive natural roles and human uses of prokaryotes. Explain their significance on the environment and in biological evolution.

Protists

16.17 Explain how the first eukaryotic cells likely originated as a community of prokaryotes.

16.18 Describe the basic types of protists. Explain why biologists currently think that they represent many kingdoms.

16.19–16.24 Describe the major protist clades, noting examples of each.

16.24 Describe the life cycle of *Ulva,* noting each form in the alternation of generations and how each is produced.

16.25 Explain how multicellular life may have evolved in eukaryotes.

Key Terms

algae	cyanobacteria	methanogens
alternation of generations	diatoms	pathogens
alveolates	dinoflagellates	peptidoglycan
amoebas	diplomonads	photoautotrophs
amoebozoans	endospore	photoheterotrophs
apicomplexans	endosymbiosis	pili
Archaea	endotoxins	plasmodial slime mold
autotrophs	euglenozoans	proteobacteria
bacilli	exotoxins	protists
Bacteria	extreme halophiles	pseudopodia
biofilms	extreme thermophiles	red algae
bioremediation	gametophytes	ribozymes
brown algae	gram-positive bacteria	RNA world
cellular slime molds	gram stain	spirochetes
chemoautotrophs	green algae	sporophyte
chemoheterotrophs	heterotrophs	stramenopiles
chlamydias	kelp	stromatolites
ciliates	Lyme disease	symbiosis
cocci	membrane infolding	water molds

Word Roots

chemo- = chemical; **hetero-** = different (*chemoheterotroph:* an organism that must consume organic molecules for both energy and carbon)

endo- = inner, within (*endotoxin:* a component of the outer membranes of certain gram-negative bacteria responsible for generalized symptoms of fever and ache)

exo- = outside (*exotoxin:* a toxic protein secreted by a bacterial cell that produces specific symptoms even in the absence of the bacterium)

gamet- = a wife or husband (*gametophyte:* the multicellular haploid form in organisms undergoing alternation of generations, which mitotically produces haploid gametes that unite and grow into the sporophyte generation)

halo- = salt; **-philos** = loving (*halophile:* microorganisms that live in unusually highly saline environments such as the Great Salt Lake or the Dead Sea)

photo- = light; **auto-** = self; **-troph** = food, nourish (*photoautotroph:* an organism that harnesses light energy to drive the synthesis of organic compounds from carbon dioxide)

pseudo- = false; **-podium** = foot (*pseudopodium:* a cellular extension of amoeboid cells used in moving and feeding)

sporo- = a seed; = **-phyto** = a plant (*sporophyte:* the multicellular diploid form in organisms undergoing alternation of generations that results from a union of gametes and that meiotically produces haploid spores that grow into the gametophyte generation)

stromato- = something spread out; **-lite** = a stone (*stromatolite:* rocks made of banded domes of sediment in which are found the most ancient forms of life)

Lecture Outline

Introduction *How Ancient Bacteria Changed the World*

    A. The evolution of life has had a profound effect on the Earth.

        1. Photosynthetic prokaryotes (cyanobacteria) evolved very early in the history of life and left unique fossilized communities called **stromatolites.**

        2. Modern-day cyanobacteria of this type are found in ponds, lakes, and shallow oceans and are virtually indistinguishable from the early forms found in stromatolites. Cyanobacteria that form thick mates or mounds are today found only in inhospitable environments.

        3. In addition to being the ancestors of today's cyanobacteria, these first photosynthetic cyanobacteria produced Earth's first oxygen-rich atmosphere.

        4. Photosynthetic prokaryotes were dominant for about 2 billion years, from nearly 3 billion years ago (bya) to about 1 bya.

        5. This chapter begins a survey of all of Earth's life forms in an evolutionary context, beginning with the evolution of life itself.

    B. The two goals of the chapters in this unit are as follows:

        1. To examine the roles that various organisms have had on the history of life on Earth.

        2. To introduce the reader to the diversity of life on earth.

I. Early Earth and the Origin of Life

    Module 16.1 Life began on a young Earth.

    A. The age of the universe is estimated to be between 10 and 20 billion years old, while Earth coalesced from gathering interstellar matter about 4.6 bya.

    B. The first atmosphere was likely to have been dominated by hot hydrogen gas. However, the Earth's gravity was not strong enough to hold onto the light H_2.

    C. Studies of modern volcanoes suggest that Earth's second early atmosphere was composed of water vapor, carbon dioxide, nitrogen, hydrogen sulfide (H_2S), and possibly some methane (CH_4) and ammonia (NH_3).

    D. Earth's crust cooled and solidified, condensing water vapor into early seas. Early Earth was also subject to intense lightning, volcanic activity, and ultraviolet radiation (Figure 16.1A).

      NOTE: It is ironic that life arose under conditions that included bombardment by UV radiation, and now a major environmental concern is the depletion of the ozone layer that protects the planet from this radiation (Modules 7.14 and 38.4).

E. Fossil evidence shows that photosynthetic prokaryotes existed by 3.5 bya (Figures 16.1B and C).

NOTE: The immensity of geological time and the very early events discussed can be made more meaningful by putting them in perspective. Borrowing an idea used by many, use a geologic time scale divided into a "life-on-Earth year." On such a scale, prokaryotic life evolves in mid-March, eukaryotes first appeared around September 1, dinosaurs flourished around Christmas, and the typical human life span of 70 years is represented by the last half-second on December 31.

F. Because cyanobacterial photosynthesis is complex and advanced, the first cells likely evolved earlier, perhaps as early as 3.9 bya.

G. An analogy of the passage of time since Earth's beginning is illustrated with a clock. (Figure 16.1D). Note the major biological events and the atmospheric changes that occurred.

Module 16.2 How did life originate?

A. Early ideas on the origin of life held that life arose by spontaneous generation.

B. Experiments in the 1600s showed that larger organisms couldn't arise spontaneously from nonliving matter.

C. In the 1860s, French scientist Louis Pasteur confirmed that all life today, including microbes, arises only from preexisting life. However, Pasteur's experiments did not deal with the question of the origin of life.

D. It is very likely that life on Earth arose between 3.9 and 3.5 bya.

E. Most biologists subscribe to the hypothesis that the earliest life forms were simpler than any that exist today and that they evolved from nonliving matter.

F. Although extraterrestrial organic molecules could have seeded Earth's early environment, most scientists think that life arose from nonorganic molecules present in Earth's early oceans and atmosphere.

G. A possible scenario: Organic monomers evolved first, then polymers, then aggregates eventually formed in a particular arrangement that allowed simple metabolism and self-replication within an enclosed membrane. Data supporting the likelihood of many of these steps exist from a number of experiments.

NOTE: The following modules detail some of the experimental evidence and theory supporting the steps in this scenario. No one has completed all the steps in order. Today's environment (even in laboratories) is very different from the environment of early Earth. Huge amounts of time are needed for these complex developments to occur.

Module 16.3 Talking about Science: Stanley Miller's experiments showed that organic molecules could have arisen on a lifeless Earth.

A. In the 1920s, Oparin and Haldane proposed that organic chemistry could have evolved in early Earth's environment because it contained no oxygen and was a reducing environment.

B. An oxidizing environment (such as Earth's O_2-rich environment today) is corrosive, tending to break molecular bonds. Thus, life could not spontaneously arise today on Earth.

C. A reducing environment tends to add electrons to molecules, building more complex forms from simple ones.

D. In 1953, Miller tested this hypothesis using an artificial mixture of inorganic molecules (H_2O, H_2, CH_4, and NH_3; see Module 16.1) in a laboratory environment that simulated conditions on early Earth (Figures 16.3A and B).

E. Within days, the mixture produced amino acids, some of the 20 amino acids that are found in organisms today (see Module 3.12).

F. More recent experiments, using modifications of Miller's setup to more closely mimic early Earth's environment, have produced most of the 20 naturally occurring amino acids, sugars, lipids, and nitrogenous bases of nucleotides including ATP.

G. Rather than the early atmosphere, many scientists think deep-sea vents and submerged volcanoes provided the chemicals required for the origin of life.

Module 16.4 The first polymers may have formed on hot rocks or clay.

A. *Review:* Polymerization occurs by dehydration synthesis (Module 3.3).

B. Although biological polymerization occurs enzymatically in organisms today, the reactions can also occur when dilute solutions of monomers are dripped on hot mineral surfaces (heat forces the dehydration synthesis) or on clays (electric charges concentrate monomers, and metallic atoms act as catalysts).

C. American biochemist Sidney Fox has made polypeptides from mixtures of amino acids dripped on hot mineral surfaces.

Module 16.5 The first genetic material and enzymes may both have been RNA.

A. *Review:* The flow of genetic information from DNA to RNA to protein is intricate and probably did not evolve as such (see Module 10.15).

B. The essential difference between cells and nonliving matter is replication.

C. A number of lines of reasoning and some experiments using artificially selected RNA molecules that can assemble nucleotides support the hypothesis that the first genes may have been made of RNA. Short RNA molecules can assemble spontaneously, without cells or enzymes, from precursor nucleotides. Some of these sequences will self-replicate if placed with additional monomer nucleotides. Further, some RNAs can act as enzymes (**ribozymes),** even one that catalyzes RNA polymerization (Figure 16.5, Module 10.10).

D. The hypothetical period in the evolution of life, when RNA played the role of both genetic material and enzyme, is termed the **RNA world.**

Module 16.6 Membrane-enclosed molecular cooperatives may have preceded the first cells.

A. Life requires the close and intricate cooperation of many different polymers. Macromolecules may have cooperated prior to the development of membranes (Figure 16.6A).

B. Experimental evidence shows that polypeptides and lipids self-assemble into microscopic spheres called **protobionts,** fluid-filled droplets with semipermeable, membranelike coatings. Though not alive, these microspheres grow by the attraction of additional polypeptides or lipids and divide when they reach a certain maximum size (Figure 16.6B).

C. Early molecular cooperation may have involved a primitive form of translation of polypeptides directly from genes in RNA. If these cooperating molecules were incorporated into a protobiont, the basic structures for self-replicating cells would be present (Figure 16.6C).

D. At this point, a primitive form of natural selection would favor those protobionts that were most efficient at growing and replicating.

E. Protobionts that relied on the environment for all their molecular needs were replaced by those that could synthesize their own monomers using sunlight or other forms of energy. Diversification was encouraged and heterotrophs developed that used the by-products of the early autotrophs or the autotrophs themselves.

F. The reign of prokaryotes started approximately 3.5 bya and lasted until 2 bya. The changes to the biosphere by prokaryotes was dramatic; for example, the addition of oxygen to the atmosphere changed the way life evolved.

II. Prokaryotes

Module 16.7 Prokaryotes have inhabited Earth for billions of years.

Review: Prokaryotic cells (Module 4.3).

A. Fossil evidence shows that prokaryotes were abundant 3.5 bya, and they evolved alone for the following 1.5 billion years.

B. Prokaryotes are ubiquitous, numerous, and small, surviving in environments that are too hot, cold, acidic, salty, or alkaline for any eukaryote (Figure 16.7).

C. Despite being small, prokaryotes influence all other life—as the cause of disease and other problems; as benign inhabitants of all environments; and more commonly, in beneficial relationships with all other living things. Bacteria that cause disease (**pathogens**) will be the focus of Module 16.14.

D. Probably the most essential activities carried out by prokaryotes are the numerous ways they function in the decomposition of dead organisms.
NOTE: See Modules 37.17 and 37.18 for the biogeochemical cycles of carbon and nitrogen.

Module 16.8 Bacteria and archaea are the two main branches of prokaryotic evolution.

NOTE: When viewed through a microscope, these two groups look similar.
Review: Classification of prokaryotes is first discussed in Module 15.10.

A. The main differences between these two groups are summarized on Table 16.8. Many of these differences concern their nucleic acids (rRNA sequences, RNA polymerase, and the presence of introns within genes).

B. Other differences between **Archaea** and **Bacteria** concern the structure of their cell walls and cell membranes. Bacteria have a true **peptidoglycan,** a polymer of sugars cross-linked with short polypeptides that functions like a cell wall.

C. In most features, archaea are more similar to eukaryotes than to bacteria.

D. *Review:* Currently, it is thought that modern archaea and eukaryotes evolved from a common ancestor (Figure 15.10B).

Module 16.9 Prokaryotes come in a variety of shapes.

A. **Cocci** (singular, *coccus*) are spherical and often occur in defined groups of two or more (Figure 16.9A). Those that occur in clusters are called staphylococci. Those that occur in chains are called streptococci.

B. **Bacilli** (singular, *bacillus*) are rod-shaped and usually occur unaggregated (Figure 16.9B). Diplobacilli occur in pairs, and streptobacilli occur in chains.

C. Vibrios resemble commas, while spirilla and spirochetes are spiral-shaped. Spirilla are shorter and less flexible than spirochetes (Figure 16.9C).

Module 16.10 Various structural features contribute to the success of prokaryotes.

A. **External Structures:**

1. The cell wall of prokaryotes provides protection, prevents lysis in a hypotonic environment, and maintains cell shape. Plasmolysis occurs in a hypertonic environment and prevents binary fission. Thus, salting is a method of preserving food.

2. The cell walls of bacteria can be differentially stained with Gram's stain, and most bacteria can be classified as Gram positive (thick peptidoglycan but simple cell wall) or Gram negative (thin peptidoglycan but complex cell wall).

3. There are more pathogenic Gram-negative bacteria than Gram-positive bacteria. This is related to the outer membrane that has a protective effect against the host defense system. The lipopolysaccharides (LPS) of the outer membrane can also be toxic. The thick outer membrane covered in polysaccharides is called a **capsule** and promotes virulence (Figure 16.10A).

4. **Pili** (also called fimbriae; singular, *fimbria*) are protein filaments thinner than bacterial flagella (Figure 16.10B). Pili help bacteria stick to each other or to surfaces in their environments. Sex pili are specialized fimbriae that are used to transfer plasmids from one bacterial cell to another (Review Module 10.22 for the three methods of DNA transfer by bacteria).

B. **Motility:** *Review:* Size, structure, and function of **prokaryotic flagella** differ from those aspects of eukaryotic flagella (Module 4.17). Flagella can be either scattered over a cell or in bunches at one or both ends. They are composed of protein in two parts:

1. External, nonmembrane-bounded filaments without microtubules.

2. Internal, rotating rings embedded in the plasma membrane and cell wall. Motion is produced as they spin on their axes like propellers (Figure 16.10C). Bacteria can move toward or away from stimuli with their flagella.

C. **Reproduction and Adaptation:** With generation times as short as several hours or less, prokaryotic populations can multiply exponentially as long as there is a ready supply of nutrients.

1. Bacteria multiply by binary fission and, under ideal conditions, divide once ever twenty minutes.

2. Some bacteria can survive adverse environmental conditions by producing a thick-walled **endospore** inside the parent cell (Figure 16.10D). Endospores are thick walls around a replicated copy of DNA and are extremely resistant to decomposition or disintegration. They can resist high temperatures; therefore, laboratory personnel use autoclaves to kill endospores (steam at 121°C and 15 pounds of pressure for 15 to 20 minutes).

3. An example of the toughness of endospores is illustrated by those of *Clostridium botulinum,* a bacterium that grows in anaerobic, low-acid environments, such as poorly canned vegetables. The toxin released by colonies of this bacterium causes botulism when consumed by humans.

D. **Internal Organization:** Review Module 4.3 for basic structure of prokaryotes.

1. The membrane of the bacterial cell can perform certain metabolic functions such as cellular respiration and photosynthesis (Figure 16.10E).

2. Prokaryotic ribosomes are smaller than their eukaryotic counterparts, containing slightly different proteins and RNA. These differences can be exploited with antibiotics that block protein synthesis in bacteria and not eukaryotes.

3. Prokaryotic DNA is smaller than eukaryotic DNA (1/1000 the size) and is usually circular. Plasmids are often present and confer extra traits such as antibiotic resistance or special metabolic capabilities. Plasmids are commonly passed between Gram-negative bacteria by conjugation.

Module 16.11 Prokaryotes obtain nourishment in a variety of ways.

A. *Review:* Cellular respiration (Chapter 6) and photosynthesis (Chapter 7).

B. **Types of Nutrition:** Modes of nutrition refer to how organisms obtain energy and carbon (Table 16.11).

1. **Autotrophs** are "self-feeders" that make carbon compounds from the carbon in CO_2 and the energy in sunlight (**photoautotrophs**) or inorganic compounds such as hydrogen sulfide (**chemoautotrophs**).
   Preview: Chemoautotrophic prokaryotes living in hydrothermal vents are discussed in the introduction to Chapter 34.

2. **Heterotrophs** are "other-feeders" that make carbon compounds from the carbon in other organic compounds and obtain energy from those same compounds (**chemoheterotrophs**) or from sunlight (**photoheterotrophs**). *E. coli* is an important chemoheterotroph that lives in the human intestine; it can live on simple sugars alone (Figure 16.11A).

C. **Metabolic Cooperation:** It was originally thought that each bacterial cell foraged for its own existence. Now it is clear that bacterial cells can cooperate metabolically.

1. Cyanobacteria can perform photosynthesis and nitrogen fixation but not simultaneously. Therefore, certain cells in a cyanobacterial colony will perform nitrogen fixation and share the nitrogen with the other cells via filamentous connections.

2. Metabolic cooperation occurs in surface coating **biofilms** (Figure 16.11B). Internal cells use channels for nutrient and waste exchange.

3. Between-species metabolic cooperation can occur. Sulfur-consuming bacteria and methane-consuming archaea coexist in the mud in the ocean floor. An estimated 300 billion kg of methane are consumed each year.

Module 16.12 Archaea thrive in extreme environments—and in other habitats.

A. **Extreme halophiles** thrive in salty places such as the Great Salt Lake (Figure 16.12A).

B. Some **extreme thermophiles** thrive in hot springs, even at temperatures above boiling (for example, deep-ocean vents). Other extreme thermophiles thrive in high-temperature, very-low-pH environments such as those found in Yellowstone National Park (Figure 16.12B).

C. The **methanogens** are a group of anaerobic, methane-producing bacteria that thrive in some vertebrate intestines and in the mud of swamps.

D. Methanogens are the organisms responsible for the production of marsh gas and are a major contributor to flatulence in humans. Methanogens also digest cellulose in the gut of animals such as cattle and deer.

E. Archaea are turning up in environments that are not so extreme. They are found at all depths in the ocean and are in equal proportions to bacteria at depths below 1,000 meters. More research needs to be conducted on this new domain.

Module 16.13 Bacteria include a diverse assemblage of prokaryotes.

A. The domain Bacteria is divided into nine groups based on molecular systematics. Five of the groups are all part of one clade and are called **proteobacteria.** The members of this clade are designated with Greek letters.

B. The alpha subgroup has members that can fix atmospheric nitrogen in the nodules of legumes (*Rizobium,* see Module 32.14). Another important member of this subgroup is *Agrobacterium,* which is used in genetic engineering studies and can produce plant tumors.

C. The gamma subgroup (largest in the proteobacteria clade) has members that can oxidize sulfur (Figure 16.13A) and is commonly found in the intestines of animals. This group has many pathogens, including *Salmonella typhi* and *Vibrio cholera. Escherichia coli,* the most-studied bacterial species, is normally found in the human intestines, but some *E. coli* serotypes can be deadly (see Module 16.14).

D. The delta proteobacteria include the slime-secreting myxobacteria that aggregate to form fruiting bodies during times of stress, releasing resistant spores. Also in this group are the *Bdellovibrios* that prey on other bacteria by attacking them at high rates of speed (Figure 16.13B).

E. **Chlamydias** form a second group and are responsible for causing blindness and a common sexually transmitted disease called nongonococcal urethritis.

F. A group of spiral bacteria move through their environment like corkscrews. Internal filaments rotate, causing **spirochetes** to spin rapidly (see Module 16.9). Most spirochetes are free-living, but others such as *Treponema pallidum* and *Borrelia burgdorferi* are pathogens causing syphilis and Lyme disease, respectively.

G. A large collection of bacteria called **Gram-positive bacteria** are as diverse as the proteobacteria. A subgroup of Gram-positive bacteria was once mistaken for fungus and is called actinomycetes. This group is found in the soil and is a major source of antibiotics (Figure 16.13C). Gram-positive bacteria also include commonly recognized pathogens such as *Staphylococcus* and *Streptococcus.* The smallest living organism is in this group and is called *Mycoplasma.* It has no cell wall and is only 0.1 micrometers (μm) in diameter (the size of a virus).

H. The **cyanobacteria** are photosynthetic bacteria that are capable of generating oxygen during photosynthesis. Their ancestors led to the oxygen-rich atmosphere we enjoy today (see Figure 16.13D, the chapter introduction, and Module 16.11).

Module 16.14 Connection: Some bacteria cause disease.

A. Bacterial **pathogens** cause about half of all known human diseases and are responsible for diseases in all other eukaryotes. Approximately 2 to 3 million people die each year from TB caused by *Mycobacterium tuberculosis,* and another 2 million people die from diarrhea caused by a variety of bacteria species.

B. Bacterial can cause disease by growth on and destruction of tissues, but they are more likely to cause disease by the release of poisons called **exotoxins** and **endotoxins.** Exotoxins are proteins released by bacteria either by secretion or when the bacteria die. Exotoxins are among the deadliest poisons known. A good example of an exotoxin is the botulinum toxin produced by the bacteria *Clostridium botulinum.*

C. *Staphylococcus aureus* is a normal microbiota found in moist skin folds, but when it grows inside a person, the exotoxin it produces can cause serious disease, such as toxic shock syndrome (Figure 16.14A). *S. aureus* can also cause food poisoning and the skin to slough off as if it has been burned (scalded skin syndrome).

D. Harmless bacteria can develop pathogenic strains. For example, *E. coli* O157:H7, normally found in cattle, may have obtained the pathogenic genes via horizontal transfer and can now produce an exotoxin that causes bloody diarrhea and may lead to death. The best prevention is to avoid undercooked meat and contaminated vegetables.

E. Endotoxins are made of glycolipids (LPSs) found in the outer membrane of Gram-negative bacteria. The signs and symptoms from all endotoxins are the same: chills, fever, aches, weakness and decreased blood pressure that can lead to shock. Species of *Salmonella* produce endotoxins that cause food poisoning and typhoid fever.

F. Sanitation, the use of antibiotics, and education are three of our defenses against bacterial diseases.

G. However, antibiotic-resistant bacteria have evolved and are now a major health issue (Module 13.13).

H. The cause of **Lyme disease,** *Borrelia burgdorferi,* is carried by a tick and elicits a distinctive set of symptoms and potential disorders (Figure 16.14B). Prevention of Lyme disease is best accomplished through public education.

Module 16.15 Connection: Bacteria can be used as biological weapons.

A. Biological organisms as weapons have played a part throughout history. As recently as October 2001, anthrax endospores (*Bacillus anthracis*) were sent through the mail to members of the media and U.S. Senate (Figure 16.15). Victims of bubonic plague (the causative agent, *Yersinia pestis*) were hurled into the ranks of opposing armies during the Middle Ages in Europe. Other examples abound.

B. The anthrax scare we experienced in the fall of 2001 was horrifying (five Americans died) yet it could have been worse. Anthrax is not as deadly as some other infectious diseases such as Ebola or smallpox. The route of infection determines the mortality rate. Cutaneous anthrax is relatively easy to treat, while pulmonary anthrax is treatable if detected early; however, it can be deadly because it is usually ignored as a common cold until it's too late.

C. An anthrax vaccine is available for personnel in harm's way, such as military personnel and foreign diplomats. Widespread vaccination programs would be too expensive and impractical. The complete genome of *B. anthracis* has been sequenced in an effort to produce new vaccines and antibiotics.

D. The United States started its own biological weapons program in 1943 and, after developing high-quality bioweapons, decided that the program was too repulsive to continue. The program was dismantled in 1969, and in 1975, the United States signed the Biological Weapons Convention that banned any future bioweapon programs. Several nations ignored the treaty even though they had signed it. The solution is diplomacy.

Module 16.16 Connection: Prokaryotes help recycle chemicals and clean up the environment.

A. Because of the variety of metabolic capabilities, prokaryotes play many beneficial roles in cycling elements among living and nonliving components of environments.

B. *Preview:* Chemical cycles are discussed more fully in Chapter 37.

C. Only prokaryotes are capable of nitrogen fixation, the conversion of N_2 gas to nitrogen in amino acids. Important nitrogen fixers include many cyanobacteria and many chemoheterotrophs in the soil.
Preview: Many plants depend on prokaryotes for nitrogen (Modules 32.13 and 32.14).

D. Bacteria can be used to clean polluted water, soil, or air. This process is referred to as **bioremediation.** The breakdown of organic wastes by decomposers is one of the most common beneficial roles of prokaryotes.

E. Prokaryotic decomposers are part of the aerobic and anaerobic communities of organisms functioning in sewage-treatment plants (Figure 16.16A).

F. Natural bacteria are encouraged, or recombinant strains are used, to decompose the remains of oil spills on beaches (Figure 16.16B).

G. Species of *Thiobacillus,* autotrophs that obtain energy from oxidizing ions in minerals, can be used to help remove toxic metals from old mines and industrial waste sites. However, their use in this role is limited since their metabolism adds sulfuric acid to the water. Other bacterial species are used to extract gold and copper from low-grade ores.

III. Protists

Module 16.17 The eukaryotic cell probably originated as a community of prokaryotes.

A. The fossil record indicates that the first eukaryotes evolved approximately 2.1 bya. There are two theories of how the membrane-enclosed organelles arose.

B. The first theory is that the endomembrane system is thought to have evolved by **membrane infolding** and resulted in the specialization of internal membranes into membrane-bounded organelles (Figure 16.17A) except mitochondria and chloroplasts. *Review:* The endomembrane system is described in Modules 4.5–4.13.

C. The second theory involves the concept of **symbiosis.** The close association between two organisms of different species is referred to as symbiosis. **Endosymbiosis** is the likely basis of the origin of mitochondria and chloroplasts (Figure 16.17B), with mitochondria evolving first. The ancestral mitochondria may have been small heterotrophic prokaryotes, and similarly, the ancestral chloroplasts may have been small photosynthetic prokaryotes.

D. Several lines of evidence support the endosymbiotic hypothesis. Mitochondria and chloroplasts are similar in size and shape to prokaryotes and include bacterial-type DNA, RNA, and ribosomes. These organelles replicate in eukaryotic cytoplasm in a manner resembling binary fission. The inner, but not the outer, membranes of these organelles contain enzymes and electron transport molecules characteristic of prokaryotes, not eukaryotes.
NOTE: Endosymbiosis is common today among protists and/or prokaryotes.

E. Evidence from RNA gene analysis indicates that eukaryotic mitochondria are closely related to alpha proteobacteria and that chloroplasts are most closely related to cyanobacteria. Eukaryotes may have obtained a nucleus from an endosymbiotic relationship with an ancient archaeal cell. Still, other evidence indicates that horizontal gene transfer may have played a significant role in the acquisition of the eukaryotic genome.

Module 16.18 Protists are an extremely diverse assortment of eukaryotes.

A. **Protists** are diverse and likely represent several kingdoms within Domain Eukarya. Protists are found in all habitats but are most common in aquatic environments (Figure 16.18).

B. As a group, protists are nutritionally diverse. Photosynthetic protists are referred to as **"algae,"** a term with no taxonomic meaning. Another useful (but informal) term describing a protist is *protozoan.* Protozoa are heterotrophs that eat bacteria and other protists. Still other protists are fungus-like, obtaining their nutrients by absorption.

C. Protists are more complex than prokaryotes because they are eukaryotes and have all the complexity of any plant or animal cell: a nucleus, organelles, cilia, and flagella with the typical 9 + 2 microtubule pattern.

D. In spite of the protists' complexities, they are still considered the simplest eukaryotes, as most are single-celled organisms.

   E. In the survey that follows, protists' taxonomic groups are presented based on the most current information obtained from molecular and cellular studies.

Module 16.19 A tentative phylogeny of eukaryotes includes multiple clades of protists.

   A. Like all scientific inquires, the phylogenic studies of protist is a work in progress. The phylogenetic tree shows the Kingdoms for plants, animals, fungi, and the groups that were once part of the Protista kingdom (Figure 16.19).

   B. Ignore the complexity of the figure, and recognize the evolutionary relationships that are represented for the protists.

Module 16.20 Diplomonads and euglenozoans include some flagellated parasites.

   A. **Diplomonads** contain two nuclei and multiple flagella and are considered the most ancient living eukaryotic lineage. *Giardia intestinalis* is a good example of this group (Figure 16.20A). What makes *Giardia* particularly interesting is its lack of mitochondria. Drinking water contaminated with *Giardia* without boiling it first will lead to intestinal cramps and severe diarrhea.

   B. **Euglenozoans** are a multiform clade containing photosynthetic autotrophs, heterotrophs, and pathogenic parasites. A pathogenic parasite in this group is the *Trypanosoma* (Figure 16.20B). It is spread by a bite from the tsetse fly and causes African sleeping sickness. Trypanosomes escape a host's immune response by frequently changing the molecular structure of the cell membranes (a process called antigenic variation).

Module 16.21 Alveolates have sacs beneath the plasma membrane and include dinoflagellates, apicomplexans, and ciliates.

   A. This clade of protists, called **alveolates,** has a membrane-bound sac under the plasma membrane.

   B. **Dinoflagellates** are uniquely shaped phytoplankton, found in both fresh and marine water, and move by two flagella in perpendicular grooves (Figure 16.21A). Some dinoflagellates are responsible for toxin-releasing blooms in warm coastal waters that are known as red tides. The toxins can cause extensive fish kills and can be harmful to humans.

   C. **Apicomplexans** have an apical structure designed to penetrate the host, and some are parasites that can cause serious human disease. *Plasmodium* is an apicomplexan that is the cause of malaria, a parasitic infection afflicting approximately 300 million people with about 2 million deaths each year. Plasmodium species are spread by mosquitoes; reproduce inside red blood cells; and cause the cells to lyse, resulting in fever and severe anemia (Figure 16.21B).

   D. **Ciliates** are the third group in the alveolates. They are a very diverse group that uses cilia for movement and for feeding. Most are free swimming, including the very common *Paramecium.* Unique to ciliates is that they have a macronucleus that performs the daily functions of the cell and micronuclei involved in reproduction. The species *Stentor* has a macronucleus that looks like a string of beads (Figure 16.12C).

Module 16.22 Stramenopiles are named for their "hairy" flagella and include water molds, diatoms, and brown algae.

   A. **Stramenopiles** are a group of protists that have flagella covered with many hair-like projections. Each hairy flagellum is associated with a smooth flagellum. This group includes heterotrophs and certain algae.

B. **Water molds** are not fungus, although they were originally classified as fungus (Figure 16.22A). They decompose dead plants and animals much like fungus and can be parasitic to fish. Downy mildew is a plant parasite related to water molds and caused the potato blight famine in Ireland during the mid 1800s.

C. **Diatoms** are unicellular, with uniquely shaped and sculptured silica walls. They are common components of watery environments (Figure 16.22B). In terms of being a food source, diatoms are to marine animals as plants are to land animals. Fossilized diatoms make up thick sediments of diatomaceous earth, which can be used either for filtering or as an abrasive.

D. **Brown algae** are the largest algae. Most species of brown algae are marine, all are multicellular, and the brown color is due to pigments in the chloroplast. Brown algae (along with red and green algae) are commonly referred to as seaweed. Brown algae are used as a food in some cultures. Large underwater forests of brown algae are called **kelp** (Figure 16.22C). Kelp can grow up to 100 meters and have the appearance of true plants but lack the typical plant structures. Kelp forests are used as feeding grounds by many marine species.

Module 16.23 Amoebozoans have pseudopodia and include amoebas and slime molds.

A. **Amoebas** move and feed by means of **pseudopodia.** Molecular analysis reveals that amoebas cross many taxonomic groups. Therefore, this section will cover only the **amoebozoans.** This group includes free-living and parasitic amoebas, and the slime molds. All members of this group have lobe-shaped **pseudopodia** (singular, *pseudopodium*).

B. Amoebas capture their prey by encasing them in their pseudopodia and engulfing them into food vacuoles (Figure 16.23A; see Module 4.11). One species of parasitic amoebas can cause dysentery, which kills approximately 100,000 people each year.

C. **Plasmodium slime molds** are brightly colored, multinucleated, branched, single-celled organisms that are commonly found anywhere there is decaying organic matter. The branching pattern seen in Figure 16.23B increases the surface area. Cytoplasmic streaming is used to distribute nutrients and can be seen under a microscope. When growing conditions are not optimal, the plasmodium differentiates into spores. When conditions are again favorable the spores release (haploid) cells that fuse to form (diploid) zygotes, and the life cycle continues (review Module 8.14).

D. **Cellular slime molds** are amoeboid cells that feed on bacteria in rotting vegetation. The three stages of the *Dictyostelium* life cycle are depicted in Figure 16.23C. Usually *Dictyostelium* exists as amoebas, but when the food supply runs out, the individual cells mass into a slug-like, multicellular aggregate. The slugs wander about for a short time; then some cells form a stalk, while others form reproductive spores above. Because *Dictyostelium* has a simple developmental sequence, it has played a role in determining the genetic mechanisms and chemical changes of cellular differentiation.

Module 16.24 Red algae and green algae are the closest relatives of land plants.

A. Molecular evidence (and other evidence) supports the following phylogenetic scenario:

1. More than 1 bya, a heterotroph developed a symbiotic relationship with a cyanobacterial cell.

2. The descendents of this cell evolved into the red and green algae.

3. Another endosymbiosis of red algae led to the alveolates and the stramenopiles.

4. Approximately 475 mya, green algae ancestors gave rise to the land plants.

B. **Red algae** are most common in tropical marine waters. Most are soft-bodied, but encrusted species are important in building coral reefs (Figure 16.24A). The red color in red algae comes from accessory pigments that mask the green color of chlorophyll.

C. The **green algae** are common inhabitants of fresh water and include a large variety of forms. Green algae can be either unicellular such as *Chlamydomonas* or multicellular such as *Volvox* (Figure 16.24B). Some multicellular green algae are large enough to qualify as seaweed.

D. The reproductive pattern of some algae (for example *ulva*, sea lettuce) involves **alternation of generations,** alternating between haploid **gametophytes** that give rise to gametes directly by mitosis and diploid **sporophytes** that give rise to flagellated spores by meiosis (Figure 16.24C).

Module 16.25 Multicellularity evolved several times in eukaryotes.

A. Single-celled protists are more complex than prokaryotes and, thus, are more diverse in form. The next big breakthrough in structural organization came when multicellular organisms developed.

B. Most multicellular organisms, including seaweed, slime molds, fungi, plants, and animals, are characterized by the differentiation of cells that perform different activities within one organism.

C. A hypothetical scenario for the evolution of a multicellular plant or animal from an early protist is presented below:
  1. Formation of ancestral colonies, with all cells the same.
  2. Specialization and cooperation among different cells within the colony.
  3. Differentiation of sexual cells from the somatic cells (Figure 16.25).

D. Multicellular organisms develop from a single cell (zygote) and contain all the genetic information necessary to develop all the other cells of the organisms. A good example of colonial protists that display specialized cells is *Volvox*. Truly multicellular organisms have a wide array of specialized cells for waste removal, nutrient acquisition, reproduction, gas exchange, protection, and structural maintenance.

E. There are three distinct eukaryotic lineages that led to multicellular organisms:
  1. One that led to brown algae.
  2. One that led to fungi and animals.
  3. One that led to red and green algae and plants.

F. Through the use of fossil records and molecular techniques, the earliest multicellular eukaryotes are thought to have been present on Earth about 1.2 billion years ago.

G. The fossil records indicate an abundance of multicellular organisms (red algae and invertebrates) dating from 600 mya. These organisms were red algae and animals resembling corals, jellyfish, and worms. Other kinds of multicellular algae probably existed as well, but their remains are yet to be found in the fossil record.

H. A mass extinction occurred between the Precambrian and Paleozoic eras. Up until 500 mya, life was aquatic and represented by diverse animals and multicellular algae, along with ancestral protists and prokaryotes. Around 500 mya, life began to move onto land as green algae. The next chapter traces the evolution of plants.

Class Activities

1. Based on the information in the text (and additional outside sources if you so desire) ask your students to first consider the basis of the recognition of protists and then have them develop a phylogenetic tree of the protistan groups discussed in the text. Have them consider the question of whether or not the different types of seaweeds should be classified as protists.

Transparency Acetates

Figure 16.1C	A clock analogy for some key events in the early history of Earth and its life
Figure 16.3B	The synthesis of organic molecules in the Miller-Urey apparatus
Figure 16.5	A hypothesis for the origin of the first genes
Figure 16.6A	The beginnings of cooperation
Figure 16.6C	Cooperation among membrane-enclosed macromolecules
Table 16.8	Differences between Bacteria and Archaea
Figure 16.10C	Prokaryotic flagella
Table 16.11	Nutritional classification of organisms
Figure 16.16A	The trickling filter system at a sewage treatment plant
Figure 16.17	A model of the origin of eukaryotes (Layer 1)
Figure 16.17	A model of the origin of eukaryotes (Layer 2)
Figure 16.19	A tentative phylogeny of eukaryotes
Figure 16.24C	A multicellular green alga: *Ulva* (sea lettuce) and its life cycle
Figure 16.25	A model for the evolution of a multicellular organism from a unicellular protist

Reviewing the Concepts, page 340: Nutritional modes of prokaryotes

Reviewing the Concepts, page 340: A eukaryotic cell

Connecting the Concepts, page 340: Stages that may have led to the origin of life

Connecting the Concepts, page 341: Important events in the history of Earth and its life

Media

See the beginning of this book for a complete description of all media available for instructors and students. Animations and videos are available in the Campbell Image Presentation Library. Media Activities and Thinking as a Scientist investigations are available on the student CD-ROM and website.

Animations and Videos	Module Number
Prokaryotic Flagella Video	16.10
Cyanobacteria Video	16.13
Euglena Video	16.20
Euglena Motion Video	16.20
Stentor Video	16.21
Stentor Ciliate Movement Video	16.21

Vorticella Cilia Video	16.21
Vorticella Detail Video	16.21
Vorticella Habitat Video	16.21
Diatoms Moving Video	16.22
Various Diatoms Video	16.22
Amoeba Video	16.23
Amoeba Pseudopodia Video	16.23
Plasmodial Slime Mold Video	16.23
Plasmodial Slime Mold Streaming Video	16.23
Dinoflagellate Video	16.23
Volvox Colony Video	16.24
Volvox Daughter Video	16.24
Volvox Flagella Video	16.24
Chlamydomonas Video	16.24

Activities and Thinking as a Scientist

Module Number

Web/CD Activity 16A: *The History of Life*	16.1
Web/CD Thinking as a Scientist: *How Might Conditions on Early Earth Have Created Life?*	16.3
Web/CD Activity 16B: *Prokaryotic Cell Structure and Function*	16.10
Web/CD Thinking as a Scientist: *What Are the Modes of Nutrition in Prokaryotes?*	16.11
Web/CD Activity 16C: *Diversity of Prokaryotes*	16.13
Web/CD Thinking as a Scientist: *What Kinds of Protists Are Found in Various Habitats?*	16.24

CHAPTER 17

Plants, Fungi, and the Colonization of Land

Teaching Objectives

Introduction   Explain the significance of mycorrhiza to plant health.

17.1   Describe the evidence linking the charophyceans to plants.

Plant Evolution and Diversity

17.2   Compare the structures of multicellular algae and plants. Explain how plants are adapted to life on land.

17.3   Compare the bryophytes, seedless vascular plants, gymnosperms, and angiosperms.

17.3   Describe the four key plant adaptations for life on land.

Alternation of Generations and Plant Life Cycles

17.4   Describe the alternation of generation life cycle. Explain why it appears that this cycle has evolved independently in algae and land plants.

17.5–17.6   Describe the key events of the moss and fern life cycles.

17.7   Explain how coal was formed.

17.7   Describe the conditions in which the gymnosperms became dominant.

17.8   Describe the stages of the pine tree life cycle.

17.9   Describe the parts of a flower and explain their functions.

17.10   Describe the stages of the angiosperm tree life cycle.

17.11   Describe examples of angiosperm adaptations that promote seed dispersal.

17.12   Describe the significance of angiosperms to humans.

17.13   Explain how flowers are adapted to attract pollinators. Define the term coevolution.

17.14   Describe the human impact on plant diversity. Explain the significance of this loss for humanity.

Fungi

17.15   Distinguish between fungi and plants. Relate the structure of fungi to their functions.

17.16   Describe and compare the asexual and sexual life cycles of fungi.

17.17   Describe and compare the five fungal phyla.

17.17   Describe the characteristics of the last common ancestor of fungi and animals.

17.18   Compare the life cycles of black bread mold and a mushroom.

17.19   Explain how parasitic fungi harm plants and animals.

17.20   Describe the structure and characteristics of lichens.

17.21   Describe a few mutualistic relationships between fungi and animals.

17.22   Describe the positive ecological and practical roles of fungi.

Key Terms

absorption
alternation of generations
angiosperms
anther
apical meristems
arbuscular mycorrhizal
  fungi
ascomycetes
basidiomycetes
bryophytes
carpel
charophyceans
chytrids
club fungi
coevolution
cuticle
dikaryotic phase
embryophytes
fossil fuels

gametangia
gametophyte
glomeromycetes
gymnosperms
heterokaryotic stage
hyphae
imperfect fungi
kingdom Fungi
kingdom Plantae
lichens
lignin
mold
mycelium
mycorrhiza
mycosis
ovary
ovules
petals
phloem

pollen
pollen grain
pollination
sac fungi
seed
seedless vascular plants
sepals
sporangia
spore
sporophyte
stamen
stigma
stomata
vascular plants
vascular tissue
xylem
yeast
zygomycetes
zygote fungi

Word Roots

bryo- = moss; **-phyte** = plant (*bryophytes:* the mosses, liverworts, and hornworts; a group of nonvascular plants that inhabit the land but lack many of the terrestrial adaptations of vascular plants)

di- = two; **-karyo** = nucleus (*dikaryotic:* a mycelium with two haploid nuclei per cell, one from each parent)

gymno- = naked; **-sperm** = seed (*gymnosperm:* a vascular plant that bears naked seeds not enclosed in any specialized chambers)

Lecture Outline

Introduction *Plants and Fungi—A Beneficial Partnership*

  A. The lives of modern plants and fungi are intertwined.
    1. We depend on plants and, indirectly, fungi for much of our food.
    2. Plants are often harmed by fungi.
    3. On the other hand, mycorrhizal fungi aid nearly all plants in the wild.
  B. Mycorrhizae are rootlike structures made of both fungi and plants. The fungi help plants obtain nutrients and water, and they protect plant roots from parasites, in exchange for food the plants make by photosynthesis.
    Preview: Mycorrhizae are also discussed in Module 32.11.
    1. Modern agricultural practices, such as killing the parasitic fungi with fungicides, may disrupt mycorrhizal fungi, forcing the need for fertilizer.

2. Some farmers try to reduce the effects of the addition of fungicides and alternate fungicides by adding mycorrhizal fungus.

C. Plants and fungi evolved together as life moved onto land. This observation is supported by the presence of mycorrhizae in the earliest plant fossils.

I. Plant Evolution and Diversity

Module 17.1 Plants evolved from green algae.

A. Plants may have evolved from green algae about 500 mya. The ancestor is not known, but analysis of nucleic acid sequences, cell structure, and biochemistry indicate that a group of green algae, the **charophyceans** (Figure 17.1A, a simple charophycean), and plants shared a common ancestor (Figure 17.1B, a complex charophycean).

B. The oldest plant fossils indicate that the correct adaptations necessary for life on land appeared about 475 mya. Early plants thrived on moist shorelines where space was essentially limitless, sunlight was unlimited, and CO_2 was abundant. Initially there were few, if any, herbivorous animals and plant pathogens.

Module 17.2 Plants have adaptations for life on land.

A. *Review:* In the two-kingdom system, Linnaeus classified algae as plants. In the five-kingdom system, algae are protists (Module 16.18). Plants (like trees, grass, and flowers) are in the kingdom **Plantae** in either system.

B. The definition of plants as multicellular, eukaryotic photosynthesizers also describes multicellular algae (Modules 16.22 and 16.24).

C. Multicellular algae, such as sea lettuce, are the most complex algae and are adapted for life in water, while plants are adapted for life on land (Figure 17.2A). For the multicellular algae, the resources, including water, carbon dioxide, and minerals, are in direct contact with their tissues, and waste products can be washed away. Water supports and suspends the body of the alga. Holdfasts anchor the alga, and all other parts can be photosynthetic. Water provides a means of dispersal for gametes and offspring.

D. Life on land imposes problems. Water and nutrients are concentrated in the ground, while carbon dioxide and light are most abundant above the ground. Air provides no support against the force of gravity and will dry out reproductive cells.

E. Adaptations to a terrestrial environment in plants include the following:

1. **Obtaining resources from two locations:** Plants have three organs (roots, stems, and leaves) that are involved with resource acquisition. Most water and nutrients are obtained from the soil via the roots (in association with mycorrhizae). Roots also provide a means to anchor the plant to the ground. Stems support the leaves that obtain CO_2 and light for photosynthesis. Growth of both the roots and shoots (stems) occurs at the **apical meristems.** Vascular tissues are used to distribute water and nutrients throughout the plant (Figure 17.2B). **Xylem,** which is made of dead cells, transports water and minerals up from the roots. **Phloem,** which is made of living cells, transports sugars.

2. **Supporting the plant body:** Plants contain a chemical called **lignin,** which thickens and strengthens the cell walls of vascular tissues that are involved in supporting the plant structure.

3. **Maintaining moisture:** In an effort to reduce moisture loss, a waxy coating called a **cuticle** covers the leaves and stems. Gases cannot easily pass through the cuticle, so small pores called **stomata** (singular, stoma) are used for the exchange of CO_2 and dioxygen. Two cells regulate the closing and opening of the stomata, open during the day and closed at night to reduce water loss.

4. **Reproducing on land:** Desiccation and dispersal are two key elements that must be overcome by land plants. **Gametangia** (singular, gametangium) are protective structures of cells that contain the eggs and prevent drying out. The sperm either swim to the egg through a thin film of water or are brought to the egg in the form of pollen. Once fertilized, the developing embryo remains attached to the parent plant for nourishment. Thus plants are classified as **embryophytes.** All plants alternate between two life cycles, haploid and diploid. Some plants produce seeds and rely on the wind or animals for dispersal. Some plants produce structures called **sporangia** (singular, sporangium), which contain haploid cells called a spores. A **spore** can produce a new plant without being fertilized.

F. A functional definition of plants is a multicellular, photosynthetic eukaryote with multiple adaptations for land including apical meristems, dependent embryos, multicellular gametangia, alternating haploid and diploid generations, and spores produced in sporangia.

Module 17.3 Plant diversity provides clues to the evolutionary history of the plant kingdom.

A. Plant phylogeny shows branching of several plant lineages, reflecting major evolutionary steps. These are previewed here, and details are added in the modules that follow (Figure 17.3A).

B. The first lineage of plants arose, most likely from ancestral charophyceans, approximately 475 mya. This lineage gave rise to modern **bryophytes,** a group of plants that includes liverworts, hornworts, and mosses. The moss lineage most likely gave rise to vascular plants.

C. Like other plants, bryophytes have a cuticle and embryos that develop within gametangia. However, many bryophytes lack vascular tissue for water conduction and internal support. Like their algal ancestors, bryophytes have flagellated sperm and depend on water for reproduction. The bryophytes are grouped together as nonvascular plants but are not one clade (Figure 17.3B).

D. Vascular plants originated approximately 420 mya from the moss lineage. The development of lignin allowed the plants to stand upright. There are two clades that are informally grouped as seedless vascular plants and include the lycophytes (club mosses, Figure 17.3C) and the widespread pterophytes (ferns, Figure 17.3C).

E. Ferns are a modern example of a seedless vascular plant and use flagellated sperm to fertilize the egg and a haploid spore for dispersal. The leaves (fronds) develop from stems that grow along the ground (Figure 17.3C). Ferns are found in shady temperate forests and are most diverse in the tropics.

F. Seed plants evolved around 360 mya and today make up more than 90% of all living plant species. There are two adaptations responsible for the success of this group.

1. **Seeds** that provide the embryonic plant with a protective coating and a food supply. Seeds promote dispersal to diverse habitats without drying out.

2. These plants also produce **pollen,** vehicles that transfer nonflagellated sperm to the female parts of plants.

G. The earliest seed plants to appear were the **gymnosperms** (naked seed). The name of these plants is based on their seeds not being contained within a specialized chamber. The largest living group of gymnosperms is the conifers (cone bearing trees) such as pine, spruce, and fir. Other gymnosperms include the cycads and ginkgo tree.

H. Flowering plants (**angiosperms**) evolved from the seed plant line approximately 140 mya. Flowers are complex reproductive structures that develop a seed in a protective chamber. The majority of modern plant species (257,000) are angiosperms.

I. Summary of land plant adaptations:

1. Dependent embryos

2. Vascular tissue with lignin

3. Production of seeds

4. Reproductive structures called flowers
    Preview: Angiosperm structure is discussed in detail in Chapter 31.

II. Alternation of Generations and Plant Life Cycles

Module 17.4 Haploid and diploid generations alternate in plant life cycles.

A. *Review:* Ulva life cycle (Figure 16.24C); human life cycle (Figure 8.13).

B. Plant life cycles alternate between multicellular, diploid (2n), and haploid (n) adults, unlike animals that are diploid after fertilization and as adults produce single-celled haploid gametes (Figure 17.4). The alternating life cycle of plants is referred to as an **alternation of generations.**

C. A **gametophyte** is the haploid generation of plants and produces gametes (sperm and eggs) by mitosis. Fertilization of the egg by sperm results in a diploid plant.

D. A **sporophyte** is the diploid generation of plants and produces spores by meiosis.

E. Some algae have an alternating life cycle (ulva); however, the closest ancestor to plants (the charophyceans) does not. It is, therefore, thought that plants developed this trait independently.
   NOTE: Compare the mosses (dominant gametophytes, semiparasitic sporophytes, flagellated sperm) to the conifers or flowering plants (dominant sporophytes, semiparasitic, reduced gametophytes, pollen).

Module 17.5 Mosses have a dominant gametophyte.

A. The green growth we see consists mostly of gametophytes (Figure 17.3B).
   NOTE: Adult gametophytes consist of nonvascular stems and leaves and threadlike holdfasts. For water and minerals, they depend on rain or on water flowing along the stem from the ground surface.

B. The moss life cycle is a five-step process (Figure 17.5):

1. Gametophytes produce sperm and eggs in male and female gametangia on separate plants. Flagellated sperm require a film of water in which to swim to female gametangia where fertilization takes place.

2. The zygote remains in the female gametangium.

3. The zygote remains attached and, dividing by mitosis, develops into a sporophyte.

4. Meiosis occurs in the sporangium and produces haploid spores at the tip of the sporophyte stalk. Spores are released from the sporangium.

5. The spores develop into haploid gametophyte plants by mitosis.
   NOTE: Adult sporophytes lose their chlorophyll and become more dependent on the female gametophytes. The sporangia are adapted to dispersing spores by means of movable teeth around the sporangium opening, on wet/dry cycles.

Module 17.6 Ferns, like most plants, have a dominant sporophyte.

NOTE: Ferns have underground stems with small roots, and all parts are vascularized. The fronds are the principal organs of photosynthesis.

A. The fern fronds we see are sporophytes. The five-step life cycle of a fern is similar to a moss (Figure 17.6):

1. Gametophytes produce flagellated sperm and eggs (like mosses). The sperm need a thin film of water to reach the egg.

2. Like mosses, fern zygotes remain in the female gametangium.

3. The zygote develops into an independent sporophyte.

4. The sporangia in clusters on the frond's underside (yellow dots) produce haploid spores by meiosis.

5. Spores are dispersed by wind and grow into small, heart-shaped gametophytes by mitosis.

   NOTE: Fern sporangia have a unique mechanism to release their spores. As the sporangia dry out, thick-walled cells along the "backs" of the sporangia pull the thin-walled "front" cells into tension. In a fraction of a second, the front cells rupture, scattering the spores into the air.

B. Today, about 95% of all plants (including seed plants) have a dominant sporophyte generation.

C. Seeded plants (as sporophytes) house the gametophyte and all reproductive stages (spores, eggs, sperm, zygote, and embryo).

Module 17.7 Seedless plants dominated vast "coal forests."

A. Two clades of seedless vascular plants once where the dominant plant on Earth. The mosses and ferns, collectively called the lycophytes, are illustrated in the painting in Figure 17.7.

B. During the Carboniferous period (360 to 290 mya) vast forests grew in tropical, swampy areas over what are now Eurasia and North America.

C. The forests included dominant lycophytes (giant woody trees) and horsetails (both seedless plants more primitive than ferns), and tree ferns (not seen in the figure).

D. The compressed remains of these forests survive as deposits of coal and other **fossil fuels.** Coal was pivotal to the industrial revolution and is still used today to generate electricity. The vast Carboniferous forest removed large quantities of CO_2, causing global cooling. Now we are adding the CO_2 back to the atmosphere by burning fossil fuels, causing global warming.

E. At the end of the Carboniferous period, the climate turned cooler and drier, providing the conditions for further plant evolution. The evolution of pollen was key to the adaptation of seed plants to dry land.

F. The most successful of the early seed plants were the gymnosperms. They grew alongside seedless plants in Carboniferous swamps. Gymnosperms survived the drying of these swamps and became the dominant type of plant. Gymnosperms (particularly the cycads) became the main food for herbivorous dinosaurs starting in the Mesozoic era.

G. **Conifers** (cone-bearing plants) are the most successful of several groups of gymnosperms because they are adapted to dry-cool climates. Conifers have needle-like leaves with a small surface area and a thick cuticle, which help them resist drying. Most conifers do not shed their leaves and, thus, are able to photosynthesize year round.

Module 17.8 A pine tree is a sporophyte with tiny gametophytes in its cones.

    A. Cones are a significant adaptation to land, protecting all reproductive structures: sporangia, microscopic gametophytes, and zygotes. The seven steps of the pine life cycle are presented in Figure 17.8.

        1. Female cones are larger. Scales bear a pair of **ovules** (sporangia with a covering, or integument). Within the ovule, one of the four products of meiosis develops into a tiny, multicellular, "female" gametophyte.

        2. Male cones are smaller, and scales bear many sporangia that make spores by meiosis. Spores develop into tiny male gametophytes **(pollen grains),** each consisting of a few cells. Pollen grains house the cells that will develop into sperm.
           NOTE: The particular pollen grains in Figure 17.8 are typical of the pine family: The central cell and cells within it compose the gametophyte. The two lateral "cells" are outgrowths of the cell wall that function as floats.

        3. Pollen is dispersed by wind. **Pollination** occurs when a pollen grain lands near an ovule and grows into it.

        4. Meiosis occurs in the ovule where a haploid spore cell begins to develop into the female gametophyte. Months later, a few of the female gametophyte's cells inside the ovule function as eggs.

        5. The pollen tube delivers a male gametophyte's nucleus (functioning as a nonflagellated sperm) to fertilize an egg. Fertilization occurs a year or more after pollination.

        6. The zygote develops into the embryonic sporophyte, and the remaining ovule develops into the other parts of the seed (the integument becomes the seed coat, and the female gametophyte becomes a food supply).

        7. Seed dispersal is by wind or animal. Under favorable conditions, the seed germinates and the embryo grows into a tree.

    B. All the reproductive stages are held in the cone, and the development of the ovule is the key adaptation. An ovule is a protective device for all the female steps and is the site of pollination, fertilization, and embryonic development. The ovule eventually becomes a seed.

Module 17.9 The flower is the centerpiece of angiosperm reproduction.

Preview: The life cycle of the flowering plant (Modules 31.9–31.15).

    A. Flowers expose an angiosperm's sexual parts and are the sites for pollination and fertilization (Figure 17.9A).

    B. Flowers are short stems with the following modified leaves: **sepals,** to protect flower buds; **petals,** to attract animal pollinators; **stamens,** the male parts (holding the **anthers,** in which pollen develops); **carpels,** the female parts (consisting of sticky **stigma** to trap pollen; and the **ovary,** which bears ovules and later develops into fruit) (Figure 17.9B).

Module 17.10 The angiosperm plant is a sporophyte with gametophytes in its flowers (Figure 17.10).

    A. The life cycle of the angiosperm is very similar to that of the gymnosperm (review Figure 17.8). The main plant is the sporophyte, and the gametophytes live on the sporophyte. Unlike gymnosperms, which have cones, angiosperms have flowers and package the seeds in fruit.

    B. Flowers protect all microscopic reproductive structures: sporangia, male and female gametophytes, and zygotes. The seven steps of the angiosperm life cycle are presented in Figure 17.10.

1. Meiosis in the anthers leads to haploid spores that undergo mitosis and develop into the male gametophytes (pollen grains).

2. Meiosis in the ovules leads to haploid spores that undergo mitosis and develop into the female gametophytes, each of which produces an egg inside the ovules.

3. Pollen is dispersed by either wind or insects. Pollination occurs when a pollen grain lands on the stigma. The pollen grows into the ovary and delivers one nucleus (again functioning as a nonflagellated sperm) to the egg nucleus in the ovule.

4. Fertilization usually occurs after pollination to form a zygote.

5. Following fertilization, the zygote develops into the embryonic sporophyte in the seed.

6. The ovary develops into the fruit.

7. Under favorable conditions, the seed germinates and the embryo develops into a mature sporophyte.

C. *Preview:* Further details about the flowering plant life cycle, including the unique adaptation of double fertilization, are covered in Modules 31.10–31.14.

Module 17.11 The structure of a fruit reflects its function in seed dispersal.

A. **Fruit** is the developed (ripened) ovary of a flower and aids in seed dispersal.

B. Fruits ripen quickly, within one growing season.

C. Some fruits are adapted for wind dispersal of seeds (Figure 17.11A).

D. Others are adapted to hitch a ride on animals (Figure 17.11B).

E. Fleshy, edible fruits are attractive to animals as food. Seeds of these fruits usually pass unharmed through the animal's digestive tract and are deposited, with fertilizer, far from the parent plant (Figure 17.11C).

Module 17.12 Connection: Agriculture is based almost entirely on angiosperms.

A. Gymnosperms supply almost all our lumber and paper, but food comes from angiosperms. Dry fruits such as corn, wheat, and rice are consumed by humans and livestock worldwide. Fleshy fruits such as tomatoes, squash, cucumbers, cherries, apples, strawberries, and oranges are also grown around the world. Humans also eat specialized stems and roots such as sweet potatoes, cassava, and potatoes.

B. Angiosperms are also used for fiber, medication, perfumes, and as a source of fine hardwoods such as oak, cherry, and walnut. Several popular drinks come from angiosperms (tea and coffee) and never forget the cacao tree, which provides cocoa and chocolate.

C. Agriculture began when humans decided to cultivate grains in an effort to control food supplies. Selective breeding produced better plants, and today, genetic engineers are developing new and improved plants.

Module 17.13 Interactions with animals have profoundly influenced angiosperm evolution.

A. The mutual evolution of two species such as flowers and bees is referred to as **coevolution** (see Chapter 36).

B. Most flowering plants depend on insects, birds, or mammals for pollination and seed dispersal.

C. Most land animals depend on flowering plants for food.

D. Pollen and nectar provide food for pollinators. Bees are one of the most highly coevolved groups of pollinators (Figure 17.13A).

E. Flowers that are pollinated by hummingbirds are usually pink or red (Figure 17.13B). The location of the nectar for some flowers is deep within the floral tube. A hummingbird can obtain the nectar with its long tongue and, in the process, collect and distribute pollen from flower to flower.

F. Flowers that are pollinated at night by bats or moths are usually large and light-colored (Figure 17.13C).

G. These mutual dependencies have been favored by natural selection and threatened by human interaction as well.

Module 17.14 Connection: Plant diversity is a nonrenewable resource.

A. Plant biodiversity is being reduced at an unprecedented rate. The majority of plant genetic diversity is found in the rain forests of the world.

B. The loss of plants is harmful in a variety of ways:

1. Twenty-five percent of all prescription medicine comes from plants, and fewer than 5,000 of the more than 295,000 known plant species have been researched as possible medicines. Table 17.14 lists just a few of the plants used as medicines.

2. Animals are perishing along with the plants.

3. Plant loss reduces air and water quality.

C. Approximately 50 million acres of forest are cleared every year. In an effort to reduce plant diversity loss, scientists have joined with the UN and an organization called the All Species Foundation in an effort to catalog all species in the next 25 years.

D. Efforts are also under way by the UN to conserve most plant species and learn how to manage forests in a sustainable and environmentally sound manner.

III. Fungi

Module 17.15 Fungi absorb food after digesting it outside their bodies.

A. The Kingdom **Fungi** includes heterotrophic eukaryotes with body structures and reproduction unlike any other organism. Like animals, fungi digest their food, but do it externally by excreting powerful enzymes to obtain the resulting small molecules as nutrients by **absorption.**

B. The close association between plants and fungi illustrates their codependence. However, fungi are more closely related to animals than plants. Fungi cannot produce their own food by photosynthesis and plants cannot decompose and return valuable nutrients to the soil (Figure 17.15A). Review the introduction to Chapter 17.

C. Fungi are ubiquitous in ecosystems and are essential decomposers. Not all fungi are beneficial, parasitizing plants and animals for nutrition.

D. Fungi are composed of **hyphae** (filamentous cell-like units, singular, *hypha*) that branch into a complex feeding network of cells called **mycelium** (plural, *mycelia,* Figures 17.15B and C).

E. The hyphae of the mycelium extend rapidly into the food source, developing a huge surface area from which digestive enzymes are secreted and through which the digested food is absorbed (Figure 17.15C).

F. Some fungi produce mushrooms, external reproductive bodies composed of above-ground tightly packed hyphae attached to underground mycelium (Figure 17.15A).

G. The hyphae cell walls are composed of chitin (nitrogen-containing polysaccharide) which is identical to the chitin in insects. The cells are attached end to end and have large pores that allow free movement of cellular components. A large mycelium can add as much as a kilometer of hyphae each day in an effort to obtain food. One fungus in Oregon covers 2,200 acres and is estimated to be 2,600 years old.

Module 17.16 Fungi produce spores in both asexual and sexual life cycles.

A. The fungal life cycle is complex but most can reproduce asexually or sexually (Figure 17.16). Fungi that reproduce sexually fuse two haploid hyphae of different mating types after sexual signaling molecules have been released. The fusion leads to the **heterokaryotic stage,** which is a cell with two distinct haploid nuclei.

B. Hours to years may pass before the nuclei fuse to form the short-lived diploid phase. Once the diploid zygote is formed, the cell undergoes meiosis and haploid spores are formed and dispersed. Spores can travel great distances by wind and water and will germinate if conditions are favorable (the presence of moisture and food).

C. **Molds** are fast growing, asexually producing fungi that produce spores at the tips of specialized hyphae. Molds are easily found on old bread or neglected fruit in the refrigerator.

D. **Yeasts** are single-celled fungi found in liquids or moist habitats including animal tissue. Yeasts reproduce asexually by cell division or by budding.

Module 17.17 Fungi can be classified into five groups.

A. Over 100,000 fungi species have been described and it is estimated by biologists that there are 1.5 million species of fungi. Classification systems for fungi are often based on the sexual reproduction structures. Those fungi that cannot reproduce sexually are informally classified as **imperfect fungi.**

B. Most fungi lack flagella, which were once used as a criterion to classify fungi. The classification systems used now rely on molecular analysis. Scientists estimate that the common ancestor of animals and fungi dates back to 1.5 bya. The oldest known fungal fossil, however, is only 460 million years old.

C. Figure 17.17A shows one hypothesis for the phylogenetic tree of fungi. Most biologists recognize five fungal phyla. The five phyla and their characteristics are presented below:

1. **Chytrids** are the only fungi with flagella and are thought to be the oldest fungi. They are found almost ubiquitously (lakes, ponds, and soil), and are decomposers of and parasitic to plants, protists, and animals.

2. **Zygote fungi (zygomycetes)** have a characteristic resistant zygosporangium with spores formed by meiosis (Figure 17.17B). This group includes the fast-growing molds that spoil food and can also be animal parasites.

3. **Arbuscular mycorrhizal fungi (glomeromycetes)** were once classified with the zygomycetes but genetic analysis indicates that they are truly a separate clade. The tips of the hyphae that invade the roots form miniature tree-like structures called arbuscles (Figure 17.17C). Most plants (90%) have a symbiotic relationship with this fungal group. The fungi deliver phosphates and other minerals to the plants and receive nutrients in return (symbiotic relationship).

4. **Sac fungi (ascomycetes)** are named for their sac-like structures called asci that produce spores sexually. Ascomycetes are found in marine, freshwater, and land environments. They range in size and structure from unicellular to complex structures such as a morel (Figure 17.17D). This group includes devastating plant pathogens and symbionts (green algae or cyanobacteria with fungi from lichen, Module 17.20).

5. **Club fungi (basidiomycetes)** include the familiar mushroom, puffball, and shelf fungi (Figure 17.17E). They are named for the spore-producing structure called a basidium. This fungal group is an excellent decomposer of woody plants (lignin). This group also has two destructive plant parasites (rust and smut).

Module 17.18 Fungal groups differ in their life cycles and reproductive structures.

A. The life cycle of the fungus zygomycetes is illustrated in Figure 17.18A. When food is plentiful, the hyphae can asexually produce haploid spores in sporangia at the tips of upright hyphae. However, when food is scarce, sexual reproduction begins.

   1. Mycelia of opposite mating types join to make cells from two parents.

   2. The zygosporangium develops into a thick-walled structure.

   3. The thick-walled structure can survive under harsh conditions for months. Once conditions improve, the parental nuclei fuse, forming a zygote.

   4. Haploid spores are produced from the zygote by meiosis.

B. The process of reproduction for ascomycetes is similar to zygomycetes. When conditions are favorable, they reproduce asexually. However, if conditions are severe, they reproduce sexually.

C. The life cycle of mushroom (a basidiomycete) is presented in Figure 17.18B and involves five steps.

   1. A heterokaryotic mycelium forms by fusion of two different mating types.

   2. A mushroom develops and grows.

   3. Specialized cells from the gills on the underside of the mushroom contain the diploid nuclei from nuclei fusion.

   4. Haploid spores are formed by meiosis and are then released. A single mushroom can release a billion spores.

   5. Provided the conditions are correct, germination takes place and a haploid mycelium grows.

D. Much of the success of fungi is due to the high asexual reproductive capacity and the ability to maintain genetic diversity through sexual reproduction.

Module 17.19 Connection: Parasitic fungi harm plants and animals.

A. Of the 100,000 species of known fungi, about 30% are parasites. Parasitic fungi are the most serious plant pests. Particularly dangerous are nonnative parasites, such as the fungus that causes Dutch elm disease (Figure 17.19A).

B. Approximately 80% of all plant diseases are caused by fungi. Between 10% and 50% of fruit harvested around the world is destroyed by fungi. Some parasitic fungi, such as corn smut, can attack developing seeds (Figure 17.19B).

C. Fungi cause a few diseases in humans. The term used for a fungal infection is **mycosis.** Flour made from grain infested with ergots can cause gangrene, nervous system disorders, and even death (Figure 17.19C). LSD (lysergic acid diethylamide) comes from one of the toxins (lysergic acid) that has been isolated from ergots.

D. Some systemic fungal infections can be fatal, particularly in people weakened by other diseases. Less serious are the fungal infections of the outer layers of the skin known as ringworm and athlete's foot. Fortunately, fungicidal ointments can control most of these fungal parasites. One type of fungus is so deadly (Coccidioides) that it is considered a potential biological weapon.

E. Yeast infections of the vagina are usually caused by some chemical, microbial, or immunologic change in the body and are classified as opportunistic infections. Other opportunistic fungal infections are on the rise due to the emergence of AIDS, which suppresses the immune system.

Module 17.20 Lichens consist of fungi living mutualistically with photosynthetic organisms.

A. **Lichens** are associations of millions of green algae or cyanobacteria held in a tangled network of fungal hyphae (Figure 17.18B).

B. The fungus receives food from the photosynthesis of its partner. The alga or cyanobacterium receives housing, water, and the minerals trapped by the hyphal network.

C. All lichen fungi and most lichen algae and cyanobacteria cannot grow independently. The relationship is so complete that they are classified together as a single species.

D. Lichens are able to survive in habitats where neither partner (nor any other multicellular organism) could grow alone (Figure 17.18A).

E. Lichens play important ecological roles in soil formation on rock surfaces and as food for animals.

F. Some lichens are thousands of years old.
NOTE: Cyanobacterium-containing lichens fix nitrogen and play important roles in the nitrogen cycle (Module 37.18).

Module 17.21 Fungi also form mutualistic relationships with animals.

A. Some fungal species have developed mutualistic relationships with animals. Ruminants have fungi in their gut to assist in the digestion of cellulose and other plant material.

B. Ants called leaf cutters have a close relationship with fungi, so much so that both depend on the other for their existence (a mutualistic association). This relationship has been evolving for more than 50 million years (Figure 17.21).

Module 17.22 Connection: Fungi have enormous ecological benefits and practical uses.

A. Plants and fungi have evolved together since they first inhabited the land. The close relationship between plants and fungi is obvious when one looks to the role played by fungi. The decomposition of matter and recycling of nutrients is essential to the survival of all plants.

B. Humans use fungi in several practical ways, such as the decomposition of pollutants and carcinogens. Fungi are also used as a source of food (e.g., mushrooms, cheese, truffles, bread, beer, and wine) (Figure 17.22A).

C. Fungi are a source of antibiotics. It was discovered that the fungus Penicillium could inhibit the growth of the bacterium Staphylococcus aureus. Subsequently, the antibiotic penicillin was developed (Figure 17.22B).

D. Fungi have played an important role in eukaryotic molecular biology, as sources of human proteins, and for industrial applications such as in the paper industry.

Class Activities

1. Have your students collect and classify examples of the different plant and fungal species found in the area in which they live. (It's a classic, but it's still a good way of familiarizing your students with the diversity of life.)

2. A considerable number of wild, cultivated, and cultured fungi are now available in many markets in the United States, both in fresh and dried condition, depending on the season and local availability of mushroom farms or proper habitat. Bring in examples to stimulate discussion and interest in the topic of fungi. Point out that the mushroom you see is like the apple of an apple tree: the "plant" (mycelium) that produces the mushroom is invisible to the naked eye. The mycelium of the most commonly available mushroom, *Agaricus campestris,* is a litter decomposer of composted straw. Oyster mushrooms and the Japanese mushroom, shiitake, are quite common in better markets and are both litter decomposers of wood (but can be grown on artificial logs made of sawdust). In season, you may be able to find golden chanterelles (the mycelium of which forms mycorrhizae, so these are not domesticated), truffles (very expensive and also mycorrhizal), or morels (a recent, secret process allows these to be cultured). The moldy cheeses (Brie, Camembert, and blue); wine, beer, and soy sauce bottles; and a loaf of bread can also be used as props to stress the diversity of our dependency on fungi for food. In health-food stores you may also be able to find tempeh, a soybean product fermented with *Rhizopus* mold.

3. Almost every region of the United States has at least one serious plant-pathogenic fungus. Contact your local agricultural extension office to obtain details about the identity of these fungi, and their classification, hosts, and controls. Featuring a specific representative will help clarify the general characteristics of the kingdom as a whole, particularly the reproductive advantage of producing spores and the ease with which their hyphae enter plant tissues. In presenting special information on local parasitic fungi, be sure to remind your students that the majority of fungal species are beneficial to humans, either in their roles as recyclers or mycorrhiza formers.

Transparency Acetates

Media

See the beginning of this book for a complete description of all media available for instructors and students. Animations and videos are available in the Campbell Image Presentation Library. Media Activities and Thinking as a Scientist investigations are available on the student CD-ROM and website.

Animations and Videos	Module Number
Bat Pollinating Agave Plant Video	17.3
Moss Life Cycle Animation	17.5
Fern Life Cycle Animation	17.6
Pine Life Cycle Animation	17.8
Flower Blooming (time-lapse) Video	17.9
Flowering Plant Life Cycle (time-lapse) Video	17.10
Bee Pollinating Video	17.13
Fungus Life Cycle Animation	17.16
Allomyces Zoospore Release Video	17.18
Phlyctochytrium Zoospore Release Video	17.18
Water Mold Oogonium Video	17.18
Water Mold Zoospores Video	17.18

Activities and Thinking as a Scientist	Module Number
Web/CD Activity 17A: *Terrestrial Adaptations of Plants*	17.2
Web/CD Activity 17B: *Highlights of Plant Phylogeny*	17.3
Web/CD Activity 17C: *Moss Life Cycle*	17.5
Web/CD Activity 17D: *Fern Life Cycle*	17.6
Web/CD Thinking as a Scientist: *What Are the Different Stages of a Fern Life Cycle?*	17.6
Web/CD Activity 17E: *Pine Life Cycle*	17.8
Web/CD Activity 17F: *Angiosperm Life Cycle*	17.10
Web/CD Activity 17G: *Connection: Madagascar and the Biodiversity Crisis*	17.14
Web/CD Thinking as a Scientist: *How Are Trees Identified by Their Leaves?*	17.14
Web/CD Activity 17H: *Fungal Reproduction and Nutrition*	17.16
Web/CD Activity 17I: *Fungal Life Cycles*	17.18
Web/CD Thinking as a Scientist: *How Does the Fungus Pilobolus Succeed as a Decomposer?*	17.18

CHAPTER 18

The Evolution of Animal Diversity

Teaching Objectives

Introduction   Describe the difficulties of classifying the duck-billed platypus and other Australian mammals. Explain how the marsupials of Australia illustrate convergent evolution.

Animal Evolution and Diversity

18.1   Define animals, and distinguish them from other forms of life.

18.1   Describe the general animal life cycle and the basic body plan.

18.2   Describe the five-stage hypothesis for the evolution of animals from protists.

18.2   Describe the Cambrian explosion, and list three hypotheses to explain its occurrence.

18.3   Explain how a hydrostatic skeleton helps an animal keep its shape and move.

18.3–18.14   Compare the nine animal phyla discussed in this chapter according to the following traits: (a) presence of true tissues; (b) no symmetry, radial symmetry, or bilateral symmetry; (c) no coelom, a pseudocoelom, or a true coelom; and (d) protostomes or deuterostomes.

Invertebrates

18.5–18.14   Describe the characteristics of and distinguish between the following phyla: Porifera, Cnidaria, Platyhelminthes, Nematoda, Mollusca, Annelida, Arthropoda, Echinodermata, and Chordata. Note several examples of each phylum.

18.10   Define segmentation, explain its functions, and note the animal phyla where it occurs.

18.11   Compare the characteristics of the four major arthropod lineages. Note examples of each.

18.12   Describe the common characteristics of insects. Distinguish between the seven insect orders described in this chapter.

Vertebrates

18.15   Describe the defining characteristics of the major chordate clades.

18.16–18.21   Describe the characteristics of and distinguish between the following vertebrate groups: lampreys, chondrichthyans, ray-finned fishes, lobe-finned fishes, amphibians, reptiles, and mammals.

18.21   Distinguish between monotremes, marsupials, and placental mammals. Note examples of each.

Animal Phylogeny and Diversity Revisited

18.22   Describe and compare the two main phylogenetic trees used to describe the evolutionary history of animals. Explain why there are differences in these two systems.

18.23   Describe the consequences of introduced species in Australia.

Key Terms

amniotes	echinoderms	molting
amniotic egg	ectoderm	monotremes
amoebocytes	ectothermic	nematodes
amphibians	endoderm	notochord
annelid	endoskeleton	open circulatory system
anterior	endothermic	operculum
arachnids	entomology	pharyngeal slits
arthropods	eutherians	placenta
bilateral symmetry	exoskeleton	placental mammals
birds	flatworms	polychaetes
bivalves	flukes	polyp
blastula	foot	post-anal tail
centipedes	free-living flatworms	posterior
cephalopods	gastropods	protostomes
chelicerates	gastrovascular cavity	pseudocoelom
choanocytes	gastrula	radial symmetry
chondrichthyans	horseshoe crabs	radula
chordate	hydrostatic skeleton	ray-finned fishes
circulatory system	incomplete metamorphosis	reptiles
clade Bilateria	ingestion	segmentation
clade Eumetazoa	invertebrates	sessile
closed circulatory system	kingdom Animalia	skull
Cnidarians	lancelets	sponges
cnidocytes	larva	suspension feeders
coelom	lateral line system	swim bladder
complete digestive tract	leeches	tapeworms
complete metamorphosis	lobe-fins	tunicates
craniates	mammals	ventral
crustaceans	mantle	vertebrae
cuticle	marsupials	vertebral column
deuterostomes	medusa	vertebrates
dorsal	mesoderm	visceral mass
dorsal, hollow nerve cord	millipedes	water vascular system
earthworms	molluscs	

Word Roots

choano- = a funnel; **-cyte** = cell (*choanocyte:* flagellated collar cells of a sponge)

cnido- = a nettle (*cnidocytes:* unique cells that function in defense and prey capture in cnidarians)

cuti- = the skin (*cuticle:* the exoskeleton of an arthropod)

deutero- = second (*deuterostome:* one of two distinct evolutionary lines of coelomates characterized by radial, indeterminate cleavage, enterocoelous formation of the coelom, and development of the anus from the blastopore)

echino- = spiny; **-derm** = skin (*echinoderm:* sessile or slow-moving animals with a thin skin that covers an exoskeleton; the group includes sea stars, sea urchins, brittle stars, crinoids, and basket stars)

ecto- = outside; **-derm** = skin (*ectoderm:* the outermost of the three primary germ layers in animal embryos)

endo- = inner; **therm-** = heat (*endotherm:* an animal that uses metabolic energy to maintain a constant body temperature, such as a bird or mammal)

gastro- = stomach; **-vascula** = a little vessel (*gastrovascular cavity:* the central digestive compartment, usually with a single opening that functions as both mouth and anus)

in- = without (*invertebrate:* an animal without a backbone)

marsupi- = a bag, pouch (*marsupial:* a mammal, such as a koala, kangaroo, or opossum, whose young complete their embryonic development inside a maternal pouch called the marsupium)

meso- = middle (*mesoderm:* the middle primary germ layer of an early embryo)

meta- = boundary, turning point; **-morph** = form (*metamorphosis:* the resurgence of development in an animal larva that transforms it into a sexually mature adult)

mono- = one (*monotreme:* an egg-laying mammal, represented by the platypus and echidna)

noto- = the back; **-chord** = a string (*notochord:* a longitudinal, flexible rod formed from dorsal mesoderm and located between the gut and the nerve cord in all chordate embryos)

proto- = first; **-stoma** = mouth (*protostome:* a member of one of two distinct evolutionary lines of coelomates characterized by spiral, determinate cleavage, schizocoelous formation of the coelom, and development of the mouth from the blastopore)

Lecture Outline

Introduction *What Am I?*

    A. Most known organisms are animals.

        1. Of the 1.7 million known species, three-fourths are animals. Animal diversity progressed through millions of years of evolution and natural selection.

        2. Humans have a tendency to appreciate and study animals, but what is an animal? Do we know one when we see one, and how do we classify different animals?

    B. What am I?

        1. The duck-billed platypus was a taxonomic nightmare when initially found by the first Europeans who visited Australia. It lays eggs and has a bill and webbed feet like a duck; it has fur and a tail like a beaver; it has mammary glands like any other mammal. So what is it? It's a monotreme (an egg-laying mammal)!

        2. Australia is full of special mammals called monotremes and marsupials. The niches that were being filled with placental mammals on other continents were left empty when Australia broke away from Pangaea. Without competition from other placental mammals, monotremes and marsupials filled in the empty niches and became the dominant mammals in Australia.

        Preview: Zoologists distinguish between animals with internal skeletons (vertebrates) and those without internal skeletons (invertebrates). All but one animal phylum (our own, phylum Chordata) are invertebrates (Module 18.14).

    I. Animal Evolution and Diversity

      Module 18.1 What is an animal?

        A. Animals are eukaryotic, multicellular heterotrophs that lack cell walls and obtain nutrition by **ingestion** (Figure 18.1A). This distinguishes animals from fungi that digest their food first and then absorb it. Animals have unique types of cell junctions (Module 4.18). Most animals have muscle cells for movement and nerve cells for sensory perception. Animals are, with the exception of the gametes, composed of diploid cells.

B. The life cycle of most animals includes a dominant, diploid adult that produces eggs or sperm by meiosis. These gametes fuse to form a zygote. The zygote develops into the adult animal, passing through a series of embryonic stages, many of which are shared by most members of the animal kingdom (Figure 18.1B).

C. In all animals, the embryonic stages include the **blastula** (hollow ball of cells) and, in most, a **gastrula** which is a saclike embryo with one opening and two layers of cells. The two cellular layers are called **endoderm,** which develops into the digestive tract, and the **ectoderm,** which becomes the outer layer of the animal and for some the nervous system. Most animals develop an additional layer of cells called the **mesoderm,** which forms the muscles and most of the internal organs.
    Preview: Embryonic development (Modules 27.9–27.15).

D. In many animals, the gastrula develops into one or more immature stages, for example, **larvae** that develop into the sexually mature adults only after **metamorphosis.**
    NOTE: Larvae are immature individuals that look different than adults. The larval stage is used for dispersal and helps an animal's offspring find suitable habitats before continuing to grow. They are also extremely important sources of food for many other animals in aquatic habitats.

E. All eukaryotes have homeoboxes that control gene expression (Module 11.15). But only animals have special regulatory genes called *Hox* genes, which control zygote development.

Module 18.2 The ancestor of animals was probably a colonial, flagellated protist.

A. Fossils of the oldest known animals date from the late Precambrian era, 600 million years ago (mya).

B. A hypothetical evolutionary scenario leading to the first animal proceeds as follows:
    1. Colonial protists of a few identical, flagellated cells.
    2. Larger, hollow, spherical colonies that ingested organic materials suspended in the water around the colony.
    3. Colonies with cells specialized for somatic (movement, digestion, etc.) and reproductive functions.
    4. Differentiated entities with an infolded, temporary digestive region.
    5. "Protoanimals," completely infolded, with two-layered body walls (Figure 18.2A).

C. These protoanimals probably "crawled," feeding on the ocean bottom.

D. The modern animal phyla evolved during the Cambrian period, 542 mya, a 15 million–year period of explosive evolution.

E. Three hypotheses explain the rapid expansion of animal diversity during the early Cambrian era:
    1. Ecological causes: increased dependency on the predator/prey relationship.
    2. Geological changes: atmospheric oxygen may have reached a critical threshold that was high enough to support the active lifestyle of animals.
    3. Genetic causes: the development of the *Hox* genes supported the diversity associated with variations in the spatial and temporal arrangement of the genes during embryonic stages of development.
    NOTE: Some mutualistic synthesis of the three hypotheses is likely the correct answer.

F. Of the roughly 35 phyla that exist today, all are **invertebrates** but one (Chordata, named this way due to the lack of a vertebral column).

Module 18.3 Animals can be characterized by basic features of their "body plan."

A. Biologists categorize animals based on several characteristics. One characteristic is the body plan. One feature of the body plan is symmetry.

B. **Radial symmetry** is a common feature of the simple animals. Body parts radiate out from the center (Figure 18.3A).

C. A second and more common feature of complex animals is **bilateral symmetry.** Most animals show bilateral symmetry: a left and a mirrored right side; a distinct head, or **anterior,** end; a tail, or **posterior,** end; a back, or **dorsal,** surface; and a bottom, or **ventral,** surface (Figure 18.3A).

D. Form and function are related to body symmetry. The radial animal is stationary or moves passively through its environment. It senses the environment equally from all sides. On the other hand, the bilateral animal moves through its environment in a forward direction with its anterior end in front. It, therefore, makes logical sense to have the brain and most of the sensory organs located in the anterior region.

E. A second aspect of body plan is tissue organization. True tissues are cooperative collections of cells that perform a specialized function (e.g., nervous tissue). As mentioned above, tissue forms during the embryonic stages from one of three tissue types, endoderm, ectoderm, or mesoderm.

F. A characteristic of animals with all three tissues is the presence or absence of a body cavity. The cavity protects the organs and allows them to grow and move independently. A **hydrostatic skeleton** is a fluid-filled cavity that acts like a skeleton for soft-bodied animals.

G. Figures 18.3B, C, and D illustrate three types of body cavities. The flatworm has a fluid-filled body cavity, and the body is solid except for the digestive tract. The roundworm has a body cavity called a **pseudocoelom,** which is a cavity not completely lined with mesoderm. The earthworm has a true **coelom** that is completely lined with mesoderm.

H. Animals with all three tissues can be classified based on the development of the digestive tract openings during gastrulation. Those animals that develop an opening that becomes a mouth are called proteosomes, while those that develop an anus are called deuterostomes.

Module 18.4 The body plans of animals can be used to build phylogenetic trees.

A. The synthesis of a phylogenetic tree requires more than fossil records because the evolution of animals happened so rapidly. Therefore morphology is used, particularly body plan and embryonic development.

B. A morphology-based phylogenetic tree is presented in Figure 18.4. The first branch point after the ancestral animal separates animals with true tissue (**Eumetazoa**) from those without true tissue (sponges). The next branch point separates radial symmetry from bilateral symmetry (**Bilateria** clade). This method is acceptable, but with the addition of molecular data, the phylogenetic trees are being reshaped (*preview:* Module 18.23).

II. Invertebrates

Module 18.5 Sponges have relatively simple, porous bodies.

A. **Sponges** are classified in the phylum Porifera. Most are marine, live singly, and range in height from 1 cm to 1.5 m (Figures 18.3A and B).

B. Sponges can exhibit radial symmetry or be asymmetrical (Figure 18.5C). Adult sponges are attached to a substrate and do not move about **(sessile).** This creates a problem with predators. Sponges have developed mechanisms to combat predators, pathogens, and parasites.

C. The body of a sponge consists of two layers of cells. An inner layer of flagellated cells, called **choanocytes,** surround an inner chamber and sweep the water toward the larger pore; **amoebocytes** produce the skeletal fibers or proteins called spongin (Figure 18.3D).

D. Sponges are **suspension feeders** (filter feeders). The choanocyte flagella beat, creating a flow of water in through the pores and the collars, which traps bacteria in mucus. Then the water is pumped out through the large, upper opening. The choanocytes then phago-cytize the food and package it in vacuoles. Amoebocytes pick up the food vacuoles, digest the food, and carry the nutrients to other cells.

Preview: Contrast this with the structure of the digestive system of other animals (Module 21.3).

NOTE: Sponges function as complex colonies of differentiated but interchangeable cells, the amoebocytes being the central cell type that forms most of the others. If a sponge is pressed through a sieve and all the cells and skeletal elements are separated, they will reorganize themselves back into the same layers and similar shape.

E. Sponges are likely to have been a very early offshoot from the multicellular organisms that gave rise to the animals (Figure 18.4). Sponges retain several protistan characteristics, including not having a digestive tract and having intracellular digestion. Developmentally, sponges do not go through a gastrula stage. Sponge cells do not make tissues as in other animals, and sponges lack nerves and muscles, although individual cells can sense and react to changes in their surroundings.

Module 18.6 Cnidarians are radial animals with tentacles and stinging cells.

A. All animals except sponges have true tissues and, thus, belong to the clade Eumetazoa. The oldest animals in the Eumetazoan clade are the jellies, hydras, sea anemones, and corals.

B. **Cnidarians** exhibit radial symmetry. These animals may be in the form of a **polyp** (relatively fixed in position) or a **medusa** (swimming), or they may alternate between polyp and medusa forms. Both body plans have a central tubular body (surrounding a **gastrovascular cavity**), one opening ("mouth") into this cavity, and tentacles arranged around the mouth (Figures 18.6A, B, and C).

C. Along the tentacles are **cnidocytes** (stinger cells) that function in defense and the capture of food. The coiled thread in each cell is discharged, stinging or entangling the prey or predator as it brushes against the cnidocyte (Figure 18.6D).

D. Cnidarians trap food with their tentacles then maneuver it into a gastrovascular cavity where it is digested and distributed throughout the body. Undigested food is eliminated through the mouth.

E. As mentioned above, corals are cnidarians that secrete a hard external skeleton. The new generation lives on the previous generation, creating coral reefs that are home to many diverse species. Some coral have a symbiotic relationship with algae.

Module 18.7 Flatworms are the simplest bilateral animals.

   A. **Flatworms** are classified in the phylum Platyhelminthes, which is composed of approximately 20,000 species. There are three major groups of flatworms: **free-living flatworms** (planarians) that live on rocks in marine and fresh water, parasitic **flukes,** and **tapeworms.**

   B. Like cnidarians, planarians and most flukes have a gastrovascular cavity and no other body cavities. The body normally has a head end with a concentration of sensory nerves. The mouth opens from the ventral surface, and the gastrovascular cavity branches through the entire length of the body (Figure 18.7A).
   NOTE: Flatworms are not quite at the organ level of construction.

   C. Most flukes have a complex life cycle, including reproduction in more than one host and one or more larval stages. Blood flukes parasitize humans and cause the disease schistosomiasis, a debilitating disease afflicting 200 million worldwide.

   D. Tapeworms are highly adapted parasites that inhabit the digestive tracts of their hosts. Unlike other flatworms, tapeworms are segmented and lack a gastrovascular cavity, absorbing their predigested food directly. The anterior end (the head) attaches to the host with hooks and suckers, and a region behind generates segments. Sexual reproduction occurs in each segment; the oldest segments break off and leave the host via the feces. Many tapeworms produce larvae that infect the prey animal, while the adult tapeworms infect that prey animal's predator (Figure 18.7B).

Module 18.8 Nematodes have a pseudocoelom and a complete digestive tract.

   A. Nematodes, also called roundworms, make up the phylum Nematoda. Nematodes show bilateral symmetry and have three tissues and a pseudocoelom. Nematodes are numerous, diverse, and found in most environments. Most are important decomposers or parasites of plants or animals.

   B. The nematode body is cylindrical, includes a **complete digestive tract** with an opening at both ends, and is covered by a tough, nonliving **cuticle** (Figure 18.8A).

   C. Food passes in one direction along a digestive tract that includes regions specialized for certain functions: food intake, breakup, digestion, absorption, and waste elimination.
   NOTE: Roundworms are tending toward the organ level of construction.

   D. One free-living species, *Caenorhabditis elegans,* is an important organism for genetic research and one of the best-understood organisms (at the molecular level). Researchers have been able to trace the developmental lineage of each of an adult's 1,000 cells. The complete genomic sequence of *C. elegans* has been determined, aiding the research of gene regulation and development.

   E. Trichinosis is a disease caused by the nematode *Trichinella spiralis*. Humans get this parasite by eating raw pork (Figure 18.8B).

Module 18.9 Diverse molluscs are variations on a common body plan.

   A. **Molluscs** are classified in the phylum Mollusca.

   B. The basic body plan of a mollusc includes bilateral symmetry, a complete digestive tract, a coelom, and many internal organs.

   C. Two distinctive characteristics of the phylum are a muscular **"foot"** and a **mantle,** an outgrowth of the body surface that drapes over the animal, functions in sensory reception, often secretes a shell, and usually houses gills that function in gas exchange and waste removal. Molluscs also have a **visceral mass,** which contains most of the internal organs (Figure 18.9A).

D. Most molluscs have a **radula,** an organ used to scrape food, such as algae, off surfaces in the environment (Figure 18.9A).

E. Molluscs also have a true **circulatory system** (in contrast to the circulatory function of the gastrovascular cavity of cnidarians and flatworms, and the pseudocoelom of round-worms) and separate sex organs. The life cycle includes a ciliated larva called a tro-chophore, a trait used in taxonomy.

F. Evolution has modified the basic body plan in different groups of molluscs. **Gastropods** include snails and slugs (Figures 18.9B and C). **Bivalves** include clams, scallops, and oysters (Figure 18.9D). **Cephalopods** include octopuses and squids (Figures 18.9E and F).

G. Cephalopods are built for speed and have large brains and sophisticated sense organs, especially their eyes, which can focus a clear image on the retina. A new species of squid, the colossal squid, was discovered in 2003 and is thought to be the largest cephalopod on record.

Module 18.10 Annelids are segmented worms.

A. These worms are classified in the phylum Annelida. They live in the sea, in most fresh-water habitats, and in damp soil. **Annelids** usually have one or more anterior segments specially modified into a head region. Annelids and other vertebrates have a **closed circulatory system,** unlike molluscs, which have an open circulatory system that bathes the organs in blood.

B. **Earthworms and their relatives:** The segmentation of the earthworm is illustrated in Figure 18.10A.

   1. This group of annelids is adapted to life in soil. They consume the soil, digest the organic parts, and eliminate undigested soil and other waste products in their feces, improving soil texture in the process.

   2. The segments in an earthworm are clearly visible from the outside, outlining the repeating pattern of organs inside. The nervous, circulatory, and excretory systems have repeating, mostly identical parts in each segment.

   3. Advantages of segmentation include greater body flexibility and mobility. For exam-ple, in the earthworm, rhythmic alternating contractions and elongations of segments propel the worm into or along the ground.

C. **Polychaete** worms are mostly marine inhabitants. They are characterized by having segments with broad, paddlelike appendages and bristles. Some polychaetes show modi-fication of anterior segments. The appendages show specialization in gas exchange and have a rich supply of blood (Figures 18.10B and C).

D. **Leeches** are free-living carnivores of aquatic animals or blood-sucking parasites on ver-tebrates (Figure 18.10D). A blood-sucking leech cuts the skin with razor-sharp jaws and secretes an anesthetic and an anticoagulant. Leeches are still used to remove blood from bruises or from pooled blood when appendages are attached.

Module 18.11 Arthropods are segmented animals with jointed appendages and an exoskeleton.

A. In terms of diversity, geographical distribution, and sheer numbers, the phylum Arthro-poda is the most successful that has ever lived. It is estimated that there are a billion billion **arthropods** on the Earth.

B. Arthropods are segmented (often fused), have jointed appendages, and have an **exoskeleton** composed of chitin and proteins (Figure 18.12A).

C. Arthropods have an open circulatory system that uses a tube-like heart to pump blood to and around the organs. Either gills or specialized tubes are used to exchange gases.

D. Fossil and molecular evidence suggest that there are four lineages. Three lineages are discussed in this module; the fourth is discussed in Module 18.12.
Preview: To facilitate movement, muscle tissue is attached to the inside of the exoskeleton (Module 30.2).

E. To grow, arthropods shed their exoskeleton, swell in size, and secrete a new, developing exoskeleton. This process is called **molting.**

F. **Chelicerates: Horseshoe crabs** are "living fossil" life forms that have survived for hundreds of millions of years with little change (see Module 14.8: equilibrium). A very close relative of the modern genus was abundant 300 mya (Figure 18.11B).

G. **Arachnids** are modern chelicerates and include scorpions, spiders, ticks, and mites. Their ancestors were among the first terrestrial carnivores. Except for mites, arachnids are carnivores (Figure 18.11C).

H. **Millipedes and Centipedes:** Millipedes have segments with two pairs of appendages each and feed on decaying plants. Centipedes have segments with one pair of appendages each and are carnivorous. Both groups are terrestrial (Figure 18.11D).

I. **Crustaceans:** Crabs, shrimps, lobsters, crayfish, and barnacles have a hardened cuticle made of calcium carbonate; they are mostly aquatic (Figure 18.11E).

Module 18.12 Insects are the most diverse group of organisms.

A. About one million insect species are known to biologists (**entomology** is the study of insects), representing perhaps half of those that exist. Insects have been important aspects of terrestrial life, but less so in aquatic and, especially, marine habitats.

B. Insects are united as a group in having a three-part body plan: head, thorax, and abdomen. The head has sensory appendages and mouthparts specialized for a particular diet. The thorax contains three pairs of walking legs and, usually, one or two pairs of wings (Figure 18.12A). The wings are an extension of the exoskeleton, which is one of the reasons that insects have been so successful.

C. Metamorphosis is common to many insects. **Incomplete metamorphosis** (Orthoptera, Odonata, and Hemiptera) results in an adult that resembles the young but is larger and has different body proportions. **Complete metamorphosis** (Coleoptera, Lepidoptera, Diptera, and Hymenoptera) occurs when a larval form specialized for eating and growing develops into a very different adult form that is specialized for reproduction and dispersal. The transition from larva to adult takes place during the pupal stage.

D. Seven of the most common orders of insects are presented below:

1. **Orthoptera:** Grasshoppers have biting and chewing mouthparts. Most species are herbivorous (mantids are an exception). They have two pairs of wings. The forewing is thickened, and the hind wing is membranous. Males typically make courtship sounds by rubbing their large back legs (Figure 18.12A).

2. **Odonata:** Damselflies and dragonflies have chewing mouthparts and are carnivorous. They have two identical pairs of wings (Figure 18.12B).

3. **Hemiptera:** True bugs have piercing, sucking mouthparts, and most species feed on plant sap (bedbugs feed on blood). They have two pairs of wings (Figure 18.12C).

4. **Coleoptera:** Beetles make up the largest order in the animal kingdom, with some 350,000 species known worldwide from all types of habitats. They have biting and chewing mouthparts and are carnivorous, omnivorous, or herbivorous. They have two pairs of wings, and the forewings serve as protective covering for the hindwings (Figure 18.12D).

5. **Lepidoptera:** Moths and butterflies have drinking-tube mouthparts for sipping nectar or other liquids, and they have two pairs of scale-covered wings (Figure 18.12E). After touching a member of Lepidoptera, the dust particles on your fingers are the scales that covered the wings of butterflies and moths.

6. **Diptera:** Flies, gnats, and mosquitoes have lapping mouthparts and feed on nectar or other liquids (mosquitoes have piercing, sucking mouthparts and suck blood). They have a single pair of functional wings, with the hindwings reduced to halteres to maintain balance (Figure 18.12F).

7. **Hymenoptera:** Ants, bees, and wasps are the third most numerous insects. They have chewing and sucking mouthparts, and many are herbivorous. They have two pairs of wings. Many in this group display complex behavior and social organization (Figure 18.12G).

   NOTE: These social groups function as "superorganisms." Some aspects of their social behavior are covered in Module 35.20.

Module 18.13 Echinoderms have spiny skin, an endoskeleton, and a water vascular system for movement.

A. The phylum Echinodermata includes sea stars, sand dollars, and sea urchins (all marine) and represents a second branch of evolution in the animal kingdom. Similarities in embryonic development (bilateral symmetry) suggest that this phylum is closely related to our own, the phylum Chordata.

B. **Echinoderms** lack segmentation and bilateral symmetry as adults, but larvae are bilaterally symmetrical. Members of this phylum are noted for their regenerative capacity. Most have tubular **endoskeletons** composed of fused plates lying just under the skin. Unique to this phylum is the presence of a water vascular system. This is a network of water-filled canals that branch into extensions called tube feet that function in movement, ingestion, and gas exchange (Figure 18.13A).

C. Sea stars have flexible "arms" that bear the tube feet. They wrap these arms around a bivalve prey, pull the valves apart, extrude their stomach out their mouth and into the opening, and digest the soft parts (Figure 18.13B).

D. Sea urchins are spherical, with five double rows of tube feet running radially, with which they pull themselves along. They eat algae (Figure 18.13C).

E. Other examples of echinoderms are brittle stars, sea lilies, and sea cucumbers.

Module 18.14 Our own phylum, Chordata, is distinguished by four features.

A. A **chordate** is distinguished by four characteristics found in the embryo and often in the adult:

1. A **dorsal, hollow nerve cord.**
2. A **notochord,** which is a flexible, longitudinal rod located between the digestive tract and the nerve cord.
3. **Pharyngeal slits,** which are gill structures (slits and supports) in the pharynx region behind the mouth.
4. A muscular **postanal tail.**

B. The most diverse chordates are vertebrates. However, there are several invertebrate chordates in this phylum.

C. **Tunicates** (sea squirts) are a group of marine chordates (Figure 18.14A). As adults, they do not exhibit the chordate pattern of notochord and nerve cord. As stationary filter feeders, they use a large opening to draw in water that passes over the gill slits and empties into a large cavity. Larval tunicates exhibit the complete chordate pattern and look very much like adult lancelets.

D. **Lancelets** are small, bladelike chordates that live anchored by their tails in marine sands and expose their heads and mouths, filtering and trapping organic particles in mucus around the gill slits. These animals show the clearest presentation of the chordate body plan (Figure 18.14B). They also show segmentation, which is not unique to chordates but is one of the characteristics. Molecular evidence indicates that lancelets are the closest living relatives of vertebrates. Lancelets express the same genes during the development of the anterior end as those genes expressed by vertebrates during brain development.

III. Vertebrates

Module 18.15 Derived characteristics define the major clades of chordates.

A. The use of molecular, anatomical, and fossil evidence has led to the development of new hypotheses for chordate evolution (Figure 18.15).

B. The following characteristics, in ascending order, were used to develop the cladogram for the chordates.

1. All chordates have a brain.

2. The development of a head came next, which included the brain in a **skull** connected to the dorsal nerve cord, eyes, and sensory organs. This group is called the craniates. This development allowed active predation.

3. A more extended skull came next along with a **vertebral column** composed of **vertebrae** (singular, *vertebra*). This group is called **vertebrates.**

4. The development of the jaw came next, which opened up even more feeding opportunities.

5. The lungs and muscular lobed fins supported by the endoskeleton made life on land possible.

6. Tetrapods were the first vertebrates on land, and they developed the amniotic egg to enhance reproduction.

C. The vertebrate skeleton is an endoskeleton of cartilage and/or bone. These nonliving materials contain living cells and grow as the animal grows, unlike the exoskeletons of arthropods, which must be molted prior to growth.

Module 18.16 Lampreys are vertebrates that lack hinged jaws.

A. Lampreys are the oldest living lineage of vertebrates, living in streams as larva and migrating to lakes or seas as adults.

B. The lampreys lack jaws but have skeletal supports between their gill slits, and they lack paired appendages. Otherwise, they are superficially similar to fishes. Most are parasites on fish, boring a hole in the host and sucking its blood (Figure 18.16A).

C. Fossil records indicate that there was a diverse array of related jawless vertebrates that became extinct 360 mya.

D. Jaws evolved by modification of the first two pairs of skeletal supports of the gill slits. Similar events occur during the embryonic development of all fishes today (Figure 18.16B).

E. The oldest fossils of jawed vertebrates appear in rocks that were formed 470 mya. Jaws enabled vertebrates (mostly fish) to catch and consume a wider variety of foods than were available to filter feeders, thus replacing the jawless vertebrates.

F. But where did the hinge come from? One hypothesis states that it may have evolved from modifications of the anterior pharyngeal slits (Figure 18.16B).

Module 18.17 Jawed vertebrates with gills and paired fins include sharks, ray-finned fishes, and lobe-fins.

A. Fish extract oxygen from water with their gills. Their paired fins help stabilize their bodies (Figure 18.18C).

B. **Chondrichthyans:** The cartilaginous fishes include the sharks and rays and have skeletons of flexible cartilage. Sharks have a keen sense of smell and sharp vision and can sense minute vibrations with a pressure-sensitive **lateral line system.** Because they cannot pump water through their gills, they must swim in order to move the water (Figure 18.17A).

C. **Ray-finned fishes:** These fishes are more common and diverse and have a stiff skeleton of bone reinforced by hard calcium salts. Like sharks, they have a keen sense of smell and a lateral line system. They also have a keen sense of sight, and a bony flap over the gills called an **operculum** that helps move water through the gills when the fish is stationary (Figure 18.17B).

D. Ray-finned fishes also have a **swim bladder** that can act as a buoyant counterbalance to their heavier bones. Sometimes this is connected to the digestive tract, enabling certain species to gulp air to increase oxygen intake.

E. Thin, flexible skeletal rays support the fins of ray-finned fishes.

F. **Lobe-fins:** The fins of lobe-finned fishes are muscular and supported by bones. Three lineages of lobed-fins survive today as descendents of the Devonian period: lungfish, coelacanths, and terrestrial tetrapods.

Module 18.18 Amphibians were the first tetrapods—vertebrates with two pairs of limbs.

A. Amphibians were the first land vertebrates and evolved about 400 mya, possibly from lobe-fins. Structurally, ancestral lobe-fins had strong fins, which may have been used to paddle and wriggle over dense vegetation. A good example of a transition animal (from fish to amphibian) is the fossil record of *Acanthostega,* a four-legged fish from the Devonian era (Figure 18.18A). The early amphibians encountered a lush environment rich with food and the chance to diversify. The amphibian expansion was of such great magnitude that the Carboniferous period is sometimes called the amphibian age (Module 17.7).

B. **Amphibians** include frogs, caecilians, and salamanders. Most amphibians are tied to water because their eggs and larvae (tadpoles) develop in water.

C. Some salamanders are entirely aquatic, but those that do live on land walk by bending their bodies from side to sided with a swagger (John Wayne style, just kidding) (Figure 18.18B). Frogs are well equipped for life on land and use their powerful back legs to hop about. Caecilians are almost blind and are legless burrowers that live in the moist, tropical soil.

D. Tadpoles are aquatic, legless scavengers with gills, a tail, and a lateral line system (Figure 18.18C).

E. Tadpoles undergo a radical metamorphosis (Figure 18.18C) to change into an adult that is often a terrestrial hunter, with paired legs, external eardrums, air-breathing lungs, and no lateral line system (Figure 18.18D).

F. The documented decline of the amphibian population worldwide over the past 25 years has zoologists concerned. The decline may be attributable to acid rains that harm the eggs and larvae of amphibians (*review:* Module 2.16).

Module 18.19 Reptiles are amniotes—tetrapods with a terrestrially adapted egg.

    A. Reptiles, birds, and mammals are called **amniotes** because they have developed an **amniotic egg** (Figure 18.19A). This development allowed a life cycle free of water.

    B. **Reptiles** include snakes, lizards, turtles, alligators, crocodilians, and birds. Lizards are the most numerous and diverse reptile group, crocodiles and alligators are the largest, snakes likely descended from lizards, and turtles have changed little since they evolved. *Review:* Reptiles are not a monophyletic group. Cladistic analysis groups birds with crocodiles, and lizards with snakes (Module 15.8).

    C. Reptiles have skin protected with protein (keratin), eggs with coatings that retain water, an internal fluid-filled sac (amnion) that bathes the embryo, and a food supply (yolk) in the amniotic egg. The young hatch as juveniles, bypassing the need for the free-living larval stage (Figure 18.19A).

    D. Most modern reptiles are **ectothermic.** They warm up by absorbing external heat, rather than generating much of their own metabolic heat as endothermic animals do (Figure 18.19B).

    E. Following the decline of prehistoric amphibians, reptilian lineages expanded and dominated Earth during the Age of Reptiles for 200 million years. These dinosaurs may have been **endothermic** (Figure 18.19C).

    F. When the dinosaurs died off 65 mya (Module 15.5), one line survived and evolved into birds.

Module 18.20 Birds are feathered reptiles with adaptations for flight.

    A. **Birds** have amniotic eggs, scales on their legs, and a reptilian body form. Birds evolved from small, two-legged, dinosaurs called theropods.

    B. Feathers, the most distinctive characteristic of birds, are derived from scales. Feathers shape bird wings into airfoils that create lift and enable birds to maneuver in the air.

    C. *Archaeopteryx* is an extinct bird with feathers and characteristics of bipedal dinosaurs such as teeth, claws, and a tail with many vertebrae (Figure 18.20A). With its heavy body, *Archaeopteryx* is more likely to have been a glider or walker than a flier.

    D. Many bird groups became extinct about 65 mya, along with the rest of the dinosaurs during the Cretaceous mass extinction.

    E. Modern birds have additional adaptations for flight, including an absence of teeth, no claws on their wings, very short tailbones, hollow bones, large breast muscles, efficient lungs, and an extremely high rate of metabolism to provide energy. Birds also have relatively large brains and possibly the best vision of all vertebrates (Figure 18.20B). The amniotic egg of birds has a hard outer shell and the male and female share responsibility for the incubation and care of the young. Birds are fabulous fliers, though some birds are flightless (Figure 18.20C).

Module 18.21 Mammals are amniotes that have hair and produce milk.

    A. Mammals evolved about 200 mya from the early amniotic lineage but occupied minor parts of habitats during the Age of Reptiles. Once the dinosaurs died off, the mammalian lineages underwent adaptive radiation. *Review:* Adaptive radiation (Module 14.8).

    B. Most mammals are terrestrial, with a number of winged and totally aquatic species. The largest animal that has ever existed is the blue whale, a species that can reach 30 m in length.

C. Mammals are endothermic, and they have hair and mammary glands.

D. The **monotremes,** such as the platypus, are egg-laying mammals that live in Australia and Tasmania (Figure 18.21A).

E. The **marsupials,** such as the American opossum and the kangaroo, give birth to embryonic young that complete development in their mother's pouch (marsupium). Most marsupials live in Australia, on neighboring islands, and in North and South America (Figure 18.21B).
   NOTE: Both groups evolved in isolation from other mammals in areas that were part of the Pangaean supercontinent, Gondwana (see Module 15.3).

F. **Eutherians (placental mammals)** comprise nearly 95% of all mammalian species, include dogs, cats, cows, rodents, bats, and whales. Their embryos are nurtured inside the mother by a placenta, an organ that includes both maternal and embryonic vascular tissue (Figure 18.21C).

G. Humans are eutherian mammals belonging to the order Primates. The relationship of humans to other primates is discussed in Chapter 19.
   Preview: Unit V will cover many other details of the lives of animals, emphasizing humans, mammals, and vertebrates, in that order.

IV. Animal Phylogeny and Diversity Revisited

Module 18.22 An animal phylogenetic tree is a work in progress.

A. Construction of a phylogenetic tree should be based on several lines of evidence such as molecular data, morphology, embryology, and fossil records.

B. Figure 18.4 conveniently illustrates the major evolutionary steps of the animal phyla in a phylogenetic tree using a traditional approach.
   1. Like most phylogenetic trees, this one is hypothetical and serves mainly to stimulate research and focus discussion.
   2. Colonial protists were the ancestors of the animal kingdom.
   3. Sponges may be a separate line of evolution: no true tissues.
   4. Two lines of tissue-level animals evolved: radially symmetrical animals, represented by cnidarians, and bilaterally symmetrical animals, the most primitive of which are represented by the flatworms.
   5. Among the bilateral animals, two lines evolved: those with pseudocoeloms, represented by the roundworms, and those with coeloms, the most primitive of which are represented by the molluscs.
   6. Among the coelomate animals, two lines evolved: those whose coelom developed from hollow outgrowths of the digestive tube—the echinoderms and chordates (deuterostomes); and those whose coelom developed from solid masses of cells—the molluscs, annelids, and arthropods (protostomes).

C. The molecular phylogenetic tree is based on molecular evidence (Figure 18.22).
   1. There are several similarities between the traditional tree and the molecular-based tree. For example, the earliest branching in both trees recognizes those that have true tissues and those that do not. Bilateral and radial symmetry is a branch point in both trees. Deuterostomes are recognized in both trees.
   2. One major difference in the molecular tree is that the protostomes are divided into two separate branches. The Lophotrochozoa have similarities in molecular sequence data and are named for the feeding apparatus and larva. The members of the other branch of the protostomes, the Ecdysozoa, share a common feature: They need to shed their exoskeleton.

D. Three important concepts to remember about the phylogenetic trees for animals are as follows:

1. It is a work in progress.

2. The animal kingdom's great diversity arose through the process of evolution.

3. All animals exhibit characteristics similar to their ancestors.
   Review: Gene expression and embryonic development (Chapter 11).

Module 18.23 Connections: Humans threaten animal diversity by introducing nonnative species.

A. The introduction of a nonnative species to a new environment can result in only two scenarios: The species will die, or it will survive and have devastating effects on the ecosystem into which it was introduced. In 2003, 65 quolls were relocated to an island were the cane toad has not been introduced (Figure 18.23A). They are thriving.

B. Rabbits, foxes, and cane toads (Figure 18.23B) have been introduced to Australia, and all three have ended in the second scenario.

C. Millions of dollars are now being spent each year by the Australian government in an effort to combat the ecological disaster caused by human intervention and reduce the loses of native species affected by nonnative species (Figures 18.23C and D).

Class Activities

1. Ask your students to consider the advantages (and disadvantages) of cephalization. While this seems like a simple question, I find that students often struggle with developing a scientifically sound response.

2. To have your class gain a real appreciation of insect diversity, have your students start an insect collection.

Transparency Acetates

Figure 18.1B	The life cycle of a sea star
Figure 18.2A	A hypothesis for the evolution of animals from a colonial flagellated protist
Figure 18.3A	Radial (left) and bilateral (right) symmetry
Figure 18.3B	No body cavity (a flatworm)
Figure 18.3C	Pseudocoelom (a roundworm)
Figure 18.3D	True coelem (a segmented worm)
Figure 18.3E	A choanoflagellate colony (about 0.02 mm high)
Figure 18.4	One hypothesis of animal phylogeny based on morphological comparisons
Figure 18.5	Bilateral symmetry
Figure 18.5D	Structure of a simple sponge
Figure 18.6D	Cnidocyte action
Figure 18.7A	A free-living flatworm, the planarian (most are about 5–10 mm long)
Figure 18.7B	A tapeworm, a parasitic flatworm
Figure 18.9A	The general body plan of a mollusc
Figure 18.10A	Segmentation and internal anatomy of an earthworm

---

Media

See the beginning of this book for a complete description of all media available for instructors and students. Animations and videos are available in the Campbell Image Presentation Library. Media Activities and Thinking as a Scientist investigations are available on the student CD-ROM and website.

Animations and Videos	Module Number
Hydra Releasing Sperm Video	18.6
Jelly Swimming Video	18.6
Thimble Jellies Video	18.6
Hydra Eating *Daphnia* (time-lapse) Video	18.6
Manta Ray Video	18.7
Rotifer Video	18.8
C. Elegans Crawling Video	18.8
C. Elegans Embryo Development (time-lapse) Video	18.8
Nudibranchs Video	18.9
Lobster Mouth Parts Video	18.11
Butterfly Emerging Video	18.12
Echinoderm Tube Feet Video	18.13
Bat Licking Nectar Video	18.20

Activities and Thinking as a Scientist

CHAPTER 19

Human Evolution

Teaching Objectives

Introduction   Describe the relationship between Neanderthals and modern humans.

Primate Diversity

19.1   Compare the three main groups of primates. List their characteristics and describe their evolutionary relationships.

19.2   Distinguish between monkeys and apes. Compare the different groups of apes to each other and to humans.

Hominid Evolution

19.3   Distinguish among hominoids, hominids, australopiths, and members of the genus *Homo*.

19.3   Describe five major features that emerged in the evolution of humans.

19.4   Describe the evidence that suggests when upright posture first evolved in humans.

19.5   Describe and compare the different species of *Homo*.

19.6   Describe the evidence that indicates where and when *Homo sapiens* first evolved.

19.7   Explain why a reduction in body hair and an increase in dark pigmentation might have evolved in hominids.

19.8   Explain how the *FOXP2* gene may have influenced human evolution.

Our Cultural History and Its Consequences

19.9   Describe the three major milestones that highlight the evolution of *Homo sapiens*. Explain the significance of human culture.

19.10   Explain how humans have acquired food over the past 100,000 years. Describe the impact of these activities on other organisms.

19.11   Describe the early development of agriculture and its impact on human culture.

19.12   Describe the impact of the Industrial Revolution on human culture and natural resources.

Key Terms

anthropoids	hominids	paleoanthropology
australopiths	hominoid	
culture	opposable thumb	

Word Roots

homin- = man (*hominid:* a term that refers to mammals that are more closely related to humans than to any other living species)

paleo- = ancient; **anthrop-** = man; **-ology** = the science of (*paleoanthropology:* the study of human origins and evolution)

Lecture Outline

Introduction *How Are We Related to the Neanderthals?*
Review: The role of molecular biology in systematics (Chapter 12 and Module 15.12).

A. Focus on the role of molecular biology in systematics.

1. Neanderthals lived in Europe until approximately 30,000 to 40,000 years ago. They had a large brain, could make tools with stone and wood, and were short in stature with heavy muscles. The Neanderthal skull (left) was markedly different from the Cro-Magnon skull (which is a direct ancestor of modern Europeans; right).

2. A question was raised recently regarding the possibility of interbreeding between Cro-Magnons and Neanderthals. To help answer the question, molecular techniques were used to sequence the DNA from a piece of Neanderthal bone. The results were compared to DNA of modern humans, regardless of location on Earth.

3. Little, if any, genetic contribution from Neanderthal to modern humans was seen in the comparison.

4. DNA from another Neanderthal bone (an infant) was analyzed, and the previous result was corroborated (no interbreeding occurred).

5. The DNA comparison was repeated with four more Neanderthal bones, and the results were the same: no similarities, no recognizable interbreeding between Cro-Magnon and Neanderthal occurred.

B. The central issues of this chapter are tracing our primate heritage, the not-entirely-worked-out evolutionary pathway of humans, and the pathway of cultural evolution and its effect on the environment.

I. Primate Diversity

Module 19.1 The human story begins with our primate heritage.
Review: Geological timeline (Module 15.1) and the comparison of human and baboon skeletons (Module 30.3).

A. Primates include lemurs, tarsiers, monkeys, and apes. Humans are part of the ape group. The earliest primates were small, arboreal creatures that lived at the end of the Age of Dinosaurs, 65 million years ago (mya) (Module 15.1).

B. Most living primates are arboreal, and humans (never strictly arboreal) retain in their bodies many traits that evolved with our arboreal relatives. Primitive primate characteristics, as exhibited by the slender loris (Figure 19.1A), include flexible shoulder and hip joints, maneuverable hands and feet, opposable thumbs and big toes, sensitivity to touch in the hands and feet, short snout, and eyes close together at the front (enhancing three-dimensional vision).

C. The lorises, pottos, and lemurs form one group of primates (Figure 19.1B). All live in tropical forests, and all are threatened by habitat destruction. Of approximately 50 species of lemur to live on Madagascar, 18 are extinct because of human incursion into their habitat about 2,000 years ago.

D. The tarsiers are the second group of primates that live in Southeast Asia and are ancestrally close relatives of anthropoids (Figure 19.1C).

E. The **anthropoids** include monkeys, apes, and humans. Anthropoids differ from the other two groups in having relatively larger brains and depending more on eyesight than on smell. Anthropoids have a fully opposable thumb, though the human thumb is designed less for power and more for manipulation. Anthropoids began diverging from other primates about 50 mya.

F. Monkeys differ from apes and humans in having a tail and equal-length forelimbs and hind limbs. They originated in Africa and migrated to other countries in Asia and the Americas. New World monkeys have nostrils that are wide open and far apart, and they often have prehensile tails (Figure 19.1E).

G. The phylogenetic tree of primates indicates several interesting possibilities (Figure 19.1D).
   1. Anthropoids diverged from other primates around 50 mya.
   2. Old World monkeys and New World monkeys diverged onto separate paths about 30 mya.
   3. Apes evolved from Old World monkeys around 20–25 mya.
   4. Humans diverged from an ancestor of chimpanzees approximately 5–7 mya.

H. Old World monkeys can be recognized by their narrow, close-set nostrils; many have a tough seat pad; and if a tail is present, it is not prehensile (Figure 19.1F).

Module 19.2 Hominoids include humans and four other groups of apes.

A. Primates (also called apes) include gibbons, orangutans, gorillas, chimpanzees, bonobos, and humans. All are tropical, lack tails, have longer forelimbs than hind limbs, have relatively large brains, and—apart from humans—have a limited geographical range. This group is formally referred to as **hominoids.**
   Review: Figure 15.9C illustrates a relationship between humans and apes based on molecular data.

B. Gibbons are the only apes that are entirely arboreal and monogamous for life. Nine species are found in Southeast Asia (Figure 19.2A).

C. The orangutan is a shy, solitary ape that is mostly arboreal, living in forests in Sumatra and Borneo (Figure 19.2B).

D. The gorilla is the largest of all primates and spends most of its time on the ground in African rain forests (Figure 19.2C). When they walk, their knuckles touch the ground.

E. The chimpanzee (and the very similar bonobo) inhabits rain forests in central Africa. Like gorillas, chimpanzees and bonobos are knuckle walkers. Many aspects of chimpanzee behavior resemble human behavior. They are fully capable of innovative behavior, can learn human sign language, and very likely have complex self-awareness. Recent biochemical evidence shows that chimpanzees and humans share 99% of their DNA sequences (Figure 19.2D).
   Preview: In Module 35.19, Jane Goodall discusses dominance hierarchies and cognition in chimpanzees.

NOTE: Consider how different the classification of humans and chimpanzees might be were humans not doing the classifying, or how the classification scheme might differ if two nonhuman species exhibiting the same evolutionarily close relationship were being considered.

II. Hominid Evolution

Module 19.3 The human branch of the primate tree is only a few million years old.

A. Hominids diverged evolutionarily from a common ancestor, probably about 5–7 mya (Figure 19.1D).

B. The study of human evolution is called **paleoanthropology.** Three words not to confuse are **hominids** (human species), hominoids (apes and humans), and anthropoids (apes, humans, and monkeys).

C. Five major characteristics distinguishing humans from other hominoids are as follows:

1. *Larger brain* size, capable of *language* and *symbolic thought,* and *make* and use *complex tools.*

2. *Shorter jaws* and flatter faces.

3. *Bipedal* posture and upright position.

4. Long-term pair bonding between mates.

5. Extended child care.

NOTE: Emphasize that humans did not descend from apes but, instead, share a recent common ancestor with apes (chimpanzees).

D. There are several different species (and several genera) in the human lineage. Evolutionary connections among the species illustrated (and others not illustrated) are hotly debated. The figure shows when each species lived (as determined from the known fossil record) but does not join them in a phylogenetic tree (Figure 19.3). It is only a time line.

E. Hominid diversity increased dramatically between 4 and 2 mya. The *Australopithecus anamensis* (4–4.5 mya) showed leg bones that were increasingly bipedal. Many of the early hominids are collectively called **australopiths;** however, this does not imply a monophyletic group.

F. *Homo sapiens* (that's us) is the only extant hominid. A common misconception is that humans evolved in direct lineage from an ancestor that separated from the apes and went directly to *Homo sapiens*. There were many dead ends along the way.

Module 19.4 Upright posture evolved well before an enlarged brain in hominids.

A. In what is now Tanzania, footprints left by *Australopithecus afarensis* indicate that hominids have been bipedal for at least 3.5 million years (Figure 19.4).

B. An important clue to bipedalism is the position of the skull in relationship to the spinal cord exit. The exit is at the base of the skull, allowing an upright position.

C. One of the most complete fossils of an australopith, nicknamed Lucy (Figure 19.4), dates back to 3.24 million years ago. *A. afarensis* was a small-brained (and small in stature) bipedal hominid that lived for about one million years.

D. What was the selective pressure that led to bipedalism? Was it an increase in the savanna or a way to reach low-hanging fruit from the ground? Irrespective of the reason, the hands of the early hominids were freed for other uses, such as tool production. Regardless, brain enlargement was preceded by bipedalism.

Module 19.5 Homo—the evolution of larger brains and reduced sexual dimorphism.

A. Brain enlargement was first evident in fossils from East Africa dated at around 2.4 mya. The larger skull also had a shorter jaw and was associated with stone tools. Thus the fossil has been assigned to the species *Homo habilis* ("handy man").

B. A fossil that dates back to 1.9 to 1.6 mya was discovered and is called *H. ergaster*. The brain size was much larger than *H. habilis,* its legs and hips were well designed for walking long distances, and the difference between the sizes of the sexes was less prominent (see Module 13.17, sexual dimorphism). Reduction in sexual dimorphism is often associated with pair-bonding (perhaps monogamy) and shared child-raising responsibility.

C. The teeth of *H. ergaster* were smaller, indicating a change in eating habits (more meat and less plant material) or perhaps some food preparation. More sophisticated tools were also used by *H. ergaster.*

D. *H. erectus* ("upright man") lived from about 1.8 mya to 250,000 years ago. *H. erectus* was taller and had a larger brain and a more advanced culture than *H. habilis. H. erectus* lived in huts or caves, built fires, wore clothes, and made more complex tools.

E. *H. erectus* spread out of Africa to Eurasia. With its broad geographic distribution, *H. erectus* became regionally diverse. One or more populations probably gave rise to our own species, *Homo sapiens.*
   Review: Chapter 14 discusses geographic patterns of speciation.

Module 19.6 When and where did modern *Homo sapiens* arise?

A. Evidence from fossil records and from DNA analysis indicates that all living *Homo sapiens* originated from Africa.

B. Ancestors of humans also came from Africa and date back as far as 600,000 years ago. The oldest fossil of *H. sapiens* found in Ethiopia dates back to 160,000 years (Figure 19.6A).

C. DNA studies indicate that Asians and Europeans are more closely related and that many African lineages represent earlier branches on the human family tree. This strongly suggests that all living humans have ancestors that originated as *H. sapiens* in Africa.

D. The conclusion regarding the origin of *H. sapiens* from Africa is further supported by the data from mitochondrial DNA and Y-chromosome analysis. Mitochondrial DNA analysis suggests that we all came from a "woman" that lived approximately 150,000 years ago. Y-chromosome analysis also suggests divergence from a common ancestor less than 100,000 years ago.

E. Evidence suggests that humans left Africa more than once, spreading to Asia first, then to Europe and Australia (oldest fossil outside Africa is approximately 50,000 years old). Arrival in the Americas is not certain but may have been between 30,000 and 15,000 years ago.

F. The rapid expansion of humans may have been related to their creativity and increased cognition. Neanderthal was a good tool-maker but showed little creativity or symbolic thought. Art from humans dates back to 77,000 years ago (Figure 19.6B).

G. Advanced thinking may have increased reproductive fitness, and other hominids could not compete when encountering humans. A good example of this is the extinction of the Neanderthal in Europe.

Module 19.7 Connection: Human skin colors reflect adaptation to varying amounts of sunlight.

A. Skin color of early hominids was probably similar to chimpanzees, light and covered with hair. As the early species (e.g., *H. ergaster*) evolved and began walking longer distances, less hair was an advantage when trying to stay cool. Damage from overexposure to UV radiation leading to skin cancer happened after reproductive age; thus this was not a selective factor for darker skin.

B. Folate (folic acid) is destroyed by UV. Therefore darker skin would be a positive selection factor to protect folate, which is needed during fetal development. UV also promotes calcium absorption, which is also needed for fetal development. In the intense sun of Africa, enough calcium would be absorbed even with dark skin. In other climates with less sun (northern latitudes), light skin would be more adaptive.

Module 19.8 Connection: A genetic difference helped humans start speaking.

A. The adaptation to speak and communicate with one another is one of the human characteristics that may have helped the global spread of humans (Figure 19.8).

B. A gene called *FOXP2* has been shown to be critical for brain development. The species with the closest DNA sequence to our *FOXP2* gene are birds. Like birds that learn their song from other birds, humans teach their young to speak.

C. Molecular evidence indicates that the *FOXP2* gene arose about 100,000 years ago, which coincides with the early fossils of *H. sapiens*.

D. Other genes are involved in speech, such as those used to shape proper anatomy and brain function. But researchers think that *FOXP2* is the critical gene for linguistics, which binds us together. This capacity to communicate allows the older members of human society to pass on large amounts of information to the next generation. Language is the basis of civilization.

III. Our Cultural History and Its Consequences

Module 19.9 Culture gives humans enormous power to change the environment.
Preview: Human population growth (Module 36.9), the impact of outside disturbances on community structure (Module 37.7), and the sociobiology of culture (Modules 35.15 and 35.19).

A. Three milestones highlight human evolution:
1. Erect stance, requiring skeletal remodeling.
2. Brain enlargement, with prolonged post-birth development of the skull and its contents.
3. Evolution of a prolonged childhood, during which cultural information is passed between generations (Module 15.7).

B. The upright stance limits the pelvic opening, creating a problem during childbirth due to the overly large heads of babies.

C. **Culture** includes the accumulated knowledge, customs, beliefs, arts, crafts, and ideas that are passed between generations. More than any other human feature, our culture can change the environment to meet our (selfish) needs at a faster rate than biological evolution. Our culture has allowed our species to transcend the limitations imposed on other species at the expense of other species and the environment.
Preview: Population dynamics is discussed in Chapter 36. The impact of human culture on the environment is discussed in Chapter 38.

Module 19.10 Scavenging, gathering, and hunting were the earliest human endeavors.

 A. This way of life began with the earliest hominids and continued to be the way of life for the australopiths and species of *Homo* until about 100,000 years ago. Hunting became important only with the advent of sophisticated tools 50,000 years ago.

 B. Some extant cultures (e.g., the !Kung of southwestern Africa) still practice hunting-gathering (Figure 19.10).

 C. With the development of more sophisticated hunting tools comes evidence of human-caused decimation of species such as the woolly rhinoceroses and giant deer of Europe.

 D. Humans reached Australia about 50,000 years ago, an event that may have been responsible for the extinction of the giant kangaroos.

 E. Nomadic hunters migrated from Asia to North America about 30,000 years ago. Their actions are likely to have caused the extinction of many large animal species.

 F. Other characteristics of this level of culture include the organization into communal groups that divided labor, the use of semipermanent homes, trading among populations, and (toward the end of the period) the growing of a few simple crops.

Module 19.11 Agriculture was a major development in human history.

 A. Agriculture developed in Africa, Eurasia, and the Americas 10,000 to 15,000 years ago. Forests were cleared and crops were planted with little damage done to the soil.
Review: The effects of deforestation on tropical forests are discussed in Module 34.18.

 B. About 5,000 years ago, farmers started using primitive plows (Figure 19.11). This opened up new areas for agriculture and increased productivity. Increases in population size made possible by improved agriculture, and the use of more advanced plows and overgrazing, and climate changes turned the Fertile Crescent from a rich forest area into a desert.
Review: Runoff from the overuse of fertilizers can result in algal blooms (Module 16.13). Also review soil conservation (Module 32.9) and organic farming (Module 32.10).

 C. Agriculture changed forever the relationship between humans and the biosphere. Large areas of native vegetation have been converted to farming use. Agriculture allows the establishment of permanent settlements and cities, and it frees many members of cultures to specialize in other activities (such as teaching college courses).

Module 19.12 Development of complex tools impacts human culture and the world.
Preview: Human population growth (Modules 36.9–36.10).

 A. The change from small hand tools to large-scale machines produced major effects on most human activities (Figure 19.12).
NOTE: The first industries built up around the fabrication of metal tools for hunting and farming long before the machine age.

 B. Complex machines further reduced the need for agricultural workers. Energy consumption increased. Medical advances reduced deaths.

 C. During all these cultural changes, humans have not changed genetically in any significant way. Rapid cultural change has changed environments in which humans and other species live. Nothing is new about this environmental change except the *speed* of the change, which now vastly outpaces the rate of biological evolution.
Preview: The effects of human interaction on the environment will be discussed in Chapter 38.

Class Activities

1. Have your class consider the following: Humans and chimpanzees are placed in different genera. Why? If any species other than humans were doing the classifying, would humans and chimpanzees be placed within the same genus?

2. Considering that insects are the most successful of all animal taxa in an evolutionary sense, in terms of species diversity and numbers, of what good is the large human brain? Over the long term will the human brain prove to have staying power and enable us to avoid extinction? What does evolution hold for the future of humans—i.e., how might the descendants of modern humans differ both anatomically and physiologically?

3. Has technology placed us in a fourth major stage of human culture? Are we now in the information/computer age?

Transparency Acetates

Figure 19.1B   A phylogenetic tree of primates

Figure 19.3   A time line for some hominid species

Reviewing the Concepts, page 409: *Homo sapiens* and *Homo neanderthalensis*

Connecting the Concepts, page 409: Phylogenetic tree of primates

Media

See the beginning of this book for a complete description of all media available for instructors and students. Animations and videos are available in the Campbell Image Presentation Library. Media Activities and Thinking as a Scientist investigations are available on the student CD-ROM and website.

Animations and Videos	Module Number
Gibbons Brachiating Video	19.2

Activities and Thinking as a Scientist	Module Number
Web/CD Activity 19A: *Primate Diversity*	19.2
Web/CD Activity 19B: *Human Evolution*	19.6

CHAPTER 20

Unifying Concepts of Animal Structure and Function

Teaching Objectives

Introduction   Explain how geckos are able to walk on walls and ceilings.

The Hierarchy of Structural Organization in an Animal

20.1   Explain how the structure of a bird is adapted for flight.
20.2   Describe the levels of organization in an animal's body.
20.3   Define a tissue, and list the four animal tissue types.
20.4–20.7   Describe the four main animal tissues, noting their structures and their functions.
20.8   Explain how artificial tissues are created and used.
20.9   Explain how the structure of organs represents cooperative interactions.
20.10   Describe the general structures and functions of the eleven major organ systems in vertebrate animals.
20.11   Compare the advantages and disadvantages of X-ray, CT, MRI, MRM, and PET imaging technologies. Also explain how each system works.

Exchanges with the External Environment

20.12   Describe the systems that help exchange materials between an animal and its environment. Describe examples of adaptations to increase the surface-to-volume ratio.
20.13   Define the concept of homeostasis.
20.14   Distinguish between negative and positive feedback. Explain how thermoregulation is an example of homeostasis.

Key Terms

adipose tissue	excretory system	neuron
anatomy	fibrous connective tissue	organ
basement membrane	homeostasis	organ system
blood	immune system	organism
bone	integumentary system	physiology
cardiac muscle	interstitial fluid	reproductive systems
cartilage	loose connective tissue	respiratory system
circulatory system	mucous membrane	skeletal muscle
connective tissue	muscle tissue	skeletal system
digestive system	muscular system	smooth muscle
endocrine system	negative feedback	tissue
epithelial tissue	nervous system	
epithelium	nervous tissue	

Word Roots

ecto- = outside; **-therm** = heat (*ectothermic:* organisms that do not produce enough metabolic heat to have much effect on body temperature)

endo- = inside (*endothermic:* organisms with bodies that are warmed by heat generated by metabolism; this heat is usually used to maintain a relatively stable body temperature higher than that of the external environment)

fibro- = a fiber (*fibrous connective tissue:* a dense tissue with large numbers of collagenous fibers organized into parallel bundles)

homeo- = same; **-stasis** = standing, posture (*homeostasis:* the steady-state physiological condition of the body)

inter- = between (*interstitial fluid:* the internal environment of vertebrates, consisting of the fluid filling the space between cells)

Lecture Outline

Introduction *Climbing the Walls*

    A. Each animal species is an accumulation of different structural and functional adaptations to life in its particular environment.

    B. This is particularly evident when one studies animals in extreme environments or with unique adaptations such as the gecko (chapter-opening photo).

        1. Most vertebrates cannot walk up a wall or on a ceiling, so how does a gecko accomplish this feat?

        2. Much discussion went in to speculating how geckos walk on ceilings, but it wasn't until a team of scientists and engineers examined the feet carefully that the answer became clear.

        3. The pictures illustrate specialized structures (setae and spatulae) at the end of each toe that allow the unique walking function. The answer can be found at the molecular level and is due to attractions between a special protein, keratin, and a force called the van der Waals force (see Chapter 3).

    C. This chapter introduces the unit on animals. Each succeeding chapter examines how animals meet needs such as nutrition, obtainment and distribution of oxygen, response to stimuli, waste removal, movement, and reproduction.

    D. In this chapter, the general, overall body organization is discussed: cells to tissues to organs to organ systems.

  I. The Hierarchy of Structural Organization in an Animal

    Module 20.1 Structure fits function in the animal body.

      A. **Anatomy** and **physiology** are the studies of structure and function, respectively.

      B. Feathers are dead protein called keratin (just like the keratin at the ends of gecko toes) formed into complex three-dimensional structures by special pits in a bird's skin. These form airfoils (Figure 20.1).

      Review: Birds' feathers are derived from scales (Module 18.20).

C. The bones of a bird's wing are homologous with those of the human arm (Module 13.4) but have been modified for flight. A bird's bones are reduced in number and motility, allowing the wing to function as a unit, and they are hollow but strongly reinforced, to reduce weight.

D. Flight muscles sit below the bird, mostly off the wings, so the wings do not have to work hard to move the weight. This position also provides balance.

Module 20.2 Animal structure has a hierarchy.
   Review: Hierarchy of organization (Module 1.1; Figure 1.1) and cells in Chapter 4.

A. In the whole animal, the hierarchy of structure is as follows: cells, tissues, organs, organ systems, organism (Figure 20.2). Each level of complexity reinforces the relationship between form and function.

B. A cell is the smallest living unit of life that can live independently or collectively (Figure 20.2A).

C. A **tissue** is a cooperating group of similar cells all performing a specialized function (Figure 20.2B).

D. An **organ** is a collection of tissues that perform a specific task (Figure 20.2C).

E. An **organ system** is composed of a collection of organs and other parts that perform a vital body function (Figure 20.2D).

F. An **organism** is a cooperating collection of organ systems that function in an integrative fashion (Figure 20.2E).

Module 20.3 Tissues are groups of cells with a common structure and function.
   Review: Animal cell junctions (Module 4.18; Figure 4.18B).

A. The cells composing a tissue (from the Latin word for *weave*) are specialized: Their particular structure enables them to perform their particular function.

B. Cells in tissues are held together, within the context of the nonliving material they organize, with sticky glue that coats the cells or with special membrane junctions.

C. There are four major categories of tissue: epithelial, connective, muscle, and nervous.

Module 20.4 Epithelial tissue covers the body and lines its organs and cavities.
   NOTE: Epithelial tissue is avascular.

A. **Epithelial tissue** (epithelium) occurs as sheets of closely packed cells. One "free" surface forms a barrier or exchange surface; the other surface is attached to underlying tissues by a basement membrane.

B. Tissues are categorized according to the number of cell layers and the shape of the individual cells (Figures 20.4A–D). Simple epithelium consists of a single layer of cells, and stratified epithelium consists of multiple layers of cells. Cells may be squamous, cuboidal, or columnar in shape.
   NOTE: A third type of layering is pseudostratified; as the name implies, it consists of a single layer of cells that give, the impression of being layered. Some epithelium consists of transitional cells (e.g., the bladder), which do not maintain a single shape.

C. The structure of each type of epithelium fits its function.

D. Stratified squamous epithelium regenerates rapidly by division of the cells at its attached surface; it covers surfaces that are subject to abrasion, such as the lining of the esophagus and the epidermis (Figures 20.4D and E). The latter is a special type of stratified squamous epithelium that has a layer of dead cells at the surface.

E. Simple squamous epithelium is thin and leaky, suitable for the exchange of materials by diffusion; it lines our lungs and blood vessels (Figure 20.4A).
    Preview: The lungs, a component of the respiratory system, are discussed in Chapter 22.

F. Cuboidal epithelium and columnar epithelium have large cells that make secretory products and form large, often folded, surface areas (Figures 20.4B and C). They line the digestive tract and air tubes, where they form a moist epithelium, a mucous membrane.

G. Epithelial tissues that secrete chemicals are called **glandular epithelia** and are found in glands and in the lining of the respiratory and digestive tracts. The **mucous membranes** of air tubes are important for keeping debris out of the lungs. Particles get trapped in the mucoid secretions, and cilia beat them up and out of the air tubes.
    NOTE: Smoking paralyzes cilia and, thus, allows debris that would otherwise be trapped and removed to reach the lungs. Furthermore, the paralysis of cilia in the oviducts probably contributes to the higher incidence of ectopic pregnancies among smokers.

Module 20.5 Connective tissue binds and supports other tissues.

A. There are six **connective tissue** types that consist of a sparse population of cells scattered in a nonliving matrix that is synthesized by the cells.
    NOTE: Connective tissue contains three fiber types. Collagen fibers provide strength; elastic fibers, resilience; and reticular fibers, a supportive network. The function of a given connective tissue can be deduced from the relative abundance of each of these types of fiber.

B. **Loose connective tissue** is a loose weave of the protein collagen; it holds many other tissues and organs in place (Figure 20.5A). It is the most common connective tissue.

C. **Adipose tissue** contains fat stored in closely packed adipose cells that are used to pad and insulate the body and store energy (Figure 20.5B).

D. **Fibrous connective tissue** consists of densely packed collagen fibers that form tendons (muscles to bone) and ligaments (bone to bone) (Figure 20.5C).
    NOTE: The type of fibrous connective tissue discussed here is dense regular connective tissue. Another type, dense irregular connective tissue, is found (for example) in the deeper (reticular) layer of the dermis. As their names imply, a difference between the two is the regular versus scattered arrangement of collagen fibers.

E. **Cartilage** is strong but flexible skeletal material with collagen fibers embedded in a rubbery matrix (Figure 20.5D). It is found at the end of bones and between the vertebrae and supports the nose and ears.
    NOTE: There are three types of cartilage: hyaline cartilage (e.g., embryonic skeleton), elastic cartilage (e.g., outer ear), and fibrocartilage (e.g., intervertebral discs).

F. **Bone** is rigid tissue made of collagen fibers embedded in calcium salts (Figure 20.5E).
    Preview: Bone tissue is discussed in more detail in Modules 30.4 and 30.5.

G. **Blood** has a fluid matrix (plasma, consisting of water, salts, and proteins) and red and white blood cells. It functions in transport and immunity (Figure 20.5F).
    Preview: Blood, a component of the circulatory system, is discussed in more detail in Chapter 23. Immunity is discussed in greater detail in Chapter 24.

Module 20.6 Muscle tissue functions in movement.
    Preview: Skeletal muscle is discussed in more detail in Modules 30.7–30.10.

A. **Muscle tissue** consists of bundles of long muscle cells (muscle fibers) and is the most abundant tissue in most animals (Figure 20.6). Parallel strands of contractile proteins exist within the cytoplasm of muscle fibers.

B. **Skeletal muscle** is attached to bones by tendons and is responsible for voluntary movement. Its cells are multinucleate, striated (from sarcomeres), and unbranched (Figure 20.6A).

C. **Cardiac muscle** causes the involuntary contractions of the heart. Its cells are striated, interconnected at special junctions, and branched (Figure 20.6B).

D. **Smooth muscle** is found in the walls of the digestive tract, urinary bladder, and arteries. Its cells are unstriated, spindle-shaped, and cause slow but strong involuntary movements (Figure 20.6C).

Module 20.7 Nervous tissue forms a communication network.
Preview: The nervous system is discussed in more detail in Chapters 28 and 29.

A. **Nervous tissue** functions to relay information regarding the internal and external environments and to relay information from one part of the body to another.
NOTE: The nervous system (Chapter 28) and the endocrine system (Chapter 26) are the control and communication systems of the body. The difference is that the nervous system acts more rapidly than the endocrine system, and the effects of nervous system activity are not as long lasting as those of the endocrine system.

B. Nervous tissue consists of interconnected **neurons;** nerve cells specialized to conduct electrical nerve impulses (Figure 20.7).

C. Each neuron has a cell body, dendrites that transfer messages to the cell body, and axons that transfer messages away from the cell body (Module 28.2).

D. One type of supportive cell in nervous tissue nourishes the neurons, while others insulate axons and promote faster signals.

Module 20.8 Artificial tissues have medical uses.

A. Most tissue can repair itself. However, if tissue is severely damaged, the repair process may be inadequate, leading to an improper or failed repair.

B. Artificial skin has been developed and shown to be very effective at assisting the healing process and warding off infections, particularly for burn victims.

C. Current areas of research into artificial tissue include cartilage and teeth.

Module 20.9 Organs are made up of tissues.

A. All animals except sponges (and some cnidaria) have some organs.
Review: Sponges are discussed in greater detail in Module 18.5.

B. Organs consist of several tissues adapted to perform specific functions as a group. They perform functions that none of the component tissues can perform alone.

C. The heart consists of muscle (the major portion, providing the contractile, pumping force), epithelial tissue (providing a smooth, low-friction inner surface), connective tissue (tying all the tissues together into a strong, elastic structure), and nervous tissue (directing the contractions).

D. The small intestine consists of layers of tissues (Figure 20.9). The lumen is lined with columnar epithelium that secretes mucus and digestive enzymes. The epithelial layer is surrounded by connective tissue, which contains nerves and blood vessels. Two perpendicular layers of smooth muscle surround the connective tissue. Two more layers, connective tissue and epithelium, surround the muscle layers.

E. The coordinated effort of the tissues within the small intestine performs a function that no single tissue could do on its own.

Module 20.10 Organ systems work together to perform life's functions.

A. An organ system is a group of several organs that work together to perform a vital body function.

B. In vertebrates, there are eleven organ systems. Each one is introduced below, followed by the chapter in which it is covered (Figures 20.10A–K).

C. **Digestive system.** Organs of the digestive tract ingest food, break it down into smaller chemical units, absorb these units, and eliminate the unused parts (Chapter 21).

D. **Respiratory system.** The lungs and associated breathing tubes exchange gases with the environment (Chapter 22).

E. **Circulatory system.** The heart and blood vessels supply nutrients and O_2 to the body and carry away wastes and CO_2 (Chapter 23).

F. **Immune and lymphatic systems.** Lymph vessels and nodes supplement the work of the cardiovascular system, particularly as components of the immune system, a diffuse system of cells (including lymphocytes and macrophages, both of which are types of white blood cells) and processes that protect the body from foreign invasion (Chapter 24). The lymphatic system supplements the function of the circulatory system. Lymph fluid that has leaked out of blood vessels and into the tissue is returned to the blood via the lymph vessels.

G. **Excretory system.** The kidneys, bladder, and urethra remove nitrogen-containing wastes from the blood and maintain osmotic balance (Chapter 25).

H. **Endocrine system.** The endocrine glands secrete hormones into the blood that regulate most other activities (Chapter 26).

I. **Reproductive systems.** There are two separate systems, one in females and one in males. Ovaries and testes and associated organs produce female and male gametes, and they help in fertilization and embryo development (Chapter 27).

J. **Nervous system.** The brain, spinal cord, nerves, and sense organs work together with the endocrine system to sense the outside environment, affect responses, and coordinate body activities (Chapters 28 and 29).

K. **Muscular system.** All skeletal muscles provide movement as they work with the skeletal system (Chapter 30).

L. **Skeletal system.** Bones and cartilage provide support and protection, and work with the muscular system to provide movement (Chapter 30).

M. **Integumentary system.** Skin, hair, and nails protect the internal body parts from mechanical injury, infection, extreme temperatures, and drying out (Chapters 24 and 29).

Module 20.11 Connection: New imaging technology reveals the inner body.

A. **X-rays** show shadows of hard structures but fail to image soft tissues; X-rays produce flat, two-dimensional images.

B. **CT** (computerized tomography) **scan** uses computers to combine the images produced by many weak X-ray sources. This technology can detect small differences between normal and abnormal tissues in many organs (Figures 20.11A and B). A modified version of the CT scanner is the ultrafast CT, which shows actual movements and volumes of the organs. This technique is very useful for the detection of heart disease.

C. **MRI** (magnetic resonance imaging) measures changes in the magnetic signal when the hydrogen atoms in living materials are excited. MRI images soft tissues extremely well.

D. A powerful application of MRI is **MRM** (magnetic resonance microscopy), which can create 3-D images of very small structures (Figure 20.11C). Functional MRM can track small changes in blood flow within the brain.

E. PET (positron-emission tomography) yields information about metabolic processes by imaging the pattern of radioactivity from isotope-labeled glucose or other metabolic precursors. PET is most valuable for measuring metabolic activity in the brain (Figure 20.11D).

II. Exchanges with the External Environment

Module 20.12 Structural adaptations enhance exchange between animals and their environment.

A. Animals are not closed systems; from the cellular through the organismal level of organization, they must obtain materials from the outside environment and excrete metabolic wastes into that same environment.

B. In simple animals with gastrovascular cavities (cnidarians and flatworms, Modules 18.5 and 18.6), virtually every cell has a plasma membrane exposed directly to an aqueous environment.

C. Most other animals have relatively smaller outer surfaces compared to their volumes. They rely on specialized, inner surfaces for the exchange of materials (Figure 20.12A). The **interstitial fluid** mediates the exchange of materials between the blood and the body's inner cells (see circular enlargement in Figure 20.12A).

D. Surface areas of the lungs (Figure 20.12B), intestines, and kidneys provide for the exchange of materials between the outer environment and the blood. Bodies with greater numbers of cells to be serviced have correspondingly larger total surfaces of exchange.

E. Two basic concepts in animal biology are illustrated in Figure 20.12A:

1. Complex animals with cells out of direct contact with the external environment must have a system of internal structures to service those cells.

2. Interdependent organ systems must work cooperatively to have a functional organism.

Module 20.13 Animals regulate their internal environment.

A. An animal's homeostatic control systems maintain internal conditions within a range where life's metabolic processes can occur. For example, the ptarmigan can survive the cold winter by maintaining proper water and salt balance and an internal temperature of approximately 40°C (Figure 20.13A). Our bodies maintain salt and water balance and also keep our internal fluids at about 37°C.

B. **Homeostasis** is the maintenance of an organism's steady state in the face of environmental fluctuations (Figure 20.13B).

C. The term "steady state" should not be taken to mean unchanging. Homeostasis maintains the body in a dynamic equilibrium. Slight fluctuations within the body are normal, but changes outside the normal range can be devastating. For example, the normal range of blood pH is between 7.35 and 7.45. A blood pH above or below this very narrow range can cause severe illness and even death.
Preview: The classic example of homeostasis is the regulation of blood glucose levels. After a meal, when blood glucose levels rise, the body releases insulin to lower blood glucose levels by storing it as fat or glycogen. Between meals, when blood glucose levels have fallen, the body releases glucagon to stimulate the release of glucose from fat or glycogen into the blood (Module 26.7).

Module 20.14 Homeostasis depends on negative feedback.

A. Most control mechanisms in our body use **negative feedback** to maintain equilibrium. A good example is a thermostat, which uses negative feedback control to keep the room temperature constant. When a sensor falls below a set temperature, the heat turns on. When the sensor rises above that point, the heat turns off.

Review: Negative feedback with regard to cell metabolism is discussed in Module 5.8.

B. Maintenance of blood temperature in mammals (and most homeostatic mechanisms) functions by negative feedback. The brain senses temperature and raises or lowers body temperature by sending nervous signals to two sets of structures in the skin: sweat glands and blood vessel networks (Figure 20.14).

Preview: Thermoregulation (Module 25.2) and thermoreceptors (Module 29.3).

Class Activities

1. Throughout this unit, the projection of material onto a monitor to illustrate structures seen under a dissecting or compound microscope can be used to great advantage. Your own internal cheek epithelial cells and blood cells (previously included in many laboratory exercises but now banned from most student labs because of AIDS) can be rapidly prepared and examined in front of a class. The arrangement of tissues in organs (lung, heart, striated muscle, kidney, brain, and other material from slaughterhouses) can be demonstrated under a dissecting microscope to very large classes. Combine a living surface view of human skin with the details seen under a prepared slide showing a cross section of skin. Activities such as feeding, responses to stimuli, various kinds of movement, and the circulation of blood can be demonstrated in invertebrates, or with fish, frogs, and small reptiles.

2. Have groups of students choose an organ and discover what tissues make up this organ and how these tissues contribute to the function of that organ.

3. Although negative feedback is important in the regulation of homeostasis, the human body also exhibits positive feedback. After describing positive feedback, see if your class can determine which human physiological processes are regulated by positive feedback mechanisms.

Transparency Acetates

Figure 20.1	The structure of a bird wing
Figure 20.2	An example of structural hierarchy in a pelican
Figure 20.4	Types of epithelium
Figure 20.5	Types of connective tissue
Figure 20.6	The three types of muscle
Figure 20.9	Tissue layers of the small intestine wall
Figure 20.10A–F	Summary of the functions of human organ systems
Figure 20.10G–L	Summary of the functions of human organ systems
Figure 20.12A	Direct exchange between the environment and the cells of a structurally simple animal (a hydra)

Media

See the beginning of this book for a complete description of all media available for instructors and students. Animations and videos are available in the Campbell Image Presentation Library. Media Activities and Thinking as a Scientist investigations are available on the student CD-ROM and website.

Animations and Videos	Module Number
Negative Feedback Animation	20.14
Positive Feedback Animation	20.14

Activities and Thinking as a Scientist	Module Number
Web/CD Activity 20A: *Correlating Structure and Function of Cells*	20.1
Web/CD Activity 20B: *The Levels of Life Card Game*	20.2
Web/CD Activity 20C: *Overview of Animal Tissues*	20.3
Web/CD Activity 20D: *Epithelial Tissue*	20.4
Web/CD Activity 20E: *Connective Tissue*	20.5
Web/CD Activity 20F: *Muscle Tissue*	20.6
Web/CD Activity 20G: *Nervous Tissue*	20.7
Web/CD Activity 20H: *Regulation: Negative and Positive Feedback*	20.14

CHAPTER 21

Nutrition and Digestion

Teaching Objectives

Introduction Describe the nature of humpback whale feeding.

Obtaining and Processing Food

21.1 Define and distinguish among carnivores, herbivores, omnivores, suspension feeders, substrate feeders, fluid feeders, and bulk feeders.

21.2 Describe the four stages of food processing. Explain how animals avoid the risk of self-digestion.

21.3 Compare the structures and functions of a gastrovascular cavity and an alimentary canal. Describe the specialized digestive systems of an earthworm, a grasshopper, and a bird.

Human Digestive System

21.4 Describe the main components of the human alimentary canal and the associated digestive glands.

21.5 Describe the functional components of saliva and the types and functions of the teeth in humans.

21.6 Explain how swallowing occurs and how food is directed away from the trachea.

21.7 Explain how the Heimlich maneuver is performed.

21.8 Explain how the structure of the esophagus functions to propel food.

21.9 Relate the structure of the stomach to its functions. Describe the functions of the secretions of the stomach. Finally, explain the causes of heartburn and why the stomach does not digest itself.

21.10 Describe the most common cause of stomach ulcers and the primary forms of treatment.

21.11 Describe the different types of chemical digestion that occur in the small intestine. Explain how the structure of the small intestine promotes nutrient absorption. Describe the roles of the liver and gall bladder in these processes.

21.12 Describe the structure and functions of the colon and rectum. Note the causes of diarrhea and constipation.

Diets and Digestive Adaptations

21.13 Compare the digestive tracts of carnivores and herbivores. Describe the cellulose digesting specializations of the digestive tracts of a koala and cow.

Nutrition

21.14 Describe the three common nutritional needs of all animals.

21.15 Define "basal metabolic rate," explain how it is measured, and explain how energy is obtained and stored in the body.

21.16 Distinguish between undernourishment and malnutrition. Describe the four classes of essential nutrients.

21.17 Explain why vegetarians cannot rely upon a single type of plant food.

21.18 Define a vitamin, and distinguish between water-soluble and fat-soluble vitamins.

21.19 Define the essential minerals, and explain why each is important in our diet.
21.20 Define the Recommended Dietary Allowances, and explain how they contribute to good health.
21.21 Describe the types of information found on food labels.
21.22 Describe the obesity epidemic in the United States. Describe the role of leptin in weight management. Explain why cravings for fat may have once been adaptive.
21.23 Describe the best approach to weight control.
21.22 Explain how diet can influence the risks of cardiovascular disease and cancer.

Key Terms

absorption	feces	mouth
acid chyme	fluid feeders	omnivores
alimentary canal	gallbladder	pancreas
anus	gastric juice	peristalsis
appendix	gastric ulcers	pharynx
basal metabolic rate (BMR)	gastrovascular cavity	pyloric sphincter
bile	gizzards	Recommended Dietary
bulk feeders	herbivores	Allowances (RDAs)
carnivores	high-density lipoproteins	rectum
cecum	(HDLs)	ruminant mammals
colon	ingestion	saliva
crop	intestine	small intestine
digestion	kilocalories (kcal)	stomachs
duodenum	large intestine	substrate feeders
elimination	liver	suspension feeders
esophagus	low-density lipoproteins	trachea
essential amino acids	(LDLs)	villi
essential fatty acids	microvilli	vitamin
essential nutrients	minerals	

Lecture Outline

Introduction *Getting Their Fill of Krill*

   A. Feeding (ingesting food) is a distinctive characteristic of the animal kingdom.

   B. The humpback whale, from an unusual habitat, shows how an animal's structure and behavior are directly tied to feeding and food processing.

   1. Humpback whales are suspension feeders that strain small fish and crustaceans from the ocean. A 72-ton whale processes as much as 2 tons of food a day.

   2. These whales use "bubble nets" to help concentrate their food at the surface. The mouth has a tremendous volume when expanded and uses the brushlike baleen to sift the food from the water. The stomach can hold up to half a ton of food at a time.

   3. For four months in the summer, these whales feed in the rich, cold oceans of polar regions and store up vast fat reserves. In the winter, they migrate to warm, southern oceans to breed. They eat little for eight months until they return to the polar regions.

I. Obtaining and Processing Food

   Module 21.1 Animals ingest their food in a variety of ways.

   A. All animals eat other organisms. Eating can be by absorption (as in a few parasitic worms) or by ingestion.

   B. Animals can be classified into one of three dietary categorized.
      1. **Herbivores** (e.g., deer or sea urchins) eat plants or algae.
      2. **Carnivores** (e.g., lions and spiders) eat only other animals.
      3. **Omnivores** (e.g., humans and crows) eat both plants and animals.

   C. Animals can also be classified based on the size and location of the food that is ingested.
      1. **Suspension feeders** ingest small animals, such as microscopic protists, and plants (whales, clams, oysters and tubeworms, Figure 21.1A).
      2. **Substrate feeders** ingest by burrowing into their food (earthworms and caterpillars; Figure 21.1B).
      3. **Fluid feeders** obtain nutrients from plant sap (aphids) or animal fluids (mosquitoes; Figure 21.1C).
      4. **Bulk feeders** are those that consume larger prey whole or in pieces (most animals; Figure 21.1D).

   Module 21.2 Overview: Food processing occurs in four stages.

   A. Food processing can be divided into four stages (Figure 21.2A).

   B. Stage 1: **Ingestion** is the act of eating.

   C. Stage 2: **Digestion** is the breakdown of food into molecules small enough to be absorbed. Digestion occurs in two steps: mechanical and chemical breakdown. Mechanical digestion occurs in the mouth. During digestion, larger polymers are chemically digested into smaller components by hydrolysis (Module 3.3; Figure 3.3B). Specific enzymes catalyze each step of digestion (Figure 21.2B). The products of digestion are then used for either cellular respiration or biosynthesis (Modules 6.14 and 6.15).

   D. Food consists of large polymeric fats, carbohydrates, proteins, and nucleic acids that animals cannot absorb directly. All animals need the same monomers: fatty acids, simple sugars, amino acids, and nucleotides.

   E. Stage 3: **Absorption** is the assimilation of these small nutrient molecules (monomers). Once in the body, cells can use the monomers to synthesis the macromolecules necessary to perform cellular functions.
      NOTE: Food does not actually enter the body until it is absorbed. Prior to absorption, food is in a tube (in the case of animals with an alimentary canal) that runs through the body.

   F. Stage 4: **Elimination** is the release of undigested material from the digestive tract.

   Module 21.3 Digestion occurs in specialized compartments.

   A. A single-celled organism, such as an amoeba, has specialized compartments for digestion called food vacuoles. Sponges, like these single-celled organisms, carry out all of their digestive functions within their cells (Module 18.5).

   B. Simple animals, such as cnidarians and flatworms, have a single digestive compartment, a **gastrovascular cavity,** in which digestion and absorption occur, with a single opening, the **mouth,** for ingestion and elimination (Figure 21.3A).

C. Other animals have a series of compartments (organs) arranged along a digestive tube (**alimentary canal**) that extends between the mouth and anus. Three examples are presented in Figure 21.3B.

D. Ingested food passes to the first cavity via a muscular **pharynx** and **esophagus.**

E. The first cavity may be a **crop** (a pouchlike organ for temporary storage and food softening), a **gizzard** (a muscular pouch that contains grinding structures), or a **stomach** (a muscular pouch without grinding structures).

F. Chemical digestion and nutrient absorption occur mainly in the **intestine.** Intestines typically have modifications that increase their inner surface area and thus increase the absorptive surface.

G. Undigested material is expelled through the **anus.**

H. The exact nature of an animal's alimentary canal reflects its diet. An earthworm is an omnivorous substrate feeder with an intestine that has an inner, dorsal fold to increase its absorptive area. A grasshopper is an herbivore with a number of adaptations for the efficient processing of plant material. Different birds eat different foods, but most store food in a crop and use a gravel-containing gizzard to grind food that has been swallowed whole.

II. Human Digestive System

Module 21.4 The human digestive system consists of an alimentary canal and accessory glands.

A. The main parts of the alimentary canal are the mouth, oral cavity, tongue, pharynx, esophagus, stomach, small intestine, large intestine, rectum, and anus (Figure 21.4).

B. Digestive glands—the salivary glands, pancreas, and liver—secrete digestive enzymes into the cavities with which they are associated.
    NOTE: These glands secrete into a duct; this makes them exocrine glands. In contrast, endocrine glands secrete into the blood (Module 20.10).

C. Food is propelled through the alimentary canal by **peristalsis,** wavelike contractions of smooth muscle.

D. Sphincter muscles control the passage of food from one cavity to the next. The **pyloric sphincter** regulates movement of food from the stomach to the small intestine, where digestion and absorption is completed in 5 to 6 hours.

E. The total digestive process takes about 12–24 hours. Any undigested food passes through the large intestines and is expelled through the anus as feces.
    NOTE: Lipids take longer and require less energy to digest than carbohydrates and proteins do.

Module 21.5 Digestion begins in the oral cavity.

A. **Saliva** contains lubricants, buffers, antibacterial agents, and a digestive enzyme (salivary amylase) that hydrolyzes starch. The sight or smell of food triggers the release of salivary juices.
    NOTE: Oral stimulation and the thought of food also trigger the secretion of saliva. Other functions of saliva include helping keep teeth clean, dissolving food so that it can be tasted, and aiding in the formation of the bolus.

B. Mechanical and chemical digestion begins in the oral cavity as food is chewed (Figure 21.5).

C. Humans have four kinds of teeth (arranged in four sets, right and left in the upper and lower jaw): two bladelike incisors for biting, one pointed canine for tearing, two premolars, and three molars for grinding and crushing food.
NOTE: Only animals with a palate and cheeks chew their food; the palate prevents food from entering the nasal cavity while chewing, and the cheeks prevent food from falling out of the mouth. Compare how a crocodile gulps its food with how a human chews its food. Vertebrates vary greatly in their complement of teeth. A pattern of dentition is related to an animal's diet. For example, horses have incisors to shear off and molars to grind the grass they eat, but they have no canines. Rodents have strong, continually growing incisors for gnawing on cellulose-rich plant materials. Lions and other carnivores have prominent canines with which they tear large hunks of flesh from their prey.

D. The tongue tastes the food, manipulates the food, and shapes the food into a bolus, which it then pushes to the back of the oral cavity and into the pharynx where it is swallowed.

Module 21.6 The food and breathing passages both open into the pharynx.

A. Most of the time, when not eating, the human pharynx opens into the **trachea** (windpipe) for breathing and speaking (air vibrates vocal cords in the voice box, or larynx, and causes sound).

B. When a bolus of food passes into the pharynx, the swallowing reflex is triggered. The esophageal sphincter muscle relaxes, the epiglottis closes off the tracheal opening, the food passes into the esophagus, and the esophageal sphincter muscle contracts as the bolus passes farther into the esophagus (Figure 21.6).

Module 21.7 The Heimlich maneuver can save lives.

A. Food or other objects can become lodged in the pharynx and block the air passageway (trachea).

B. A procedure called the Heimlich maneuver (invented by Dr. Henry Heimlich) can be used to dislodge the object.

C. From behind the choking victim, place your fist in the upper abdomen; grab your fist with your other hand; and press into the victim's abdomen with a quick, upward jerk (Figure 21.7). Air is forced out of the lungs. The maneuver should be repeated until the object is dislodged.

D. Perform this maneuver on drowning victims to clear water from the lungs prior to performing CPR.

Module 21.8 The esophagus squeezes food along to the stomach by peristalsis.

A. Esophageal muscles are arranged in two layers of smooth muscle, one circular and the other longitudinal. The muscle layers contract alternately.

B. Peristalsis moves the bolus down the esophagus to the stomach (Figure 21.8).
NOTE: The esophagus itself has no digestive function. However, salivary amylase continues to act on the food during its passage through the esophagus. Carbohydrate digestion stops upon entering the stomach, which is very acidic. Carbohydrate digestion then continues in the small intestine.

Module 21.9 The stomach stores food and breaks it down with acid and enzymes.

A. The stomach can store up to 2 liters of food. It empties its contents slowly (after 2–6 hours) by opening the pyloric sphincter.

B. The inner surface of the stomach is highly folded and has pits that terminate in gastric glands (Figure 21.9).

C. Chemical digestion continues in the stomach and is aided by contractions of smooth muscle in the stomach wall. The digestion of proteins into smaller polypeptides occurs by the action of the enzyme pepsin.

D. **Gastric juice** also includes mucus, which lubricates and protects the stomach lining, and hydrochloric acid, which converts pepsinogen to pepsin and provides the proper pH for the action of pepsin.
   NOTE: The HCl secreted by the stomach has a pH of 1. HCl is also important in denaturing proteins that allow greater exposure of peptide bonds to pepsin, deactivating hormones present in food and killing bacteria. Further, HCl is important for the absorption of nutrients such as vitamin B_{12} and iron.

E. Gastric activity is initiated by a nervous signal from the brain (after seeing, tasting, or smelling the food) and is continued by the secretion of **gastrin,** a gastric gland hormone, when food is actually present in the stomach.

F. The release of gastric juice by the gastric glands, under the control of gastrin, is a negative-feedback mechanism (see Module 20.14).

G. Occasional backflow of the stomach contents (**acid chyme**) into the esophagus causes acid reflux.

H. Exposure of the esophagus to the acid contents of the stomach can cause what is commonly referred to as heartburn but more accurately called esophageal-burn. Chronic exposure to the acid contents of the stomach can lead to gastroesophageal reflux disease (GERD), which damages the lining of the esophagus.
   NOTE: The buildup of scar tissue at the base of the esophagus can decrease the diameter of this region of the esophagus (peptic stricture). Ironically, the discomfort of chronic heartburn is relieved with the development of Barrett's esophagus (the growth of abnormal tissue in the esophagus), which increases the risk of esophageal cancer (adenocarcinoma).

I. The pyloric sphincter regulates the passage of acid chyme from the stomach to the small intestine, allowing the passage of only a small amount at a time. It takes 2 to 6 hours for the stomach to empty and longer if the diet was rich in fat.

J. A hormone is released from the small intestine, slowing down the digestion of fat in the stomach. Other hormones are released from the small intestine, which regulate the pancreas and gallbladder secretions.

Module 21.10 Connection: Bacterial infections can cause ulcers.

A. A **gastric ulcer** is an open sore on the stomach lining. The major symptom is pain in the upper abdomen associated with eating.

B. Ulcers were originally thought to be due to overproduction of pepsin and/or acid. However, evidence now indicates that the major cause of ulcers and gastritis (70 to 90%) is the prokaryote *Helicobacter pylori* (Figure 21.10).
   NOTE: In addition to *H. pylori,* the other major cause of ulcers is the (over) use of nonsteroidal anti-inflammatory drugs (NSAID) such as aspirin and ibuprofen. NSAID reduce inflammation by inhibiting prostaglandin synthesis. Prostaglandins play a major role in cytoprotection (protecting the cells lining the stomach from damage by HCl).

C. The body's response to a *H. pylori* infection results in stomach inflammation (gastritis). Gastritis may progress to an ulcer.

D. *H. pylori* infection is also associated with an increased cancer risk.

E. Gastric ulcers usually respond to antibiotic therapy in combination with drugs such as bismuth (the active ingredient in Pepto Bismol). Vaccines against *H. pylori* are in development.
NOTE: Not only is this treatment protocol more effective than the older methods; it is also less expensive.

F. Ulcers may also form in the small intestine (duodenum) and the esophagus.

Module 21.11 The small intestine is the major organ of chemical digestion and nutrient absorption.

A. All remaining chemical digestion and most absorption of nutrients occur in the **small intestine.** This organ is about 6 meters long and 2.5 cm in diameter. Peristalsis moves the mixture.
NOTE: The chyme that enters the small intestine from the stomach has a pH of 2–3.

B. Digestion continues in the first 25 cm (the duodenum).

C. Glandular secretions are released into the duodenum from the **liver,** the **gallbladder** (the liver produces bile that contains salts to make fats more soluble; bile is stored in the gallbladder until it is needed in the small intestine), the **duodenum** wall, and the **pancreas** (which produces enzymes and bicarbonate ions to neutralize the acid chyme and raise its pH) (Figure 21.11A).
Preview: The role of the liver in homeostasis is discussed in more detail in Module 25.7.
NOTE: Folic acid (a B vitamin that is of great importance during pregnancy; Table 21.18) is secreted along with bile and is reabsorbed in the small intestine. Anything that inhibits this reabsorption can result in a folate deficiency (neural tube defects).

D. Each type of macromolecule (carbohydrates, proteins, fats, and nucleic acids) is digested sequentially by specific enzymes. The digestion of carbohydrates and proteins continues on fragments produced by previous chemical breakdown. The digestion of fats and nucleic acids starts here (Table 21.11).

E. The surface area of the lower part of the small intestine is huge, with several levels of folding. The wall is folded into circular pleats. These pleats contain projections of cells called **villi** (singular, *villus*), and the cells have further projections called **microvilli.** The total surface area is about 300 m^2 (Figure 21.11B).

F. The core of each villus contains capillaries and lymph ducts. Nutrients diffuse from the intestine chamber to blood, or they are moved across microvillous membranes against concentration gradients.

G. Water-soluble nutrients pass into the capillaries, lipid-soluble nutrients pass into the intestinal lymphatics (lacteals). Nutrient-laden blood from the small intestine passes to the liver, which gets the first chance to process or store the nutrients, particularly storing excess glucose as animal starch (glycogen).

Module 21.12 The large intestine reclaims water and compacts the feces.

A. The **large intestine** or **colon** is about 1.5 m long and 5 cm in diameter (Figure 21.12).

B. About 7 liters of digestive contents pass into the large intestine each day. About 90% of the water is absorbed back into the blood and tissue fluids.

C. The **appendix** is a gland at the top of the large intestine, above the **cecum** (a blind pouch), that has a minor immune system function. Appendicitis occurs if the appendix becomes infected following irritation, or when its opening is blocked by undigested food.

D. Prokaryotes that normally live in the colon, including *E. coli,* live in the undigested material. They produce and release important vitamins (biotin, folate, B vitamins, and vitamin K) that humans cannot make themselves.

NOTE: The amount of a vitamin synthesized by the intestinal fauna that is available for absorption is not the same for each vitamin. For example, intestinal bacteria can meet 50% of an adult's need for vitamin K, whereas it is not yet known how much of the biotin synthesized by intestinal prokaryotes is absorbed.

E. The remaining undigested material (fiber) is compacted by peristalsis and stored in the **rectum** until it is defecated as **feces.** Irritation of the colon lining by a pathogen can cause diarrhea, and the lack of fiber and exercise can cause constipation.

NOTE: A lack of fiber in the diet can also cause outpouchings (diverticula) in the wall of the colon. If the diverticula become inflamed, the result is diverticulitis.

III. Diets and Digestive Adaptations

Module 21.13 Adaptations of vertebrate digestive systems reflect diet.

A. Herbivores and omnivores have longer alimentary canals than carnivores, to allow more time and surface area for digesting plant material (Figure 21.13A).

B. Dietary needs change from the larval stage to the adult stage in amphibians. The alimentary canal of the larva is proportionally longer relative to body size than that of the adult.

C. Most herbivores rely on the cellulose-digesting enzymes of prokaryotes and protists. Populations of these organisms are housed in parts of the animals' alimentary canals.

D. Rabbits, and some rodents, produce soft fecal pellets first, which include microorganisms that have digested the cellulose in the cecum (a pouchlike region where small and large intestines meet). They reingest these pellets, absorb the digested cellulose (glucose molecules) through their small intestines, and then defecate hard fecal pellets.

E. **Ruminant mammals,** such as cattle, sheep, and deer, have an elaborate, four-chambered stomach, part of which houses the microorganisms. Ingested grass enters the rumen and reticulum, where prokaryotes and protists begin to digest the cellulose. Periodically, a cow regurgitates some of this material and helps mechanically digest it by "chewing the cud." The cud is then swallowed into the omasum, where water is absorbed, passing to the abomasum, where the enzymes from the cow complete the digestion process (Figure 21.13B).

IV. Nutrition

Module 21.14 Overview: A healthy diet satisfies three needs.

A. All animals must meet three basic nutritional requirements through the process of digestion:

1. Fuel to power all body activities.
2. Raw materials needed to make an animal's own molecules.
3. Essential nutrients (substances the animal cannot make itself).

B. Digestion breaks the bonds of polymers, making them available for absorption and use by cells. Monomers can be either a source of energy via oxidation or assemblage via hydrolysis into their own macromolecules to maintain cell structure and function.

Module 21.15 Chemical energy powers the body.

Review: Cellular respiration in Chapter 6.

A. The energy content of food (carbohydrates, fats, and, proteins) is measured in **kilocalories (kcal),** the accurate form of the popular word *calories.*
   NOTE: A calorie is the amount of energy required to raise one gram of water one degree Celsius. One kcal = 1,000 calories.

B. The **basal metabolic rate (BMR)** is the amount of energy required to maintain cellular metabolism in a resting animal. The average BMR for adult humans is 1,300–1,800 kcal per day (females, 1,300–1,500 kcal/day; males, 1,600–1,800 kcal/day).

C. Various levels of activity add to a human's caloric requirements, and various foods supply these requirements (Table 21.15).

D. The liver and muscles store chemical energy in the form of glycogen, a complex carbohydrate.

E. Excess chemical energy is also stored as fat. The liver can make fat from carbohydrates and proteins even if there is little fat in the diet. The average person could survive on stored fat for several weeks (0.3 kg of fat burned per day on a starvation diet).

Module 21.16 An animal's diet must supply essential nutrients.

A. Some substances (**essential nutrients**) cannot be made and must be obtained directly from food. The four classes of essential nutrient are essential fatty acids, essential amino acids, vitamins, and minerals.

B. *Malnourished* is the lack of an essential nutrient (more common) while *undernourished* is the lack of sufficient calories. Causes for these two afflictions can be as diverse as war, natural disaster, and disease (e.g., anorexia nervosa).

C. Fatty acids that our body cannot make for itself and that are required in the diet are called **essential fatty acids.** Fat is an essential component of the human body. One important essential fatty acid is linoleic acid because it is a major precursor in membrane phospholipids.

D. The human body can make a great variety of organic molecules (including 12 amino acids) from basic sources of organic carbon and nitrogen provided in digested food. But eight amino acids must be obtained through our diet. Meat, egg, and milk products provide all eight **essential amino acids.** The lack of one or more of the essential amino acids is the most common form of malnutrition, particularly in children.

Module 21.17 Connection: Vegetarians must be sure to obtain all eight essential amino acids.

A. The majority of the human population is vegetarian and, therefore, must be careful to obtain all essential nutrients in their diet. Protein deficiency is the most common form of malnutrition.

B. A combination of the right plants can provide all eight essential amino acids (Figure 21.17).

Module 21.18 A healthy diet includes 13 vitamins.

A. A **vitamin** is an organic nutrient that is essential but required in much smaller quantities than the essential amino acids. Extreme deficiencies of each vitamin cause specific sets of symptoms.

B. Most vitamins serve as part of a coenzyme or are themselves coenzymes, which are reused in metabolic reactions or in a variety of roles in maintaining cellular health.
   Review: Enzyme function is discussed in Modules 5.5–5.9.

C. Vitamins are grouped into two groups; those that are water soluble and those that are fat soluble (Table 21.18). Unlike water-soluble vitamins, which when in excess are usually eliminated in the urine, excess fat-soluble vitamins are not easily eliminated from the body and build up in body fat, where they may have toxic effects.

Module 21.19 Essential minerals are required for many body functions.

A. **Minerals** are chemical nutrients other than carbon, hydrogen, oxygen, and nitrogen (e.g., iron, calcium, iodine, and potassium).

B. Depending on their roles in structure and function, the essential minerals are required in various amounts (Table 21.18). For example, iodine is needed for thyroxine synthesis (Module 26.5). An enlarged thyroid (goiter) will develop with iodine deficiency.

C. Too much of some minerals can cause abnormal function; for example, too much sodium in salt promotes high blood pressure in humans.
    NOTE: Recent studies are showing that only a subset of the population is sodium sensitive and that those individuals who are not sodium sensitive have less need to be concerned about their sodium intake (but shouldn't overdo it).

Module 21.20 Connection: Do you need to take vitamin and mineral supplements?

A. The **Recommended Dietary Allowances (RDAs)** is an established list of minimal standards that if taken daily should prevent nutritional deficiencies.

B. Taking supplements as a way to obtain the RDAs of vitamins and minerals will not be harmful and is probably not necessary provided a healthful, balanced diet is maintained.

C. The debate over the use of megavitamins as a way to gain health benefits is ongoing (Figure 21.20). It is well established, however, that some minerals and vitamins in large quantities can be harmful (e.g., iron and vitamin A).

Module 21.21 Connection: What do food labels tell us?

A. Food labels provide several pieces of information for the consumer (Figure 21.21):
    1. Serving size for the type of food (e.g., one slice of bread) and servings per container.
    2. A list of ingredients arranged according to weight, from the greatest amount to the least amount.
    3. The number of kilocalories, carbohydrates (total and dietary fiber and sugars), proteins, fats (total and saturated fats and cholesterol), and selected vitamins and minerals supplied in one serving appear on the label and are expressed as percentages of a daily value.

B. Some labels will also emphasize nutrients that are of health concern or associated with disease such as total, saturated, and unsaturated fats; cholesterol; and sodium.

Module 21.22 Connection: Obesity is a human health problem.

A. The World Health Organization (WHO) has recognized obesity as a global health problem. A combination of more fatty foods and a sedentary lifestyle has contributed to the obesity issue. In the United States, 30% of the population is obese, up from 15% two decades ago.

B. Obesity contributes to a number of health problems such as diabetes, colon cancer, breast cancer, and cardiovascular disease.

C. The rise in obesity has stimulated research efforts to discover its genetic bases. A hormone produced by adipose tissue (Figure 21.22A), called leptin was discovered (along with the gene). The function of this hormone is to suppress the appetite in mice (Figure 21.22B). It is produced in humans, but the effects are not the same as in mice.

D. The lack of appetite suppression by high leptin levels may be related to our evolutionary history as gatherers and hunters (scavengers). It is only recently that large populations have had enough to eat on a consistent basis (including fatty foods); that is contributing to the obesity epidemic.

Module 21.23 Connection: What are the health risks and benefits of fad diets?

A. There is a direct correlation between increase in obesity and increase revenues in the weight loss industry.

B. The fact that a diet may help you shed pounds may not guarantee that the weight loss is healthful or permanent.

C. Low-carbohydrate diets have become popular and have proven effective at weight loss. However, the low-carbohydrate diet has innate risks. Low vegetable and fruit intake reduces the essential nutrients in the diet and increases the risk of cancer. Carbohydrate calories are replaced with protein and fat calories, which may increase the risk of heart disease.

D. A previously popular diet was the low-fat diet. As discussed in Module 21.16, essential fatty acids are required for good health. Removal of fats from the diet was often accompanied by reduced protein intake. This combination can be harmful due to the reduction in essential amino acids and an inability to adsorb fat-soluble vitamins.

E. Ideally, fat should be 20–25% and 15–19% of the body weights of women and men, respectively.

F. The best protocol to lose weight and then maintain the desired weight is a combination of regular aerobic exercise and a restricted (1,200 kcal or more per day) but balanced diet (Table 21.23).

Module 21.24 Connection: Diet can influence cardiovascular disease and cancer.

A. We can choose to improve our health by regular exercise and weight loss using a restricted but balanced diet. What we choose to eat can also alter the risk of cardiovascular disease and cancer.

B. Linked to cardiovascular disease are diets low in fruits and vegetables and rich in saturated fats, which, in turn, correlate with high levels of blood cholesterol. Cardiovascular disease is linked to high levels of **low-density lipoproteins (LDLs),** while increased concentrations of **high-density lipoproteins (HDLs)** are correlated with lower risk of cardiovascular disease. Exercise tends to increase HDL, while smoking decreases HDL levels (Figure 21.24).

C. Hydrogenated vegetable oils have elevated concentrations of trans-fats, which increase LDL and decrease HDL. Using oils rich in unsaturated fats such as fish oil or vegetable oils (olive, corn, and soybean oils) may increase HDL and decrease LDL. These oils are also rich in vitamin E, which is an antioxidant.
NOTE: Inherited (familial) hypercholesterolemia is discussed in Modules 5.20 and Table 9.9. However, as discussed here, lifestyle (lack of exercise, a high-fat diet) may also result in hypercholesterolemia.

D. Foods rich in vitamins that have antioxidant characteristics may reduce the incidence of cancer by helping cells avoid the damage caused by free radicals. High levels of dietary fat and low levels of dietary fiber are linked to some forms of cancer (Table 21.24).
Review: See Modules 11.16–11.20 for a discussion of the cellular basis of cancer and lifestyle and cancer risk.

NOTE: The benefits of fiber include slowing glucose absorption and lowering blood cholesterol levels. In addition, foods high in fiber tend to be lower in fats. Until the body adapts to a high-fiber diet, the result can be diarrhea or constipation, gas, and abdominal discomfort. A diet can also be too high in fiber; the result can be insufficient consumption of energy or nutrients, inhibition of nutrient absorption, and formation of phytobezoars (fiber balls that can obstruct the GI tract).

Class Activities

1. Have your students create a model of the human digestive system illustrating the major functions of each component of the system.

2. Have your students choose two different vertebrate species and explore how differences in their diet are reflected in differences in the structure of their digestive systems.

3. There is a great deal of misinformation/misrepresentation concerning nutrition in the popular press. Have students bring in articles to critique.

4. Have students analyze and critique the diets they consume (there are many good diet analysis programs available) and discuss ways to improve their diet.

Transparency Acetates

Figure 21.2A	The four main stages of food processing
Figure 21.2B	Chemical digestion: The breakdown of polymers to monomers
Figure 21.3A	Digestion in the gastrovascular cavity of a hydra
Figure 21.3B	Three examples of alimentary canals
Figure 21.4	The human digestive tract
Figure 21.5	The human oral cavity
Figure 21.6	The swallowing reflex (Layer 1)
Figure 21.6	The swallowing reflex (Layer 2)
Figure 21.6	The swallowing reflex (Layer 3)
Figure 21.7	The Heimlich maneuver for helping choking victims
Figure 21.8	Peristalsis moving a food bolus down the esophagus
Figure 21.9	The stomach and its production of gastric juice
Table 21.11	Enzymatic digestion in the small intestine
Figure 21.11A	The small intestine and related digestive organs
Figure 21.11B	Structure of the small intestine
Figure 21.12	The relationship of the small and large intestine
Figure 21.13A	The alimentary canal in a carnivore (coyote) and an herbivore (koala)
Figure 21.13B	The digestive system of a ruminant mammal
Table 21.15	Exercise required to "burn" the Calories (kcal) in common foods
Figure 21.17	Essential amino acids
Table 21.18	Vitamin requirements of humans
Table 21.19	Mineral requirements of humans

Figure 21.21   Whole wheat bread label
Table 21.23   Types of weight loss diets
Figure 21.24   Risk factors associated with cardiovascular disease
Reviewing the Concepts, page 450: Structure of the small intestine
Connecting the Concepts, page 450: Functions of organs and glands
Connecting the Concepts, page 450: A healthy diet
Applying the Concepts, page 451: Nutrition Facts label

Media

See the beginning of this book for a complete description of all media available for instructors and students. Animations and videos are available in the Campbell Image Presentation Library. Media Activities and Thinking as a Scientist investigations are available on the student CD-ROM and website.

Animations and Videos	Module Number
Whale Eating a Seal Video	21.1

Activities and Thinking as a Scientist	Module Number
Web/CD Activity 21A: *Digestive System Function*	21.11
Web/CD Thinking as a Scientist: *What Role Does Amylase Play in Digestion?*	21.11

CHAPTER 22

Gas Exchange

Teaching Objectives

Introduction Explain how geese can fly at altitudes as high as or higher than Mt. Everest. Explain how humans adjust to life at high altitudes.

Mechanisms of Gas Exchange

22.1 Describe the three main phases of gas exchange in a human.

22.2 Describe the properties of respiratory surfaces. Describe four types of respiratory surfaces and the types of animals that use them.

22.3 Explain how the amount of oxygen available in air compares to that available in cold and warm fresh water and saltier water.

22.3 Explain how the structure and functions of fish gills maximize oxygen exchange.

22.4 Explain how breathing air is easier than using water for gas exchange.

22.4 Describe the tracheal system of insects.

22.5 Describe the structures and corresponding functions of a mammalian respiratory system. Explain why the lungs of a mammal are proportionally larger and more complex than the lungs of a frog.

22.6 Describe the impact of smoking on human health.

22.7 Compare the mechanisms and efficiencies of lung ventilation in humans and birds.

22.8 Explain how breathing is controlled in humans.

Transport of Gases in the Body

22.9 Explain how blood transports gases between the lungs and tissues of the body.

22.10 Describe the functions of hemoglobin and explain how carbon dioxide is transported in the blood.

22.11 Explain how a human fetus obtains oxygen prior to and immediately after birth.

Key Terms

alveoli	gas exchange	pharynx
breathing	gills	respiration
breathing control centers	hemoglobin	respiratory surface
bronchi	hyperventilating	trachea
bronchioles	larynx	tracheal system
countercurrent exchange	lungs	ventilation
diaphragm	negative pressure breathing	vital capacity
emphysema	partial pressure	vocal cords

Word Roots

alveol- = a cavity (*alveoli:* one of the dead-end, multilobed air sacs that constitute the gas exchange surface of the lungs)

counter- = opposite (*countercurrent exchange:* the opposite flow of adjacent fluids that maximizes transfer rates)

Lecture Outline

Introduction *Surviving in Thin Air*

    A. *Review:* Cellular respiration: Animals need to obtain oxygen and glucose and rid themselves of waste carbon dioxide (Chapter 6; Figures 6.2, 6.3, and 6.6).

    B. Life at high altitude imposes many changes on the organs and tissues that function in respiration.

        1. People born in and adapted to high altitudes have relatively large lungs and hearts, more red blood cells, and elevated hemoglobin concentrations.

        2. A short period of conditioning will help those living in lower altitudes acclimate to higher altitudes. Faster heart rate and larger capillary diameter are replaced over time with deeper and more rapid rates of breathing, more capillaries, and higher numbers of red blood cells and levels of hemoglobin.

        3. Many animals are capable of exchanging gases from environments humans would find inhospitable. Some birds can stand the cold and low oxygen concentrations of altitudes of 20,000–30,000 feet. They have more efficient lungs, hemoglobin with a very high affinity for oxygen, a larger number of capillaries, and muscle proteins that hold oxygen.

    C. **Gas exchange** (respiration) is the transposition of oxygen with CO_2 between an animal and its environment.

I. Mechanisms of Gas Exchange

    Module 22.1 Overview: Gas exchange involves breathing, the transport of gases, and exchange of gases with tissue cells.

    A. The process of breathing (the intake of oxygen and removal of CO_2) makes it possible to use the nutrients obtained from digestion. There are three steps to gas exchange:

        1. Breathing involves inhaling O_2 and exhaling CO_2 (Figure 22.1).

        2. The transport of gases involves diffusion into and transport by hemoglobin in the red blood cells of the circulatory system.

        3. Blood supplies every cell with O_2 and picks up waste CO_2.

    B. There must be a constant supply of oxygen and removal of CO_2 at the cellular level. The process requires the combined efforts of the circulatory and respiratory systems.

    Module 22.2 Animals exchange O_2 and CO_2 across moist body surfaces.

    A. The portion of an animal where gas exchange with the environment takes place is called the **respiratory surface.** Respiratory surfaces vary among animal groups. However, what all respiratory surfaces have in common is that they must be moist, thin, and extensive. Gases must be dissolved in water before they can diffuse across a body surface. In each part of Figures 22.2A–D, the circle represents a cross section of the animal's body in the region of the respiratory surface, and the yellow color represents the respiratory surfaces.

B. Earthworms (Module 18.10) and other "skin breathers" must live in moist environments to keep their skin moist. Small size or flatness provides the high ratio of respiratory surface to body volume required for efficient gas exchange between environment and cells (Figure 22.2A).

C. **Gills** have evolved in most aquatic animals to increase the respiratory surface. They generally project from the body surface (Figure 22.2B).

D. A system of branching tubes is used by insects and is called a **tracheal system** (Module 18.12). These branched tubes bring external gases directly to the inner cells without the aid of the circulatory system (Figure 22.2C).

E. **Lungs** are found in the majority of terrestrial vertebrates (Figure 22.2D). They are composed of branched tubes ending in tiny internal sacs lined with a moist epithelium. Gases are carried between the lungs and body cells by the circulatory system.

Module 22.3 Gills are adapted for gas exchange in aquatic environments.

A. The chief advantage of exchanging gases with water is that energy does not have to be expended to keep the transfer surface wet.

B. However, the concentration of O_2 is only 3–5% of its concentration in air, and the warmer and saltier the water, the less O_2 it can carry. Consequently, gills must be very efficient to extract O_2 from water.

C. Energy is expended as a fish covers its gill surfaces with water by "inhaling" water with its opercula closed and mouth opened, and "exhaling" the water across the gills with its mouth closed and opercula opened. The process of increasing contact of the surface area with oxygen is called **ventilation** regardless of if it's a fish, bird, or any other animal.

D. Oxygen-poor blood enters each gill filament and crosses the lamellae (red blood cells travel single file here), picking up O_2 and leaving CO_2 (Figure 22.3).

E. **Countercurrent exchange** is a general principle of transfer found in many animal systems.
NOTE: For example, a countercurrent system is used in thermoregulation (Module 25.2) and to enhance water reabsorption in the kidneys (Module 25.10).

F. Countercurrent exchange is the transfer of a substance from a fluid flowing in one direction to another fluid moving in the opposite direction.

G. Opposite flows maintain a diffusion gradient that enhances the transfer of the substance, O_2 in the case shown (Figure 22.3 circle to the right).
NOTE: To impress students with the efficiency that results from this arrangement, diagram a transfer system in which both fluids flow in the same direction.

H. This mechanism is so efficient in fish that their gills remove more than 80% of the oxygen dissolved in the water flowing through them.

Module 22.4 The tracheal system of insects provides direct exchange between the air and body cells.

A. Air contains much more O_2 than an equal volume of water, and air is easier to move than water. Thus, terrestrial animals expend less energy in ventilating their respiratory surfaces.

B. Tracheae in an insect branch throughout the body, conveying air directly to body cells (Figure 22.4A).

C. Included in the system are tracheal air sacs that work like bellows when muscles around them alternately contract and relax, moving air out and in.

D. Water is conserved and respiratory surfaces remain moist because only the narrowest tubes, the tracheoles, contain fluid. It is across the tracheoles that gas exchange occurs.

E. An insect in flight may use up to 200 times more oxygen than when at rest. To improve oxygen exchange rates, the flight muscles pump air through the tracheal system (Figure 22.4B).

Module 22.5 Terrestrial vertebrates have lungs.

A. Since lungs are restricted to one part of the body, unlike tracheae, the circulatory system must be involved in transporting the gases to and from body cells.

B. Amphibians supplement their lungs with skin breathing, but all other terrestrial vertebrates (and aquatic reptiles and mammals) have efficient lungs only.

C. The human respiratory system is in the chest cavity and is bounded at the bottom by the **diaphragm** (Figure 22.5A). The human respiratory system includes:

1. The nasal cavity (filters, warms, humidifies, and samples odors of incoming air).

2. The **pharynx** (controls the passage of air through the mouth region and into the **larynx** [Module 21.6]).

3. A branched system of tubes (**tracheae** and **bronchi**) that lead into the lungs.

D. Exhaling through the **vocal cords** of the larynx produces sounds. High-pitched sounds are produced by tightening the vocal cords, which will vibrate rapidly when air passes over them. Conversely, low-pitched sounds are made with relaxed vocal cords.
NOTE: This branched system is another example of the hierarchical organization of life (Module 1.1).

E. Lungs include the ultimate branches of the **bronchioles** and the grapelike clusters of **alveoli.** Gas exchange occurs across the alveolar surfaces (Figure 22.5B).

F. All surfaces of the respiratory system are lined by moist epithelium. In all but the alveoli and smallest bronchioles, cilia and a thin film of mucus that helps eliminate dust, pollen, etc., cover this tissue.

G. A muscular diaphragm helps move air in and out of the lungs.

H. O_2 in inhaled air dissolves in a film of moisture lining the alveoli, then diffuses across the epithelial cells and into a web of capillaries that surrounds the alveolus. CO_2 diffuses the other way (Figure 22.5C).

Module 22.6 Connection: Smoking is a deadly assault on our respiratory system.

A. Mucus covering the epithelium of the respiratory system traps particles and microorganisms that are then swept out of the respiratory system by the action of cilia.
Review: Cilia (Module 4.17).

B. Microorganisms and particles are also phagocytized by macrophages inhabiting the lining of the respiratory system.

C. A breath of air in a polluted city may contain thousands of chemicals, many potentially harmful. Air pollutants such as sulfur dioxide, carbon monoxide, and ozone are associated with serious respiratory diseases, and asbestos fibers and radioactive radon gas have been linked with lung cancer.

D. Tobacco smoke is one of the worst sources of toxic air pollutants. Components are known to irritate epithelial cells and inhibit or destroy cilia and macrophages. This allows more of the toxins to reach the lungs' alveoli; the frequent coughing of smokers is the respiratory system's attempt to clean itself.

E. Of all cases of lung cancer, 90% are caused by smoking. Most people diagnosed with lung cancer caused by smoking will die within the first year (Figure 22.7A, normal lung; Figure 22.7B, lung with cancer caused by smoking).

F. **Emphysema** is a disease of cigarette smokers characterized by the alveoli becoming brittle and eventually rupturing. Nearly half a million people die each year from smoking. The life expectancy of a smoker is 13 to 14 years less than that of a nonsmoker.

G. Nonsmokers exposed to cigarette smoke are at risk, and children exposed to cigarette smoke have an increased rate of asthma, bronchitis, and pneumonia.

Module 22.7 Breathing ventilates the lungs.

A. Breathing is the inhalation of air followed by exhalation of air. During inhalation, the rib cage expands, the rib muscles and diaphragm contract, and the chest expands. The lungs also increase in size. These changes reduce the air pressure within the alveoli, and air moves in as a result of the higher pressure outside (Figure 22.7A). This is called **negative pressure breathing.**

B. During exhalation, both the rib muscles and diaphragm relax, decreasing the volume of the rib cage and forcing air out.
NOTE: The elastic cartilage holding the rib cage together helps increase and decrease the rib cage's volume.

C. The normal volume of each breath (at rest) is about 500 mL. The maximum volume that one can inhale and exhale, the **vital capacity,** is about 3.4 L and 4.8 L for college-age females and males, respectively. The air that remains in the lungs after complete exhalation is the residual volume. This is proportionally greater (relative to vital capacity) in older and more-diseased people.

D. Gas-exchange systems of birds are more efficient than most mammals' gas-exchange systems are. Birds maintain a one-way flow of air between two air sacs in addition to lungs. The sacs act like bellows and are not involved with gas exchange. The air tubes within the lungs have no residual volume of air because all the air travels through the lungs in one direction (Figure 22.7B). Birds can extract about 5% more oxygen from the air than humans.

Module 22.8 Breathing is automatically controlled.

A. Although breathing can be consciously controlled, most of the time automatic control centers in our brain regulate our breathing movements (Figure 22.8).

B. **Breathing control centers** are located in the lower parts of the brainstem, the pons and the medulla oblongata (Module 28.15). About 10–14 times a minute, nerves from those areas signal the diaphragm and rib muscles to contract.

C. Increased cellular respiration causes increased concentrations of CO_2 in the blood. CO_2 reacts with water to form carbonic acid, lowering the pH. The medulla senses the pH drop and increases the rate and depth of breathing, thus eliminating more CO_2 from the blood in the lungs. **Hyperventilating** also causes an increase in the pH of the blood.
NOTE: This is one of the mechanisms that results in panting during and after strenuous exercise. Lactic acid buildup also contributes to the acidity of the blood during strenuous exercise (Module 6.13).

D. A secondary set of controls, which monitor oxygen and CO_2 levels are located in the aorta and the carotid arteries. During severe depression of O_2 levels in the blood, sensors on arteries near the heart signal the breathing control center. This response may occur at high altitudes, where required levels of O_2 cannot be obtained by normal breathing.

II. Transport of Gases in the Body

Module 22.9 Blood transports respiratory gases.

A. The human circulatory system functions in gas transport. One side of the heart pumps O_2-poor, CO_2-rich blood from the body to the lungs, and the other side of the heart pumps O_2-rich, CO_2-poor blood from the lungs to the rest of the body (Figure 22.9).

B. Every gas in a mixture accounts for a portion (that gas's **partial pressure**) of the mixture's total pressure. At each location (lungs and tissues), gases are exchanged as they diffuse along their own partial pressure gradient.

Module 22.10 Hemoglobin carries O_2 and helps transport CO_2 and buffer the blood.

A. O_2 is not very soluble in water. **Hemoglobin** in red blood cells has a much higher affinity for O_2 than water. Hemoglobin consists of four polypeptide chains (of two types); each chain is attached to a heme group with an iron atom in its center. Each iron atom can carry one O_2 molecule (Figure 22.10).

B. Hemoglobin not only transports oxygen, but also carries CO_2 and can help buffer harmful pH changes in the blood.

C. Within red blood cells, CO_2 reacts with water to form carbonic acid (H_2CO_3). This breaks into acidic hydrogen ions and basic bicarbonate ions more quickly in red blood cells under the control of an enzyme (carbonic anhydrase). Hemoglobin picks up most of the hydrogen ions and allows most of the bicarbonate to diffuse back into the plasma. This provides a buffer in the blood that will react with any hydrogen ions that are picked up elsewhere.

D. When blood flows through the lungs, the process is reversed. Hydrogen ions are given up by the hemoglobin, reacting with the bicarbonate (HCO_3^2) ions to form carbonic acid. This is then converted back into CO_2, and the CO_2 diffuses from the blood to the air.

Module 22.11 Connection: The human fetus exchanges gases with the mother's bloodstream.

A. The fetus lies within a watery bath of amniotic fluid. Its lungs are filled with this fluid.

B. Capillaries from the fetal blood supply (through the umbilical cord) mix with capillaries of the uterus in the placenta (Figure 22.11).

C. A fetus also has a different type of hemoglobin from the mother. This fetal hemoglobin has a higher affinity for oxygen than normal adult hemoglobin, thus enhancing the transfer of O_2 from mother to fetus.

D. When the baby is born and placental transfer stops, CO_2 concentration in the blood increases, lowering the pH and stimulating the breathing center, causing the baby to take its first breath.

E. An infant's switch from living in water and exchanging gases with its mother is a phenomenal feat on par with the ability of geese to fly at high altitudes for long distances. Both took millions of years of adaptation to accomplish.

Preview: Refer to this module when discussing fetal changes that take place during the third trimester of pregnancy (Module 27.17).

Class Activities

1. A bell-jar model of lungs with a diaphragm can be built or purchased from biological supply companies. To build a model, take a Y-shaped tube and place balloons on the two ends (these will be the lungs), secure the stem of the Y-shaped tube in a stopper, and place this in the neck of the bell jar. Secure a piece of rubber across the wide, open end of the bell jar (this will be the diaphragm); the bell jar itself plays the role of the thoracic cavity. When the rubber diaphragm is pulled on, the volume of the bell jar increases and air will enter the balloons. When the rubber diaphragm is allowed to return to its original position, the volume of the bell jar will decrease and air will be forced out of the balloons. This is an elegantly simple way of demonstrating the forces that fill and empty mammalian lungs.

2. Find the average pulse rate and blood pressures of the nonsmokers versus the smokers in the class. Let the smokers go outside to smoke and when they come back, see how their average pulse rate and blood pressure have changed.

Transparency Acetates

Media

See the beginning of this book for a complete description of all media available for instructors and students. Animations and videos are available in the Campbell Image Presentation Library. Media Activities and Thinking as a Scientist investigations are available on the student CD-ROM and website.

Videos and Animations	Module Number
Transport of Respiratory Gases, Step 1	22.10
Transport of Respiratory Gases, Step 2	22.10
Transport of Respiratory Gases, Step 3	22.10
Transport of Respiratory Gases, Step 4	22.10

Activities and Thinking as a Scientist	Module Number
Web/CD Activity 22A: *The Human Respiratory System*	22.5
Web/CD Activity 22B: *Transport of Respiratory Gases*	22.10
Biology Labs On-Line: *Transport of Gases in the Body*	22.10

CHAPTER 23

Circulation

Teaching Objectives

Introduction Explain how gravity affects the circulation of terrestrial vertebrates.

23.1 Describe the general need for and functions of a circulatory system.

Mechanisms of Internal Transport

23.2 Compare the structures and functions of gastrovascular cavities, open circulatory systems, and closed circulatory systems.

23.3 Compare the cardiovascular systems of a fish, an amphibian, a reptile, a bird, and a mammal.

The Mammalian Cardiovascular System

23.4 Describe the pathway of blood through the mammalian cardiovascular system. Note the names of all blood vessels and heart chambers identified in Figure 23.4.

23.5 Relate the structure of blood vessels to their functions.

23.6 Distinguish between diastole and systole. Explain what keeps blood moving in the correct direction within the heart and what causes heart "beats."

23.7 Explain how heartbeats are controlled.

23.8 Define a heart attack and cardiovascular disease. Explain how these problems are caused and what can be done to reduce the chances of developing cardiovascular diseases.

23.9 Explain how and why blood pressure changes as blood moves away from the heart. Explain how blood is moved back to the heart.

23.10 Explain how blood pressure is measured. Note normal and high blood pressure readings. Describe lifestyle changes that can help to reduce high blood pressure.

23.11 Explain how blood flow through capillaries is regulated.

23.12 Explain how the structure of a capillary is related to its functions.

Structure and Function of Blood

23.13 Describe the components of blood and their functions.

23.14 Describe the structure, function, and production of red blood cells. Explain how training at high altitudes, injecting synthetic EPO, and blood doping increase red blood cell concentrations.

23.15 Describe the process of blood clotting.

23.16 Define leukemia and describe the most common forms of treatment.

Key Terms

anemia	circulatory system	plasma
aorta	closed circulatory system	platelets
arteries	diastole	pulmonary arteries
arterioles	double circulation	pulmonary circuit
artificial pacemaker	erythrocytes	pulmonary veins
atherosclerosis	erythropoietin (EPO)	pulse
atrium	fibrin	red blood cells
AV (atrioventricular) node	fibrinogen	SA (sinoatrial) node
blood	heart attack	stem cells
blood pressure	hypertension	superior vena cava
capillaries	inferior vena cava	systemic circuit
capillary beds	leukemia	systole
cardiac cycle	leukocytes	veins
cardiac output	open circulatory system	ventricle
cardiovascular disease	pacemaker	venules
cardiovascular system	phagocytes	white blood cells

Word Roots

atrio- = a vestibule; **-ventriculo** = ventricle (*atrioventricular node:* a region of specialized muscle tissue between the right atrium and right ventricle; it generates electrical impulses that primarily cause the ventricles to contract)

cardi- = heart; **-vascula** = a little vessel (*cardiovascular system:* the closed circulatory system characteristic of vertebrates)

fibrino- = a fiber; **-gen** = produce (*fibrinogen:* the inactive form of the plasma protein that is converted to the active form fibrin, which aggregates into threads that form the framework of a blood clot)

Lecture Outline

Introduction *How Does Gravity Affect Blood Circulation?*

    A. Most animals have a **circulatory system** for the internal transport of gases, nutrients, and waste.

    B. Gravity has had major effects in shaping the evolution of circulatory systems in terrestrial organisms as different as corn snakes and giraffes.

        1. Strong hearts are able to pump against the force of gravity, even in tall animals.

        2. Muscles used in normal activities contract around veins and force blood back to the heart through one-way valves.

        3. In the corn snake, veins have no valves, but tail vessels constrict during a climb, and a snake will wriggle after a climb to increase circulation.

Module 23.1 The circulatory system connects with all body tissues.

Review: Chemical exchange between an animal and its environment (Module 20.11).

A. Diffusion is inadequate for transporting chemicals over distances greater than a few cell widths. A circulatory system is used to transport material over long distances and bring those needed materials close enough for diffusion to work.

B. **Capillaries** are the smallest vessels and form an intricate network of vessels among the cells of every tissue (Figures 23.1A and 23.12A).

C. The various components of blood, particularly red blood cells, come in close enough contact with associated cells that materials can diffuse between them, via the interstitial fluid (Figure 23.1B).

D. In most tissues, O_2 and nutrients diffuse from blood to tissue, and CO_2 and metabolic wastes diffuse from tissue to blood.

E. The circulatory system also functions in homeostasis by exchanging molecules with the interstitial fluid and by moving the blood through organs such as the liver and kidneys, where the blood's contents are regulated.

I. Mechanisms of Internal Transport

Module 23.2 Several types of internal transport have evolved in animals.

A. The body plan of the hydra and other cnidarians does not require a circulatory system (Module 21.3). The body wall and gastrovascular cavity are only two to three cells thick; therefore, diffusion can transport molecules directly to the cells. In jellyfish, the gastrovascular cavity is intricately branched, radiating from the mouth to a circular canal (Figure 23.2A).

B. Many invertebrates (including arthropods and molluscs) have **open circulatory systems. Blood** is pumped by one or more hearts through open-ended vessels and flows out among the cells. There is no separate interstitial fluid. Pores in the hearts function as valves, opening when the hearts relax to pull in blood from the tissues (Figure 23.2B).

C. Other invertebrates and all vertebrates have **closed circulatory systems** (also called a **cardiovascular system**). Blood is confined to vessels, which keeps it distinct from the interstitial fluid (Figure 23.2C).

D. In closed systems, **arteries** carry blood away from the heart, **veins** return blood to the heart, and capillaries convey blood between these two vessel types within each organ.

E. A fish system includes four gills, each with thousands of gill capillaries, on each side of the head and a two-chambered heart (**atrium** receives and **ventricle** pumps out). Large arteries branch out into smaller **arterioles** and then out into the **capillary beds.** Once past the capillaries, the blood converges into **venules,** which then finally join together to form veins.

Module 23.3 Vertebrate cardiovascular systems reflect evolution.

A. The switch from gill breathing in aquatic vertebrates to lung breathing in terrestrial vertebrates was accompanied by drastic changes in the circulatory systems.
NOTE: Fish and mammal systems are compared in this module, while a progression of evolutionary adaptations in the circulatory systems of amphibians and reptiles links these two extremes.

B. Fish have a single circuit of blood flow, with the heart receiving and pumping only O_2-poor blood (Figure 23.3A).
   NOTE: Point out that the overhead transparencies show the circulatory system as though the animal were facing you, with its right side on your left. Historically, such illustrations are oriented to illustrate animal dissections, with the open body cavity facing up.

C. The cardiovascular system of terrestrial vertebrates is a more vigorous system with **double circulation.** The heart pumps blood to the lungs (**pulmonary circuit**) and through the first capillary bed and then one more time to the rest of the body (**systemic circuit**).

D. Amphibians have a three-chambered heart that pumps blood from the right atrium to the lungs and the skin to be oxygenated (a pulmocutaneous circuit). The oxygen-rich blood returns to the left atrium then flows to the ventricle where it mixes with low-oxygenated blood and is pumped to the rest of the body (Figure 23.3B). Reptiles also have a three-chambered heart, but the ventricle is partly closed and less mixing occurs.

E. Mammals and birds have a four-chambered heart with two atria and two ventricles. The pulmonary circuit carries blood from the right side of the heart to the lungs, and the systemic circuit carries blood from the left side of the heart to the rest of the body. This improved double-circulation system provides rapid delivery of O_2-rich blood to body tissues of highly active animals, endotherms (Figure 23.3C). Endotherms use approximately 10 times more energy than ectotherms; therefore, they need comparable amounts of oxygen and nutrients for the cells to be delivered by a large and powerful heart. Birds and mammals evolved from different ancestors, and their cardiovascular systems evolved independently (convergent evolution, Module 15.6).

II. The Mammalian Cardiovascular System

Module 23.4 The human heart and cardiovascular system are typical of mammals.

A. The heart (Figure 23.4A) is composed mostly of cardiac muscle tissue (Module 20.6). *Review:* Specialized cell junctions connect cardiac muscle fibers to one another (Module 4.18). These specialized cell junctions are called intercalated discs. Intercalated discs are a combination of anchoring junctions and communicating junctions.

B. Thin-walled atria receive blood then pump the blood to the ventricles.

C. Thick-walled ventricles pump blood to the lungs and other organs.

D. Valves between chambers and between ventricles and main arteries maintain the flow in one direction.

E. The flow of blood through the body (Figure 23.4B) follows this path:
   1. Right ventricle to lungs
   2. Via two **pulmonary arteries**
   3. Blood in the lungs passes though capillary beds exchanging CO_2 for O_2
   4. Lungs to left atrium via two **pulmonary veins**
   5. Left atrium to left ventricle
   6. Left ventricle to all body organs via the **aorta**
   7. The head, chest, and arms to right atrium via **superior vena cava**
   8. Lower body to right atrium via **inferior vena cava**
   9. Right atrium to right ventricle

F. The flow of blood is always from the heart to the lungs, back to the heart (the pulmonary circuit), from the heart out to the body, and then back to the heart (systemic circuit). In the middle of each circuit are capillary beds where the exchange of chemicals takes place.

G. The first arteries that branch off the aorta supply blood to the heart itself (coronary arteries) and then the head, including the brain and many sense organs.

Module 23.5 The structure of blood vessels fits their functions.

A. Capillaries, which supply cells, have thin walls composed of a single layer of epithelial cells wrapped in a thin basement membrane (Figure 23.5). Such a thin surface facilitates the diffusion of molecules to and from the cells through the interstitial fluid.

B. Arteries, arterioles, veins, and venules are composed of three tissue layers (Figure 23.5). The inner layer is the same as that found in capillaries (epithelium). The outer layer is connective tissue with elastic fibers to allow stretch and recoil during heart beats. The middle layer is composed of smooth [missing word?].

C. Arteries have thicker walls than veins to accommodate the rapid flow of blood and high pressure exerted by the heart. Arterial smooth muscle can regulate blood flow by constriction or relaxation.

D. Veins are thinner and are under less pressure and slower blood flow. Larger veins also have flaps of tissue that act as valves to prevent back flow.

Module 23.6 The heart contracts and relaxes rhythmically.

A. The heart passively fills with returning blood and actively contracts, pumping out blood. The whole sequence is called the **cardiac cycle** (Figure 23.6). One cycle takes about 0.8 seconds at a heart rate of 75 beats per minute.

B. During **diastole** (which lasts about 0.4 sec), the heart is relaxed and blood flows into all four chambers, with all valves open.

C. **Systole** begins as the atria contract (about 0.1 sec), forcing blood into the ventricles, and continues as the ventricles contract (about 0.3 sec), forcing the atrioventricular (AV) valves closed and the semilunar valves open.
NOTE: The AV valves are opened by the weight of the blood in the atria. Therefore, most ventricular filling is accomplished prior to atrial contraction. This is why atrial fibrillation is not as immediately serious as ventricular fibrillation (though atrial fibrillation is an indicator of risk of stroke).

D. **Cardiac output** is about 75 mL per beat, or 5.25 liters per minute in the average resting person. Cardiac output can vary with exercise and chemical stimulants such as caffeine.

E. The *lub-dup* sound of a beating heart is from the closure of the AV valves (*lub*) and the closure of the semilunar valves (*dup*).

F. A heart murmur sounds like a quiet hiss to the trained ear and occurs when a valve malfunctions, allowing blood to squirt back into a preceding chamber. Murmurs can be related to congenital defects or a result of infection (rheumatic fever).

Module 23.7 The pacemaker sets the tempo of the heartbeat.

A. The **pacemaker** is a specialized region of cardiac muscle in the wall of the right atrium, also known as the **sinoatrial (SA) node** (Figure 23.7).

B. When the SA node contracts, it sends out electrical signals, first to the atria, making them contract, and then to the **AV (atrioventricular node),** which acts as a relay. *NOTE:* The relay function of the AV node is needed because the atria and ventricles are separated by nonconductive connective tissue. Also note that the conduction system of the ventricles is more extensive than that of the atria.

C. The signals are delayed 0.1 sec in the AV node and then travel along specialized muscle fibers to the cardiac muscles of the ventricles, causing them to contract. The delay ensures that the atria empty prior to ventricular contraction.

D. The SA node sets the normal rate of contractions. The brain also can send signals to modify the basic rate, depending on body activity.

E. If the pacemaker does not function correctly, an **artificial pacemaker** can be implanted next to the heart. This provides a regular electrical signal to trigger the beat. *Preview:* The medulla oblongata is also involved in the regulation of heart rate (Module 28.15).

Module 23.8 Connection: What is a heart attack?

A. A **heart attack** is the death of cardiac muscle cells and the resulting failure of the heart to deliver enough blood to the rest of the body. Heart attacks follow clogging of the coronary arteries, blocking blood flow to regions of cardiac muscle (Figure 23.8A). *Review:* Dietary influence (Module 21.24) and the influence of smoking (Module 22.6) on cardiovascular fitness.

B. Such clogs occur if blood clots back up behind constrictions (due to lipid buildup) in these arteries.

C. Cardiac muscle cells do not regenerate but leave noncontracting scar tissue.

D. The sudden onset of a heart attack (myocardial infarction, or MI) takes the patient by surprise because the buildup of plaques on the inner epithelial lining of the artery **(atherosclerosis)** is asymptomatic. Plaques are composed of lipids and appear for a variety of reasons (Module 21.24; Table 9.9; and Modules 3.8, 3.9, and 3.10).

E. Lifestyle changes can reduce the risk of heart disease. Increase exercise, lower fat intake, increase fruit and vegetable consumption, and don't smoke.

F. Relief to heart disease patients includes treatment with clot-dissolving enzymes, coronary artery bypass surgery, and angioplasty and laser surgery to open up constricted coronary arteries. Identification of patients at risk of heart attack with simple blood tests and with advances in imaging technologies has improved patient outcome. Heart transplants are possible, but the shortage of donor hearts restricts the procedure. Artificial hearts are under development as alternatives to transplants.

G. Cardiovascular disease has decreased somewhat (50% in the past 50 years) as a result of increased awareness of the roles of diet and exercise in health, early diagnosis of problems, and the availability of automatic external defibrillators (AED).

Module 23.9 Blood exerts pressure on vessel walls.
Preview: The hypothalamus plays a role in the regulation of blood pressure (Table 28.15).

A. **Blood pressure** is caused by the pumping of the heart against the resistance offered by smaller vessels in the tissues supplied with blood.

B. **Pulse** is the rhythmic stretching of the arteries caused by the pressure of blood from the heart during systole.

C. Blood pressure is greatest in the aorta and decreases along the path back to the venae cavae (Figure 23.9A). Blood pressure depends on several factors, such as physical and emotional stress, and is controlled by changes in hormone levels and arteriole constriction and dilation.

D. Velocity decreases sequentially from the aorta to the capillaries, where the velocity is very low. The low velocity is necessary for efficient exchange of chemicals. The velocity increases as the blood leaves the capillaries and enters the venules in the pattern shown because of frictional resistance and because the cross-sectional area of the capillary beds is greater than that of larger veins.

E. Blood pressure in veins is near zero, but blood returns to the heart with the aid of muscular contraction, valves, and the lifting of the chest cavity during breathing (Figure 23.9B).

Module 23.10 Connection: Measuring blood pressure can reveal cardiovascular problems.

A. A blood pressure of 120/70 indicates that the force of the heart's beat during systole is 120 mm of mercury (mm Hg) and the general background pressure of the blood in arteries during diastole is 70 mm Hg. Blood pressure below 120/80 is an indication of a healthy cardiovascular system. Conversely, abnormal blood pressure (too high or too low) is an indication of cardiovascular disease or some other serious condition such as an endocrine disorder.

B. Blood pressure is measured with a sphygmomanometer. The pressure of the cuff cuts off the blood flow in outer arteries (no pulse is heard). Pressure is reduced in the cuff until the force of systole first pushes blood through (the turbulent sounds of blood flow are heard). Further reduction in the cuff's pressure reaches a point where the sounds of turbulent blood flow are no longer heard; this marks diastole (Figures 23.10 and 23.9A). *NOTE:* The sounds that are heard when measuring blood pressure are referred to as Korotkoff sounds.

C. High blood pressure (hypertension) is a persistent blood pressure of 140/90. It makes the heart work harder against greater resistance due to blockages and reduced flexibility.

D. Hypertension is called the silent killer because its damaging effects take many years to be clinically apparent. Once the damage is done, it is often too late to fix the problem. Hypertension-related diseases include heart failure, stroke, heart attack, and kidney failure.

E. Causes of hypertension can be difficult to diagnose; however, in spite of a predisposition for hypertension, one can reduce the risk factors by the following changes in lifestyle:

1. Eat a heart-healthy diet.
2. Lose excess weight and maintain the ideal body weight once obtained.
3. Exercise several times each week.
4. Do not smoke or indulge in excessive drinking.

F. If these lifestyle changes fail to reduce blood pressure readings, then antihypertensive medication may help.

Module 23.11 Smooth muscle controls the distribution of blood.
Review: Types of muscle, including smooth muscle, are discussed in Module 20.6.

A. In all tissues except the brain, liver, kidneys, and heart, blood supply varies greatly depending on the need of the organ or tissue.

B. Arteriole constriction can reduce the flow to capillaries. This flow is under the control of nerves and hormones.

C. In another mechanism, some blood flows through the center of a capillary bed (a thoroughfare channel), but precapillary sphincter muscles control the passage of most blood into the bed. For example, after a meal, precapillary sphincters let more blood pass into the capillaries that supply the villi of the small intestine (Figure 23.11).
NOTE: At the same time, blood supply may be diverted from the outer extremities. Thus, on a cold day, you will feel extra chilled after a meal.

Module 23.12 Capillaries allow the transfer of substances through their walls.
Review: Movement of materials across membranes by diffusion, endocytosis, and osmosis (Modules 5.14–5.16 and 5.19).

A. Capillaries are the only vessels with walls thin enough to allow transfer of substances though the epithelium (Figure 23.12A).

B. Some substances simply diffuse across the capillary wall to and from blood and interstitial fluid; others are moved across by endo- and exocytosis.

C. Water and some small dissolved molecules (salts, sugars, and small proteins) "leak" through small cracks between the epithelial cells surrounding capillaries.
Preview: This fluid is returned to the cardiovascular system via the lymphatic system (Module 24.3).

D. Blood pressure tends to actively force fluid out of capillaries. Osmosis (Module 5.16) tends to cause fluids to move in. At the arterial ends of capillary beds, blood pressure is relatively high, exceeding osmotic pressure and forcing water out of the capillaries. At the venous ends, osmotic pressure is higher than blood pressure, which allows water to return to the capillaries (Figure 23.12B).

III. Structure and Function of Blood

Module 23.13 Blood consists of red and white blood cells suspended in plasma.

A. An average adult human contains 4–6 liters of blood (Figure 23.13).

B. About 45% of blood is cellular (red and white blood cells and platelets).

C. About 55% of blood is plasma, of which 90% is water and 10% is dissolved molecules. Ions of salts and albumin maintain osmotic balance and pH and regulate the permeability of membranes. Proteins help in blood clotting and are important in body defense, among other things (such as transport of substances).
Preview: The function of these important immune system proteins is covered in Chapter 24.

D. **Erythrocytes (red blood cells)** are the most numerous blood cell type; there are about 25 trillion present at one time in the average person (Figure 23.13).
Review: The function of red blood cells in exchanging and carrying gases (Modules 22.10 and 22.11).

E. Five types of **leukocytes (white blood cells)** are distinguished by nuclear shape and staining properties. They are also produced in the bone marrow. As a group, they spend most of their time outside the circulatory system, fighting infections and preventing cancer cells from growing. These types of white blood cells are called **phagocytes.**

F. The five types of leukocytes are basophils, neutrophils, monocytes, eosinophils, and lymphocytes (Figure 23.13).

G. The third type of cellular element in the blood is **platelets,** which are involved in clot formation (Figure 23.13).

Module 23.14 Too few or too many red blood cells can be unhealthy.

A. Adequate numbers of RBCs are needed for proper health. RBCs have a normal life span of 3 to 4 months, at which time they die and the components (particularly iron) are recycled (Figure 23.14).

B. Low levels of hemoglobin or a low number of red blood cells is known as **anemia.** A person who is anemic feels tired and has no energy. There are a variety of causes for anemia, the most common of which is iron deficiency. Iron deficiency can usually be treated with iron supplements.

C. Red blood cell production is under the control of a negative-feedback mechanism that is sensitive to the amount of oxygen reaching tissues. This mechanism is mediated by production of the hormone **erythropoietin** (EPO) in the kidneys. Kidney dialysis patients often receive EPO shots to stimulate RBC production.

D. A result of living at high altitudes is an increased RBC count. Athletes will train at high elevations in an effort to improve performance. In an alternative way to improve performance, some athletes take injections of EPO; however, the consequences can be lethal.

Module 23.15 Blood clots plug leaks when blood vessels are injured.

A. The blood-clotting mechanism involves materials carried in the blood: platelets, the plasma protein **fibrinogen,** and clotting factors.
NOTE: Blood clotting also requires Ca^{2+}.

B. Minor damage to a blood vessel exposes connective tissue to blood. Platelets adhere to this tissue and release a substance that makes nearby platelets sticky. If major damage occurs, a chain of enzymatically regulated reactions form a more complex plug, a fibrin clot (Figure 23.15A).

C. The platelet clot activates a series of enzymes, which in turn convert fibrinogen into the threadlike protein **fibrin.** These fibrin threads trap additional blood cells (Figure 23.15B). Within an hour after clot formation, contraction, which reduces the repair site, occurs. Chemicals released by the platelets stimulate muscle and connective tissue cell division and promote repair.
NOTE: Blood clotting is one of the few examples of a positive-feedback mechanism; another is labor (Module 27.18).

D. Hemophilia is an inherited disease in which individuals lack this mechanism (Module 9.24). The opposite effect of hemophilia is the spontaneous formation of clots without injury. The result is a thrombus, which, if dislodged from the site of formation, can travel through the blood to organs such as the heart, brain, or lungs and cause heart attacks, stroke, or pulmonary embolism, respectively.

Module 23.16 Connection: Stem cells offer a potential cure for blood cell diseases.

A. White blood cells, red blood cells, and platelets all arise in the bone marrow from stem cells (Figure 23.16).

B. **Leukemia** is cancer of the bone marrow cells that produce white blood cells. The leukocytes are in abnormally high numbers, and these in turn may interfere with red blood cell production, causing the person to be anemic.

C. Standard treatment for leukemia involves radiation and chemotherapy (Module 8.10) or bone marrow replacement (following radiation, removal, and the introduction of donor marrow). Bone marrow replacement requires the patient to be on lifelong treatment with drugs that suppress the rejection of transplanted cells. Such drugs are not selective and suppress all immune function, making individuals who take these drugs more susceptible to infections.

D. A potential variation on the latter treatment involves a technique to remove and purify bone marrow from a patient with leukemia, isolating the stem cells. These are then reintroduced in bone marrow that has been radiated to kill off all cancerous leukocytes. Since these are the patient's own cells, there is no risk of rejection.

E. Three methods are commonly used to harvest stem cells:

1. Bone marrow aspiration.
2. Chemically induced stem cell migration to the blood.
3. Stem cell harvesting from umbilical cord blood.

F. Regardless of the method used, stem cells are powerful cells and can completely repopulate a patient's immune system as well as have other applications. The medical implications are far reaching.

Class Activities

1. To see the effect of the unidirectional valves in veins, let an arm hang down the side of the body. After a short period of time, the veins will be visibly filled with blood. Raise the arm above the head, and the veins will empty of blood.

2. Do the classic: Have the students trace the path of a red blood cell through the body. You can divide the class into groups and give each group a different starting point. Perhaps you can reward the group that comes up with the shortest route, the longest route, or that finds the most alternative routes.

3. Challenge your students to try and think of blood vessels, other than pulmonary vessels, where veins carry oxygenated blood and arteries carry deoxygenated blood.

Transparency Acetates

Figure 23.1B	Diffusion between blood and tissue cells
Figure 23.2A	The gastrovascular cavity (salmon color) in a jelly
Figure 23.2B	The open circulatory system (vessels in gold) in a grasshopper (combined with Figure 23.2A)
Figure 23.2C	The closed circulatory system in a fish
Figure 23.3A	Diagram of the cardiovascular system of a fish
Figure 23.3B	Diagram of the cardiovascular system of an amphibian
Figure 23.3C	Diagram of the cardiovascular system of a mammal
Figure 23.4A	Blood flow through the human heart
Figure 23.4B	Blood flow through the human cardiovascular system
Figure 23.5	Structural relationships of blood vessels
Figure 23.6	The cardiac cycle
Figure 23.7	Control of the heart's rhythm (top) and an electrocardiogram (bottom). (Yellow color represents electrical signals.)
Figure 23.8A	Blockage of a coronary artery, resulting in a heart attack
Figure 23.9A	Blood pressure and velocity in the blood vessels
Figure 23.9B	Blood flow in a vein

Figure 23.10   Measuring blood pressure (Layer 1)

Figure 23.10   Measuring blood pressure (Layer 2)

Figure 23.10   Measuring blood pressure (Layer 3)

Figure 23.11   The control of capillary blood flow by precapillary sphincters

Figure 23.12A   A capillary in cross section

Figure 23.12B   The movement of fluid into and out of a capillary

Figure 23.13   The composition of blood

Figure 23.15A   The blood-clotting process

Reviewing the Concepts, page 482: Blood vessel structure

Connecting the Concepts, page 482: The flow of blood in the human cardiovascular system

Testing Your Knowledge, page 482: A blood sample that has been spun in a centrifuge

---

Media

See the beginning of this book for a complete description of all media available for instructors and students. Animations and videos are available in the Campbell Image Presentation Library. Media Activities and Thinking as a Scientist investigations are available on the student CD-ROM and website.

Animations and Videos	Module Number
Path of Blood Flow in Mammals	23.4

Activities and Thinking as a Scientist	Module Number
Web/CD Activity 23A: *Mammalian Cardiovascular System Structure*	23.4
Web/CD Activity 23B: *Path of Blood Flow in Mammals*	23.4
Web/CD Activity 23C: *Mammalian Cardiovascular System Function*	23.7
Web/CD Thinking as a Scientist: *Connection: How Is Cardiovascular Fitness Measured?*	23.10
Biology Labs On-Line: *The Mammalian Cardiovascular System*	23.10
Biology Labs On-Line: *Structure and Function of Blood*	23.14

CHAPTER 24

The Immune System

Teaching Objectives

Introduction Explain how the transmission of AIDS from mother to child can be reduced, and describe the experiments that revealed cost-effective ways to do so.

Innate Defenses Against Infection

24.1 Describe the nature of innate defenses against infection.

24.2 Describe the events of the inflammatory response, and explain how it helps to prevent the spread of disease.

24.3 Describe the structure and functions of the lymphatic system.

Acquired Immunity

24.4 Describe the specific nature of an immune system response. Define antigen, antibody, passive immunity, and active immunity.

24.5 Describe the development and functions of B and T lymphocytes.

24.6 Describe the nature of antigens. Explain how an antigen and antibody interact.

24.7 Describe the process of clonal selection, and compare a primary immune response to a secondary immune response.

24.8 Relate the specific structure of an antibody to its functions.

24.9 Describe four effector mechanisms. Explain how antibodies work with innate defenses to form a complete defense system.

24.10 Describe the production of and uses for monoclonal antibodies.

24.11 Describe the specific functions of cytotoxic T cells and helper T cells. Note their interactions with other cells.

24.12 Explain how HIV infects cells, multiplies, and causes disease.

24.13 Explain how cytotoxic T cells destroy infected body cells.

24.14 Explain how the immune system helps to fight cancer.

24.15 Explain how the immune system identifies the body's own molecules and how this system creates problems for organ transplantations.

Disorders of the Immune System

24.16 Describe examples of how the malfunction or failure of the immune system can cause disease.

24.17 Explain why allergies occur and what causes anaphylactic shock.

Key Terms

acquired immunity
active immunity
allergens
allergies

anaphylactic shock
antibody
antigen
antigen receptors

antigen-binding site
antigenic determinant
antigen-presenting cells
 (APCs)

antihistamines	inflammatory response	neutrophils
autoimmune diseases	innate immunity	nonself molecules
B cells	interferons	opportunistic infections
cell-mediated immunity	lymph	passive immunity
clonal selection	lymphatic system	perforin
complement system	lymphocytes	plasma cells
cytotoxic T cells	macrophages	primary immune response
effector cells	major histocompatibility	secondary immune response
helper T cells	complex	self protein
histamine	mast cells	T cells
humoral immunity	memory cells	vaccination
immune system	MHC	vaccine
immunity	monoclonal antibodies	
immunodeficiency diseases	natural killer cells	

Word Roots

an- = without; **-aphy** = suck (*anaphylactic shock:* an acute, life-threatening, allergic response)

anti- = against; **-gen** = produce (*antigen:* a foreign macromolecule that does not belong to the host organism and that elicits an immune response)

macro- = large; **-phage** = eat (*macrophage:* an amoeboid cell that moves through tissue fibers, engulfing bacteria and dead cells by phagocytosis)

mono- = one (*monocyte:* an agranular leukocyte that is able to migrate into tissues and transform into a macrophage)

neutro- = neutral; **-phil** = loving (*neutrophil:* the most abundant type of leukocyte; neutrophils tend to self-destruct as they destroy foreign invaders, limiting their life span to but a few days)

perfora- = bore through (*perforin:* a protein that forms pores in a target cell's membrane)

Lecture Outline

Introduction *An AIDS Uproar*

    A. A good scientific study should be based on proper scientific methods. However, ethics and public policy sometimes influence how and if a study is conducted. This was the case with a study done to see if the dosage of AZT (typically $800) used to decrease the HIV infection rate from mother to infant could be reduced to an economical level ($80).

    B. Preliminary results from the studies showed a 50% reduction in the HIV infection rate for infants at the low AZT dose, which prompted scientists to stop the use of the controversial placebo and administer AZT to the remaining mothers who had not yet given birth.

    C. AIDS selectively destroys T-lymphocytes, which are a critical component of our bodies' defense mechanisms. Our immune system is severely weakened without T-lymphocytes, making our body vulnerable to a variety of opportunistic infections.

    D. Humans and other animals depend on several elaborate systems of defense, which can be divided into two main categories:

        1. Innate immune defenses: nonspecific defenses do not distinguish individual infectious agents.

        2. Acquired immune defenses: this part of the immune system recognizes specific invaders and attacks and eliminates them.

I. Innate Defenses Against Infection

Module 24.1 Innate defenses against infection include the skin and mucous membranes, phagocytic cells, and antimicrobial proteins.

    A. The initial line of defense that our body has is not adaptive and does not discriminate between invading pathogens. It is, therefore, called **innate immunity.**

    B. The skin provides a tough, physical barrier. It also provides general chemical defenses (acidic pH) in the form of glandular secretions (tears, sweat, and other secretions) that inhibit or kill microbes. Sweat, saliva, and tears contain lysozyme.

    C. Mucous membranes protect organ systems (digestive and respiratory) that are open to the external environment. Stomach acid kills bacteria that are swallowed. Nose hair filters air, and mucus in the respiratory passages traps microbes and debris. Cilia propel the mucus to the throat, where it is swallowed.
Review: The details of the functioning of cilia are discussed in Module 4.17.

    D. **Neutrophils** and **macrophages** phagocytize bacteria and viruses in infected tissue. Macrophages develop from monocytes and phagocytize bacteria and virus-infected cells (Figure 24.1A). **Natural killer cells** attack cancer cells and virus-infected cells by releasing proteins that induce apoptosis (Module 27.13). All of these types of white blood cells leave the blood and scavenge invading cells in the interstitial fluid and body tissues.
Review: White blood cells (Module 23.13).

    E. **Interferons** are antimicrobial proteins produced by virus-infected cells that help other cells resist viruses. The mechanism of how interferon works is illustrated in Figure 24.1B. The infected cell induces cells in close proximity to produce antiviral proteins, which protect against viral infections. This is a good example of nonspecific defense because the interferon made by the infected cell induces resistance against unrelated viruses.

    F. The **complement system** is another type of antimicrobial proteins. Inactive complement proteins circulate in the blood and are activated by microbes. Some coat the microbes, making the microbes more susceptible to attack by macrophages; others lethally damage microbial membranes, causing lysis. The complement system also amplifies the inflammatory response.

Module 24.2 The inflammatory response mobilizes nonspecific defense forces.

    A. Any infectious agent or break in the barrier triggers the **inflammatory response.**

    B. The damaged cells release chemical such as **histamine.** Histamine induces blood vessels to dilate and become leakier, facilitating the flow of blood and fluid to the affected region (Figure 24.2).

    C. Other chemicals, such as complement proteins, attract phagocytes.

    D. Local clotting reactions seal off the infected region and allow repairs to begin.
Review: Clotting (Module 23.15).

E. Local action of this response is the disinfection and cleaning of injured areas that become hot, red, and swollen as a consequence of the increased blood supply, fluid, and cells. *NOTE:* Swelling presses against nerves and causes pain that is associated with inflammation. The accumulation of fluid also dilutes any toxins that may be present.

F. Systemic action of the response, due to microbes or their toxins circulating in the blood, results in a rapid increase in white blood cells and a high fever. High fevers can be dangerous, but moderate fevers may stimulate phagocytosis and inhibit the growth of microbes.

G. Overwhelming bacterial infection of an organ or an organ system results in septic shock and often ends in death.

Module 24.3 The lymphatic system becomes a crucial battleground during infection.

A. The **lymphatic system** consists of an open branching network of vessels, lymph nodes, the thymus, tonsils, appendix, adenoids, spleen, and bone marrow. The system has two main functions: to return excess fluid from the interstitial fluid to the circulatory system and to fight infection through both immune defense systems (Figure 24.3).

B. **Lymph** (the fluid of the lymphatic system) enters the system through lymphatic capillaries (Figure 24.3, bottom right). The largest lymph ducts empty into circulatory system veins in the shoulders (Figure 24.3).

C. Lymph is similar to interstitial fluid, except that it is lower in oxygen and contains fewer nutrients. As it circulates through the lymphatic organs, microbes from infected sites and cancer cells may be phagocytized by macrophages. Also, within these lymphoid organs, lymphocytes may be activated to mount a specific immune response. *NOTE:* With age, the glandular tissue of the thymus is replaced with connective tissue.

D. **Lymph nodes** are concentrated areas of branched ducts containing large numbers of lymphocytes (B cells and T cells) and macrophages. During an infection, these areas become activated and swell, causing the tenderness and aches and pains associated with a systemic infection (Figure 24.3, top right).

E. Swollen and tender lymph nodes are an overt sign that your body is responding to an infection.

II. Acquired Immunity

Module 24.4 The immune response counters specific invaders.

A. The **immune system** recognizes specific invaders more efficiently than the nonspecific defenses, and it amplifies the inflammatory and complement responses. Extreme specificity, memory, and prompt response on second exposure to an antigen characterize the immune system.

B. An **antigen** is any molecule that elicits an immune response. Such molecules include those found on the surfaces of viruses, bacteria, mold, etc.
Preview: An autoimmune response occurs when the antigen(s) that elicit(s) an immune response is (are) that body's own molecule(s). Autoimmune diseases include insulin-dependent diabetes mellitus, lupus, multiple sclerosis, and rheumatoid arthritis (Module 24.16).

C. The system responds to an antigen by producing a specific type of **antibody** that attaches to the antigen and helps counter its effects.

D. In the future, the primed system remembers the antigen and reacts to it.

E. **Immunity** refers to resistance to specific invaders. This type of immunity is gained only after exposure to the antigen and is, therefore, called **acquired immunity. Active immunity** is achieved by exposure to the invader or to parts of the invader incorporated in **vaccinations** in the form of an injection called a **vaccine. Passive immunity** is achieved when a person receives the antibodies from someone else. For instance, a fetus may achieve passive immunity to antigens from its mother through the placenta, or a baby through breast milk.

Module 24.5 Lymphocytes mount a dual defense.

A. **Lymphocytes** arise from stem cells in the bone marrow (Modules 23.15 and 30.5; Figure 24.5).

B. There are two major categories of lymphocytes:

1. **B cells** (B lymphocytes) mature in the bone and release antibodies that function when dissolved in the blood.

2. **T cells** (T lymphocytes) mature in the thymus (a gland found in the upper chest).
   Preview: B cells produce a clone of cells, plasma cells, which secrete antibodies in much higher quantity than B cells can (Module 24.8).

C. **Humoral immunity** is defense against bacteria and viruses free in the blood or interstitial fluid. Humoral immunity can be transferred passively by injecting antibody-containing plasma to a nonimmune individual, or by antibodies moving across the placenta (Module 24.4). Cell-surface antigens bound by antibodies are marked for destruction by phagocytes.

D. **Cell-mediated immunity** is a defense mounted by T cells against bacteria and viruses inside body cells, against fungi and protozoans, and against cancer cells. T cells circulate in the blood and mount a cellular attack on repeated foreign invaders. T cells promote phagocytosis by other white blood cells. Furthermore, by promoting antibody secretion by B cells, T cells also play a role in humoral immunity.
   Preview: There are several types of T cells (Module 24.11).
   Preview: The functioning of the thymus gland is also discussed in Module 26.3.

E. Both B cells and T cells must mature before they are able to function in defense of the body. This involves a process by which certain genes are turned on, which allows them to produce proteins that are incorporated into the plasma membrane. These cells become capable of recognizing and responding to a specific antigen. Mature T and B cells have surface proteins called **antigen receptors** that can bind antigens. There are about 100,000 antigen receptors on a single lymphocyte, all identical and capable of binding only one antigen.

F. A human has millions of different kinds of B cells and T cells. Most are in a standby mode, ready to come to the defense of the body when the right antigen is present.
   NOTE: Modules 24.6–24.10 describe humoral immunity, and Module 24.13 describes cell-mediated immunity.

Module 24.6 Antigens have specific regions where antibodies bind to them.

A. Antigens are usually proteins or large polysaccharides on viruses or foreign cells.

B. An antibody usually identifies a localized region on the antigen called an **antigenic determinant** (or epitope) by means of a "lock-and-key" fit (Figure 24.6).

C. An antigen may have several antigenic determinants and can, therefore, elicit several distinct antibodies. Each antibody has two identical antigen-binding sites.

Module 24.7 Clonal selection musters defensive forces against specific antigens.

A. Each B cell has a specific antigen receptor on its surface before it is exposed to an antigen. The function of the immune system is dependent on the diversity of antigen receptors and the ability of an antigen to induce **clonal selection.**

B. Upon exposure to an antigen, a tiny fraction of the lymphocytes are able to bind to it and are activated (Figure 24.7A). These cells proliferate, forming a clone of genetically identical effector cells called plasma cells. Plasma cells may secrete up to 2,000 antibody molecules per second during their 4-to-5-day lifetime.

C. The effect of the proliferation of the effector cells is the **primary immune response.** There is a delay between exposure to the antigen and the secretion of antibodies, and this first exposure results in the release of modest levels of antibodies (Figure 24.7B).

D. During the primary response, some of the cloned cells function as effector cells, while some become **memory cells.** The memory cells remain in the lymph nodes, ready to be activated by a second exposure to the antigen.

E. The **secondary immune response** occurs when the body is exposed again to the same antigen. This response is faster than the primary response, lasts longer, and produces much higher levels of antibodies that may be more effective than those antibodies produced during the primary response. During a secondary response, memory cells bind antigens and rapidly produce a new clone of plasma cells.

F. Overall, the system works by combining clonal selection and immunologic memory. A clone is composed of some effector (plasma) cells that immediately produce antibodies to the antigen (primary response), and a smaller number of memory cells that prepare the immune system for a secondary response (Figures 24.7A and 24.7B).

Module 24.8 Antibodies are the weapons of humoral immunity.
Review: Protein structure (Module 3.14).

A. The cells responsible for antibody production are the **plasma cells** (the effector cell from Module 24.7), which is a product of B cell clonal selection.

B. The symbol used for an antibody is a "Y" because the actual quaternary structure of an antibody resembles a Y (Figure 24.8A). Each antibody is made of two identical "heavy" polypeptide chains and two identical "light" polypeptide chains (Figure 24.8B).

C. Each of the four chains of an antibody has a C (constant) region and a V (variable) region. A pair of V regions, at the tip of each arm of the Y, forms the **antigen-binding site** (Figure 24.8B).
NOTE: Genetically, these variable regions are assembled following transcription and translation of combinations of a few each of several dozen genes. Each B cell or T cell line activates one set of such genes and continues to activate the same set over its lifetime.

D. The antibody has two main functions in humoral immunity:

1. To bind to its antigen, this occurs at the antigen-binding site.

2. To assist in the elimination of the antigen, this occurs at the C region of the heavy chains.

E. Based on the nature of the C region, human antibodies are divided into five major classes—IgA, IgD, IgE, IgG, and IgM—each with a particular role. Ig is the abbreviation for *immunoglobulin,* which is synonymous with *antibody.*

Module 24.9 Antibodies mark antigens for elimination.

    A. Antibody-antigen complexes are eliminated by several mechanisms (Figure 24.9):

        1. Neutralization physically blocks harmful antigens, making them harmless.

        2. Agglutination clumps groups of cells (or viruses) to ease their capture by phagocytes.

        3. Precipitation clumps dissolved antigens together so they precipitate out of solution and can be captured by phagocytes.

        4. Antigen-antibody complexes activate complement proteins. Activated complement proteins attach to foreign cells, prompting cell lysis.

    B. All mechanisms involve a *specific* recognition phase (the antibodies of humoral immunity) followed by a *nonspecific* destruction phase (phagocytosis and complement proteins).

Module 24.10 Connection: Monoclonal antibodies are powerful tools in the lab and clinic.

    A. Antibodies used in clinical diagnosis, treatment, and research were first produced in animals by injecting the antigen and then removing some blood that contained polyclonal antibodies.

    B. Techniques were developed to stimulate B cells for specific antigens. These cells were fused with immortal tumor cells to form hybrid cells that can be cultured indefinitely and produce **monoclonal antibodies** (Figure 24.10A). The antibodies are screened for the desired antigen-binding properties.

    C. Monoclonal antibodies are useful in medical diagnoses, such as pregnancy tests, which test for the presence of a specific hormone (HCG). Monoclonal antibodies also provide a way to target drugs (toxins) to certain cells that cause cancer. Herceptin is a genetically engineered monoclonal antibody that is used against breast cancer.
NOTE: They are also used with fluorochromes, such as fluorescein, thus allowing the molecular (antigen) positions to be determined within a cell by a technique called immunofluorescence.

Module 24.11 Helper T cells stimulate humoral and cell-mediated immunity.
Review: The role of T cells in attacking antigens from bacteria and viruses inside body cells and those of protozoans and fungi (Module 24.5).

    A. The mechanism of the T-cell system results from the close cooperation of a number of cell types.

    B. **Cytotoxic T cells** attack pathogen-infected cells (Module 24.13).

    C. **Helper T cells** play a role in the activation of cytotoxic T cells, B cells, and macrophages.

    D. Macrophages are **antigen-presenting cells (APCs)** that combine with and display on their cell surface **"self proteins"** and a **nonself molecule** consisting of a small peptide from an antigen that it has ingested and processed.

    E. Helper T cells recognize only one combination of self protein and foreign antigen as presented by an APC (Figure 24.11). The binding to a self-nonself complex is one of the ways helper T cells are activated. Other signals, such as the secretion of interleukin-1 by the APC, enhance the activation of helper T cells.

F. Activated helper T cells secrete proteins that promote an immune response. For example, interleukin-2 has three major effects:

1. It stimulates helper T cells to grow and divide, producing both memory cells and more helper T cells (cell-mediated immunity).

2. It stimulates B cells (humoral immunity).

3. It stimulates cytotoxic T cells (cell-mediated immunity).

Module 24.12 Connection: HIV destroys helper T cells, compromising the body's defenses.

A. Human immunodeficiency virus (HIV) causes AIDS (acquired immune deficiency syndrome). The cell most likely killed by the virus is the helper T cell, which, as we saw in Module 24.11, is a critical component of the immune system.

B. HIV is a retrovirus that is transmitted through body fluids, usually by sexual intercourse, with contaminated needles, or from mother to child (opening essay). Once inside the body, the viruses attach to cells (particularly helper T cells), enter, and start to replicate. The infection can take years to show any signs or symptoms.

C. The selectivity of the virus for helper T cells makes those with the infection very susceptible to **opportunistic infections** such as *Pneumocystis carinii* and Kaposi sarcoma.

D. Despite intense efforts in research, no cure or vaccine for HIV has been developed. Some drugs such as AZT slow the progress of AIDS, but the virus mutates rapidly; therefore, attempts at vaccination fail and drug-resistant strains of HIV are common.

E. The best way to stop the spread of HIV is through education, practice of safe sex (although condoms do not completely prevent the transmission of HIV or other viruses such as hepatitis B), practice of abstinence, and monogamous relationships.

Module 24.13 Cytotoxic T cells destroy infected body cells.

A. Two types of T cells are involved in cell-mediated immunity: helper T cells and cytotoxic T cells. Helper T cells activate cytotoxic T cells when stimulated with interleukin-2 (Module 24.11).

B. Cytotoxic T cells are the only T cells that actually kill other cells. Activated cytotoxic T cells recognize and bind to infected body cells in much the same way that helper T cells bind to APCs: They recognize only a combination of a self protein (different from the APC self protein) and the foreign antigen as presented by the infected cell.

C. The cytotoxic T cells then secrete **perforin,** a protein that makes holes in the target cell, causing lysis. T-cell enzymes enter the infected cell and trigger apoptosis (programmed cell death), causing cell lysis and death (Figure 24.13).

Module 24.14 Cytotoxic T cells may help prevent cancer.
Review: The molecular and cellular bases of cancer (Modules 8.10, 8.23, and 11.16–11.20).

A. Genetic changes that occur in cancer cells can result in the production of new proteins that are expressed on the outer membrane. These proteins are referred to as tumor antigens.

B. If these changes result in the cancer cell's not appearing as "self" to the T-cell system, they may be eliminated by the cytotoxic T cells (Figure 24.14).

C. How often this built-in system functions and why it sometimes fails are the subjects of considerable research on possible cancer cures.

Module 24.15 The immune system depends on our molecular fingerprints.

    A. The ability of our immune system to distinguish self from nonself enables it to battle foreign invaders without harming healthy body cells.

    B. There are two types of self proteins. Class I proteins occur on all nucleated body cells. Class II proteins are found only on B cells, activated T cells, and macrophages. Both are unique to each individual.

    C. The main self proteins are determined on multiple chromosomal loci, each with hundreds of alleles. Thus, with the exception of identical twins, it is (effectively) impossible for two individuals to have an identical set of self proteins. Self proteins are coded for by **MHC (major histocompatibility complex)** genes.

    D. This diversity can cause problems when a person receives an organ transplant. The donated organ displays different self proteins, is recognized as foreign, and is, thus, subject to immune attack and organ rejection.

    E. The risk of rejection is minimized by finding a donor whose self proteins match the recipient's as closely as possible, and by using drugs that suppress the immune response against the transplant. Most such drugs interfere with the beneficial effects of the system. Cyclosporine suppresses only the cell-mediated response.
      NOTE: Cloning (Modules 11.10–11.12) has the potential to make possible autologous organ transplants.

III. Disorders of the Immune System

Module 24.16 Connection: Malfunction or failure of the immune system causes diseases.

    A. In **autoimmune diseases,** the immune system turns against its own body cells. Such diseases include insulin-dependent diabetes (insulin-producing cells are subjected to a cell-mediated response; Module 26.8), rheumatoid arthritis (antibody-mediated damage to joints, bones, and cartilage), lupus (production of antibodies against molecules such as histones and DNA), and multiple sclerosis (T cells attack myelin; Module 28.2).
      NOTE: Autoimmune diseases, such as insulin-dependent diabetes, appear to be triggered by an infection.

    B. In **immunodeficiency diseases,** part or all of the immune system is lacking. SCID (severe combined immunodeficiency) is an inherited disorder in which both T cells and B cells are absent or inactive. Hodgkin's disease is a cancer of lymphocytes; treatment of this disease can suppress the immune system. HIV infection, leading to AIDS, is discussed in Module 24.12.

    C. Physical and emotional stress may also weaken the immune system.

Module 24.17 Connections: Allergies are overreactions to certain environmental antigens.

    A. **Allergies** are abnormal sensitivities to antigens in our environment. These antigens are called **allergens** (e.g., pollen, dust mite feces, insect toxins, cat saliva, and proteins).
      NOTE: Children subjected to cigarette smoke as well as children who were exposed prenatally to cigarette smoke are more likely to develop allergies. Also, feeding young children nuts or peanuts (a legume) may increase the risk of the development of allergies in susceptible individuals.

    B. Allergic reactions follow two stages:

      1. Sensitization: A person is first exposed to the allergen, eliciting B cells to form an immunologic clone against the allergen. The antibodies produced attach to histamine-producing **mast cells** that trigger an inflammatory response by releasing histamines.

2. Second exposure: The person is secondarily exposed to the same allergen. The antibodies on the mast cell bind to the allergen and release histamine in greater amounts than in a normal inflammatory response. This causes the symptoms of allergies: nasal irritation, itchiness, and tears (Figure 24.17).

C. **Antihistamines** interfere with histamine action and give temporary relief from the symptoms.

D. The response to allergens can range from mild and seasonal to severe. The precipitous release of histamine can cause **anaphylactic shock** in some people, which can result in a dramatic drop in blood pressure and may lead to death. Fortunately, the effect of the allergen can be counteracted with a shot of epinephrine.

Class Activities

1. Have your students consider why emerging viruses are so dangerous. Based on what they have learned about the functioning of the immune system, is it possible that there is a naturally existing pathogen that can evade everyone's immune system? Is it possible to genetically engineer a pathogen that can evade the immune system?

2. Inflammation is a normal part of the nonspecific response against infection. It is also very uncomfortable, so people tend to take analgesics to reduce inflammation. In terms of dealing with the infection, is it always a good idea to reduce inflammation?

Transparency Acetates

Figure 24.1B	The interferon mechanism against viruses
Figure 24.2	The inflammatory response
Figure 24.3	The human lymphatic system
Figure 24.5A	The development of B cells and T cells
Figure 24.6	The binding of antibodies to antigenic determinants
Figure 24.7A	Clonal selection of B cells in the primary and secondary immune responses (Layer 1)
Figure 24.7A	Clonal selection of B cells in the primary and secondary immune responses (Layer 2)
Figure 24.7A	Clonal selection of B cells in the primary and secondary immune responses (Layer 3)
Figure 24.7A	Clonal selection of B cells in the primary and secondary immune responses (Layer 4)
Figure 24.7B	The two phases of the immune system
Figure 24.8B	Antibody structure
Figure 24.9	Effector mechanisms of humoral immunity
Figure 24.10A	The procedure for making monoclonal antibodies
Figure 24.11	The activation of a helper T cell and its roles in immunity
Figure 24.13	How a cytotoxic T cell kills an infected cell (Layer 1)
Figure 24.13	How a cytotoxic T cell kills an infected cell (Layer 2)
Figure 24.13	How a cytotoxic T cell kills an infected cell (Layer 3)
Figure 24.17	The two stages of an allergic reaction

Reviewing the Concepts, page 500: The immune response

Connecting the Concepts, page 500: The body's defenses

Media

See the beginning of this book for a complete description of all media available for instructors and students. Animations and videos are available in the Campbell Image Presentation Library. Media Activities and Thinking as a Scientist investigations are available on the student CD-ROM and website.

Animations and Videos	Module Number
Role of B Cells Animation	24.7
Antibodies Animation	24.9
Helper T Cells Animation	24.11
T Cell Receptors Video	24.13
Cytotoxic T Cells Animation	24.13

Activities and Thinking as a Scientist	Module Number
Web/CD Thinking as a Scientist: *Connection: What Causes Infections in AIDS Patients?*	24.12
Web/CD Thinking as a Scientist: *Connection: Why Do AIDS Rates Differ Across the U.S.?*	24.12
Web/CD Activity 24A: *Immune Responses*	24.13
Web/CD Activity 24B: *HIV Reproductive Cycle*	24.17

CHAPTER 25

Control of the Internal Environment

Teaching Objectives

Introduction Explain how bear physiology adjusts during a time of dormancy.

Thermoregulation

25.1 Describe the four ways that heat is gained or lost by an animal.

25.2 Describe the five general categories of adaptations that help animals thermoregulate. Note examples of each.

25.3 Define and distinguish between hibernation and torpor, noting examples of each.

Osmoregulation and Excretion

25.4 Describe the osmoregulatory problems and associated adaptations of freshwater and saltwater fish, terrestrial arthropods, and terrestrial vertebrates.

25.5 Describe the daily human requirements for water. Note the sources of water in our diet, and describe some of the common misperceptions about water consumption.

25.6 Describe the three ways that animals eliminate nitrogenous wastes and the advantages and disadvantages of each method.

25.7 Describe the many functions of the liver.

25.8 Describe the consequences of heavy, repeated exposure of the liver to dietary alcohol.

25.9 Describe the general and specific structure of the human kidney. Explain how this organ promotes homeostasis.

25.10 Describe the four major processes by which the human excretory system produces and eliminates urine.

25.11 Describe the key events in the process of converting filtrate into urine in the kidneys.

25.12 Explain how a dialysis machine functions.

Key Terms

ammonia	filtrate	renal cortex
antidiuretic hormone (ADH)	filtration	renal medulla
Bowman's capsule	glomerulus	secretion
collecting duct	hepatic portal vessel	thermoregulation
countercurrent heat	hibernation	torpor
exchanger	loop of Henle	urea
dialysis	nephrons	ureter
distal tubule	osmoconformer	urethra
ectotherms	osmoregulation	uric acid
endotherms	osmoregulators	urinary bladder
estivation	proximal tubule	urine
excretion	reabsorption	

Word Roots

counter- = opposite (*countercurrent heat exchanger:* a special arrangement of blood vessels that helps trap heat in the body core and is important in reducing heat loss in many endotherms)

ecto- = outside; **-therm** = heat (*ectotherm:* an animal, such as a reptile, fish, or amphibian, that must use environmental energy and behavioral adaptations to regulate its body temperature)

endo- = inner (*endotherm:* an animal that uses metabolic energy to maintain a constant body temperature, such as a bird or mammal)

glomer- = a ball (*glomerulus:* a ball of capillaries surrounded by Bowman's capsule in the nephron and serving as the site of filtration in the vertebrate kidney)

osmo- = pushing; **-regula** = regular (*osmoregulation:* adaptations to control the water balance in organisms living in hypertonic, hypotonic, or terrestrial environments)

Lecture Outline

Introduction *Let Sleeping Bears Lie*

A. Animals survive fluctuations in the external environment because they have internal, homeostatic controls.
1. **Thermoregulation** is the control of internal temperature within narrow limits.
2. **Osmoregulation** is control of the concentration of water and dissolved solutes.
3. **Excretion** is the disposal of nitrogen-containing wastes.

B. Animals vary in the ways they control body temperature.
1. The concept of cold-blooded and warm-blooded animals is better replaced by the terms **ectothermic** and **endothermic** because these terms focus on the processes animals use to control body heat.
2. Endotherms derive most of their body heat from their own metabolism. This group includes mammals, birds, some reptiles and fish.
3. Ectotherms warm themselves by absorbing heat from the surrounding environment. This group includes most invertebrates, fishes, reptiles, amphibians, and other birds.
4. Some animals hibernate during the winter, and their body temperature may drop as much as 30°C.
5. Bears do not hibernate but instead go dormant and maintain body temperatures only a few degrees below their normal temperature.
6. Bears have several adaptations that allow a state of dormancy such as:
   a. Change in eating habits prior to dormancy to increase weight and store the excess energy as fat.
   b. Reduced blood flow to the extremities.
   c. Fetal position during dormant sleep.
   d. Dense fur and fat for excellent insulation.
   e. No eating, expelling waste, or urinating during the dormant state.

C. This chapter covers the homeostatic control mechanisms of thermoregulation, osmoregulation, and excretion.

I. Thermoregulation

Module 25.1 Heat is gained or lost in four ways.

A. An animal can exchange heat with the environment in four ways; any or all can happen at the same time (Figure 25.1).

   1. *Conduction* is the direct transfer of heat between surfaces in contact.

   2. *Convection* is the transfer of heat from air or liquid moving past a surface.

   3. *Radiation,* the emission of electromagnetic energy, can transfer heat between two bodies not in contact.

   4. *Evaporative* cooling is the loss of heat from a surface of liquid as the liquid is transformed into gas.

B. In each mechanism, heat is conducted from an area of higher temperature to one of lower temperature.

Module 25.2 Thermoregulation involves adaptations that balance heat gain and loss.
Preview: Thermoreceptors (Module 29.3).

A. Each species has an optimal internal temperature range. There are five categories of thermoregulation in which most animals can be placed.

B. **Metabolic heat production:** A change in the metabolic rate induced by altered hormonal levels is common among mammals and birds during cold weather. Movement and shivering are methods used to increase internal temperatures (Figure 25.2A).

C. **Insulation:** Thick layers of fat, fur, feathers or hair all act as good insulators. The ability to fluff the fur or feathers is a way to improve the insulation property by adding pockets of air.

D. **Circulatory adaptations:** Blood vessels can change diameters with changes in external temperature, wide to cool the body and constricted to warm the body. The use of a **countercurrent heat exchanger** is a method used by birds such as geese to reduce heat loss (Figure 25.2B). This method is also common among large fish such as sharks, tuna, and swordfish.

E. **Evaporative cooling:** Adaptations such as sweating, panting, or even spreading saliva on the body are methods used to stay cool during warm temperatures. Honeybees bring water to the hives and then fan it to cool the hive by evaporation and convection.

F. **Behavioral responses:** Bathing cools by convection and then later by evaporation. Relief from heat or cold can be obtained by seeking shelter, migrating to more suitable climates, or basking in the sun on cold days.

Module 25.3 Reducing metabolic rate and body temperature saves energy.

A. Ectotherms, such as the gray tree frog, can spend much of the winter frozen. The extremely low metabolic rate means that the frog uses almost no energy all winter. A frog version of antifreeze (cryoprotectants) prevents ice crystals from rupturing its cells (Figure 25.3).

B. In contrast to ectotherms, endotherms can remain active during severe weather. However, a large expenditure of energy is required to keep the body warm. Endotherms have several different adaptations that reduce energy needs.

   1. **Torpor** is the temporary reduction in body activity to bypass times of cooler temperatures. Bats and hummingbirds use torpor to escape the requirements of keeping their bodies warm during cold days (bats) and nights (hummingbirds).

   2. **Hibernation** is a type of long-term torpor practiced by squirrels and other small mammals during cold winter months. Hibernating animals can stay alive for many months by reducing their metabolic rates, lowering their body temperatures, and using fat stores for energy.

II. Osmoregulation and Excretion

Module 25.4 Osmoregulation: Animals balance the gain and loss of water and solutes.
Review: Mechanisms of transport: diffusion, osmosis, and active transport (Modules 5.14–5.19).

A. Osmoregulation is dependent on a balance between water and solute gain and loss. Water follows the movement of solutes by osmosis. Because of this property, cells will burst if in dilute solutions due to water uptake and will crenate (shrivel) in concentrated solutions due to water loss.

B. **Osmoconformers** are all aquatic animals that maintain their cells at solute concentrations essentially the same as the surrounding water. Examples include invertebrates such as jellies, flatworms, molluscs, and arthropods.

C. **Osmoregulators** maintain their body fluids with solute concentrations different from those of their surroundings. Examples include all freshwater animals, all land animals, and most marine vertebrates.

D. Freshwater fish constantly take in fresh water by osmosis. They control internal water and solute balance by taking up ions from food in the digestive system and gills, and by the production of large amounts of dilute urine via the excretory system (Figure 25.4A).

E. Saltwater fish have the opposite problem: They lose water by osmosis to their surroundings. They control internal solute concentration by drinking water, pumping out ions through the gills, and producing concentrated urine (Figure 25.4B).

F. Some fish, such as salmon, inhabit both fresh water and salt water at different phases in their lives. When they change habitats, they change strategies, using the freshwater or saltwater mechanisms as necessary.

G. Land animals have osmoregulatory problems like marine fish. Only two groups of animals are successful land dwellers: the arthropods and the vertebrates. Both have solved osmoregulatory problems by having thick skins that inhibit water loss, complex excretory systems, and adaptations that protect fertilized eggs and developing embryos from drying out.

Module 25.5 Connection: Do we need to drink eight glasses of water each day?

A. Conventional wisdom has been that eight glasses (8 ounces each) of water each day will promote good health (Figure 25.5). This old adage was recently examined by The Institute of Medicine and found not to be true.

B. The average male needs approximately 3.8 liters each day, while the average woman needs 2.6 liters. Most men take in approximately 3.1 liters from drinks (of all types), and women will average 2.1 liters each day. Most people will also consume an additional 0.5 to 0.7 liters from water-rich foods.

C. Additional fluid intake is not necessary unless excessive exercise or work that induces sweating takes place or if one lives in a warm, arid climate. The most prudent action one can take is to simply obey the thirst reflex. The instinct to drink is part of the body's osmoregulation system.

Module 25.6 Animals must dispose of nitrogenous wastes.

A. Nitrogen-containing wastes come mostly from the breakdown of proteins and nucleic acids. Nitrogenous wastes, as with most waste products, must be removed from the body dissolved in water. This process will impact water balance.

B. Aquatic animals can dispose of nitrogenous wastes in the form of toxic **ammonia,** which diffuses readily in water (Figure 25.6).

C. Terrestrial animals must use energy to convert amino groups of proteins into less toxic compounds.

D. **Urea** is highly soluble in water, 100,000 times less toxic than ammonia, and excreted by mammals, amphibians, and a few fishes.

E. **Uric acid** is also less toxic than ammonia and is excreted by birds, insects, many reptiles, and snails. Because it is almost insoluble in water, uric acid is excreted in crystalline form and, thus, has the benefit of conserving water.

F. The type of reproduction that a species has influences the method of nitrogen disposal. Live births or births from soft-shelled eggs can use urea, but birth from hard-shelled eggs must use uric acid.

Module 25.7 The liver performs many functions, including the production of urea.

A. This organ can perform many functions because its cells are capable of a wide range of metabolic activities. The strategic location of the liver aids in the cleansing process of the blood prior to the blood's reaching the heart and the rest of the body.

B. Substances absorbed by the GI tract travel to the liver via the **hepatic portal vessel** (or hepatic portal vein) (Figure 25.7). The liver then modifies and detoxifies absorbed substances prior to their distribution to the rest of the body via the heart.

C. The liver prepares nitrogenous wastes (synthesizes urea from ammonia) for disposal by the kidneys.

D. The liver regulates glucose levels in the blood by controlling glycogen and fat stores. The liver also makes lipoproteins to bind to and transport lipids and cholesterol throughout the body.

Module 25.8 Alcohol consumption can damage the liver.

A. The liver converts certain toxic compounds (alcohol and drugs) into inactive compounds that the kidneys will remove. The toxic compounds, however, can and do harm the liver during the detoxification process. This can lead to cirrhosis of the liver, which can be fatal if allowed to proceed unchecked. Approximately 25,000 people die each year in the United States from alcohol-induced cirrhosis.

Module 25.9 The excretory system plays several major roles in homeostasis.

A. The major roles include forming and excreting wastes in urine, and regulating the concentrations of water and solutes in body fluids.

B. The human excretory system includes two kidneys, a bladder, interconnecting ducts, and the associated vessels of the circulatory system. The system extracts about 180 liters of fluid, also called filtrate, from the 1,100–2,000 liters of blood passing through it per day, concentrating and storing 1.5 liters of urine for disposal (Figure 25.9A).

C. The kidney is the processing center of the excretory system. Blood enters and leaves each kidney through the renal artery and renal vein. Urine passes from the kidney to the **urinary bladder** via the **ureter** and from the bladder to the outside through the **urethra** (Figure 25.8A).

D. The kidney is composed of the outer **renal cortex** and the inner **renal medulla** (Figure 25.8B).

E. Thousands of blood-filtering units, **nephrons,** are within the kidney. Each nephron is composed of tubules and associated blood vessels. Each extracts and refines a small amount of filtrate and releases a small quantity of urine (Figure 25.8C).

F. The nephron consists of a blood-filtering region (**Bowman's capsule**) and a filtrate refinery (the **proximal tubule, loop of Henle,** and **distal tubule**). At the far end of the nephron is the **collecting duct,** which gathers the urine and takes it to the renal pelvis (Figure 25.8D).

G. The blood vessel parts of the nephron include a ball of capillaries **(glomerulus),** where blood pressure forces water and solutes out of the blood and into the tubule, and a second, looser capillary network that surrounds the region of the loop of Henle and helps refine the filtrate. It is the close association of the blood capillaries with the nephron that is critical to nephron function.

Module 25.10 Overview: The key functions of the excretory system are filtration, reabsorption, secretion, and excretion.

A. The process of producing urine occurs in four major steps, as illustrated in Figure 25.9.

B. During **filtration,** water and other small molecules are forced by blood pressure through capillary walls into the nephron tubule.

C. During **reabsorption,** water and solutes still valuable to the body are reclaimed from the filtrate.

D. During **secretion,** excess ions, drugs, and toxins (such as urea) are secreted from the blood into the nephron tubule. This is the step that controls blood pH.

E. Upon **excretion,** the urine passes from the kidneys to the outside, by the ureters, urinary bladder, and urethra.

Module 25.11 From blood filtrate to urine: A closer look.

A. In Figure 25.10, capillaries are not shown; red arrows represent reabsorption by active transport, passive diffusion or osmosis; blue arrows pointing in represent secretion; and the intensity of the beige represents solute concentration in the interstitial fluid—light beige in the cortex (low solute concentration) and darker beige in the medulla (high solute concentration).

B. Small molecules travel between blood and nephron filtrate through the interstitial fluid.

C. Blood pressure forces water and most solutes into the Bowman's capsule of the nephron tubule from the glomerulus.

D. NaCl and H_2O are reabsorbed from, and excess hydrogen ions secreted into, the filtrate in the proximal and distal tubules. The proximal and distal tubules are also the sites of secretion of toxins such as ammonia. The proximal tubule reabsorbs water and nutrients such as glucose and amino acids. The distal tubule may also secrete drugs or their metabolites such as penicillin.

E. The loop of Henle is the principal site of water reabsorption. NaCl and urea reabsorption along the descending limb of the loop of Henle only heightens the rate at which water is reabsorbed from the filtrate. The blood removes excess water in the interstitial fluid. The ascending limb of the loop of Henle is impermeable to water, and NaCl is first passively and then actively reabsorbed, maintaining the concentration gradient encountered by the descending limb of the loop of Henle (another example of a countercurrent mechanism). *NOTE:* The type of environment in which an animal lives, and thus its need to conserve water, can be approximated by looking at its loops of Henle. The longer the loops of Henle, the greater the need for water conservation, and the more arid the environment in which the animal lives.

F. This results in a high concentration of NaCl in the interstitial fluid surrounding the distal tubule and the first part of the collecting tubule. Water can then be reabsorbed from the filtrate in the upper collecting duct.

G. Until the collecting duct enters the medulla, urea tends to remain in the filtrate because the nephron is relatively impermeable to it.

H. In the medulla, the collecting duct is permeable to urea, and some urea moves into the interstitial fluid. This increases the concentration of the interstitial fluid of the medulla, enhancing (even more) water reabsorption.

I. Much of the reabsorption of water is under the control of **ADH (antidiuretic hormone).** ADH is released from a control center in the brain. Excessive urine production is called diuresis, and ADH counters this problem.

   Preview: ADH is produced by the hypothalamus and released from the posterior pituitary (Table 26.3; Module 26.4).

   NOTE: The reason alcohol acts as a diuretic is that alcohol consumption inhibits the release of ADH.

Module 25.12 Connection: Kidney dialysis can be a lifesaver.

A. Kidney failure or impaired function can lead to death from a buildup of solutes and toxins in the blood. The most common causes of kidney failure are hypertension and diabetes (Modules 23.10 and 26.8).

B. Kidney dialysis machines function like kidneys, but receive and return blood from a person's vein. The word *dialysis* means "to separate."

C. The machine removes small molecules from the blood, using selectively permeable membranes to allow only water and desired solutes to pass out with the dialyzing solution (Figure 25.11).

D. Dialysis does not cure the afflicted individual; it only prolongs life. Kidney transplant from a cadaver or live donor is the only cure, for now (discuss stem cells).

Class Activities

1. Some fish move between saltwater and freshwater environments. Have your class consider how these fish might cope with these contrasting osmoregulatory problems.

2. Ask your class to consider what the length of the loop of Henle can tell you about the environment in which an animal lives. Perhaps you can approach this by showing your class images of kidneys.

Transparency Acetates

Figure 25.1   Mechanisms of heat exchange
Figure 25.2B   Countercurrent heat exchange
Figure 25.4A   Osmoregulation in a freshwater fish, a perch
Figure 25.4B   Osmoregulation in a saltwater fish, a cod
Figure 25.6   Nitrogen-containing metabolic waste products
Figure 25.7   The hepatic portal system
Figure 25.9   Anatomy of the human excretory system
Figure 25.10   Major processes of the excretory system
Figure 25.11   Reabsorption and secretion in a nephron
Figure 25.12   Kidney dialysis

Reviewing the Concepts, page 516: Thermoregulation

Reviewing the Concepts, page 516: The excretory system

Connecting the Concepts, page 516: Homeostasis

Connecting the Concepts, page 516: Urine production in a nephron

Media

See the beginning of this book for a complete description of all media available for instructors and students. Animations and videos are available in the Campbell Image Presentation Library. Media Activities and Thinking as a Scientist investigations are available on the student CD-ROM and website.

Animations and Videos	Module Number
Nephron Introduction Animation	25.9
Bowman's Capsule Animation	25.9
Loop of Henle Animation	25.9
Collecting Duct Animation	25.9
Effect of ADH Animation	25.11

Activities and Thinking as a Scientist	Module Number
Web/CD Thinking as a Scientist: *How Does Temperature Affect Metabolic Rate in* Daphnia?	25.2
Web/CD Activity 25A: *Structure of the Human Excretory System*	25.8
Web/CD Activity 25B: *Nephron Function*	25.10
Web/CD Activity 25C: *Control of Water Reabsorption*	25.10
Web/CD Thinking as a Scientist: *What Affects Urine Production?*	25.10

CHAPTER 26

Chemical Regulation

Teaching Objectives

Introduction   Explain how testosterone affects humans and the behavior of cichlid fish.

The Nature of Chemical Regulation

26.1   Compare the mechanisms and functions of the endocrine and nervous systems, noting areas of overlap.

26.1   Distinguish between hormones, local regulators, pheromones, and neurotransmitters.

26.2   Distinguish among the three types of vertebrate hormones, and compare the two general mechanisms by which hormones trigger changes in target cells.

The Vertebrate Endocrine System

26.3   Describe the different types and functions of vertebrate endocrine organs.

26.4   Describe the functions of and interrelationships among the hypothalamus and the anterior and posterior pituitary glands.

Hormones and Homeostasis

26.5   Describe the functions of the thyroid gland. Describe the symptoms of hypothyroidism, hyperthyroidism, and a goiter.

26.6   Explain how the thyroid and parathyroid glands maintain calcium homeostasis.

26.7–26.8   Explain how insulin and glucagon manage blood glucose levels. Compare the causes and symptoms of type I diabetes, type II diabetes, and hypoglycemia.

26.9   Compare the functions of the hormones released by the adrenal medulla and the adrenal cortex.

26.10   Describe the benefits and risks of using glucocorticoid drugs.

26.11   Describe the three major categories of sex hormones and their functions.

Key Terms

adrenal cortex
adrenal glands
adrenal medulla
adrenocorticotropic hormone (ACTH)
androgens
antagonistic hormones
anterior pituitary
antidiuretic hormone (ADH)
calcitonin
corticosteroids

diabetes mellitus
endocrine glands
endocrine system
endorphins
epinephrine
estrogens
follicle-stimulating hormone (FSH)
glucagon
glucocorticoids
goiter
gonads

growth hormone (GH)
hormone
hypoglycemia
hypothalamus
inhibiting hormones
insulin
islets of Langerhans
local regulators
luteinizing hormone (LH)
mineralocorticoids
neurosecretory cells
neurotransmitter

norepinephrine
oxytocin
pancreas
parathyroid glands
parathyroid hormone (PTH)
pheromones
pineal gland
pituitary gland

posterior pituitary
progestins
prolactin (PRL)
releasing hormones
steroid hormones
target cells
testosterone
thymus gland

thyroid gland
thyroid-stimulating hormone (TSH)
thyroxine (T$_4$)
TRH (TSH-releasing hormone)
triiodothyronine (T$_3$)

Word Roots

andro- = male; **-gen** = produce (*androgens:* the principal male steroid hormones, such as testosterone, which stimulate the development and maintenance of the male reproductive system and secondary sex characteristics)

endo- = inside (*endorphin:* a hormone produced in the brain and anterior pituitary that inhibits pain perception)

epi- = above, over (*epinephrine:* a hormone produced as a response to stress; also called adrenaline)

lut- = yellow (*luteinizing hormone:* a gonadotropin secreted by the anterior pituitary)

para- = beside, near (*parathyroid glands:* four endocrine glands, embedded in the surface of the thyroid gland, that secrete parathyroid hormone and raise blood calcium levels)

pro- = before; **-lact** = milk (*prolactin:* a hormone produced by the anterior pituitary gland; it stimulates milk synthesis in mammals)

tri- = three; **-iodo** = violet (*triiodothyrodine:* one of two very similar hormones produced by the thyroid gland and derived from the amino acid tyrosine)

Lecture Outline

Introduction *Testosterone and Male Aggression: Is There a Link?*

A. The male sex hormone testosterone has been associated with male aggression in a variety of species. The difficulty for researchers in the field of endocrinology is to definitively prove the association between aggression and testosterone levels.

B. The cichlid fish *(Oreochromis mossambicus)* has been extensively studied. Its testosterone levels rise when in battle over territory. Even spectator cichlid fish demonstrate elevated levels of testosterone when viewing other male cichlid fish in a battle over territory.

C. Testosterone in males develops and maintains the reproductive organs and secondary sex characteristics. But how does one define aggression in humans? Is it a desire to fight, or can it be determined through psychological testing? At best, researchers agree that testosterone has little, if any, direct measurable effect on humans and aggressive behavior.

D. Testosterone is classified with a group of chemical signals (hormones) that coordinate body functions at the basic level, including such activities as metabolism, energy usage, and growth. This chapter will cover the subject of hormones and other chemical signals with an emphasis on homeostasis.

I. The Nature of Chemical Regulation

Module 26.1 Chemical signals coordinate body functions.

A. **Hormones** are chemical signals secreted into body fluids, usually blood, and have a regulatory effect on the body via specific **target cells.** Hormones are produced mainly by **endocrine glands** (Figure 26.1A).

B. Collectively, all hormone-secreting tissues constitute the **endocrine system.** This system is particularly important in controlling whole-body activities such as metabolic rate, growth, maturation, and reproduction. Hormones also control the response to stimuli such as stress, dehydration, and low body glucose.

C. **Local regulators** are secreted into the interstitial fluid and cause changes in cells near the point of secretion. **Pheromones** transmit messages between individuals, particularly during mating season.
Preview: The nervous system is the subject of Chapters 28 and 29.

D. The two systems, endocrine and nervous, coordinate most of their activities. The nervous system provides split-second control, and the endocrine system provides control over longer duration, from minutes to days.

E. **Neurosecretory cells** secrete **neurotransmitters** that play a role in nerve impulse conduction (Modules 28.6–28.8) and are also transported in the blood to target cells. For example, epinephrine is the fight-or-flight hormone and is also a neurotransmitter (Figures 26.1B and C).

Module 26.2 Hormones affect target cells by two main signaling mechanisms.

A. Three types of molecules make up hormones:
   1. Protein and polypeptides; made from amino acids, are water soluble.
   2. Amine; made from amino acids, are water soluble.
   3. Steroids; made from cholesterol, are lipid soluble.

B. All hormones prompt three key cellular events:
   1. *Reception;* acceptance of the signal happens when the hormone binds a specific receptor on/in the cell.
   2. *Signal transduction;* binding of the signal to the receptor elicits a series of events within the cell.
   3. *Response;* the final event changes the behavior of the cell.

C. The mechanisms used by the hormones to elicit a response are different, and the difference is related to the molecular makeup of each hormone.

D. Water-soluble hormones bind to a receptor on the surface of the plasma membrane. A signal is passed through the plasma membrane to a series of proteins that ultimately ends with a protein that induces a change in the cell's behavior (Figure 26.2A).

E. Lipid-soluble hormones can pass directly through the plasma membrane and bind to the cytoplasmic or nuclear receptors. The receptor carries out the transduction of the hormonal signal via transcription factor (a gene activator). The hormone-receptor complex binds to the DNA and stimulates transcription, which leads to protein synthesis and altered cell behavior (Figure 26.2B). All steroid hormones alter gene function.

F. Hormones are promiscuous when binding to receptors. Therefore, the same hormone can stimulate an assortment of cells with different receptors while eliciting varied responses.

II. The Vertebrate Endocrine System

Module 26.3 Overview: The vertebrate endocrine system.

   A. Endocrine glands secrete into the blood.
   Review: Contrast this with the nonendocrine (exocrine) glands of the GI tract (Chapter 21), which secrete into body cavities.

   B. The endocrine system is composed of glands spread throughout the body (Figure 26.3). Some (e.g., pituitary and thyroid) are endocrine specialists. Others (e.g., the pancreas) have both endocrine and nonendocrine (exocrine) functions.
   NOTE: Structures with endocrine functions that are missing from Figure 26.3 include the heart (atrial natriuretic factor) and the kidneys (erythropoietin).

   C. General features shared by the endocrine systems of all vertebrates are listed in Table 26.3.

   D. Only the sex organs and the adrenal cortex produce steroid hormones that enter the target cells directly. Most hormone action is by means of signal transduction.

   E. Some hormones (e.g., sex hormones) affect body tissues generally. Some have specific targets in or out of the endocrine system.

   F. The endocrine and nervous systems are closely associated (see the "Regulated by" column in Table 26.3).

   G. The **pineal gland** secretes melatonin, which links environmental light conditions with activities that show daily or seasonal rhythms. A major role is to cue reproductive activity. Rising levels prompt reproduction in sheep and deer that breed in the fall. Lowering levels cue reproduction in mammals that breed in the spring.

   H. The **thymus gland** (not discussed in this chapter) is important in the immune system, stimulating the development and differentiation of T cells in early childhood. This gland virtually disappears but still remains functional in adults.
   Review: The role of the thymus and T cells (Module 24.5).

Module 26.4 The hypothalamus, closely tied to the pituitary, connects the nervous and endocrine systems.

   A. The **hypothalamus** is the endocrine system's master control center (Figure 26.4A). It receives information from nerves about the internal condition of the body and about the external environment. It signals the **pituitary gland,** which in turn secretes hormones that influence many body functions, including those of other endocrine glands.

   B. The **posterior pituitary** consists of an extension of the hypothalamus. Composed of nervous tissue, it stores and secretes hormones made in the hypothalamus.
   NOTE: The release of the hormones stored in the posterior pituitary is under the control of nerve impulses from the hypothalamus.

   C. The **anterior pituitary** is composed mostly of glandular tissue. The anterior pituitary synthesizes its own hormones, several of which control other endocrine glands.

   D. The hypothalamus controls the pituitary by secreting **releasing hormones** and **inhibiting hormones.**

   E. Neurosecretory cells extend from the hypothalamus into the posterior pituitary and synthesize the hormones **oxytocin** and **antidiuretic hormone** (**ADH;** Module 25.10). Oxytocin induces contraction of the uterine muscles during childbirth (Module 27.18) and causes the mammary glands to release milk during nursing. ADH helps the kidneys retain water (Figure 26.4B).

F. A set of neurosecretory cells of the hypothalamus secretes releasing and inhibiting hormones that are carried by small vessels to the anterior pituitary (Figure 26.4C). Under the control of releasing hormones, the anterior pituitary can release **thyroid-stimulating hormone (TSH), adrenocorticotropic hormone (ACTH), follicle-stimulating hormone (FSH),** and **luteinizing hormone (LH),** all of which activate other endocrine glands. These glands' hormonal secretions all exhibit negative-feedback control on the anterior pituitary.

G. Secretion of **TRH (thyroid-releasing hormone)** by the hypothalamus induces the anterior pituitary to secrete **TSH (thyroid-stimulating hormone).** TSH causes the thyroid to release **thyroxine** into the blood. Thyroxine increases the metabolic rates of most cells. Increased thyroxine and TSH levels have negative-feedback (Module 20.14) control on the release of TRH (Figure 26.4D).

H. Other hormones produced by the anterior pituitary include the following:

1. **Growth hormone (GH)** promotes the development and enlargement of all body parts in young children. Too much in children leads to gigantism, too little leads to dwarfism. Too much in adults leads to acromegaly.

2. **Prolactin (PRL)** stimulates mammals to produce milk, regulates fat metabolism and reproduction in birds, regulates larval development of amphibians, and regulates salt and water balance in fishes. PRL is probably an ancient hormone.

3. **Endorphins,** the body's natural painkillers, bind to brain receptors that perceive pain and dull the effect. The runner's high may be due to endorphin release. The drug morphine has similar effects on the brain.

III. Hormones and Homeostasis

Module 26.5 The thyroid regulates development and metabolism.

A. The **thyroid gland** is located underneath the larynx (voice box). Thyroid hormones affect virtually all vertebrate tissues. Two very similar iodine-containing amine hormones are produced by the thyroid gland: **Thyroxine (T_4)** and **triiodothyronine (T_3)** have four and three iodine atoms per molecule, respectively.

B. In amphibians, thyroid hormones trigger tissue reorganization during metamorphosis.

C. In mammals, thyroid hormones control the early development of bone and nerve cells. Congenital deficiency of thyroxine leads to mental and physical retardation in children (cretinism).

D. In adult mammals, thyroid hormones maintain normal blood pressure, heart rate, muscle tone, and digestive and reproductive functions (homeostatic function).

E. *Hyperthyroidism* causes overheating, profuse sweating, irritability, high blood pressure, and weight loss.

F. *Hypothyroidism* causes lethargy, intolerance to cold, and weight gain. Hypothyroidism is often accompanied by enlargement of the thyroid, a condition called a **goiter,** which occurs when too little iodine is consumed in the diet (Figure 26.5A). This condition results from an interruption of normal negative-feedback control on TSH release by the pituitary (Figure 26.5B). A goiter can be avoided/eliminated with the addition of iodine to the diet. *NOTE:* Severe hypothyroidism in adults results in myxedema.

Module 26.6 Hormones from the thyroid and parathyroids maintain calcium homeostasis.

A. Appropriate levels of calcium in the blood and interstitial fluids are essential for nerve and muscle cell functions, blood clotting, and active transport across cell membranes.

B. Secretions from the **thyroid** and **parathyroid glands** keep Ca^{2+} ions at a concentration of 9–11 mg per 100 mL of blood.

   C. **Calcitonin** from the thyroid and **parathyroid hormone (PTH)** from the parathyroid glands are **antagonistic hormones;** that is, they have opposite effects (Figure 26.6).

   D. PTH raises the Ca^{2+} level whenever that level falls below normal. It causes Ca^{2+} to be released from bone, absorbed more by the intestine, and reabsorbed more by the kidneys.

   E. In the kidneys, PTH promotes the conversion of vitamin D to its active form. In turn, vitamin D promotes the absorption of calcium and phosphate from the alimentary canal (Module 21.4), the retention of these minerals by the kidneys, and their release from bone into blood.

   F. Calcitonin lowers the Ca^{2+} level whenever that level rises above normal. It causes Ca^{2+} to be deposited in bone and absorbed less by the intestine, and it causes the kidneys to reabsorb less Ca^{2+} as they form urine.

   G. Antagonistic hormones maintain calcium levels. Low levels of PTH result in low levels of calcium in the blood. Decreased calcium blood levels can lead to convulsive contractions of skeletal muscle; a condition called tetany.
    NOTE: The effects of hyperparathyroidism include demineralization of bone.

Module 26.7 Pancreatic hormones regulate blood glucose levels.

   A. **Insulin** and **glucagon** are antagonistic hormones produced by cells clustered together in the **pancreas** (Figure 26.7). The cell clusters are called **islets of Langerhans.**

   B. Insulin is a protein hormone produced by beta islet cells. Glucagon is a peptide hormone produced by alpha islet cells.

   C. The set point that controls hormone balance is about 90 mg glucose/100 mL.

   D. Rising blood glucose levels (after a meal) stimulate the beta islet cells to secrete insulin. The blood glucose level falls because insulin stimulates all body cells to take more glucose from the blood. The liver converts most glucose into stored glycogen. Muscle cells will also convert excess glucose to glycogen. Other cells metabolize glucose into energy, stored fats, or proteins.

   E. Falling blood glucose levels (during a fast or between meals) stimulate the alpha islet cells to secrete glucagon. The blood glucose level rises because glucagon stimulates the liver cells to convert glycogen to glucose, as well as convert fatty acids and amino acids to glucose.

Module 26.8 Connection: Diabetes is a common endocrine disorder.

   A. Much of the function of insulin has been discovered in people with **diabetes mellitus,** which occurs in about 5% of the population in the United States.

   B. This disease occurs when there is not enough insulin produced to maintain proper absorption of glucose from the blood or when body cells do not respond to normal levels of insulin. The glucose concentration of blood becomes so high (hyperglycemia) that glucose is excreted by the kidneys.

   C. Type I diabetes (insulin-dependent diabetes) develops during childhood and involves the destruction of beta islet cells by T cells. Therefore, it is classified as an autoimmune disease (Module 24.16). Type I diabetes is controlled with injections of recombinant human insulin.

   D. Type II diabetes (non-insulin-dependent diabetes) is usually associated with people who are older (at least 40 years old) and obese and occurs when body cells do not respond correctly to insulin or when there is a true deficiency. Type II diabetes is usually controlled by diet, antidiabetic drugs, and exercise.

E. Early signs of diabetes include lethargy, a craving for sweets, frequent urination, and thirst. A glucose-tolerance test is used to detect diabetes (Figure 26.8). A less traumatic procedure is a two-hour postprandial glucose determination in conjunction with a fasting glucose level.
NOTE: These early signs are frequently referred to as polyphagia (excessive hunger), polyuria (excessive urination), and polydipsia (frequent thirst).

F. **Hypoglycemia** occurs in some people who secrete too much insulin. Symptoms appear 2–4 hours after a meal and include hunger, weakness, sweating, and nervousness. In severe cases, convulsions can lead to death in people whose brains do not receive enough glucose.

Module 26.9 The adrenal glands mobilize responses to stress.

A. The **adrenal glands** are associated with the kidneys and are composed of two functionally different parts: the **adrenal medulla** in the center produces the fight-or-flight hormones; the **adrenal cortex** at the outside produces hormones that provide slower, longer-term responses to stress.

B. Stress produces a cascade effect. Stressful stimuli (negative or positive) activate certain hypothalamus cells. These cells send signals along nerve cells through the spinal cord to stimulate the adrenal medulla (Figure 26.9).

C. The adrenal medulla ensures a rapid, short-term response to stress. When stimulated, the adrenal medulla releases **epinephrine** (adrenaline) and **norepinephrine** (noradrenaline) into the bloodstream. Both hormones stimulate liver and muscle cells to release glucose, making more energy available for cellular fuel. They increase blood pressure, breathing rate, and metabolic rate and change blood-flow patterns. Epinephrine dilates blood vessels in the brain and skeletal muscles but constricts vessels elsewhere, directing blood to critical areas.
NOTE: The secretion is mostly of epinephrine.

D. The adrenal cortex causes slower responses. It responds to endocrine signals (ACTH) from the pituitary. When stimulated, the adrenal cortex secretes a family of steroid hormones, the **corticosteroids.** These hormones help the body function normally, whether stressed or not. **Mineralocorticoids** affect salt and water balance. **Glucocorticoids** promote the synthesis of glucose from noncarbohydrate sources. In addition, high levels of the glucocorticoids can suppress the body's defense system and can control excessive inflammation. Cortisone can be administered to relieve symptoms of inflammation.
NOTE: Hypersecretion of the adrenal cortex can cause Cushing's disease. Symptoms of Cushing's disease include a pendulous (fatty) abdomen and a fatty hump on the back of the neck. Hyposecretion of the adrenal cortex can cause Addison's disease. Symptoms of Addison's disease include dehydration and weight loss.
NOTE: The adrenal cortex also secretes both androgens and estrogens.

Module 26.10 Connection: Glucocorticoids offer relief from pain, but not without serious risks.

A. Physicians often prescribe glucocorticoids to relieve the pain of athletic injuries (Figure 26.10).

B. Unfortunately they depress the activity of the adrenal glands and may have dangerous side effects, such as psychological changes.

Module 26.11 The gonads secrete sex hormones.

   A. Sex hormones are steroid hormones produced by the **gonads** that affect growth and development and regulate reproductive cycles and sexual behavior.

   B. The three categories of sex hormones—**androgens, estrogens,** and **progestins**—are all found in both females and males, but in different proportions.

   C. Females have a high ratio of estrogens to androgens. Estrogens stimulate the development and maintenance of the female reproductive system and secondary sex characteristics, such as smaller body size, higher voice, breasts, and wider hips. Progestins (progesterone) are most active in human females, where they prepare the uterus to support the developing embryo.
     Preview: The role of these hormones in the menstrual and ovarian cycles is discussed in Module 27.5.

   D. Males have a high ratio of androgens (e.g., testosterone) to estrogens. Androgens stimulate the development of the embryo at week seven to become a male. Androgens develop and maintain the male reproductive system and secondary sex characteristics, such as a deeper voice, more body hair, and larger skeletal muscles. Androgens affect different species in a variety of ways. The cichlids respond with aggressive behavior (Figure 26.11), and the elephant seals have a drastically modified body compared to the female
     Review: Anabolic steroids, artificial analogs of testosterone (Module 3.10).
     Preview: The role of these hormones in regulating sperm production is discussed in Module 27.3.

   E. The hypothalamus and anterior pituitary control the release of sex hormones. The anterior pituitary synthesizes FSH and LH, which stimulate the ovaries and testes to synthesize and secrete sex hormones.
     Preview: Module 27.3.

Class Activities

1. Engage the students in thought experiments concerning the potential effects of hypersecretion or hyposecretion of the hormones discussed in this chapter.

2. Ask your students if they can think of situations under which a genetic predisposition to Type II diabetes might be an advantage. (Ask your students if, historically, food has been as plentiful and easily obtainable as it is in the U.S. today.)

Transparency Acetates

Figure 26.1A	Hormone from an endocrine cell
Figure 26.1B	Hormone from a neurosecretory cell (combined with Figures 26.1A and 26.1C)
Figure 26.1C	Neurotransmitter (combined with Figures 26.1A and 26.1B)
Figure 26.2A	A hormone that binds a plasma-membrane receptor
Figure 26.2B	A hormone that binds an intracellular receptor
Figure 26.3	The major endocrine glands in humans
Table 26.3	Major human endocrine glands and some of their hormones

Media

See the beginning of this book for a complete description of all media available for instructors and students. Animations and videos are available in the Campbell Image Presentation Library. Media Activities and Thinking as a Scientist investigations are available on the student CD-ROM and website.

Animations and Videos	Module Number
Nonsteroid Hormone Animation	26.2
Steroid Hormone Animation	26.2

Activities and Thinking as a Scientist	Module Number
Web/CD Activity 26A: *Overview of Cell Signaling*	26.2
Web/CD Activity 26B: *Nonsteroid Hormone Action*	26.2
Web/CD Activity 26C: *Steroid Hormone Action*	26.2
Web/CD Thinking as a Scientist: *How Do Thyroxine and TSH Affect Metabolism?*	26.5
Web/CD Activity 26D: *Human Endocrine Glands and Hormones*	26.11

CHAPTER 27

Reproduction and Embryonic Development

Teaching Objectives

Introduction Explain how the increased use of fertility drugs has impacted the number of multiple births in the United States. Describe the increased health risks of multiple births.

Asexual and Sexual Reproduction

27.1 Compare the types, advantages, and disadvantages of asexual and sexual reproduction.

Human Reproduction

27.2–27.3 Describe the structures and functions of the female and male human reproductive tracts.
27.4 Describe and compare the processes and products of spermatogenesis and oogenesis.
27.5 Describe the events of and control of the menstrual cycle. Note the specific functions of the five hormones listed in Table 27.5.
27.6 Describe the four stages of the human sexual response. Explain how the reproductive cycle of humans is different from animals that experience estrus.
27.7 Describe the nature of the eight most common sexually transmitted diseases. Note their agents of infection, symptoms, and forms of treatment.
27.8 Describe the most common forms of birth control, and explain how each works. Compare the failure rates and advantages and disadvantages of each method.

Principles of Embryonic Development

27.9 Relate the structure of sperm to its roles in fertilization. Describe the mechanisms that prevent more than one sperm from fertilizing an egg.
27.10–27.11 Describe the processes of and results of cleavage and gastrulation.
27.12 Explain how organs form after the development of a gastrula.
27.13 Explain how changes in cell shape, cell migration, and apoptosis contribute to development.
27.14 Describe the role of induction in the formation of the vertebrate eye.
27.15 Explain how the one-dimensional information in DNA is used to direct the three-dimensional form of an embryo.

Human Development

27.16 Describe the initial embryonic stages and the formation and functions of the extraembryonic membranes.
27.17 Describe the main changes that occur during each of the trimesters of human development.
27.18 Explain how labor begins, and describe the main events of the three labor stages.
27.19 Describe the common causes of infertility and the variety of technologies available to help couples get pregnant.

Key Terms

acrosome
allantois
amnion
apoptosis
archenteron
asexual reproduction
assisted reproductive
    technology (ART)
barrier methods
Bartholin's glands
birth control pills
blastocoel
blastocyst
blastopore
blastula
budding
bulbourethral gland
cervix
chorion
chorionic villi
cleavage
clitoris
contraception
copulation
corpus luteum
ectoderm
ectopic pregnancy
egg
ejaculation
ejaculatory duct
embryo
endoderm
endometrium
epididymis
excitement phase
external fertilization
extraembryonic membranes
fertilization

fertilization envelope
fetus
fission
follicles
fragmentation
gametes
gametogenesis
gastrula
gastrulation
gestation
glans
hermaphroditism
human chorionic
    gonadotropin (HCG)
hymen
impotence
in vitro fertilization
induction
infertility
internal fertilization
labia majora
labia minora
labor
menstrual cycle
menstruation
mesoderm
morning-after pills (MAPs)
natural family planning
neural tube
notochord
oogenesis
oral contraceptives
orgasm
ova
ovarian cycle
ovaries
oviduct
ovulation

ovum
pattern formation
penis
placenta
plateau phase
prepuce
primary oocyte
primary spermatocytes
programmed cell death
prostate gland
regeneration
reproduction
resolution phase
rhythm method
scrotum
secondary oocyte
secondary spermatocytes
semen
seminal vesicles
seminiferous tubules
sexual reproduction
sexually transmitted
    diseases (STDs)
sperm
spermatogenesis
spermicididal
testes
trimesters
trophoblast
tubal ligation
uterus
vagina
vas deferens
vasectomy
withdrawal
yolk plug
yolk sac
zygote

Word Roots

arch- = ancient, beginning (*archenteron:* the endoderm-lined cavity, formed during the gastrulation process, that develops into the digestive tract of an animal)

blast- = bud, sprout; **-pore** = a passage (*blastopore:* the opening of the archenteron in the gastrula that develops into the mouth in protostomes and the anus in deuterostomes)

blasto- = produce; **-cyst** = sac, bladder (*blastocyst:* a hollow ball of cells produced one week after fertilization in humans)

contra- = against (*contraception:* the prevention of pregnancy)

-ectomy = cut out (*vasectomy:* the cutting of each vas deferens to prevent sperm from entering the urethra)

endo- = inside (*endometrium:* the inner lining of the uterus, which is richly supplied with blood vessels)

epi- = above, over (*epididymis:* a coiled tubule located adjacent to the testes where sperm are stored)

extra- = beyond (*extraembryonic membrane:* four membranes that support the developing embryo in reptiles, birds, and mammals)

fertil- = fruitful (*fertilization:* the union of haploid gametes to produce a diploid zygote)

gastro- = stomach, belly (*gastrulation:* the formation of a gastrula from a blastula)

labi- = lip; **major-** = larger (*labia majora:* a pair of thick, fatty ridges that enclose and protect the labia minora and vestibule)

oo- = egg; **-genesis** = producing (*oogenesis:* the process in the ovary that results in the production of female gametes)

soma- = a body (*somites:* paired blocks of mesoderm just lateral to the notochord of a vertebrate embryo)

tri- = three (*trimester:* a three-month period)

tropho- = nourish (*trophoblast:* the outer epithelium of the blastocyst, which forms the fetal part of the placenta)

Lecture Outline

Introduction *Baby Bonanza*

> *Review:* Human life cycle (Module 8.13; Figure 8.13), meiosis (Module 8.14), fertilization (Module 8.16), mitosis (Module 8.6), and the genetic control of embryonic development (Modules 11.1–11.9 and 11.13–11.15).

A. One out of 7 couples in the United States is diagnosed with **infertility,** the inability to conceive and have a child after one year of unprotected sex.

B. There has been a dramatic increase in the rate of multiple births between 1980 and 2002 (up 83% for twins and up more than 550% for super twins). This increase is due to the ability to manipulate ovulation with drugs.

C. As with any medical intervention, there are risks involved with infertility: multiple births, increased mortality, low birth weight, birth defects, and premature birth of the infants.
NOTE: There are also some risks to the mother, such as increased ovarian cancer. There are also ethical questions raised when the couple is faced with the possibility of multiple births and selective reduction (a polite term for abortion) or how to dispose of leftover eggs or embryos.

D. Reproductive diversity and development will be examined first, followed by the reproductive process in humans.

I. Asexual and Sexual Reproduction

Module 27.1 Sexual and asexual reproduction are both common among animals.

A. **Reproduction** (the creation of new individuals from existing ones) allows a species to transcend the finite life span of its individuals.

B. **Asexual reproduction** is the creation of offspring whose genes all come from one parent. Asexual reproduction can be accomplished by **budding, fission** (Figures 27.1A and B), or **fragmentation,** and it is often accompanied by the **regeneration** of missing parts.
Review: Budding by hydras is discussed in Module 8.11; binary fission by bacteria is discussed in Module 8.3.
Preview: Reproduction by fragmentation by plants is discussed in Module 31.14.

C. Asexual reproduction allows animals to reproduce without mates, to produce offspring quickly without expending energy for gamete production or fertilization, and to produce large numbers of successful genotypes. But populations developing from asexual reproduction are genetically homogeneous.
NOTE: Relate this to Module 17.14 and Chapter 38. Forests are logged and then replanted. Are they replanted with a diversity of trees or with trees of a single species? If the replanted trees are of a single species, is the population genetically diverse or genetically homogeneous (clones)? How does this relate to resistance to environmental factors (e.g., extremes of weather and pests) and biodiversity?

D. **Sexual reproduction** is the reproduction of offspring by the fusion of two **gametes** (**ovum** and **sperm**). The **zygote** and the offspring that develop from it contain a unique combination of genes from the parents. Species may alternate between sexual and asexual reproduction (e.g., rotifer and hydra) or reproduce with a process called **hermaphroditism** (e.g., earthworms). Most fishes and amphibians use **external fertilization,** while most terrestrial animals use **internal fertilization** that requires **copulation** (Figures 27.1C, D, and E).
Review: Modules 8.16 and 8.18 discuss how meiosis and random fertilization increase genetic variation.

E. Sexual reproduction increases genetic variation in a population and, thus, leaves the population better able to deal with changing environmental conditions. But animals must find mates and expend extra energy to produce gametes and ensure that fertilization takes place.

II. Human Reproduction

Module 27.2 Reproductive anatomy of the human female.

A. Eggs develop in **ovaries.** Each ovum develops in a separate follicle that contains other cells to protect and nourish the egg, and to produce estrogen.
Review: The hormones released by the ovarian follicles are discussed in Module 26.11.
Preview: As illustrated in Module 27.4, the ovary never contains an egg; it does, however, contain cells that have the potential to develop into eggs. An egg is not actually formed until the secondary oocyte is stimulated by a sperm cell to complete meiosis II.

B. Women are born with up to 400,000 **follicles,** but only several hundred will release eggs, one every 28 days, starting at puberty (Figure 27.2B).

C. Following **ovulation,** the remaining follicular tissue temporarily develops into the **corpus luteum,** which secretes progesterone and estrogen to maintain the uterine lining if pregnancy occurs.

D. The released egg traverses a short space to the oviduct opening. Fertilization normally occurs in the **oviduct.** Abnormal, **ectopic pregnancies** often occur in the oviduct, where they must be surgically removed.

E. The fertilized egg, the zygote, begins to develop and moves into the **uterus.** The **embryo** implants in the **endometrium,** and development is completed there. (After the eighth week, when body structures begin to appear, the embryo is known as a **fetus.**)

F. The uterus opens into the **vagina** through the **cervix.** The vagina receives the sperm during sexual intercourse and serves as the birth canal through which the newborn baby leaves the uterus (Figure 27.2A).

G. A number of external structures **(hymen, labia major, labia minor, clitoris,** and **Bartholin's glands)** are associated with the vaginal opening, and most function during sexual arousal and intercourse (Figure 27.2C).

H. The clitoris is homologous to the penis, consisting of a **glans** with a large number of nerve endings and a **prepuce** (foreskin). Like the penis, the clitoris (along with the vagina and the labia minor) becomes engorged with blood during sexual activity. The clitoris can trigger orgasms when stimulated properly.
   NOTE: In addition to the homology of the clitoris and the penis, the ducts of the male and female reproductive system and the gonads are homologous. Thus, true hermaphroditism (reproductively functional as both female and male) is not possible in humans.

Module 27.3 Reproductive anatomy of the human male.

A. Sperm cells are continuously produced in the **testes** and held outside the abdominal cavity in the **scrotum,** which keeps the sperm below body temperature (Figure 27.3A).
   NOTE: This is why males with low sperm counts are told to wear boxer shorts rather than briefs.
   NOTE: Marine mammals keep their testes cool while retaining them within the body cavity. The question arises as to the evolutionary basis of keeping sperm cooler and why in a scrotum? Remember, female gametes develop within the body cavity.

B. The path sperm travel is from the testes to the **epididymis,** where they are stored while they develop motility and fertilizing ability. During ejaculation, sperm leave the epididymis and are moved by muscular contractions (peristalsis) to the **vas deferens.** The vas deferens passes into the body cavity and loops around the urinary bladder, where it merges with a duct from the **seminal vesicle** (one of the male sex glands). The union of the vas deferens with the duct from the seminal vesicle forms the **ejaculatory duct.** The ejaculatory ducts from the right and left sides of the body empty into the urethra. The urethra conveys both urine and sperm to the outside, through the penis (Figure 27.3B).
   NOTE: The site where the vas (ductus) deferens passes into the body cavity is the inguinal canal. The inguinal region is a weak area in the abdominal wall and is often the site of a rupture (hernia).

C. In addition to the testis and ducts, the male reproductive system contains three sets of glands:
   1. Paired **seminal vesicles** secrete a thick, clear fluid that lubricates the spermatic ducts and nourishes sperm.
   2. The **prostate gland** secretes a milky, alkaline fluid, which neutralizes the acidity of both the male and female reproductive tracts.
   3. Paired **bulbourethral glands** secrete a few drops of fluid into the urethra during sexual arousal.
   NOTE: The seminal vesicles lie at the base of the urinary bladder. The prostate gland surrounds the first part of the urethra and is where the ejaculatory ducts merge into the urethra. The bulbourethral glands are found beneath the prostate gland. Enlargement of the prostate gland, benign prostatic hypertrophy (BPH), is an almost inevitable consequence of male aging (starting at about age 45).

D. **Semen** consists of sperm and the secretions of these glands. There are about 50–130 million sperm in one teaspoon of semen discharged during a typical ejaculation. A zygote is a product of one sperm and one egg.

E. During sexual arousal, erectile tissue in the **penis** swells with blood. Erection is essential for the insertion of the penis into the vagina. Like the clitoris, the penis consists of a glans that is richly supplied with nerve endings and a prepuce (foreskin) that covers the glans.

F. Ejaculation occurs in two stages. First, at the peak of sexual arousal, muscles in the epididymis, seminal vesicles, prostate gland, and vas deferens contract, forcing sperm and secretions into the vas deferens behind a closed sphincter at the base of the penis and urethra. Second, that sphincter opens, and strong muscular contractions force the semen along the urethra and out of the penis (Figure 27.3C).

G. Production of sperm and androgens are under the control of hormones from the pituitary (FSH and LH) (Figure 27.3D). FSH increases sperm production by the testes. LH promotes the secretion of androgens, mainly testosterone. Androgens stimulate sperm production.
   Review: These hormones are also discussed in Module 26.11.

H. Unlike in females, the hormonal regulation of sperm production permits the testes to produce hundreds of millions of sperm every day from puberty onward.

Module 27.4 The formation of sperm and ova requires meiosis.
   Review: Meiosis (Modules 8.12–8.14; Figure 8.14).

A. Both sperm and ova (gametes) are haploid and develop by meiosis from diploid cells in the gonads (testes and ovaries). This process is called **gametogenesis.**

B. **Spermatogenesis** takes about 65–75 days. Diploid cells in the **seminiferous tubules** of the testes ultimately develop into sperm cells.

C. Diploid cells near the outer tubule wall multiply by mitosis. About 3 million per day develop into **primary spermatocytes.** Each primary spermatocyte divides by meiosis, passing through a **secondary spermatocyte** stage after the first meiotic division. Immature sperm develop full motility in the epididymis (Figure 27.4A).
   NOTE: If mature sperm are not ejaculated, they are broken down and reabsorbed in the epididymis tissue.

D. **Oogenesis** of all ova begins before birth. Diploid cells in the ovaries develop by mitosis into **primary oocytes,** one per follicle. Meiosis begins but is arrested in prophase at the time of a female's birth. Meiosis continues once a woman is mature, producing a single egg each month, until menopause.
   NOTE: Some of your students may be under the misconception that menopause occurs when a female runs out of potential ova. This is not true; menopause occurs as a result of changes in the pattern of release of hypothalamic and pituitary hormones and ovarian response to these hormones. Ask your students to consider the evolutionary basis of menopause. A healthy (postpubescent) male, while secreting lower levels of testosterone with age, can father a child at any age; why doesn't the same hold for females?

E. At birth, each ovary contains all the follicles a woman will have, each with an egg at the beginning of meiosis, at the primary oocyte stage. FSH from the pituitary stimulates one dormant follicle to develop. The first meiotic division of the primary oocyte results in one **secondary oocyte** and one polar body. The second meiotic division produces an ovum and three polar bodies (one from the second oocyte and two from the first polar body). The polar bodies receive virtually no cytoplasm and are nonfunctional (Figures 27.4B and C).

NOTE: Ask your class why three polar bodies are produced if only one functional gamete is produced.

F. One cell at a time develops and is induced (in mid-meiosis, as a secondary oocyte) to leave the ovary (ovulate) by secretion of LH from the pituitary. This hormone continues to cause the ruptured follicle to develop into a corpus luteum, which begins to secrete estrogen and progesterone to prepare and maintain the uterine lining for implantation of the fertilized egg. The final meiotic division of the secondary oocyte occurs immediately following fertilization.

G. Spermatogenesis and oogenesis are alike by producing haploid gametes, but differ in three ways:

1. The number of gametes produced by each meiotic division (four for males versus one for females).

2. How often meiosis occurs (continuously for males versus once per month for females).

3. How many primary cells there are (unlimited for males versus a set number, present at birth for females).

Module 27.5 Hormones synchronize cyclical changes in the ovary and uterus.
Review: The hormones released by the follicles are discussed in Module 26.11.

A. The reproductive cycle in females involves an integrated process between the ovaries and the uterus. The **menstrual cycle** involves the monthly changes in the uterus. The **ovarian cycle** produces the oocyte, occurs approximately every 28 days, and coincides with the menstrual cycle.

B. **An Overview of the Ovarian and Menstrual Cycle:**

1. Day one is defined as the first day of menstrual bleeding when, due to the decline in estrogen and progesterone levels, the endometrium breaks down and is shed through the vagina. Menstrual discharge (**menstruation**) consists of blood, endometrial cells, and mucus. This usually lasts for 3–5 days and corresponds with the preovulatory phase of the ovarian cycle (Figure 27.5).
NOTE: This corresponds to the menstrual phase of the menstrual cycle.

2. After menstruation, the endometrium regrows (the proliferative phase) under the influence of estrogen. This regrowth reaches a maximum at about 20 to 25 days.
NOTE: This corresponds to the proliferative phase of the menstrual cycle.

3. FSH initiates the preovulatory phase of the ovarian cycle. During the preovulatory phase, the secondary oocyte is developing and the follicle is stimulated to secrete low levels of estrogen. As the follicle grows, its secretion of estrogen increases, but estrogen levels are still relatively low. This exerts negative-feedback control on the pituitary and keeps FSH and LH levels low.

C. **Hormonal Events before Ovulation:**

1. Estrogen levels peak just before ovulation; this results in a surge in LH and FSH levels.

2. LH stimulates the completion of the development of the secondary oocyte. This surge in LH is required for ovulation.

D. **Hormonal Events at Ovulation and After:**

1. Ovulation occurs on day 14, after which the ruptured follicle develops into the corpus luteum.

2. The corpus luteum secretes both estrogen and progesterone. The resultant high levels of progesterone and estrogen maintain the uterus for the possibility of implantation of a fertilized egg. The high levels of estrogen and progesterone also inhibit the secretion of FSH and LH. Thus, FSH and LH levels fall, and as a result, new ovarian and menstrual cycles cannot be initiated.
    NOTE: This corresponds to the secretory phase of the menstrual cycle.

3. Next, if fertilization and implantation do not occur, the corpus luteum gradually degenerates. This leads to a fall in estrogen and progesterone levels, which allows FSH and LH levels to increase and new ovarian and menstrual cycles to be initiated.

E. **Control of the Menstrual Cycle:** Estrogen and progesterone are the controlling hormones that maintain the endometrial lining and the thickening that occurs as ovulation is approaching. Once ovulation has occurred, the endometrium is stable as long as enough estrogen and progesterone is present (supplied by the corpus luteum). When these levels start to decline, the endometrium starts to slough off, menstrual bleeding begins, and the cycle starts over.

F. If an embryo is implanted in the uterus, the degeneration of the corpus luteum is delayed, and levels of estrogen and progesterone remain high. The corpus luteum is maintained by secretion of human chorionic gonadotropin (HCG) by the developing embryo.
    NOTE: With degeneration of the corpus luteum, the endometrium is maintained, while the onset of a new ovarian and menstrual cycle is delayed by the secretion of estrogen and progesterone by the placenta.

Module 27.6 The human sexual response occurs in four phases.

A. Most female mammals are receptive to males only on certain days and for only a brief period once or twice a year, when they are "in estrus."

B. Humans and several other primates are unusual in having no distinct breeding periods.
    NOTE: Have your students consider the evolutionary basis of this and its affects on the evolution of human culture.

C. Human sexuality is emotional as well as physical. The behavior surrounding sexual activity may have evolved as a way to strengthen bonding between mates.

D. Sexual response during intercourse occurs in four phases, which involve changes in sensitivity of the nerves supplying and activating the muscle groups associated with the sex organs and other tissues. The four phases are as follows:

1. **Excitement phase:** increase in sexual passion, engorgement of erectile tissues with blood, vagina secretes lubricating fluids, arm and leg muscles tighten.

2. **Plateau phase:** increase in the response in the excitement phase, corresponding increase in breath and heart rate.

3. **Orgasm:** rhythmic involuntary contraction of the reproductive structures and extreme pleasure.

4. **Resolution phase:** sexual response reverses, passion subsides, and organs return to normal size.
    NOTE: The anti-impotence drug Viagra® works by affecting nitric oxide (NO) levels.
    NOTE: Sexual response is one of the few examples of a positive-feedback system; others are blood clotting and labor.

Module 27.7 Connection: Sexual activity can transmit disease.

A. **Sexually transmissible diseases (STDs)** are contagious infections transmitted by sexual contact. A list of STDs is presented in Table 27.7.

B. HIV (the cause of AIDS), genital herpes, and genital warts are all viruses. These diseases can cause death or at least long-term problems if not treated. Most of these diseases infect both partners. Viral STDs are not curable, but bacterial, protozoan, and fungal STDs generally are.

C. The most common age groups reporting STDs are teenagers and young adults. Abstinence is the best way to stop the spread of STDs, but latex condoms can provide "safer sex," although viruses can pass through latex.

Module 27.8 Connection: Contraception can prevent unwanted pregnancy.

A. Contraception is the deliberate prevention of pregnancy. Only complete abstinence is completely effective at preventing pregnancy. Contraceptive methods vary in their reliability when used correctly and when used typically (Table 27.8).

B. In females, sterilization involves **tubal ligation,** cutting a section out of each oviduct. Sterilization in males is called a **vasectomy.** This involves cutting a section out of each vas deferens.
NOTE: A vasectomy is done under local anesthesia and does not noticeably alter the volume of the ejaculate. The procedure is reversible, but fertility may not be restored. Some studies indicate that following a vasectomy, an immune response to sperm may occur.

C. Methods that are known to have a high failure rate include the **rhythm method** or **natural family planning,** which involves abstaining from intercourse from a few days before to a few days after ovulation, and the **withdrawal** method.
NOTE: One of the reasons withdrawal is ineffective is that the secretions from the bulbourethral gland can carry a sufficient number of sperm for conception to occur.

D. **Barrier methods** physically block sperm and egg from meeting. Examples of barrier methods include a condom, a diaphragm (a cap that covers the cervix), and a cervical cap (a smaller, more closely fitting diaphragm). In order to be effective, condoms, diaphragms, and cervical caps need to be used in conjunction with **spermicidal** foam and jelly.

E. **Oral contraceptives,** or **birth control pills,** work by preventing the release of gametes. This is a highly effective method of contraception (but will not prevent any STDs). Most birth control pills contain a synthetic estrogen and synthetic progesterone (progestin). A long-term health concern is an increased risk of cardiovascular problems, especially for women at risk, such as smokers.

F. Another type of birth control pill, the minipill, contains only progestin. This pill is available as a tablet or as an injection that lasts for three months.

G. **MAPs (morning-after pills)** contain estrogen and progesterone and, if taken within 3 days after intercourse, may prevent fertilization or implantation. MAPs should be used only in emergencies, as there are significant side effects. If implantation (pregnancy) has already occurred, the drug mifepristone can induce an abortion during the first seven weeks of pregnancy. This requires a prescription and the care of a physician.

III. Principles of Embryonic Development

Review: The genetic basis of embryonic development (Modules 11.12–11.14).

Module 27.9 Fertilization results in a zygote and triggers embryonic development.

A. **Fertilization** is the union of sperm and egg to produce a diploid zygote.

B. **The Properties of Sperm Cells:** Human sperm are well-adapted for fertilization (Figure 27.9A). They have a streamlined shape; a head that contains only the nucleus and the **acrosome,** the enzyme-containing body that will help the sperm penetrate the egg; and a long, motile flagellum with one associated mitochondrion wrapped around it. Power is generated by respiration of the fructose found in semen (Figure 27.9B).

C. **The Process of Fertilization:** To reach the nucleus, the sperm must pass through three barriers around the egg: a jelly coat, a middle vitelline layer of glycoproteins, and the egg cell's plasma membrane. The acrosomal enzymes digest a hole in the jelly, species-specific proteins on the tip of the sperm bind with receptor proteins on the vitelline layer, and finally, the sperm and egg plasma membranes fuse. This triggers changes in the egg that prevent the entry of more sperm; the egg's plasma membrane becomes impenetrable, and the vitelline layer hardens and separates from the plasma membrane, forming the **fertilization envelope** (Figure 27.9C).

NOTE: Upon ejaculation, sperm are incapable of penetrating to the secondary oocyte. The process by which they gain this ability is called capacitation.

NOTE: It takes the acrosome of several hundred sperm to penetrate to the secondary oocyte. In addition, sperm mortality is high, some are abnormal, some leak out of the vagina, some are killed within the female reproductive tract, and not all (at least initially) swim toward the secondary oocyte.

D. The egg's metabolism begins to change to that needed for development at the time of membrane fusion.

E. Simultaneously, the egg and sperm nuclei fuse, producing the diploid nucleus of the zygote.

Module 27.10 Cleavage produces a ball of cells from the zygote.

A. **Cleavage** of the zygote by rapid cell division results in a ball of cells. At first, the overall size of the collection of cells remains the same. In the sea urchin, doubling occurs every 20 minutes. In 3 hours, a small ball of cells is produced. Then the ball becomes hollow (the **blastula**), forming a fluid-filled cavity, the **blastocoel** (Figure 27.10).

B. Decreasing the size of the cells increases the surface-to-volume ratio of each cell, thus enhancing the flow of materials in and out of the cells.

C. During cleavage, the embryo is partitioned into sections that differ in size and chemistry. These sections activate different genes to guide the development of different parts of the animal.

Review: Embryonic development (Module 11.13).

Module 27.11 Gastrulation produces a three-layered embryo.

A. **Gastrulation** adds more cells and sorts them into three distinct cell layers in the gastrula: ectoderm, endoderm, and mesoderm (Figure 27.11).

B. **Ectoderm** forms the outer skin of the gastrula and ultimately the outer layer of the adult skin and the nervous system.

C. **Endoderm** lines the embryonic digestive tract and ultimately that of the adult.

    D. **Mesoderm** partially fills in the space between ectoderm and endoderm and ultimately forms most other tissues and organs, including the skin's inner lining, the muscles, and the excretory system.

    E. The mechanics of gastrulation differ among species. Gastrulation involves the migration of outer cells across the blastula surface and into a small pore or groove, the **blastopore.** Once the gastrula has formed, some of the inner cells break off of the primitive gut **(archenteron)** to form the mesoderm layer. Ultimately, the blastocoel is filled with mesoderm and endoderm cells. The ectoderm covers the outer layer except for the **yolk plug** (endoderm), which marks the blastopore (the future site of the anus).

Module 27.12 Organs start to form after gastrulation (Table 27.12).
    NOTE: The formation of organs is called organogenesis.

    A. Frog: A few hours after gastrulation, the **notochord** (cartilage-like material) forms from mesodermal cells. It supports the length of the embryo, and later the backbone forms around it (Figures 27.12A and C).

    B. The **neural tube** forms when two ridges of ectoderm cells above the notochord fuse and move below the remaining ectoderm (Figures 27.12A, B, and C).
    NOTE: This process is referred to as neurulation.

    C. **Somites** form as blocks of mesoderm that will give rise to segmented muscles and bone along the backbone and ribs. At this time, a hollow space develops in the mesoderm that will become the **coelom** (Figure 27.12C).
    Review: Two basic features shared by all chordates are segmentation and a coelom (Modules 18.2, 18.3, and 18.15).

    D. Further development will result in actual muscle cells, a heartbeat, blood in an early circulatory network, and a tail fin.

    E. A recognizable tadpole is visible after 5–8 days of development (Figure 27.12D).

Module 27.13 Changes in cell shape, cell migration, and programmed cell death give form to the developing animal.

    A. Cells of the ectoderm elongate and become wedge-shaped. This change in size and shape forces the surface into a groove and then into a neural tube that is the start of the brain and spinal cord (Figure 27.13A).

    B. Many embryonic cells migrate to specific destinations by following chemical trails and moving by pseudopodia.

    C. Once migrating cells reach their destination, surface proteins on similar cells cause them to aggregate and become glued together.

    D. The cells then differentiate and take on the characteristics of the tissue appropriate to their location.
    Review: Patterns of gene expression in differentiated cells (Modules 11.13–11.15).

    E. **Programmed cell death (apoptosis),** controlled by suicide genes, is also essential for development (Figure 27.13B). A good example of apoptosis is the timely death of specific cells resulting in the formation of the spaces between fingers and toes.

Module 27.14 Embryonic induction initiates organ formation.
    Review: Cell signaling and signal transduction (Modules 11.12 and 11.13).

    A. When cells differentiate, some genes are activated and others remain inactive.

B. Cells may be activated by **induction,** the influence of one group of cells on another. Induction may occur either by physical contact (cell-surface interaction) or by chemical influence through diffusion. Mechanisms of induction involve signal molecules and signal-transduction pathways.

C. For example, a lobe (optic cup) of the early brain area induces the formation of the lens of the eye from outer ectodermal cells above. The developing lens, in turn, induces the cornea to form from other ectodermal cells (Figure 27.14).
   NOTE: Another example is the induction of the neural tube by the notochord.

Module 27.15 Pattern formation organizes the animal body.
   Review: Homeotic genes (Module 11.13).

A. The overall goal of the research described here is to find out how the one-dimensional information encoded in DNA directs **pattern formation,** the emergence of a three-dimensional body with specialized organs and tissues in the proper locations.

B. Different positional signals arise from different patterns of cells surrounding a developing region in the embryo.

C. Vertebrate limbs develop from embryonic limb buds. These buds develop into limb patterns in the right place when each cell within the bud receives the correct chemical signal from the correct surrounding cells (Figures 27.15A and B).

D. By experimentally removing wing pattern-forming zones from one animal and grafting them on another prior to complete wing formation, cells of the host's wing bud are induced to form two wing structures. The cells on either side of the wing bud are getting similar chemical signals from the host pattern-forming zone and the grafted donor pattern-forming zone.

IV. Human Development

Module 27.16 The embryo and placenta take shape during the first month of pregnancy.

A. **Gestation** is the carrying of developing young in the female reproductive tract. The human gestation period averages 38 weeks. Gestation is another name for pregnancy.
   NOTE: This is 9.5 months, not 9 months. The human gestation period of 40 weeks includes the two weeks prior to ovulation.

B. Gestation begins with fertilization in the oviduct. Cleavage begins 24 hours later. By the time the embryo has reached the uterus, it is a **blastocyst** of about 100 cells. These cells are partitioned into an inner cell mass that will develop into the baby and an outer layer of cells, the **trophoblast** (Figures 27.16A and B).

C. About a week after conception, the trophoblast secretes enzymes that help the embryo implant in the uterine endometrium lining. The trophoblast and endometrium tissues then begin to build the **placenta,** as the embryo develops further from the inner cells (Figures 27.16C and D).

D. The embryo develops as a pad of cells with layers that will undergo gastrulation to form ectoderm, mesoderm, and endoderm.

E. A series of **extraembryonic membranes** protect the embryo and help it interact with its environment. Moving from outermost to innermost:

   1. The **chorion** forms the embryo's part of the placenta; it is formed by the trophoblast and cells derived from the yolk sac.

   2. The **amnion** protects the embryo in a bag of fluid.

3. The **yolk sac** produces the first blood cells and cells that will give rise to gamete-producing cells of the gonads.

4. The **allantois** is important in waste disposal; it develops from an extension of the yolk sac. In other animals, these membranes may have other functions. For example, the yolk sac of birds and reptiles stores food that is used as an energy source for development (Figures 27.16D, E, and F).

F. Cells of the chorion secrete **human chorionic gonadotropin (HCG),** which ensures that the corpus luteum continues to produce estrogen and progesterone during the first three months of pregnancy. The chorion also forms the embryonic part of the placenta, the **chorionic villi** that contain embryonic blood vessels that interweave with the maternal blood supply in the placenta's margin. Here nutrients, gases, and antibodies are absorbed from the mother's blood, and wastes diffuse from the fetus into the mother's blood.

G. A number of viruses, including HIV, can cross the placenta. Other harmful substances that can cross the placenta include blood alcohol, prescription and nonprescription drugs, and toxins from smoke.

Module 27.17 Human development from conception to birth is divided into three trimesters. *NOTE:* Human development is divided into three-month periods called **trimesters.**

A. **First Trimester:** During the first trimester (conception to 12 weeks), all organs and appendages are built in essentially a human pattern. At the very beginning, a notochord, gill pouches, limb buds, and a tail appear. The notochord is subsumed into the developing spine, the gill pouches grow into parts of the middle ear and throat, the limb buds develop into tiny arms and legs with fingers and toes, and the tail is lost (Figures 27.17A and B). By the end of the first trimester, the fetus can make suckling motions with its lips, frown, move its arms and legs, and has a heart beat.

B. **Second Trimester:** Main changes during the second trimester (13 weeks to 27 weeks) involve an increase in size and a general refinement of human features. The placenta stops producing HCG and takes over the job of secreting progesterone and estrogen from the corpus luteum. By the end of this time, the fetus has the face of an infant and a definite heartbeat (Figures 27.17C and D).

C. **Third Trimester:** During the third trimester (28 weeks to birth), the fetus grows in size and strength, and the circulatory and respiratory systems go through changes that will enable the baby to switch to breathing air. The fetus gains the ability to maintain internal temperature; its bones harden, and its muscles thicken.
Review: Module 22.12 discusses the switch that a baby must endure at birth, from exchanging gas with the placenta to breathing air.

D. A typical baby is born 20 inches long and weighing from 6 to 8 pounds (Figure 27.17E). *NOTE:* Human baby birth weight is an example of stabilizing selection (Module 13.16).

Module 27.18 Childbirth is hormonally induced and occurs in three stages.

A. Estrogen reaches very high levels during the final weeks of pregnancy. This induces the formation of receptors on the uterus that are sensitive to oxytocin, the hormone that stimulates the contraction of smooth muscles during labor. At the appropriate time, cells of the fetus, and later the pituitary, produce oxytocin (Module 26.4), and cells of the placenta produce local regulators, the prostaglandins. Positive feedback results in the uterine contractions, causing the release of increasingly larger amounts of hormones (Figure 27.18A).
NOTE: Sometimes contractions do not signal true labor but are false labor.

B. The three stages of labor are presented below:

1. *Dilation of the cervix:* during the first stage of childbirth, the cervix dilates to about 10 cm.

2. *Expulsion:* during the second stage, strong uterine contractions of about 1-minute duration occur at 2- to 3-minute intervals, and the baby is born. The total time of labor varies from 20 minutes to more than 1 hour.

3. *Delivery of the placenta:* the third stage usually occurs no later than 15 minutes after the birth of the baby (Figure 27.18B).

C. Following childbirth, decreasing levels of progesterone and estrogen cause the uterus to start returning to normal. Lower levels of progesterone induce the pituitary to produce prolactin, a hormone that, along with oxytocin, promotes milk production.

Module 27.19 Connection: Reproductive technology increases our reproductive options.

A. Approximately 15 percent of couples are unable to conceive after one year of unprotected sex because of male (more likely) or female infertility. The inability to maintain an erection is called **impotence.**

B. Hormone therapy can be used to induce ovulation, drugs such as Viagra® can promote erections, and surgery can sometimes correct infertility. But what can be done if these procedures fail?

C. Alternatives are available that can be used to assist couples in the quest for a child of their own genetic makeup. The process is called **assisted reproductive technology (ART).**

D. *In vitro* **fertilization (IVF)** is the most common method chosen by couples seeking medical assistance with their infertility problems. In IVF, ova removed from a woman using hormone therapy are mixed with sperm that results in an embryo (or embryos) that can be implanted in the woman's (or a surrogate's) uterus after about 2 days (at the eight-cell stage) (Figure 27.19).

E. Other ART choices could be made by couples seeking medical assistance, for example, or TET (tubal embryo transfer), ZIFT (zygote intrafallopian transfer), and GIFT (gamete intrafallopian transfer). These procedures are expensive ($10,000 or more regardless of success), but it has resulted in the conception and birth of thousands of babies. Price of the procedure is one concern. A second concern raised by recent studies indicates a higher rate of birth defects may be associated with ART than with natural means.

F. As with many issues related to medicine and improvements in technology, there are ethical and legal issues surrounding assisted reproductive technology.

Class Activities

1. What are the evolutionary advantages and disadvantages of parthenogenesis?

2. Relate the material in this chapter to that covered in Chapter 24. During pregnancy, nonself tissue is housed within the female's body. Why isn't this foreign tissue attacked by the immune system? Remind your students of problems that can occur when the mother is Rh− and the fetus is Rh+.

Transparency Acetates

Reviewing the Concepts, page 562: Spermatogenesis and oogenesis

Reviewing the Concepts, page 562: Cleavage and gastrulation

Connecting the Concepts, page 563: Rise and fall of pituitary and ovarian hormones during the human ovarian cycle

---

Media

See the beginning of this book for a complete description of all media available for instructors and students. Animations and videos are available in the Campbell Image Presentation Library. Media Activities and Thinking as a Scientist investigations are available on the student CD-ROM and website.

Animations and Videos	Module Number
Female Reproductive Anatomy Animation	27.2
Male Reproductive Anatomy Animation	27.3
Male Hormones Animation	27.3
Ovulation Animation	27.5
Post Ovulation Animation	27.5
Sea Urchin Embryonic Development (Time-Lapse) Video	27.11
Frog Embryo Development Video	27.12
Structure and Function of the Eye Animation	27.14

Activities and Thinking as a Scientist	Module Number
Web/CD Activity 27A: *Reproductive System of the Human Male*	27.3
Web/CD Thinking as a Scientist: *Connection: What Might Obstruct the Male Urethra?*	27.3
Web/CD Activity 27B: *Reproductive System of the Human Female*	27.5
Web/CD Activity 27C: *Sea Urchin Development Video*	27.11
Web/CD Activity 27D: *Frog Development Video*	27.12
Web/CD Thinking as a Scientist: *What Determines Cell Differentiation in the Sea Urchin?*	27.14

CHAPTER 28

Nervous Systems

Teaching Objectives

Introduction Explain how spinal cords are injured and the approaches to repairing the damage.

Nervous System Structure and Function

28.1 Describe the structural and functional subdivisions of the nervous system. Describe the three parts of a reflex, noting the three types of neurons involved in the reaction.

28.2 Describe the structure and functions of neurons.

Nerve Signals and Their Transmission

28.3 Define a resting potential, and explain how it is created.

28.4 Explain how an action potential is produced and the resting membrane potential restored.

28.5 Explain (a) how an action potential propagates itself along a neuron, (b) why action potentials move in only one direction, and (c) how action potentials relay different intensities of information.

28.6 Compare the structures, functions, and locations of electrical and chemical synapses.

28.7 Compare excitatory and inhibitory neurotransmitters. Explain how the number and location of bound neurotransmitters influence a receiving cell.

28.8 Describe the types and functions of neurotransmitters known in humans.

28.9 Explain how drugs can alter chemical synapses.

An Overview of Animal Nervous Systems

28.10 Describe, with examples, the diversity of animal nervous systems. Explain how the structure of the nervous system relates to the ways animals interact with their environment.

28.11 Describe the general structure of the brain, spinal cord, and associated nerves of vertebrates. Describe the formation, location, and functions of cerebrospinal fluid.

28.12 Compare the functions of the somatic and autonomic nervous systems.

28.13 Compare the structures, functions, and interrelationships of the parasympathetic, sympathetic, and enteric divisions of the peripheral nervous system.

28.14 Describe two trends in the evolution of the vertebrate brain. Explain how the human forebrain changes during development.

The Human Brain

28.15–28.16 Describe the parts and functions of the human brain. Note the detailed structures and functions of the cerebral cortex.

28.17 Explain how injuries, illness, and surgery provide insight into the functions of the brain.

28.18 Explain how the brain regulates sleep and arousal. Compare slow-wave and REM sleep.

28.19 Describe the structure and functions of the limbic system. Describe the properties of short-term, long-term, and skill memories.

28.20 Describe the causes, symptoms, and treatments of schizophrenia, depression, Alzheimer's disease, and Parkinson's disease.

Key Terms

acetylcholine
action potential
Alzheimer's disease (AD)
amygdala
autonomic nervous system
axon
basal ganglia
biogenic amines
biological clock
bipolar disorder
blood-brain barrier
brain
brainstem
cell body
central canal
central nervous system
(CNS)
centralization
cephalization
cerebellum
cerebral cortex
cerebral hemispheres
cerebrospinal fluid
cerebrum
circadian rhythms
corpus callosum
cranial nerves
dendrites
effector cells

electroencephalogram
(EEG)
enteric division
forebrain
ganglia
glia
gray matter
hindbrain
hippocampus
integration
interneurons
lateralization
limbic system
long-term memory
major depression
medulla oblongata
membrane potential
memory
meninges
midbrain
motor neurons
motor output
myelin sheath
nerve
nerve cords
nerve net
nervous systems
neuron
neurotransmitter

nodes of Ranvier
parasympathetic division
Parkinson's disease
peripheral nervous system
(PNS)
pons
reflexes
REM sleep
resting potential
reticular formation
schizophrenia
sensory input
sensory neurons
short-term memory
sodium-potassium
(Na^+-K^+) pumps
somatic nervous system
spinal cord
spinal nerves
supporting cells
sympathetic division
synapse
synaptic cleft
synaptic terminal
synaptic vesicles
thalamus
threshold
ventricles
white matter

Word Roots

auto- = self (*autonomic nervous system:* a subdivision of the motor nervous system of vertebrates that regulates the internal environment)

bio- = life; **-genic** = producing (*biogenic amines:* neurotransmitters derived from amino acids)

cephalo- = head (*cephalization:* the clustering of sensory neurons and other nerve cells to form a small brain near the anterior end and mouth of animals with elongated, bilaterally symmetrical bodies)

dendro- = tree (*dendrite:* one of usually numerous, short, highly branched processes of a neuron that conveys nerve impulses toward the cell body)

inter- = between (*interneurons:* an association neuron; a nerve cell within the central nervous system that forms synapses with sensory and motor neurons and integrates sensory input and motor output)

neuro- = nerve; **trans-** = across (*neurotransmitter:* a chemical messenger released from the synaptic terminal of a neuron at a chemical synapse that diffuses across the synaptic cleft and binds to and stimulates the postsynaptic cell)

para- = near (*parasympathetic division:* one of two divisions of the autonomic nervous system)

soma- = body (*somatic nervous system:* the branch of the motor division of the vertebrate peripheral nervous system composed of motor neurons that carry signals to skeletal muscles in response to external stimuli)

syn- = together (*synapse:* the locus where a neuron communicates with a postsynaptic cell in a neural pathway)

Lecture Outline

Introduction *Can an Injured Spinal Cord Be Fixed?*

   A. The nervous system is basic to the functioning of any animal.

      1. In order to survive and reproduce, an animal must respond appropriately to environmental stimuli, both internal and external.

      2. The nervous system coordinates immediate responses to stimuli with long-term responses from the endocrine system (Chapter 26).

   B. The spinal cord acts as a conduit for information flow between the brain and the rest of the body. But what happens if the spinal cord is injured?

      1. Minor injuries to the spinal cord can be healed; however, severe injuries can be devastating physically, monetarily, and emotionally to the victim and the victim's family.

      2. Previously, patients suffering a severe injury to the spinal cord were often left paralyzed and without hope for a cure.

      3. Recently, with the advances in growth factors, cell transplantation, and stem cell research, the possibility of a cure has become closer to a reality (Module 11.12).

   C. Structure, function, and evolution of the nervous system are reviewed in this chapter. Emphasis will be placed on the vertebrate nervous system and on the human brain.

I. Nervous System Structure and Function

   Module 28.1 Nervous systems receive sensory input, interpret it, and send out appropriate commands.

   A. The **nervous systems** of animals are the most complex data processing systems on Earth. The human brain contains approximately 100 billion neurons. A **neuron** is the functional unit of the nervous system containing a cell body; a nucleus; organelles; and long, thin neuron fibers that convey signals.

   B. The two main divisions of nervous systems are the **central nervous system (CNS)** and the **peripheral nervous system (PNS).** The CNS consists of the brain and (in vertebrates) spinal cord. The PNS carries information from sensory receptors to the CNS and from the CNS to effector cells. A **nerve** (part of the PNS) is a bundle of neuron fibers wrapped in connective tissue that carries information into and out of the CNS. The PNS also has clusters of neuron cell bodies called **ganglia.**
   NOTE: Clusters of nerve cell bodies within the CNS are called nuclei.

   C. The nervous system is organized with three interconnecting functions (Figure 28.1A):

      1. **Sensory input** is triggered by stimulation of receptors and involves the conduction of signals from the receptors to integration centers.

      2. **Integration** is the interpretation of these signals and the formulation of responses by the processing centers.

      3. **Motor output** is the conduction of signals from the processing center to **effector cells** (muscles or glands) that respond to the stimuli.

D. PNS nerves that convey information from sensory receptors to the CNS are called **sensory neurons.** PNS nerves that convey information from the CNS to effector cells are called **motor neurons.** Nerves that convey information from one region of the CNS to another are called **interneurons** (Figure 28.1B).

E. A simple **reflex** originates with the stimulation of a receptor. The impulse is then conveyed along a sensory neuron (PNS) to the CNS (where integration occurs), to a motor neuron (PNS), and to an effector cell (Figure 28.1B).

Module 28.2 Neurons are the functional units of nervous systems.

A. Each neuron consists of the following components (Figure 28.2):

1. The **cell body** houses the nucleus and most of the organelles.

2. **Dendrites** are short, numerous, and highly branched; they convey signals toward the cell body.

3. **Axons** are long and usually unbranched (except at the very end); they convey signals away from the cell body toward other neurons or effector cells. Each axon ends in a **synaptic terminal** that relays the signal. The signal must pass to the next cell across a space called the **synapse.**

B. Neurons are found with **supporting cells** or **glia.** There may be as many as 50 supporting cells for every neuron. These cells protect, insulate, or reinforce the neurons.
NOTE: These supporting cells are also called neuroglia (or glial cells). There are six major types of neuroglia. For example, astrocytes are supportive cells within the CNS that connect neurons to blood vessels. Astrocytes have many functions, including neurotransmitter metabolism and K^+ balance. Recent studies have implicated astrocytes in learning and memory. Oligodendrocytes form the myelin sheath of the CNS. However, unlike Schwann cells, which form the myelin sheath of the PNS, oligodendrocytes do not guide the regrowth of damaged neurons. Microglia are phagocytic cells found within the CNS. There is evidence that microglia play a role in Alzheimer's disease. Ependymal cells are ciliated cells that aid in the circulation of cerebrospinal fluid (CSF). Satellite cells support clusters of nerve cell bodies (ganglia) in the PNS.

C. Those nerves in the PNS that convey signals very quickly are enveloped by special supporting cells *(Schwann cells)* that form a **myelin sheath.** The Schwann cells are arranged like beads on a string, wrapped around the axon but leaving periodic, unmyelinated **nodes of Ranvier.** On axons of this type, the myelin sheath insulates the axon, and the nodes of Ranvier are the only places on the axon where signals are transmitted (where the plasma membrane of the axon is depolarized).
NOTE: Schwann cells are also called neurolemmocytes. Nodes of Ranvier are also called neurofibril nodes.

D. In the human nervous system, impulses travel along myelinated axons at about 150 m/sec and along nonmyelinated axons at about 5 m/sec.

E. In people who have the debilitating autoimmune disease multiple sclerosis, the myelin sheaths are gradually degraded by the person's immune system.
Review: Autoimmune diseases are discussed in Module 24.16.

II. Nerve Signals and Their Transmission

Module 28.3 A neuron maintains a membrane potential across its membrane.

A. Like a battery, a neuron maintains potential energy (Module 5.1) as a difference in electrical charge across the plasma membrane. This potential energy across the plasma

membrane is called a **membrane potential.** Cells in general have a negative **resting potential,** with more negative charges inside the cell than outside. A neuron has a resting potential of −70 millivolts (mV) (Figure 28.3A).
NOTE: Remind the students that this is a localized charge and that the cell as a whole is not negatively charged; moreover, the interstitial fluid as a whole is not positively charged (ask your students if they stick to magnets).

B. The resting potential is maintained by negatively charged, large organic molecules (proteins) remaining inside the cell and an excess of K^+ ions inside and Na^+ ions outside the cell. The K^+ ions are free to diffuse in both directions through K^+ channels across the membrane. Na^+ ions are actively transported out of the cell as K^+ ions are transported in by the **sodium-potassium pump (Na^+-K^+)** (Figure 28.3B).

C. The membrane potential (voltage difference) across the plasma membrane is produced by the ion gradient. When stimulated, the plasma membrane becomes permeable to the Na^+, and the membrane potential changes.
Review: Active transport (Module 5.18).

Module 28.4 A nerve signal begins as a change in the membrane potential.

A. In the 1940s, Hodgkin and Huxley worked out the details of nerve signal transmission using squid giant axons (fibers).

B. A **stimulus** is any factor (electric shock, light, sound, a tap on the knee, etc.) that results in triggering a nerve signal. A nerve signal involves carrying formation of the **action potential** along an axon.

C. The graph traces the electrical changes over time at one point along an axon. These changes can lead to an action potential (Figure 28.4).

D. A typical action potential shows the following changes relative to the resting potential of −70 mV. Following a stimulus, the voltage rises to the **threshold,** the minimum rise that will generate an action potential (in this case, to −50 mV). The threshold triggers the action potential, causing a reversal in the membrane potential, a rapid upswing to about +35 mV. The voltage then drops slightly below the resting potential (hyperpolarization), and returns to resting potential a few milliseconds after the stimulus.
NOTE: It is only the axon that can achieve an action potential. The potentials that travel along dendrites and nerve cell bodies are graded potentials. Graded potentials travel only a short distance before dying out. However, graded potentials can be added together (summation) to result in an action potential.

E. The specific ion movements that generate this action potential are controlled by the opening and closing of voltage-gated channels. The stimulus triggers the opening of Na^+ channels. At first, a few Na^+ ions move into the axon. If enough ions move in to reach the threshold, the increasingly positive charge within causes more and more Na^+ channels to open. The peak voltage triggers the closing of Na^+ channels and the opening of K^+ channels, allowing K^+ to diffuse out rapidly, thereby balancing the inward movement of Na^+. Next, there is a brief period during which the membrane potential is below −70 mV (due to slow closure of the K^+ channels), followed by a return to the resting potential.
NOTE: This hyperpolarization (below −70 mV) prior to a return to the resting potential is due to the slow closure of the K^+ channels. Also, keep in mind that the activity at a point on the axon is being described here; this is not a description of the actual conduction of a nerve impulse.

Module 28.5 The action potential propagates itself along the neuron.

   A. The local spreading of the electrical changes is caused by Na^+ flowing into the cell (Figure 28.5).

   B. These changes trigger the opening of Na^+ channels just ahead of the action potential, generating a second action potential a little farther along the axon.

   C. But the changes cannot be induced in the region behind the action potential where K^+ ions are moving out because the Na^+ channels have been inactivated, therefore the action potential travels in just one direction.

   D. Action potentials are *all-or-none* events. A signal with higher intensity reaches no higher peak voltage, but instead consists of an increase in the number of action potentials per millisecond.

Module 28.6 Neurons communicate at synapses.

   A. Action potentials generally stop at the end of the axon and do not transmit their signal to the next cell. A synapse is the region of communication between two neurons, or between a neuron and an effector cell. Synapses come in two varieties, electrical and chemical.

   B. At electrical synapses, action potentials travel directly from one cell to another. In humans, electrical synapses are common in the heart and digestive tract, associated with cardiac and smooth muscle cells.

   C. At chemical synapses, action potentials are converted into a chemical signal. This chemical signal takes the form of **neurotransmitter,** which is stored in **synaptic vesicles.** The neurotransmitter carries the message across a small gap (**synaptic cleft**) between the cells. The synaptic cleft prevents the spread of the action potential between cells.

   D. The arrival of the action potential triggers the fusion of the synaptic vesicles with the plasma membrane, releasing the neurotransmitter into the cleft. The molecules diffuse across and bind to cell surface receptors on the receiving cell. The neurotransmitters produce their effect by causing the opening of ion channels through which ions can diffuse and trigger a new action potential. The neurotransmitters are then broken down enzymatically or recycled back to the signaling cell for later use, and as a result the ion channels close (Figure 28.6).
   NOTE: The fusion of the vesicles containing neurotransmitters with the plasma membrane requires an influx of Ca^{2+}.
   Preview: These events are similar to those that occur at a neuromuscular junction (Module 30.10).

Module 28.7 Chemical synapses make complex information processing possible.

   A. Neurotransmitters can either open ion channels in the receiving cell's plasma membrane or trigger a signal-transduction mechanism that will result in the opening of ion channels.
   Review: The mechanism of signal transduction is discussed in Module 11.14.

   B. Excitatory neurotransmitters open Na^+ channels and trigger a new action potential in the receiving cell.

   C. Inhibitory neurotransmitters open Cl^- or K^+ channels that decrease the tendency of the receiving cell to develop action potentials.

D. One cell receives input from numerous synaptic terminals from hundreds of neurons. The cell receives various magnitudes and numbers of both inhibitory and excitatory signals. The behavior of the receiving cell depends on the summation of all incoming signals (Figure 28.7). The more neurotransmitters that bind or the closer the synapse is to the receiving cell's axon, the stronger the effect.
NOTE: Temporal summation is when the signals impinging on the receiving cell are separated in time. Spatial summation occurs when the signals impinge on different regions (different dendrites) of the receiving cell.

Module 28.8 A variety of small molecules function as neurotransmitters.

A. The ability to send a nerve signal across a chemical synapse is dependent on the type of neurotransmitter. Several small molecules are capable of performing this function.

B. Most neurotransmitters are small, nitrogen-containing molecules. For example, **acetylcholine** slows heart rate (inhibitory) and causes muscle cells to contract (excitatory).

C. Several neurotransmitters are **biogenic amines** (derived from amino acids) that also function as hormones: epinephrine, norepinephrine (increases heart rate), serotonin, and dopamine (affects sleep, mood, attention, and learning).

D. Biogenic amines are associated with various diseases. For example, Parkinson's disease is caused by a lack of dopamine, whereas schizophrenia has been linked to an excess of dopamine.

E. Aspartate, glutamate, glycine, and gamma aminobutyric acid (GABA) are amino acids with neurosecretory functions in the brain. Aspartate and glutamate are excitatory. Glycine and GABA are inhibitory.
NOTE: Glutamate has been implicated in stroke-induced neuronal death.

F. Peptides (short chains of amino acids) such as endorphins (natural painkillers) and substance P (excitatory) are also neurotransmitters.

G. The toxic gases NO (nitric oxide) and CO have also been shown to serve as neurotransmitters. NO is released from neurons into erectile tissue, thus producing penile erection (Viagra® promotes the effect of NO). NO may play a role in learning.
NOTE: NO affects many other aspects of physiology, including playing a role in the regulation of blood pressure.

Module 28.9 Connection: Many drugs act at chemical synapses.

A. Drugs often produce their effect by altering the neurotransmitter or the receptor to the transmitter.

B. The effects of several commonly used drugs are as listed below:
1. Caffeine increases alertness by countering the effects of inhibitory signals.
2. Nicotine activates acetylcholine receptors and is a stimulant.
3. Alcohol may increase the inhibitory effects of GABA.

C. Prescription drugs also can act on the neurotransmitters and are used effectively in the treatment of psychological disorders. Popular antidepressants inhibit the removal of serotonin from the receptor and are called SSRIs (selective serotonin reuptake inhibitors; see Module 28.20, Prozac®).

D. Illegal drugs have a wide range of effects and include stimulants, depressants, and hallucinogenics. The problem with drugs that alter the effects of neurotransmitters is their addictive potential.

III. An Overview of Animal Nervous Systems

Module 28.10 Nervous system organization usually correlates with body symmetry.

A. Neurons function in essentially the same way in all animals, but they are arranged in different patterns that provide different levels of integration and control.

B. Animals such as sponges do not have a nervous system.

C. Cnidarians have a **nerve net** (Figure 28.10A). The nerve net provides overall sensory function and control over limited muscular activity. The nerve net of hydras lacks central and peripheral divisions. The structure of the nervous system is suited to the hydra's radially symmetrical body plan and limited activity.

D. Like the hydra, radially symmetrical echinoderms have radially symmetrical nervous systems.
   Review: At the phylum level, echinoderms are chordates' closest relatives (Chapter 18).

E. With bilateral symmetry comes the tendency for one end to encounter new environments first. The result of this is a concentration of nervous tissue at the head end, **cephalization,** and the presence of distinct central and peripheral nervous systems, **centralization.**

F. Flatworms are the first animal phylum to show cephalization and centralization. Their CNS is composed of a brain composed of ganglia and two parallel **nerve cords** that communicate with smaller nerves of the PNS (Figure 28.10B). This CNS pattern is further developed in leeches (Figure 28.10C).

G. Insects have large, complex brains, integrating ganglia in each body segment, and many more complex sense organs (Figure 28.10D).

H. The nervous system of the squid and octopus parallels that of vertebrates (large brain, image-forming eyes, and rapid signaling axons) and is well suited for a predatory lifestyle (Figure 28.10E).

Module 28.11 Vertebrate nervous systems are highly centralized and cephalized.

A. This system is highly centralized into brain and spinal cord, all protected inside bony skeletal elements (Figure 28.11A). The **brain** is the master control center, directing output through the spinal cord and including homeostatic centers, sensory centers, and centers of emotions and intellect. The **spinal cord** runs lengthwise inside the vertebral column, conveying information to and from the brain and integrating simple stimuli.

B. The brain and spinal cord both include hollow regions that are filled with **cerebrospinal fluid** (CSF). These spaces in the brain, **ventricles,** are continuous with the **central canal** of the spinal cord (Figure 28.11B).
   NOTE: This stems from the developmental source of the nervous system as the ectoderm folds into a hollow nerve tube (Modules 27.12 and 27.13).

C. The brain is kept from direct contact with blood by the **blood-brain barrier.** The brain and spinal cord are also protected by the **meninges.** CSF flows between layers of the meninges and cushions the CNS.
   NOTE: CSF also exchanges materials with the CNS and provides information, read by regions of the brain, on the status of the body.

D. The CNS is divided between white matter, with concentrations of myelinated axons and their synapses, and gray matter, with concentrations of neuron cell bodies and dendrites. In the mammalian brain, the cerebral cortex, the region of higher brain function, is gray matter.

E. Information is carried to and from the brain by **cranial nerves.** Information is carried to and from the spinal cord by **spinal nerves.** All spinal nerves and most cranial nerves contain both sensory and motor neurons.

Module 28.12 The peripheral nervous system of vertebrates is a functional hierarchy.

A. The PNS is divided into two functional groups, the somatic nervous system and the autonomic nervous system (Figure 28.12).

B. The **somatic nervous system** carries messages to skeletal muscles under voluntary control in response to external stimuli or involuntarily through reflexes.

C. The **autonomic nervous system** manages the internal environment by controlling smooth muscle, cardiac muscle, the digestive tract, and the exocrine and endocrine systems. The autonomic nervous system is divided into three divisions, the sympathetic, parasympathetic, and enteric divisions.
Preview: The somatic nervous system controls voluntary muscular movement (Module 30.10).

D. All spinal and most cranial nerves carry both sensory and motor neurons.

Module 28.13 Opposing actions of sympathetic and parasympathetic neurons regulate the internal environment.

A. The **parasympathetic division** of the autonomic nervous system primes the body for digesting food and resting, activities that gain and conserve the body's energy supply. These include stimulation of all digestive processes and slowing the heart and breathing rates (Figure 28.13).
NOTE: The parasympathetic division is associated with relaxation and absorption of nutrients, "rest and digest."

B. Neurons from this system leave the basal part of the brain and the lower part of the spinal cord. Most neurons release the neurotransmitter acetylcholine to affect their target organs.

C. The **sympathetic division** prepares the body for intense, energy-consuming activities, such as fighting a competitor or fleeing a predator. These include inhibition of digestive activity, increasing the heart and breathing rates, and stimulating the liver to release glucose and the adrenal glands to release the fight-or-flight hormones, epinephrine and norepinephrine.
NOTE: The sympathetic division is associated with "fight or flight."

D. Neurons from this system leave the middle part of the spinal cord. Most neurons release the neurotransmitter norepinephrine to affect their target organs.

E. The **enteric division** of the autonomic nervous system controls the digestive process. The digestive tract, pancreas, and gallbladder are under control by the enteric system including the smooth muscles that control peristaltic movement. Although the enteric division can function independently, it is under the control of the other two divisions of the autonomic nervous system.

Module 28.14 The vertebrate brain develops from three anterior bulges of the neural tube.

A. Embryonic development of the vertebrate brain shows three anterior bulges on the neural tube: **forebrain, midbrain,** and **hindbrain.** These subdivisions can be distinguished in early stages of brain development in all vertebrates (Figure 28.14).

B. In the process of evolution, the forebrain and hindbrain become structurally and functionally distinct. The evolution of complex vertebrate behavior paralleled increases in forebrain integrative power. The **cerebrum** is an outgrowth of the forebrain and is the most complex part of the brain controlling homeostasis and integration.

C. Major changes of the forebrain occur during embryonic development. There is a rapid increase in size during the second and third trimesters that covers most of the brain. There is also an increase in the surface area due to extensive folding. The folds form the cerebral cortex.

D. In birds and mammals, the cerebral cortex is highly folded, increasing the surface area of gray matter. Porpoises and primates have a larger and more complex cerebral cortex than all other vertebrates. Of all animals, humans have the largest brain surface area relative to body size.

IV. The Human Brain

Module 28.15 The structure of a living supercomputer: The human brain.
NOTE: A great deal of the human brain is given over to relaying information.

A. The human brain is composed of around 100 billion neurons, with a much larger number of supporting cells.

B. The three ancestral lobes of the brain are present, but they are highly evolved (Figure 28.15A). Brain structures and functions are listed in Table 28.15.

C. The hindbrain: The **pons** and **medulla oblongata** conduct information to and from the more forward portions through sensory and motor neurons. This region also controls such involuntary activities as breathing (Chapter 22), heart rates (Chapter 23), and digestion (Chapter 21) and helps coordinate whole-body movement (Chapter 30). The **cerebellum** coordinates muscular movement of the limbs and is responsible for learned motor responses (Chapter 29).

D. The midbrain integrates auditory information, coordinates visual reflexes, and relays sensory data to higher brain centers (Chapter 29). Together, the hindbrain and midbrain form the brainstem.

E. The **brainstem** filters sensory information sent on to higher brain centers, regulates sleep and arousal, and coordinates muscular movements and balance.

F. The forebrain is the site of the most sophisticated integration. The **thalamus** contains cell bodies of neurons that relay information to the cerebral cortex and filter signals that pass through it. The hypothalamus regulates homeostasis, particularly in controlling the hormonal output of the pituitary gland. It is particularly sensitive to some addicting drugs such as cocaine. The hypothalamus (Module 26.4) controls the pituitary gland, body temperature (Chapter 25), blood pressure (Chapter 23), hunger, thirst (Chapter 25), sexual urges, and responses to danger. It is involved in the experiences of emotions such as rage and pleasure. The hypothalamus contains a **biological clock** (the suprachiasmatic nuclei), which regulates **circadian rhythms** such as the sleep and wake cycle. *NOTE:* Much of the brain functions in relaying information from one part of the brain to another in the process of integration.

G. The **cerebrum** is composed of two **cerebral hemispheres** connected by the **corpus callosum** (Figure 28.15B).

H. **Basal ganglia,** found beneath the corpus callosum, function in motor coordination. Degeneration of cells in the basal ganglia occurs in Parkinson's disease, a symptom that results in uncontrollable shaking.

Module 28.16 The cerebral cortex is a mosaic of specialized, interactive regions.

A. The **cerebral cortex** is a highly folded sheet of gray matter occupying more than 80% of total brain mass. The cerebral cortex contains about 10 billion neurons and hundreds of billions of synapses. Its neural circuitry produces our most distinctive human traits: reasoning, language, imagination, artistic talent, and personality. It also creates our sensory perceptions by integrating sensory information with memory and analysis.

B. The cerebral cortex is split into right and left sides that communicate with each other through the corpus callosum. Interestingly, the right hemisphere of the cerebral cortex controls and receives information from the left side of the body and vice versa.

C. Localization of function within the cortex comes mostly from studying the effects of tumors, strokes, and accidental damage; from studying direct stimulation during surgery; and from studying brain activity using PET scans (Module 20.11). The cortex has no pain sensors.

D. Both hemispheres are divided into four discrete lobes, each of which has several functional areas. Regions often combine centers that receive signals with association areas that help integrate our sensory perceptions. These association areas are the sites of higher mental activities: evaluating consequences, making judgments, and planning for the future. Language also results from interactions among several areas, especially those areas associated with reading and speech (Figure 28.16).

E. **Lateralization** refers to the specialization of the hemispheres during infant and child development. The right brain (right cerebral hemisphere) is involved with emotional processing, spatial relationships, and pattern recognition. While the left brain (left cerebral hemisphere) specializes in fine motor skills, logic, language, problem solving, and processing fine visual and auditory details.

Module 28.17 Connection: Injuries and brain operations provide insight into brain function.

A. The lack of appropriate animal models or computer simulations makes studying the human brain the most difficult task in anatomy and physiology. PET scans and MRIs have enhanced research efforts toward understanding brain function.

B. The practice of studying injured brains has also increased the understanding of normal brain function.

C. Much has been learned about the brain during surgery. Patients can be operated on awake, during which time they can be questioned while stimulated with electrical probes.

D. A radical procedure to alleviate the symptoms of severe epilepsy is a hemispherectomy. This procedure surgically removes half of the brain, with few long-term side effects other than partial paralysis on the opposite side of the body. The younger the patient is that needs this type of surgery (less than 5 to 6 years old) the better the recovery. Successful recovery after this type of surgery indicates the plasticity of the brain.

Module 28.18 Several parts of the brain regulate sleep and arousal.

A. Humans require *sleep,* a brain state in which stimuli are received and, in part, acted on, but without awareness of the stimuli. Arousal is the state of consciousness, perceiving the outside world.

B. Sleep/wake cycles are regulated by the hypothalamus. Centers in the pons and medulla oblongata produce sleep when stimulated. A center in the midbrain causes arousal when stimulated.

C. Serotonin may be the key to why milk may induce sleepiness. Milk contains tryptophan, the precursor used to synthesize serotonin.

D. The **reticular formation** is a dispersed network that functions in sleep and arousal (Figure 28.18A). It filters familiar and repetitive stimuli, keeping them from impinging on consciousness. In general, the more active the reticular formation, the more aroused you are.

E. Brain waves (electrical signals on the head's surface recorded by an **electroencephalogram,** or **EEG**) depend on mental activity. The less the mental activity, the more regular the EEG (Figure 28.18B).

F. Alpha waves are characteristic of quiet, awake individuals. Beta waves are more agitated and characteristic of awake individuals solving complex mental problems (Figure 28.18C).

G. During sleep, activity cycles between two alternating types of sleep. Slow-wave (SW) sleep is characterized by delta waves and regular strong bursts of brain-wave activity. **REM (rapid-eye-movement) sleep** is characterized by rapid, less regular brain-wave activity. It is during REM sleep that most dreams occur. Sleep seems to play a role in consolidating memories and learning.

Module 28.19 The limbic system is involved in emotions, memory, and learning.

A. The **limbic system** is a functional unit of several integrating centers and interconnecting neurons in the forebrain, including the thalamus, and parts of the hypothalamus and cerebral cortex (Figure 28.19).

B. Feelings of emotions, pleasure, and punishment are associated with the limbic system. Stimulation of these areas evokes intense reactions and is associated with basic survival mechanisms such as feeding, aggression, and sexuality.

C. **Memory** is essential for learning and requires the ability to store and recall information related to prior experiences. The **hippocampus** is involved in memory formation, learning, and emotions. The hippocampus interacts closely with the **amygdala,** hypothalamus, brainstem, and prefrontal cortex. The amygdala appears to function as a memory filter, tying memory to a particular event or emotion. The prefrontal cortex functions in complex learning, reasoning, and personality.

D. The limbic system is closely associated with olfaction, as evidenced by the ability of odors to evoke both memories and emotions.

E. **Short-term memory** lasts only short periods of time (minutes).

F. **Long-term memory** requires the ability to store and retrieve information. The prefrontal cortex appears to be involved in the retrieval of stored information. Long-term memory can be improved with rehearsal and association with other long-term memories.

G. There is a difference between factual memories and skills. Skill memories involve muscular activities that have been learned by repeated use of a set of muscles. Overall, the process of memory formation and retrieval appears to be highly complex.

Module 28.20 Changes in brain physiology can produce neurological disorders.

A. Diseases of the nervous system are common in our society. Cures for neurological disorders have not been discovered, but limited treatments are available. Four neurological disorders are discussed below.

B. **Schizophrenia:** Approximately 1% of the population suffer from this disease. Schizophrenia causes the patient to be unable to distinguish reality. There is a genetic tendency for members of a family to be positively diagnosed if another member of the family has schizophrenia. The cause is unknown and treatments are not very effective.

C. **Depression:** Once thought to be purely psychological, it is now clear that depression is physiological as well. Two types of depression have been characterized. **Major depression,** which occurs in 5% of the population, is characterized by extreme and prolonged sadness and thoughts of suicide. **Bipolar depression,** or manic-depressive disorder, affects 1% of the population. It involves extreme mood swings and has genetic connections within families. Treatments are available; for example, SSRIs such as Prozac® (Figure 28.20A) are often used.

D. **Alzheimer's disease:** This disease leads to deterioration of the brain and eventual death. Symptoms include confusion, memory loss, and lack of facial recognition even of family members. Alzheimer's disease is age related—10% of the population at age 65 and 35% by age 85. Diagnosis is confirmed with a brain autopsy that shows senile plaques (aggregates of beta-amyloid) and neurofibrillary tangles (bundles of degenerated brain cells) in the remaining brain tissue (Figure 28.20B).

E. **Parkinson's disease:** Approximately one million people suffer from Parkinson's disease; it is age related and fatal (Figure 28.20C). The disease is a result of the degeneration of midbrain neurons. Symptoms include difficulty in initiating movement, slow movement, rigidity, muscle tremor, poor balance, and a shuffling gait. Treatments are available that slow the symptoms (e.g., L-Dopa).

F. The challenge to neurobiologists is to unravel the causes and find effective cures for these and other neurological diseases.

Class Activities

1. Compare two types of nervous systems by using the cnidarian *Hydra* and the planarian flatworm *Dugesia*. Place several individuals of each species in a watch glass on an overhead projector, and leave the preparation alone as you talk about the systems. The animals will (hopefully) demonstrate their capabilities very well. Add a few *Daphnia* to introduce an even more sophisticated system, and to induce additional behavior of *Hydra*.

2. An impromptu demonstration of the "all-or-nothing" and cascading nature of the transmission of action potentials can be done with chalkboard erasers (make sure you have plenty on hand). Line them up as though they were dominoes (you can also use dominoes, but erasers work better), with each eraser upright on its narrow end and with a space of about two-thirds of an eraser length between them. A slight push of the leading eraser will cause it to rock back and forth, but if it doesn't surpass the "threshold" push, the signal will not be passed further. A certain strength of push will surpass the "threshold potential" and induce the transmission of an " action potential" (the sequential tipping over of all the erasers).

3. There are numerous reflexes that are fun to demonstrate. For example, tapping the patellar tendon will cause the knee-jerk reflex, tapping the Achilles tendon will cause the foot to move, gently stroking the back of the hand will cause a change in the size of the pupils, and I am sure that there are many others you can think of.

4. Ask your students to consider the evolutionary advantages and disadvantages of cephalization. Have the class show how a particular type of nervous system reflects an organism's lifestyle.

Transparency Acetates

Media

See the beginning of this book for a complete description of all media available for instructors and students. Animations and videos are available in the Campbell Image Presentation Library. Media Activities and Thinking as a Scientist investigations are available on the student CD-ROM and website.

Animations and Videos	Module Number
Resting Potential Animation	28.3
Action Potential Animation	28.4
Synapse Animation	28.6

Activities and Thinking as a Scientist	Module Number
Web/CD Activity 28A: *Neuron Structure*	28.2
Web/CD Thinking as a Scientist: *What Triggers Nerve Impulses?*	28.4
Web/CD Activity 28B: *Nerve Signals: Action Potentials*	28.5
Web/CD Activity 28C: *Neuron Communication*	28.6

CHAPTER 29

The Senses

Teaching Objectives

Introduction Explain how salmon navigate to and from streams during their life cycles.

   29.1 Define and compare sensations and perceptions, noting where each is formed.

Sensory Reception

   29.2 Define sensory transduction, a receptor potential, and sensory adaptation. Illustrate each with examples.

   29.3 Describe the five general categories of sensory receptors found in animals. Note examples of each.

Vision

   29.4 Compare the structures and functions of the eye cup of planarians, the compound eyes of insects and crustaceans, and the single-lens eyes of squids.

   29.5 Describe the parts of the human eye and their functions.

   29.6 Compare the mechanisms used to focus the eyes of a squid and a human.

   29.7 Explain the causes and symptoms of myopia, hyperopia, presbyopia, and astigmatism.

   29.8 Compare the structures, functions, distributions, and densities of rods and cones. Explain how light is perceived in the retina.

Hearing and Balance

   29.9 List the structures of the ear in the order in which they participate in hearing. Describe the possible causes of hearing loss. Explain how the cochlea distinguishes sounds of different pitch.

   29.10 Explain how body position and movement are sensed in the inner ear.

   29.11 Explain what causes motion sickness and what can be done to prevent it.

Taste and Smell

   29.12 Explain how odor and taste receptors function.

   29.13 Explain how the sensitivity of taste and smell change with age.

   29.14 Describe the role of the central nervous system in sensory perception.

Key Terms

accommodation	chemoreceptors	cornea
aqueous humor	choroid	eardrum
astigmatism	ciliary body	electromagnetic receptors
auditory canal	cochlea	Eustachian tube
basilar membrane	compound eye	eye cup
blind spot	cones	farsightedness

fovea	perceptions	sensations
hair cells	photopsin	sensory adaptation
inner ear	photoreceptors	sensory receptors
iris	pinna	sensory transduction
lens	pupil	single-lens eye
mechanoreceptors	receptor potential	stretch receptors
middle ear	retina	thermoreceptors
nearsightedness	rhodopsin	utricle
organ of Corti	rods	visual acuity
outer ear	saccule	vitreous humor
oval window	sclera	
pain receptors	semicircular canals	

Word Roots

aqua- = water (*aqueous humor:* the clear, watery substance that fills the anterior cavity of the eye)

chemo- = chemical (*chemoreceptor:* a receptor that transmits information about the total solute concentration in a solution or about individual kinds of molecules)

electro- = electricity (*electromagnetic receptor:* receptors of electromagnetic energy, such as visible light, electricity, and magnetism)

fovea- = a pit (*fovea:* the center of the visual field of the eye)

mechano- = an instrument (*mechanoreceptor:* a sensory receptor that detects physical deformations in the body's environment associated with pressure, touch, stretch, motion, and sound)

omma- = the eye (*ommatidia:* the facets of the compound eye of arthropods and some polychaete worms)

photo- = light (*photoreceptor:* receptors of light)

rhodo- = red (*rhodopsin:* a visual pigment consisting of retinal and opsin)

sacc- = a sack (*saccule:* a chamber in the vestibule behind the oval window that participates in the sense of balance)

thermo- = heat (*thermoreceptor:* an interoreceptor stimulated by either heat or cold)

utric- = a leather bag (*utricle:* a chamber behind the oval window that opens into the three semicircular canals)

vitre- = glass (*vitreous humor:* the jellylike material that fills the posterior cavity of the vertebrate eye)

Lecture Outline

Introduction *An Animal's Senses Guide Its Movements*

    A. Sensory information gathered by sensory receptors guides animals in their activities.

    B. Bears learn as cubs to feed at certain streams. They find the same streams year after year, using their well-tuned sense of smell. Their sense of smell and very fast reflexes make up for poor eyesight to aid in the capture of food.

        NOTE: Compare the relatively large size of the nasal area of a bear's head to ours.

C. Salmon form a memory of the chemical "scent" of the stream where they hatch. After migrating downstream and spending several years feeding and growing in the open ocean, they use a variety of senses to return to their home spawning grounds. They use sight of the sun's angle and possibly the magnetic field of the Earth to find the river's ocean mouth. Once in the river, they use smell to follow the increasing concentration of the spawning ground's scent as they make the correct turns up the stream's branches.

Module 29.1 Sensory inputs become sensations and perceptions in the brain.

A. Receptor cells detect stimuli such as chemicals, light, muscle tension, sounds, electricity, cold, heat, and touch. They trigger action potentials that travel to the central nervous system.

B. **Sensations** are the action potential it receives from sense receptors.

C. **Perceptions** are constructed by the brain as it processes sensations and integrates them with other information, forming a meaningful interpretation of sensory data. For instance, the perception of a fragrant red rose results from the sum total of interconnected neurons in the visual and odor centers, and their associated memory areas in the brain.

D. The visual demonstration provided may first be sensed as just splotches and later (after suggestion) integrated into the perception of a person riding a horse (Figure 29.1).

I. Sensory Reception

Module 29.2 Sensory receptors convert stimulus energy to action potentials.

A. **Sensory receptors** are found on all sensory organs and are specialized cells (neurons) that identify stimuli.

B. This conversion, known as sensory transduction, occurs in the plasma membrane of the receptor cell. For example, in a taste bud sensing sugar, the sugar molecules enter the region of the sensory receptor cells, bind to specific proteins in the cell's membrane, cause some ion channels to open and others to close, and induce a change in membrane potential. The result is the production of a **receptor potential** as a consequence of signal transduction (Figure 29.2A).
Review: Signal transduction (Module 11.14).

C. Unlike action potentials, the stronger the stimulus, the larger the receptor potential.

D. Receptors synapse with sensory neurons and generate receptor potentials by increasing their release of neurotransmitters.
Review: Synapses and neurotransmitters (Modules 28.6–28.8).

E. A receptor normally secretes neurotransmitters at a constant, low rate. The stimulus results in some higher rate of neurotransmitter release. In the brain, the stimulus is sensed as a change in the frequency of action potentials arriving on the sensory neuron. The strength of the stimulus is also interpreted from how many sensory neurons send a signal (Figure 29.2B).

F. Signals from different sensory receptors are perceived as different (sweet versus salty) depending on which interneurons are stimulated in which region of the brain.
NOTE: Distinguishing between stimuli depends on genetically determined "hard-wired" neuronal connections between association centers and on comparison with learned memories of other similar stimuli.

G. **Sensory adaptation** is the tendency of receptor cells to become less sensitive to constant stimulation because stimuli are perceived as changes in rate. This keeps the body from becoming overloaded with background stimuli.

Module 29.3 Specialized sensory receptors detect five categories of stimuli.

A. There are five general categories of sensory receptors: pain receptors, thermoreceptors, mechanoreceptors, chemoreceptors, and electromagnetic receptors.

B. Skin contains receptors falling into three of these categories: pain receptors, thermoreceptors, and mechanoreceptors. In this case, each receptor is also the sensory neuron delivering the stimulus to the brain (Figure 29.3A).

C. **Pain receptors** indicate the presence of danger and often elicit withdrawal to safety. With the exception of the brain, all parts of the human body have pain receptors. Pain receptors may respond to excessive heat and pressure. Inflamed tissues release histamines and prostaglandins (PG) that trigger pain receptors. Aspirin and ibuprofen inhibit PG synthesis, thus reducing pain.

D. **Thermoreceptors** detect either heat or cold and also monitor blood temperature deep in the body. The hypothalamus (Module 28.15) sets and monitors body temperature. *Review:* Thermoregulation as a homeostatic mechanism is discussed in Module 20.13; also see Module 25.2.

E. **Mechanoreceptors** are diverse and respond to touch, pressure (including blood pressure), stretching of muscles (stretch receptors), motion, and sound. **Hair cells** detect movement of cilia or special projections of the cell membrane when exposed to stimuli from sound waves and other forms of movement. In one direction, more neurotransmitter molecules are released, and in the other, fewer (Figure 29.3B). Hair cells are involved in hearing and balance.

F. **Chemoreceptors** include sensory receptors in the nose and mouth, and internal receptors that monitor blood levels of chemicals. Chemoreceptors of insects can be extremely sensitive to just a few molecules (Figure 29.3C).

G. **Electromagnetic receptors** are sensitive to energy of various wavelengths, including electricity, magnetism, and light (photoreceptors). Some fishes (including salmon) are sensitive to changes in electrical fields caused by environmental interaction with electrical currents the fish produce. The heads of a number of animals contain magnetite that they may use to sense changes in magnetic fields. **Photoreceptors** are sensitive to humanly visible wavelengths, to infrared (in vertebrates such as snakes; Figure 29.3D), and ultraviolet wavelengths.

H. Photoreceptors are genetically ancient (common ancestry), based on molecular evidence and similarities in pigment structure and function.

II. Vision

Module 29.4 Several types of eyes have evolved among invertebrates.

A. The simplest form of light-detecting organ is the **eye cup,** which is found in planarian flatworms and other invertebrates. They are composed of rounded shields of dark-colored cells that shade photoreceptor cells from one side. They do not form images, but allow the animal to sense the intensity and direction of light. When the intensity and direction have equalized, the planarian moves in the opposite direction, maintaining the equilibrium and moving in the direction exactly opposite the light. The animal can then escape to shady hiding places (Figure 29.4A).

B. The **compound eye** (found in insects and other arthropods) is composed of many tiny light detectors (ommatidia), each with its own covering (cornea) and lens, that focus light onto a cluster of photoreceptor cells. Each ommatidium responds to light from a portion of a field of view. The brain then integrates this information into a visual image. Compound eyes are extremely acute motion detectors and most provide color vision (Figure 29.4B).

    C. **Single-lens eyes** (e.g., squid) function like a camera. Light rays reflected from an object enter through a small pupil and are focused into an image on the photoreceptor surface of the retina. Muscles in the eye can move the lens forward and back, focusing the image from variable distances. This produces a fine-grained, integrated image in the brain (Figure 29.4C).

Module 29.5 Vertebrates have single-lens eyes.

    A. The vertebrate eye evolved independently of the single-lens eye of invertebrates and differs in many details.
       NOTE: Many animals, including humans, have two eyes that both face forward to focus on the same object. This is known as convergence and allows for depth perception.

    B. The outermost layer of the eyeball is the **sclera.** The sclera forms the white of the eyeball, and in front, the transparent **cornea.**
       NOTE: The conjunctiva is a thin mucous membrane that lines the eyelids and the front of the eyeball, except the cornea. The conjunctiva helps keep the eye moist. The glands that keep the conjunctiva moist respond to eye irritations and emotional changes. When the blood vessels of the conjunctiva are dilated, the eyes appear to be bloodshot.

    C. The sclera surrounds a thin pigmented layer, the **choroid.** The **iris,** which gives the eye its color, is formed from the choroid. Muscles in the iris regulate the size of the **pupil,** the opening that lets light into the eye's interior.
       NOTE: The pigmented choroid absorbs light rays and prevents them from reflecting within the eyeball and blurring vision.

    D. After going through the pupil, light passes through a transparent **lens** that focuses images on the **retina,** the layer of photoreceptors that lies on the inner surface of the choroid (Figure 29.5).
       NOTE: Although transparent, the lens is composed of hundreds of cells arranged in layers like the scales of an onion.

    E. The photoreceptor cells of the retina are most highly concentrated in a region called the **fovea.**

    F. The photoreceptor cells of the retina transduce light energy into action potentials; the nerve impulses then travel along the optic nerve to the visual areas of the brain.

    G. Since there are no photoreceptors located where the optic nerve attaches to the eye, this region of the retina is a **blind spot.**

    H. The chamber in front of the lens is filled with **aqueous humor,** a liquid similar to blood plasma. The chamber behind the lens is filled with **vitreous humor,** a jellylike fluid. Humor fluid, secreted by the **ciliary body,** in both chambers maintains the shape of the eyeball, provides nutrients and oxygen, and removes waste. Excess aqueous humor is caused by glaucoma and can lead to blindness by causing excess pressure on the retina.

Module 29.6 To focus, a lens changes position or shape.

    A. In fishes, the lens moves back and forth (relative to the retina), moving the fixed point of focus.

    B. In mammals, the lens changes shape, thereby changing the distance at which images are focused. This process is called **accommodation** (allows diverging light rays from a close object to be bent and focused). Muscles attached to the choroid contract, reducing tension on the ligaments that support the lens and allowing it to take a more rounded shape and focus images of nearby objects on the retina. When the muscles relax, the lens is stretched into a more elongated shape to focus images of distant objects (Figure 29.6).

NOTE: The pupil also accommodates to near and far vision. For near vision, the iris decreases the size of the pupil so as to eliminate peripheral light rays.

Module 29.7 Connection: Artificial lenses or surgery can correct focusing problems.

A. **Visual acuity** is the ability to distinguish fine detail. So-called normal vision, or 20/20 acuity, indicates that at 20 feet, the eye can read letters on a chart normally readable at 20 feet. Acuity of 20/10 is better than normal; at 20 feet, the eye can read letters normally readable at 10 feet. And acuity of 20/50 is worse than normal; at 20 feet, the eye can read letters normally readable at 50 feet.

B. **Nearsightedness** (myopia) is the inability to focus on far objects because the eyeballs are too elongated and the lenses cannot accommodate. Corrective lenses that are thinner in the middle correct nearsightedness (Figure 29.7A). Surgery can correct nearsightedness by cutting slits in the cornea or by removing layers of the cornea with a laser.

C. **Farsightedness** (hyperopia) is the inability to focus on near objects because the eyeballs are too short and the lenses cannot accommodate. As the lenses age, they become less elastic and hyperopia becomes worse (called presbyopia, Greek for "old eyes"). Corrective lenses that are thicker in the middle correct farsightedness (Figure 29.7B).

D. **Astigmatism** is blurred vision caused by lenses or corneas that are misshapen. Asymmetrical lenses are used to correct the problem.

Module 29.8 Our photoreceptor cells are rods and cones.

A. The human eye contains about 130 million photoreceptors, which come in two types, rods and cones (Figure 29.8A).

B. **Rods** are most sensitive to dim light and distinguish shades of gray, not color, using the light-absorbing pigment **rhodopsin.** They are most common in the outer margins of the retina and completely absent from the eye's center of focus (fovea). The best night vision is thus achieved by looking at things out of the "corner of your eye."

C. **Cones** are sensitive to bright light, and they distinguish color. Three types of cones (blue cones, red cones, and green cones) can distinguish three predominant wavelengths using three kinds of the light-absorbing pigment **photopsin.** Groups of cones can distinguish thousands of different tints. Cones are less numerous in the retina's margins and are most dense in the fovea. The best color vision and most acute vision are achieved by looking right at an object in bright light.

NOTE: Rods are more sensitive to light than are cones. This is why we do not see color when there is little light available.

D. Photoreceptors detect light when light is absorbed by a pigment that changes it chemically, triggering signal transduction pathways that alter membrane permeability and result in a receptor potential. Integration of the stimuli first occurs among interneurons that interconnect the output of several neighboring rods and cones. Many such integrated signals occur in a layer of neurons (on the surface of the retina), combining to leave the eyeball via the optic nerve (Figure 29.8B).

NOTE: Is it not odd that light must pass through several layers of neurons before reaching the photoreceptors?

E. Color blindness is a result of a deficiency of one or more cone types. Red-green color blindness is most common in males.

III. Hearing and Balance

Module 29.9 The ear converts air pressure waves to action potentials that are perceived as sound.

A. The **outer ear** consists of two parts, the flap-like structure called a **pinna** and the **auditory canal.** Sound waves are collected by the pinna and channeled through the auditory canal to the **eardrum.** The **middle ear** relays the sound wave vibrations from the eardrum through three small bones—the hammer, anvil, and stirrup—to the **oval window,** a membrane that separates the middle and inner ears. Air pressure in the middle ear and outer ear is equalized by the **Eustachian tube.** The **inner ear** houses the hearing organ, which is composed of several channels of fluid wrapped in a spiral (the **cochlea**) and encased in bones of the skull. Vibrations of the oval window produce pressure waves in the fluid (Figures 29.9A and B).

B. The pressure waves travel through the upper canal to the tip of the cochlea, then enter the lower canal and gradually fade away. Pressure waves in the upper canal push down on the middle canal, causing the **basilar membrane** below this canal to vibrate. The vibrations stimulate the hair cells attached to the membrane by bending them up against the overlying shelf of tissue. This whole structure is the **organ of Corti** (Figure 29.9C). The hair cells develop receptor potentials when bent and release neurotransmitter molecules, thereby inducing action potentials in auditory neurons, grouped together as the auditory nerve. Each region of the cochlea vibrates best at a given pitch (Figure 29.9D).

C. **Volume and Pitch:** The brain perceives sound as a change in the action potential from the auditory nerve. The human ear can detect sound in two qualities.

   1. The first quality of sound is volume. The louder the volume, the higher amplitude of the pressure wave generated. Volume is measure in decibels (dB) and humans can detect and tolerate a dB range of 0 to 120.

   2. The second quality of sound is pitch. Pitch depends on the frequency of the sound wave. Frequency is measured in Hertz (Hz). Young people are sensitive to pitches between 20 (low frequency) and 20,000 Hz. Dogs can hear to 40,000 Hz, and bats echolocate with sounds as high pitched as 100,000 Hz (very high frequency).
   NOTE: Bats can use their ears much as we use our eyes. Bats can hear the patterns formed by sounds bouncing off their environment and prey. A fishing bat can hear, in three dimensions, the ripples on the surface of water, indicating the movement of a fish below the surface.

D. The organ of Corti is sensitive to a considerable range of sound amplitudes (volumes) without perceiving pain, from about 0 to 120 dB. Exposure to sounds of 90 dB (modestly amplified rock music or occupation-related noise) for long periods can cause hearing loss. Ear protection is recommended when listening to loud music and is a must for employees exposed to occupational noise.

Module 29.10 The inner ear houses our organs of balance.

A. Three **semicircular canals** lie next to the cochlea.

B. These organs detect changes in the head's rate of movement. Because they are arranged in three perpendicular planes, they detect movement in all directions. Receptor potentials are triggered when a jellylike mass of tissue (the cupula) suspended in the thick fluid in a canal moves against hair cells (Figure 29.10).

C. The **utricle** and **saccule** detect the position of the head relative to the force of gravity. Within these chambers, calcium carbonate particles are pulled by gravity in different directions (depending on the head's orientation) against hair cells.

D. The brain integrates information from the semicircular canals, the utricle, and saccule and sends signals to the skeletal muscles to balance the body.

Module 29.11 Connection: What causes motion sickness?

    A. Motion sickness seems to occur when the brain receives signals from equilibrium receptors of the inner ear and a contrary set of perceptions, usually visual. Sometimes simply closing the eyes can relieve the sick feeling.

    B. People vary considerably in what it takes to produce motion sickness. As NASA has discovered, some people are able to consciously override the sick feelings stemming from the mixed messages.

IV. Taste and Smell

Module 29.12 Odor and taste receptors detect chemicals present in solution or air.

    A. Chemoreceptors localized in taste buds detect molecules in food. There are four types of taste perception that detect sweet, sour, salty, and bitter. A fifth taste perception called umami (Japanese for "delicious") recognizes glutamate, which is found in meat and the flavor enhancer MSG. A broad range of molecules from each category stimulates each type of taste bud (Module 3.6). The brain integrates combined inputs, and we perceive a variety of flavors.

    B. Chemoreceptors in the nose detect airborne molecules, distinguishing thousands of odors (Figure 29.12). Humans have a relatively poor olfactory sense compared to other animals such as dogs, cats, and bears. Olfactory chemoreceptors are in the upper portion of the nasal cavity and send input along the axons directly to the olfactory lobe of the brain. Molecules enter the nose, dissolve in the mucus, and bind to specific receptor molecules on the chemoreceptor cilia. The binding triggers receptor potentials that our brain integrates and perceives as odor.
Review: Olfaction is tied to the limbic system, which is why it is particularly good at evoking emotions and memories (Module 28.19).

Module 29.13 Our sense of taste may change as we age.

    A. The response to odor and taste changes with age. Children and teenagers are often intensely sensitive to strong odors and flavors to the extent that they will not eat foods that older adults consider delicious (e.g., spinach salad and grilled salmon).

    B. Taste perceptions can vary between individuals and may be related to genetic traits. Some people have very sensitive bitter perceptions and avoid foods such as spinach and broccoli. This can have detrimental health implications (phytochemicals).

    C. Smell and taste have independent receptors and pathways to the brain. Yet anyone who has had a head cold knows that food does not taste as good when you're all stuffed up.

Module 29.14 Review: The central nervous system couples stimulus with response.

    A. Sensory receptors enable an animal to survive by avoiding danger, communicating with others, finding food and mates, and maintaining homeostasis.

    B. A summary of the sequence of information flow is presented as the brown bear catches the salmon (see opening essay). A flash of light stimulates the bear's photoreceptors. These cells transduce the light stimulus into action potentials that travel along sensory neurons to the brain. Additional perceptions (smell, sound, and touch) are integrated, with memories, by the brain. The brain then sends action potentials along motor neurons to effector cells and muscles in the paws, neck, and jaws. The salmon is caught!

Class Activities

1. As the optic nerve runs from the eye to the brain, the fibers from the nasal half of each optic nerve cross over to the other side of the brain. The optic nerve fibers from the nasal (left) half of the right eye cross to the left side of the brain, and the optic nerve fibers from the nasal (right) half of the left eye cross to the right side of the brain. The place at which these fibers cross is the optic chiasma. This crossing of nerve fibers can be demonstrated by placing a tube (for example, a cardboard paper towel tube) in front of one eye and looking straight ahead out of both eyes. Put the palm of the hand on the same side as the eye that is not looking through the tube at arm's length and directly in front of that eye. Slowly move the palm closer to that eye, all the while continuing to look straight ahead out of both eyes. At a certain point, it will appear that there is a hole in the palm.

2. Having ears on either side of the head allows for the direction from which a sound arose to be localized. For example, if the sound reaches the right ear before reaching the left ear, the sound must be coming from the right. This can be demonstrated by having students, with their eyes closed, determine the location of a tuning fork that is vibrating on the right or left side of their head. If the tuning fork is placed directly above their head, they will be unable to determine where the sound is coming from.

3. There is evidence that the traditional taste map is wrong, and that there is a wider variety of taste receptors than previously thought. Using cotton swabs, see if your students can create a taste map of their tongues. Also, to demonstrate the importance of smell to that which is perceived as taste, have your students taste various foods while holding their nose. Of course, these demonstrations need to be done with the eyes closed.

4. Be careful when doing this one—demonstrate equilibrium by spinning a student in a chair and then having them walk. Ask how the resulting staggered walk relates to the structure of the ear.

Transparency Acetates

Figure 29.1	Black splotches or a person riding a horse?
Figure 29.2A	Sensory transduction at a taste bud (Layer 1)
Figure 29.2A	Sensory transduction at a taste bud (Layer 2)
Figure 29.2A	Sensory transduction at a taste bud (Layer 3)
Figure 29.2B	How action potentials transmit different taste sensations
Figure 29.3A	Sensory receptors (labels in blue) in the human skin
Figure 29.3B	Mechanoreception by a hair cell
Figure 29.5	The single-lens eye of a vertebrate
Figure 29.6	How lenses focus light
Figure 29.7A	A nearsighted eye (eyeball too long)
Figure 29.7B	A farsighted eye (eyeball too short) (combined with Figure 29.7A)
Figure 29.8A	Photoreceptor cells
Figure 29.8B	The vision pathway from light source to optic nerve
Figure 29.9A	An overview of the human ear
Figure 29.9B	The middle ear and the inner ear (combined with Figure 29.9A)

Figure 29.9C   The organ of Corti, within the cochlea

Figure 29.9D   The route of sound wave vibrations through the ear

Figure 29.10   Equilibrium structures in the inner ear

Figure 29.12   Smell in humans

Reviewing the Concepts, page 602: Action potentials

Reviewing the Concepts, page 602: The eye

Connecting the Concepts, page 602: Sensory receptors

Connecting the Concepts, page 603: The human ear

Media

See the beginning of this book for a complete description of all media available for instructors and students. Animations and videos are available in the Campbell Image Presentation Library. Media Activities and Thinking as a Scientist investigations are available on the student CD-ROM and website.

Activities and Thinking as a Scientist   Module Number

Web/CD Activity 29A: *Structure and Function of the Eye*   29.6

CHAPTER 30

How Animals Move

Teaching Objectives

Introduction   Describe the field of biomechanics, noting what animal systems are studied.

Movement and Locomotion

30.1   Describe the diverse methods of locomotion and the forces each must resist.

Skeletal Support

30.2   Describe the three main types of skeletons. Note their advantages, their disadvantages, and examples of each.

30.3   Describe the common features of terrestrial vertebrate skeletons, distinguishing between the axial and appendicular skeletons and noting the special skeletal adaptations of humans. Describe three types of joints, and provide examples of each.

30.4   Describe the complex structure of a bone, noting the major tissues that contribute to bones and their functions.

30.5   Explain why bones break and how we can help them heal.

30.6   Describe the causes of osteoporosis.

Muscle Contraction and Movement

30.7   Explain how muscles and the skeleton interact to cause movement. Explain how muscles lengthen again once contracted.

30.8   Describe the structure and arrangement of the filaments found in a muscle cell.

30.9   Explain how a muscle cell contracts.

30.10   Explain how motor units control muscle contraction.

30.10   Explain how a motor neuron makes a muscle fiber contract.

30.10   Describe the role of calcium in a muscle contraction.

30.11   Explain what causes muscles to fatigue. Distinguish between aerobic and anaerobic exercise. Note the advantages of each.

30.12   Describe an example of an animal using its sensory receptors, central nervous system, skeleton, and muscles to perform an activity.

Key Terms

anaerobic exercise	ligaments	skeletal muscle
appendicular skeleton	motor units	sliding-filament model
axial skeleton	myofibril	tendons
ball-and-socket joints	neuromuscular junctions	thick filament
endoskeleton	osteoporosis	thin filament
exoskeleton	pivot joint	yellow bone marrow
hinge joint	red bone marrow	
hydrostatic skeleton	sarcomeres	

Word Roots

endo- = within (*endoskeleton:* a hard skeleton buried within the soft tissues of an animal, such as the spicules of sponges, the plates of echinoderms, and the bony skeletons of vertebrates)

hydro- = water (*hydrostatic skeleton:* a skeletal system composed of fluid held under pressure in a closed body compartment; the main skeleton of most cnidarians, flatworms, nematodes, and annelids)

myo- = myscle; **-fibro** = fiber (*myofibril:* a fibril collectively arranged in longitudinal bundles in muscle cells; composed of thin filaments of actin and a regulatory protein and thick filaments of myosin)

para- = near (*parasympathetic division:* one of two divisions of the autonomic nervous system)

sarco- = flesh; **-mere** = a part (*sarcomere:* the fundamental, repeating unit of striated muscle, delimited by the Z lines)

Lecture Outline

Introduction *Elephants Do the "Groucho Gait"*

 A. Gait analysis and the study of biomechanics began in the early 1900s with the research of Eadweard Muybridge. He used photography to explore movement. Recent studies that investigate movement are leading to new ways to help people who have difficulty (for a variety of reasons) moving.

 B. The ability to move at will (or by instinct) is a distinct feature of animals. Whether the organism is a small rodent or a giant elephant, movement is dependent on three organ systems interacting in a precise and orderly fashion.

  1. Movement is regulated by the nervous system, which can stimulate muscle contraction by sending signals (Module 28.1).

  2. Muscles respond to the signals by contracting, which causes the intended movement.

  3. The movement of the organism is dependent on a firm structure against which the force of contraction is applied.

I. Movement and Locomotion

 Module 30.1 Diverse means of animal locomotion have evolved.

  A. Animals move in a wide variety of ways: fly, crawl, swim, walk, run, and hop. The focus in this chapter is on **locomotion,** or the ability to move from place to place through the expenditure of energy. Locomotion in all its forms requires an animal to overcome two forces: friction and gravity.

  B. Some animals remain fixed in one place, letting the world come to them and, therefore, are not involved in locomotion. Sponges use flagellated collar cells to move water through their bodies. Some cnidarians (such as hydras) remain attached and move slowly during feeding activities.

  C. **Swimming:** Water supports against gravity but offers considerable frictional resistance. Swimming involves legs as oars (many aquatic insects and mammals), jet propulsion (squids), whole body side to side (fishes), and up and down (whales) (Figure 30.1A). A streamlined body is a common feature among aquatic animals.

D. **Locomotion on Land: Hopping, Walking, Running, and Crawling:** Land animals must not only overcome gravity, they must also maintain their balance whether moving forward or while at rest because air offers little support. Terrestrial locomotion includes hopping on springlike back legs, and quadrupedal or bipedal walking and running (and resting) (Figures 30.1B and C). Powerful muscles and strong supporting skeletons are common features among land animals.

E. There are some exceptions to the above statement. Animals that crawl (snakes and worms) must overcome considerable friction. These land animals crawl by undulating movements or by peristalsis. During peristalsis, longitudinal muscles shorten and thicken regions, while circular muscles constrict and elongate other regions. In an earthworm, bristles anchor the short, thick regions, and regions anterior to them lengthen (Figure 30.1D).

F. **Flying:** Air offers little resistance but provides little support. Flying (which is different from gliding) has evolved only in insects, reptiles (including birds), and mammals (bats). To fly, animals move wings in patterns that provide lift to overcome gravity. Bird wings have cross-sectional shapes of airfoils. Air flowing past an airfoil has lower pressure above relative to below, providing lift (Figure 30.1E).
NOTE: Insects, bats (most of the time), and some birds (hummingbirds) produce lift in a different way. Lift is created by fluttering (which is more like the lift a helicopter produces) or pushing their wings down against the air during a power stroke and slipping them up through the air during a return (nonpower) stroke. This type of flight enables these animals to hover, a feat the rest of the birds cannot do without fluttering, and then inefficiently. Some other animal groups (fishes, amphibians, and other mammals) have evolved gliding, which moves the animal through the air or water without producing lift.

G. All types of movement are based on either the contraction of microtubules (see cilia and flagella in Module 4.17) or the contraction of microfilaments (amoeboid movement and muscle contraction).

II. Skeletal Support

Module 30.2 Skeletons function in support, movement, and protection.

A. Skeletons have many functions, including support, protection of soft parts, and movement. There are three main types of skeletons: hydrostatic skeletons, exoskeletons, and endoskeletons.
NOTE: Skeletons can also play a role in mineral storage and blood cell production (Modules 23.15 and 30.4).

B. **Hydrostatic skeleton:** A hydrostatic skeleton consists of a volume of fluid held under pressure in a body compartment. Such skeletons work well for aquatic animals and animals that burrow by peristalsis. Earthworms have a body cavity filled with fluid (the coelom). A hydra counters muscle cell contractions against a hydrostatic skeleton of its closed gastrovascular cavity (Figure 30.2A).

C. **Exoskeleton:** An **exoskeleton** consists of a rigid, external, armorlike covering. Muscles are attached to the inner surface of the exoskeleton. At joints, the exoskeleton is thin and flexible. Clams and snails have exoskeletons (shells) that are enlarged by secretions from the body margin (mantle). The hollow, tubular exoskeletons of arthropods (Modules 18.11 and 18.12) are extremely light for their strength, but they do not grow with the animal. Periodically, during molting, the old skeleton is lost, and following body growth, a new skeleton is hardened (Figures 30.2B and C). At this time, these animals are particularly vulnerable to predators and remain so until the new exoskeleton hardens.

NOTE: Although most shell-bearing molluscs move by manipulating a muscular foot, the scallop moves by rapid opening and closing of its shells, producing a jet-propulsive movement that is somewhat random.

D. **Endoskeleton:** An endoskeleton consists of rigid, internal supports, usually consisting of noncellular material secreted by surrounding cells. Sponges support their cells on spicules. Spicules are made of materials such as calcium salts or silica. Echinoderms have an endoskeleton of calcium plates under their spines (Figure 30.2D). Vertebrates have endoskeletons made of cartilage or bone and cartilage (Figure 30.2E).

Module 30.3 The human skeleton is a unique variation on an ancient theme.

Review: Human evolution (Modules 19.1–19.8).

A. The basic skeletal pattern of vertebrates is modified according to the needs of each animal. For example, the frog sits on all four legs and hops using its powerful hind legs. A person sits on its hindquarters and walks upright.
Review: Primitive and derived characters (Module 15.8).

B. Despite the structural differences, most vertebrates share two similar skeletal features (Figure 30.3A).

1. The **axial skeleton** consists of a skull protecting the brain, the backbone (vertebral column) protecting the spinal cord and supporting the remaining skeletal elements, and the rib cage surrounding the lungs and heart.

2. The **appendicular skeleton** consists of the bones of the appendages (arms, legs, and fins) and the bones that link the appendages to the axial skeleton (the shoulder [pectoral] and pelvic girdles).
NOTE: The shoulder girdle consists of the clavicle and scapula. Coming off the shoulder girdle are the humerus, radius and ulna, carpals, metacarpals, and phalanges. The pelvic girdle is formed by the coxal bone (os coxa), which consists of three fused bones: the ilium, the ischium, and the pubis. Coming off the pelvic girdle are the femur, patella (kneecap), tibia and fibula, tarsals, metatarsals, and phalanges.
NOTE: A human skeleton can be determined to be that of a female or male by examining the pelvic girdle. There are several differences, but one of the easiest to use is the angle of the pubic arch. If the angle is between 80° and 90°, then it is the skeleton of a female; if the angle is between 50° and 60°, then it is the skeleton of a male.

C. Comparing the bipedal human skeleton with that of the quadrupedal baboon underscores the evolutionarily distinctive features. The human skull is large, flat-faced, and balanced on top of the backbone. The backbone is S-shaped. The pelvic girdle is shorter, rounder, and oriented vertically. The bones of the hands and feet are different. The hands are adapted for grasping and manipulating, and the feet are adapted to support the entire body bipedally (Figure 30.3B).

D. The versatility of the vertebrate skeleton comes in part from its movable joints. Joints are held together by strong, fibrous connective tissue called **ligaments.** There are three main types of joints (Figures 30.3C1–3):

1. **Ball-and-socket joints** allow movement in all directions.

2. **Hinge joints** are strong and restrict movement to one plane.

3. **Pivot joints** allow bones to rotate, providing ease of manipulation.

Module 30.4 Bones are complex living organs.

Review: Tissues, bone, and cartilage (Module 20.5) and the role of the thyroid and parathyroid glands in calcium homeostasis (Module 26.6).

A. Bones are composed of other tissues besides bone and cartilage. Bone tissues intermix with tissues of the circulatory system (vessels and blood) and nervous system (nerves) (Figure 30.4).

B. Most of the outside surface of a bone is covered with fibrous connective tissue. When bones break or crack, this tissue is able to form new bone through a process called remodeling.

C. At either end of most bones, cartilage replaces connective tissue, forming a surface that cushions the joint.

D. Bone is composed primarily of a hard, compression-resistant material made of calcium and phosphate. A fibrous connective tissue protein called collagen provides flexibility to the bone. Both materials in the bone are produced and maintained by living cells that surround themselves with bone matrix.

E. The shafts of long bones are made of compact bone, with a dense matrix surrounding a hollow cavity containing stored fat (**yellow bone marrow**). The ends of long bones are made of an outer layer of compact bone and an inner area of spongy bone. Within cavities in the matrix of the spongy bone, specialized tissues produce blood cells (**red bone marrow**).

NOTE: The cavity of long bones reduces the weight of the body and makes movement easier.

Module 30.5 Connection: Broken bones can heal themselves.

A. Bones have the capacity to flex to a slight degree, but when too much force is applied, they will break (Figure 30.5A). The average American will break two bones in his or her lifetime.

B. Two factors determine if a bone will break:
    1. The amount and angle of force applied to the bone.
    2. The strength of the skeleton.

C. Bone is a living, dynamic tissue that can heal itself if given the opportunity (e.g., a cast). However, sometimes the process requires surgical intervention (as seen in Figure 30.5A) in an effort to enhance the healing process. Once healed, bone is usually stronger than before the break.

D. Occasionally bone is too severely broken, fails to heal properly, or disease limits proper bone health, and the injured or diseased bone must be replaced with artificial parts or with bone grafts (Figure 30.5B).

Module 30.6 Connection: Weak, brittle bones are a serious health problem, even in young people.

A. **Osteoporosis** was once considered a disease of older women (postmenopausal), but recently more men and young people are being diagnosed with the disease. Osteoporosis is characterized by low bone mass and structural degeneration of the bone matrix.

B. The risk of bone fracture has risen recently, some speculate, because of changes in the lifestyle of many Americans. Changes in our diet, the lack of weight-bearing exercise, and an increase in diabetes are contributing to the rise in osteoporosis.

C. This disease can be treated with calcium, vitamin D, and drug therapy that reduces bone loss.

D. Lifestyle changes are also an important consideration, particularly for the young. Bone density is still increasing until age 30; therefore, calcium and weight-bearing exercise may help prevent osteoporosis.

III. Muscle Contraction and Movement

Module 30.7 The skeleton and muscles interact in movement.

A. Muscles are connected to bones by **tendons** (Module 20.6).
NOTE: At joints, bones are held together by ligaments.

B. A muscle can only contract. To extend, it must be pulled by the contraction of an opposing muscle. Thus, movements of most parts of the body require antagonistic pairs of muscles (Figure 30.7). Biceps and triceps are an antagonistic pair of muscles.
NOTE: Nerves that enervate antagonistic muscle pairs have a built-in circuitry that prevents both muscles of a pair from contracting at the same time (this is referred to as reciprocal innervation). A strong electrical shock can bypass this circuitry and cause both nerves to induce their muscles to contract at the same time. This can break bones. However, one can flex the arm and force both the biceps and triceps to contract.

Module 30.8 Each muscle cell has its own contractile apparatus.

A. **Skeletal muscle** (striated muscle) tissue was introduced in Module 20.6 (Figure 20.6A).

B. Each muscle fiber is a single cell with many nuclei. Within each fiber are numerous long **myofibrils** (Figure 30.8).

C. A myofibril is composed of contracting units called **sarcomeres,** joined end to end at Z lines.

D. Each sarcomere is composed of **thin filaments** (coiled strands of two actin proteins and one regulatory protein) and **thick filaments** (parallel strands of myosin protein). This structure produces a pattern of light and dark bands in the muscle tissue. The dark bands consist of thick filaments and thin filaments, which do not extend to the center of the dark band. The light bands have only thin filaments and straddle the Z lines that connect adjacent thin filaments.
NOTE: The regulatory protein wrapped around actin is actually two proteins, a complex of troponin and tropomyosin. Tropomyosin physically blocks binding sites for myosin on actin. These sites are unblocked when Ca^{2+} binds to troponin, forcing a conformational change, which, in turn, moves tropomyosin from its position blocking the binding sites (Module 30.9). This mechanism works essentially the same way in cardiac muscle fibers.

Module 30.9 A muscle contracts when thin filaments slide across thick filaments.

A. The **sliding-filament model** of muscle contraction relates the structure of muscle to its function.

B. Contraction shortens the sarcomere but does not shorten the thick and thin filaments, which slide between each other (Figures 30.8 and 30.9A).

C. Energy-consuming interactions between the myosin molecules of the thick filaments and the actin molecules of the thin filaments cause them to slide along one another. The process occurs in four steps (Figure 30.9B):

1. ATP attaches to the myosin head and is hydrolyzed to ADP, releasing the head from the actin.

2. The myosin head–ADP complex is a high-energy conformation (extended configuration).

3. The complex binds to a new site on the actin filament.

4. Binding causes the ADP to disassociate, and the myosin head reverts back to its low energy conformation (the power stroke).

D. The myosin molecules of the thick filament expose about 350 swollen "heads" per filament. Each head can repeatedly move at about five movements per second.

E. The process continues (detach-extend-attach-pull, detach-extend-attach-pull) as long as ATP is available, the muscle is fully contracted, or until the muscle fiber is signaled to stop contracting.

Module 30.10 Motor neurons stimulate muscle contraction.

Review: Neuron structure and function (Module 28.2).

A. Each muscle fiber is stimulated by just one neuron, but a single neuron can stimulate many fibers, up to several hundred in a large muscle moving the appendicular skeleton. Each such group of muscle fibers is known as a **motor unit** because each is stimulated to contract together (Figure 30.10A).
NOTE: The fewer the number of muscle fibers per motor unit, the greater the degree of fine control over the muscle.

B. A weak contraction is produced by the stimulation of one motor unit. A strong contraction involves the simultaneous contractions of several motor units.

C. The synapses between neuron and muscle fiber are called **neuromuscular junctions.** The action potential is transmitted to the fiber through the release of the neurotransmitter acetylcholine.
Review: Synapses and neurotransmitters (Modules 28.6–28.8).

D. At the cellular level, muscle fiber stimulation proceeds as follows. The released acetylcholine changes the permeability of the muscle fiber's plasma membrane. This induces an action potential along the muscle cell membrane and into the membranous tubular that folds inward into the cell. Within the cell, the action potentials cause the endoplasmic reticulum (ER) to release Ca^{2+} into the cytoplasm. Calcium removes the regulatory protein on actin, thus triggering the binding of myosin to actin. When action potentials stop, Ca^{2+} moves back into the ER, allowing the regulatory protein to bind actin, causing the muscle to relax (Figure 30.10B).

Module 30.11 Connection: Athletic training increases strength and endurance.

A. Hallmarks of an elite athlete are mental toughness and the ability to ignore muscle pain and fatigue. The type of training program used by elite athletes helps prepare them for enduring great mental and physical exertion.

B. Recall that the source of energy that muscles use is in the form of ATP generated from glucose in the process of aerobic respiration. Endurance improves with aerobic exercise training programs. Aerobic exercise increases blood flow and mitochondria size, and strengthens the heart and circulatory system. Bone mass and strength also increase. But aerobic exercise must be balanced with anaerobic exercise.

C. Anaerobic exercise increases muscle power and mass. Anaerobic exercise is designed to push muscle contraction to its maximum, creating an oxygen deficit and, therefore, forcing anaerobic respiration.

D. Elite athletes use balanced exercise programs ("cross-training") in an effort to increase muscle endurance, strength, and power (Figure 30.11). Even though most people will never be classified as an elite athlete, a well-balanced workout program that includes both aerobic and anaerobic exercise can improve cardiovascular health and overall body strength.

Module 30.12 The structure-function theme underlies all the parts and activities of an animal.

A. A baseball game, with its requirement for split-second decisions and precise actions, demonstrates some of the remarkable evolutionary adaptations of the human body (Figure 30.12).

B. The sequence of events that lead to the hitter making contact with the ball and the shortstop catching the ball are truly remarkable. Both players use photoreceptors to see the ball; the information is integrated in the brain through interneurons. The brain receives auditory input and integrates this information with that of the eyes. A signal from the brain tells the players' muscles how to respond. The ball is hit and then caught by the shortstop.

C. The action of the baseball field results from the nervous system responding to sensory input, sending signals to the muscles, which contract against skeletal structure resulting in rapid and precise movements.

D. The above sequence is a testament to the adaptation process, refined through natural selection, leading to the survival of our species.

Class Activities

1. Students always enjoy seeing X-rays of broken bones; the worse the break, the more they enjoy it. See if you can find a series that illustrates the various stages of the healing of a broken bone. In such a series you can see the less dense new bone become increasingly dense.

2. Ask your class how the structure of the human skeleton reflects the evolutionary history of the lineage that led to humans. Ask them how they could improve upon the structure of the human skeleton; please ask them what improvements would help prevent some of the problems associated with aging.

3. The demonstrations of skeletal structures, joints, and antagonistic muscles will be much easier, and more dramatic, if you refer to a human skeleton (and, for the material in Figure 30.3B, a baboon skeleton). Some demonstration skeletons show antagonistic muscle insertions. If one is not available, use differently colored cords to demonstrate the locations and functions of antagonistic muscles on the upper arm or leg.

4. To demonstrate the function of hydrostatic skeletons and peristaltic movement, use earthworms on an overhead projector. Place them briefly in a shallow bowl of cool water. The light and temperature of the overhead will cause them to move rapidly away from the projector's heat. Other means of invertebrate movement, such as in shrimp or bivalve mollusks, can also be demonstrated in this way. Worms are available in bait stores or backyard compost piles. The other animals may not be available in all locations.

5. Many students will be interested in the human muscle groups from an athletic and/or body-building perspective. Have a local orthopedic surgeon describe and demonstrate the areas of human musculoskeletal anatomy that are especially vulnerable to injury.

Transparency Acetates

Figure 30.1D   An earthworm crawling by peristalsis

Figure 30.1E   A bald eagle in flight

Figure 30.2E   Bone (tan) and cartilage (blue) in the endoskeleton of a vertebrate: a frog

Figure 30.3A   The human skeleton

Figure 30.3B   Bipedal and quadrupedal primate skeletons compared

Figure 30.3C   Three kinds of joints

Figure 30.4   The structure of an arm bone

Figure 30.7   Antagonistic action of muscles in the human arm

Figure 30.8   The contractile apparatus of skeletal muscle

Figure 30.9A   The sliding-filament model of muscle contraction

Figure 30.9B   The mechanism of filament sliding (Layer 1)

Figure 30.9B   The mechanism of filament sliding (Layer 2)

Figure 30.9B   The mechanism of filament sliding (Layer 3)

Figure 30.9B   The mechanism of filament sliding (Layer 4)

Figure 30.10A   The relation between motor neurons and muscle fibers

Figure 30.10B   Part of a muscle fiber (cell) at a neuromuscular junction (combined with Figure 30.10A)

Reviewing the Concepts, page 619: Locomotion in animals

Reviewing the Concepts, page 619: The sliding-filament model

Connecting the Concepts, page 619: Animal movement

Media

See the beginning of this book for a complete description of all media available for instructors and students. Animations and videos are available in the Campbell Image Presentation Library. Media Activities and Thinking as a Scientist investigations are available on the student CD-ROM and website.

Animations and Videos

	Module Number
Earthworm Locomotion Video	30.1
Flapping Geese Video	30.1
Soaring Hawk Video	30.1
Swans Taking Flight Video	30.1
Muscle Contraction Animation	30.9

Activities and Thinking as a Scientist

	Module Number
Web/CD Activity 30A: *The Human Skeleton*	30.3
Web/CD Activity 30B: *Skeletal Muscle Structure*	30.8
Web/CD Activity 30C: *Muscle Contraction*	30.10
Web/CD Thinking as a Scientist: *How Do Electrical Stimuli Affect Muscle Contraction?*	30.10

CHAPTER 31

Plant Structure, Reproduction, and Development

Teaching Objectives

Introduction Explain how angiosperms impact human life.

31.1 Define the field of systems biology, and explain how the study of *Arabidopsis* can be useful in crop plant production.

Plant Structure and Function

31.2 Compare the structures of monocots and dicots.

31.3 Compare the structures and functions of root and shoot systems. Explain how "pinching back" a plant helps make a plant bushier.

31.4 Distinguish among a taproot, runner, rhizome, tuber, bulb, petiole, and tendril, and indicate common examples of each from a vegetable garden.

31.5 Describe the general structure of plant cells. Describe the three unique plant cell structures not found in animal cells.

31.5 Compare the structures and functions of parenchyma, collenchyma, sclerenchyma, water-conducting, and food-conducting cells. Also compare the structures and functions of xylem and phloem.

31.6 Compare the structures and functions of the dermal tissue system, vascular tissue system, and ground tissue system of young dicot roots, stems, and leaves. Compare the structures of the stem of a young dicot and young monocot.

Plant Growth

31.7 Distinguish between and among (a) indeterminate versus determinate growth and (b) annuals, biennials, and perennials.

31.7–31.8 Describe and compare primary and secondary growth. Explain how a tree grows, the location of the new and old tissues, and how tree rings are produced.

Reproduction of Flowering Plants

31.9 Describe the parts of a flower and their functions. Relate this structure to the overall life cycle of an angiosperm.

31.10 Describe the processes and events that lead to double fertilization. Describe the advantages of double fertilization.

31.11 Explain how a seed forms. Compare the structures of dicot and monocot seeds, and explain the significance of seed dormancy.

31.12 Describe the formation and functions of fruit. Distinguish among simple fruits, aggregate fruits, and multiple fruits.

31.13 Describe and compare germination in pea and corn plants.

31.14 Describe four examples of vegetative reproduction in plants. Describe the advantages of asexual versus sexual reproduction.

31.15 Explain how genetic engineering has transformed agriculture.

Key Terms

aggregate fruit	ground tissue system	secondary growth
annuals	guard cells	secondary phloem
anther	heartwood	secondary xylem
apical dominance	indeterminate growth	seed coat
apical meristems	internodes	seed dormancy
axillary buds	lateral meristem	sepals
bark	leaves	shoot system
biennials	meristem	sieve plates
carpel	mesophyll	sieve-tube members
clone	monocot	simple fruit
collenchyma cells	monocultures	sporophyte
companion cell	multiple fruit	stamen
cork	nodes	stems
cork cambium	ovary	stigma
cortex	ovules	stomata
cotyledons	parenchyma cells	terminal bud
cuticle	perennials	tissue system
dermal tissue system	petals	tracheids
determinate growth	phloem	tubers
dicot	pith	vascular bundles
double fertilization	pollination	vascular cambium
embryo sac	primary growth	vascular tissue system
endodermis	primary phloem	vegetative propagation
endosperm	primary xylem	vein
epidermis	rhizomes	vessel elements
fiber	root cap	water-conducting cells
food-conducting cells	root hairs	wood
fragmentation	root system	wood rays
fruit	sapwood	xylem
gametophyte	sclereids	
germinate	sclerenchyma cells	

Word Roots

apic- = the tip; **meristo-** = divided (*apical meristems:* embryonic plant tissue on the tips of roots and in the buds of shoots that supplies cells for the plant to grow)

bienn- = every 2 years (*biennial:* a plant that requires two years to complete its life cycle)

coll- = glue; **-enchyma** = an infusion (*collenchyma cell:* a flexible plant cell type that occurs in strands or cylinders that support young parts of the plant without restraining growth)

dorm- = sleep (*dormancy:* a condition typified by extremely low metabolic rate and a suspension of growth and development)

endo- = inner; **derm-** = skin (*endodermis:* the innermost layer of the cortex in plants roots)

epi- = over (*epidermis:* the dermal tissue system in plants; the outer covering of animals)

gamet- = a wife or husband (*gametophyte:* the multicellular haploid form in organisms undergoing alternation of generations, which mitotically produces haploid gametes that unite and grow into the sporophyte generation)

inter- = between (*internode:* the segment of a plant stem between the points where leaves are attached)

meso- = middle; **-phyll** = a leaf (*mesophyll:* the ground tissue of a leaf, sandwiched between the upper and lower epidermis and specialized for photosynthesis)

perenni- = through the year (*perennial:* a plant that lives for many years)

phloe- = the bark of a tree (*phloem:* the portion of the vascular system in plants consisting of living cells arranged into elongated tubes that transport sugar and other organic nutrients throughout the plant)

proto- = first; **-plast** = formed, molded (*protoplast:* the contents of a plant cell exclusive of the cell wall)

sclero- = hard (*sclereid:* a short, irregular sclerenchyma cell in nutshells and seed coats and scattered through the parenchyma of some plants)

sporo- = a seed; = **-phyto** = a plant (*sporophyte:* the multicellular diploid form in organisms undergoing alternation of generations that results from a union of gametes and that meiotically produces haploid spores that grow into the gametophyte generation)

stam- = standing upright (*stamen:* the pollen-producing male reproductive organ of a flower, consisting of an anther and filament)

xyl- = wood (*xylem:* the tube-shaped, nonliving portion of the vascular system in plants that carries water and minerals from the roots to the rest of the plant)

Lecture Outline

Introduction *A Gentle Giant*

    A. Plants are unique organisms.
      Review: Basic characteristics of the plant kingdom (Module 17.1).

      1. Examining the giant sequoia, *Sequoiadendron gigantea,* helps underscore the unique capabilities and adaptations of plants. The tree known as General Sherman is the largest individual plant on Earth: 84 m tall, 10 m in diameter at the base, first branch at 40 m, weighing about 1,400 tons, and alive for about 2,500 years (chapter-opening photos).

      2. Humans depend on plants for a variety of needs (e.g., lumber, fabric, paper, and food), and many other organisms depend on them for nutrition and shelter.
        NOTE: Despite the importance of plants, on a worldwide basis, slightly more photosynthesis is carried out by photosynthetic protists (algae) and bacteria of aquatic habitats.

      3. Giant sequoias are gymnosperms (naked seeds; Modules 17.7 and 17.8). Because angiosperms (covered seeds; Modules 17.9–17.13) make up 90% of the world's plant species, they are the focus of this chapter.
        Review: Module 17.3 discusses the basic differences between gymnosperms and angiosperms.

    Module 31.1 Talking About Science: Plant scientist Natasha Raikhel studies the *Arabidopsis* plant as a model biological system.

      A. Dr. Natasha Raikhel is the Distinguished Professor of Plant Cell Biology at the University of California, Riverside. She recently received an award from the American Society of Cell Biology for her work on the mustard seed plant, *Arabidopsis* (Figure 31.1B).

      B. Raikhel uses the mustard seed plant to study biological systems and the structure-function relationship in plants. Raikhel is a leader in the field of plant cell biology, and she also loves to share her enthusiasm for plants with her students (Figure 31.1A).

I. Plant Structure and Function

Module 31.2 The two major groups of angiosperms are the monocots and the dicots.

A. **Monocots** include orchids, bamboos, palms, lilies, and grasses (including most of the agricultural, grain-producing plants). They are distinguished by having one seed leaf **(cotyledon)** but also usually have parallel-veined leaves, scattered vascular bundles in stems, floral parts in multiples of three, and fibrous root systems (Figure 31.2).

B. Most angiosperms are **dicots.** Dicots include most shrubs and trees (except conifers) and many herbaceous plants, including many food plants and plants domesticated for their fibers. They are distinguished by having two cotyledons but also usually have net-veined leaves, vascular bundles in a ring in stems, floral parts in multiples of four or five, and taproot systems.

C. Careful analysis of plant structure often reveals its function. Conversely, function provides insight into the logic of a plant's structure.

Module 31.3 A typical plant body consists of roots and shoots.

A. Plants, like animals, have a hierarchical structure; plants are made of organs, organs are made of tissues, and tissues are made of cells.

B. Plant structural adaptations allow them to function in terrestrial habitats without drying out. Functionally, plants need to absorb water and minerals from the soil, CO_2 from the air, and light from the sun. Plants must then create the necessary body parts from the raw materials and from the products of photosynthesis.

C. The **root system** anchors the plant, absorbs and transports minerals and water, and stores food. The fibrous roots of monocots, and the taproot plus secondary roots of dicots, are effective in anchoring and absorption. The focal point of absorption is the **root hair,** an outgrowth of the epidermal cells that increases the surface area for the absorption of water and minerals (Figure 31.3).
Preview: Most plants are also aided in nutrient uptake by mycorrhizal fungi (Module 32.12, Chapter 17 Opening Essay).

D. The **shoot system** consists of supporting stems, photosynthetic leaves, and reproductive structures (in angiosperms, flowers). **Stems** are composed of **nodes,** where leaves, flowers, or other stems are attached, and **internodes. Leaves** are composed of photosynthetic blades and short stalks that join the blade to the stem's nodes.

E. Buds are undeveloped shoots that contain potential nodes, internodes, and leaves. Two types occur: The **terminal bud** at the plant apex is the source of growth in height. The **axillary buds,** one in each angle formed by a leaf and the stem, are usually dormant but can produce new branches that add to a plant's width.

F. **Apical dominance** results from the release of hormones from terminal buds that inhibits the growth of the axillary buds. One can cause a plant to be bushier by removing the terminal bud (pinching back), thereby stimulating (removing the inhibition of) the development of the axillary buds.

Module 31.4 Many plants have modified roots, stems, and leaves.

A. In many dicots (e.g., carrots, turnips, beets, and sweet potatoes), food is stored in modified taproots (Figure 31.4A). Plants store carbohydrates, in the form of starch, as a source of food in these structures. Plants use the stored starch for flowering and fruit production.
NOTE: Animals store carbohydrate in the form of glycogen (Module 21.11).

B. Stems can be modified for several purposes. Strawberries make runners (or stolon) that provide a mean for asexual reproduction. **Rhizomes** (e.g., iris and ginger) and **tubers** (e.g., potatoes) are underground stems that store starch (Figure 31.4B).

C. Leaves may also be modified from their photosynthetic function. Some leaf bases (e.g., celery) store food. Tendrils (e.g., vetch) are modified for grasping and climbing. Spines (e.g., cactus) are modified for protection (Figure 31.4C).

Module 31.5 Plant cells and tissues are diverse in structure and function.

A. Plant cells have many of the same features as animal cells. Plants have three unique features.

1. Many are photosynthetic and contain chloroplasts.

2. They often have a large, central vacuole that helps support the cell (and plant tissues) by maintaining cell turgor (Module 5.17).

3. Plant cells have a cell wall composed mainly of cellulose that surrounds the plasma membrane.

B. Most plant cells that provide support have an additional, stronger secondary wall hardened with lignin that is laid down inside the primary wall. Pits with cytoplasmically continuous plasmodesmata (Module 4.19) often interconnect adjacent cells (Figure 31.5A).

C. Plant cells can be grouped into five types based upon the structure and function of the cells.

1. **Parenchyma cells** are the most abundant, unspecialized cells, with only primary walls that are thin and flexible. They function in food storage, photosynthesis, and aerobic respiration (Figure 31.5B). Parenchyma cells can differentiate into any other plant cell type.

2. **Collenchyma cells** resemble parenchyma cells but lack secondary walls and have thicker primary walls that are uneven. They provide flexible support for young parts of plants that are still growing (Figure 31.5C).

3. **Sclerenchyma cells** have thick, rigid primary walls, hardened with lignin, and uneven secondary walls. They function in support and protection. Lignin is the main chemical component of wood. There are two types of sclerenchymal cell. **Fibers** are long, slender, and arranged in bundles. Hemp fiber is a good example. **Sclereids** are short cells with thick, irregular, and very hard secondary walls. Sclereids are in many seed coats, nutshells, and the gritty texture of the soft tissue of pears (Figure 31.5D).

4. **Water-conducting cells** have rigid secondary walls containing lignin, and function only when dead and connected end to end. **Tracheids** are long, thin cells with tapered ends, covered with open pits. **Vessel elements** are wider, shorter, less tapered, and have completely open ends (Figure 31.5E). Either type of cell, as the name implies, forms a system of tubers that transports water from the roots to the stems and leaves.

5. **Food-conducting cells (sieve-tube members)** are also arranged end to end but have relatively thin primary walls and no secondary walls. They are alive but lack nuclei and ribosomes. The end of each cell forms a **sieve plate** containing numerous pits with plasmodesmata. Each food-conducting cell is found in association with at least one **companion cell** that makes certain proteins for it.

D. Plant cells are grouped into tissues. Two types of vascular tissues are as follows: **Xylem** tissue is largely composed of water-conducting cells. **Phloem** tissue is largely composed of these food-conducting cells. Both types of vascular tissue have other cells, for example, sclerenchyma cells for support and parenchyma cells for storage.
Preview: Xylem and phloem function (Modules 32.3 and 32.5).

Module 31.6 Three tissue systems make up the plant body.

A. Plants have three tissue systems, each made of one or more tissue type. The plant organs (roots, stems, and leaves) are made of all three tissue systems.

   1. The **dermal tissue system** is the skinlike first defense against damage or infection. In many plants, this tissue system is composed of a single surrounding layer of cells called an **epidermis.** The epidermis of leaves and most stems is covered with a **cuticle** (waxy coating) to prevent water loss.

   2. The **vascular tissue system,** composed of xylem and phloem tissues, conducts water and nutrients throughout the plant. This tissue system also provides support.

   3. The **ground tissue system** fills the spaces between the epidermis and vascular tissue system in young plants and functions variously in photosynthesis, storage, and support.

B. Each tissue system is continuous from organ to organ throughout the plant (Figure 31.6A).

C. Roots are surrounded by epidermal cells with root hairs and without a cuticle. Water and minerals must be absorbed through the epidermis. The ground tissue system forms the **cortex,** which functions in conducting materials from the root surface into the central vascular tissue and in food storage. The inner layer of the cortex is the **endodermis.** It provides a selective barrier, regulating flow into the vascular tissue (Figure 31.6A). *Preview:* Solute uptake is controlled by the plasma membranes of root cells (Module 32.2).

D. Stems of dicots and monocots differ in the relative distributions of ground tissue and vascular tissue systems. However, both types of plants have their vascular tissue systems arranged in **vascular bundles.** Monocots have vascular bundle tissues scattered in a more uniform ground tissue. A dicot has bundles of vascular tissue in an outer ring supported in a ring of ground tissue cortex that surrounds a food storage region called the **pith** (Figure 31.6A).

E. Leaves have a complex arrangement of the three tissue types that perfectly fit their function of photosynthesis. The epidermis contains **guard cells** that form a pore or **stomata** (singular, *stoma*) (Module 32.4).

F. The ground tissue system is the layer between two epidermal layers and is called the **mesophyll.** The mesophyll contains mostly photosynthetic parenchyma cells. The lower mesophyll is loosely arranged, particularly near the stomata, where most gas exchange takes place.

G. Tiny branches, or **veins,** make up the vascular tissue system of leaves and are continuous with the vascular bundles of stems. Each vein has xylem and phloem and is in close contact with photosynthetic cells providing minerals and water from the soil and removing the sugars to be transported to the rest of the plant.

II. Plant Growth

Module 31.7 Primary growth lengthens roots and shoots.

A. Unlike animals that have a **determinate growth** and only grow to a certain size, plants have **indeterminate growth;** that is, they continue to grow during their entire lives. Animals can move through their surroundings (Chapter 30), but individual plants must grow to reach other places in their environments.

B. Three seasonal growth patterns occur in plants. **Annuals** complete their life cycle in one year. **Biennials** complete their life cycle in two years. **Perennials** continue to live and reproduce for many years.

C. Indeterminate growth is the result of plants having **meristems,** unspecialized cells that continue to give rise to new cells. **Apical meristems** are found at the root and shoot tips and in axillary buds. The lengthwise growth produced by these regions is **primary growth** (Figure 31.7A). The mechanism of primary growth differs between roots and shoots.

D. The apical meristem in the root tip is covered by a **root cap** that is sloughed off during growth through abrasive soil. Just above the meristem, these tissues elongate, pushing the root tip downward.

E. The cells behind the meristem grow through three successive stages of primary growth but with no distinct boundaries:

1. Zone of cell division—includes cells of the root apical meristem and cells derived from the meristem; cells of the root cap and new root cells come from this zone.

2. Zone of elongation—root cells elongate up to ten times their original length. Elongation by water uptake is responsible for the downward progression of the root. Expansion in width is limited by the parallel arrangement of cellulose fibers.

3. Zone of maturation—the three tissue systems (dermal, ground, and vascular) develop here based on differential gene expression. The cells of the vascular cylinder differentiate into **primary xylem** and **primary phloem** (Figure 31.7B).

F. The apical meristem of the shoot is a dome-shaped mass of dividing cells at the end of the terminal bud. Elongation occurs below the terminal bud, forcing it upward. Some of the apical meristem cells remain in lateral positions and develop the apical meristems in axillary buds (Figure 31.7C).

Preview: The hormonal basis of shoot growth is discussed in Module 33.2.

Module 31.8 Secondary growth increases the girth of woody plants.

A. **Secondary growth** involves growth in stems and roots that causes thickening. It is most evident in trees, shrubs, and vines. The increase in diameter is due to another type of meristem called **lateral meristems,** which are composed of two types of dividing cells.

B. The **vascular cambium** is a cylindrical meristem that develops from two layers of parenchyma cells between the xylem and phloem of shoots. As cells in this vascular cambium divide inward, they form new layers of **secondary xylem** to the outside of the primary xylem. As cells of the vascular cambium divide outward, they form new layers of **secondary phloem** inside the primary phloem. The increase in thickness of the stem is mostly layers of secondary xylem, which form the **wood** of a tree, shrub, or vine (Figure 31.8A).

C. In regions that have distinct seasons, secondary xylem cells are larger in diameter during periods of favorable growth (early wood, growth during the spring) and smaller at other times (late summer). This results in distinct annual growth rings (Figure 31.8B).

D. The new layers of phloem external to the vascular cambium do not accumulate but are sloughed off in **bark** at about the same rate they are produced. Bark includes the secondary phloem, the cork cambium, and the cork. **Cork cambium** (a meristem tissue) is derived from parenchyma cells in the cortex and makes **cork.** Mature cork cells are dead and have waxy, thick walls that protect the stem surface from damage and infection, much like epidermal cells. However, they eventually slough off as new cork cambium develops within deeper layers (Figure 31.8B).

NOTE: This also provides a way for a woody plant to increase the circumference of its protective layer as the diameter of the stem increases.

E. Wood itself can be divided into central **heartwood,** xylem that no longer functions in transport because it is plugged with resins, and **sapwood,** younger secondary xylem that actually conducts water and minerals (xylem sap). **Wood rays** are collections of parenchyma cells that extend laterally from heartwood into the sapwood, providing channels between these two regions. The heartwood of trees acts as an endoskeleton, providing a strong, rigid, yet flexible core upon which the living plant substance is supported.

F. Wood is the source of many products useful to humans. As a building material, it is unmatched for its combination of strength, hardness, lightness, insulating properties, durability, workability, and beauty.

III. Reproduction of Flowering Plants

Review: Features of angiosperms (Modules 17.9–17.12).

Module 31.9 Overview: The sexual life cycle of a flowering plant.

A. A flower is the reproductive shoot of an angiosperm composed of modified leaves (sepals, petals, stamens, and carpels) (Figure 31.9A).

B. **Sepals** are usually green and protect flower buds. **Petals** are usually large and showy and attract pollinators.

C. **Stamens** are male structures with pollen-bearing **anthers** at the tip. Pollen grains deliver sperm nuclei to females.

D. **Carpels** are female structures composed of **stigma** and an **ovary.** Inside the ovary are the ovules, which carry the developing egg and supporting cells.

E. Pollination occurs when pollen is delivered to the stigma of another flower. Fertilization occurs in the ovule. The fertilized egg develops into an embryo, and the ovule develops into a seed that holds the embryo. The ovary develops into a fruit that aids in seed dispersal. The seed **germinates** in a favorable environment to complete the life cycle (Figure 31.9B).

Module 31.10 The development of pollen and ovules culminates in fertilization.

A. All plants, including angiosperms, alternate between diploid **sporophytes** that produce spores by meiosis (spores then divide mitotically and develop into a gametophyte) and haploid **gametophytes** that produce gametes by mitosis. The gametes unite by fertilization to form a diploid zygote, which is the first cell of the next sporophyte generation. *Review:* Diploid and haploid generations of plants (Module 17.4).

B. The mature plant we see is the sporophyte. Angiosperm gametophytes are microscopic and are found inside the flower parts (Figure 31.10).

C. The male gametophyte is the two-celled pollen grain. It develops into spores following meiosis of cells in the anther. Each resulting spore divides mitotically to produce two haploid cells, a tube cell and a generative cell. The outer wall of the pollen grain is thick and resistant.

D. The female gametophyte develops inside the ovule, a central cell surrounded by a coating of smaller cells. The central cell undergoes meiosis, but only one of the resulting haploid nuclei develops into a spore. The nucleus in the haploid spore enlarges and divides mitotically, forming the **embryo sac.** The embryo sac, housed in and protected by the sporophyte, is the female gametophyte. The embryo sac contains a large central cell with two haploid nuclei. Another of the cells is the haploid egg. All this happens in specialized ovary tissue at the base of the carpel.

E. **Pollination** is the delivery of pollen to a stigma. Pollen is usually wind- or animal-dispersed (Module 17.13).

F. After pollination, the pollen grain germinates and the tube cell grows its pollen tube downward into the stigma and ovary. The generative cell divides mitotically, forming two sperm nuclei. At the base of the ovule, the pollen tube releases both sperm nuclei.

G. The **double fertilization** that follows is a hallmark of the angiosperms. One sperm nucleus fertilizes the egg, forming the zygote ($2n$, diploid) that will develop into the embryo. The other sperm nucleus fuses with the two central nuclei, forming a triploid ($3n$) nucleus that will develop into the endosperm, tissue that nourishes the embryo.

Module 31.11 The ovule develops into a seed.

A. Within the ovule, the triploid cell develops into a nutrient-rich **endosperm,** and repeated division of the diploid zygote leads to the development of an embryo (Figure 31.11A). *NOTE:* Be sure to point out that the ovule includes everything inside the original coating of small cells that surrounded the cell that underwent meiosis to form, ultimately, the eight haploid nuclei, including the egg. All nuclei other than the zygote and endosperm do not develop further.

B. The embryo develops when the zygote first divides into two cells. One of the cells becomes the embryo. The other cell divides and becomes a thread that forces the embryo into the endosperm. Near the end of maturation, the seed loses water and develops a resistant **seed coat.**

C. **Seed dormancy** occurs when the seed develops up to a point and then further growth and development are suspended. This allows time for dispersal and for the seasonal occurrence of conditions favorable for independent growth.

D. Seeds of dicots (common bean) have two fleshy cotyledons that have absorbed the endosperm nutrients and taken over the role of nourishment. The seed of a monocot is actually a fruit with one seed. The fruit of maize (a kernel) has one cotyledon, a protective sheath over the embryonic root and shoot, and contains a large endosperm (Figure 31.11B).

Module 31.12 The ovary develops into a fruit.

A. The ovary of a flower changes into a fruit when hormones are released during fertilization. A **fruit** houses and protects seeds and helps disperse them. During development, hormonal changes make the ovary grow and thicken.

B. Pod formation follows several steps:
1. Pollination must take place first.
2. Petals drop from the flower, the ovaries start to grow, and the walls thicken.
3. The ovaries form a pod (or a fruit).

C. Fruits are highly varied in organization, depending on how many ovules, how many ovaries, how many carpels, or how many flowers are involved in the formation, and on the ultimate means of dispersal (wind, water, or animal).

D. A peach or peapod are examples of a **simple fruit** (Figures 31.12A and B).

E. A raspberry is an example of an **aggregate fruit,** fruit that develops from many united carpels.

F. A pineapple is an example of a **multiple fruit,** fruit that develops from many united flowers (Figure 31.12C).
NOTE: Plums and avocados are fruits with single seeds. The winged maple "seed" and plumed dandelion "seed" are examples of fruits modified for wind dispersal. The seed of each is at the heavy end of the fruit.

Module 31.13 Seed germination continues the life cycle.

A. New plant life does not start with seed germination. Seed dormancy is discontinued when conditions are acceptable for growth to resume. A previously developed embryo starts developing again when the seed takes up water, expands, and ruptures its coat. Endosperm or cotyledons begin to enzymatically digest stored nutrients, and the nutrients are transported to the growing parts.

B. In dicots, the embryonic root emerges first, followed by young shoots that exit the seed in a hooked shape that protects the terminal meristem from abrasion by soil particles. Once the shoot clears the soil surface, light stimulates the hook to straighten, and the first foliage leaves develop at the tip and begin photosynthesis (Figure 31.13A). In the pea, the cotyledons, having provided food for the germinating embryo, remain in the soil and decompose.

C. In monocots, the embryonic root emerges first, followed by young shoots that do not develop a hook. However, the shoots are protected from abrasion by a sheath that surrounds them until they break through the soil surface. The maize cotyledon remains in the soil and decomposes (Figure 31.13B).

D. The process of reproduction is a perilous journey for a seedling. Production of seeds in great quantities helps ensure the survival of the next generation of plants.

Module 31.14 Asexual reproduction produces plant clones.

Review: Asexual and sexual reproduction (Chapter 8 Opening Essay and Module 27.1).

A. **Vegetative propagation** (or asexual reproduction) is the production of offspring from a single parent. The offspring from asexual reproduction are called **clones** and are genetically identical to the original plant.
Review: Animal reproduction by fragmentation is discussed in Module 27.1.

B. Asexual reproduction is an extension of a plant's ability to grow throughout its life. The meristem tissue and parenchyma cells are capable of sustaining life indefinitely.

C. Asexual reproduction often involves **fragmentation** (e.g., garlic) into separate parts; each regenerates into a new plant. A garlic bulb is an underground stem that will fragment into cloves giving rise to several new plants (Figure 31.14A). A root sprout of a coast redwood will grow to take the place of the parent, if the parent is lost (Figure 31.14B). The creosote bush of southwestern deserts reproduces vegetatively from its roots, forming very old clones. (The one in Figure 31.14C is estimated at 12,000 years old.) Dune grass propagates by underground runners (Figure 31.14D).

D. There are several advantages to asexual reproduction. Offspring are well suited to their immediate environments. Early life for vegetative offspring is less hazardous than for seedlings because they are less fragile.

Module 31.15 Connection: Asexual reproduction is a mainstay of modern agriculture.

A. Many ornamental trees, shrubs, and houseplants are propagated by stem or leaf cuttings.

B. Plant tissue culture provides another way to grow offspring from a few meristematic cells (Figure 31.15), and this technique has been adapted to propagate genetically engineered plant cells. The addition of a foreign gene into a plant cell (parenchyma cell) results in a genetically modified (GM) plant. There are some environmental and health concerns related to GM plants (see Module 12.19).

C. Vegetative propagation has one main disadvantage: Crop plants developed from cloning processes have inherently low levels of genetic diversity, which exposes them to potential devastation from disease, especially when planted in **monoculture** (single plant species in a large area).

Class Activities

1. A thought experiment: Ask your students to consider what might be the evolutionary basis of the differences between monocots and dicots. Under what conditions might one be at an advantage over the other?

2. There really is no such thing as a vegetable. Have your students properly classify plant parts that are considered vegetables. For example, cucumbers are fruits, lettuce is a leaf, etc.

3. Bring in a variety of fruits and vegetables, and discuss the developmental source of the tissues in each, and their specific functions. Strawberries are separate fruits (the "seeds") on a modified flower receptacle (the red part). Coconuts have liquid endosperm. Some fruits have been bred without seeds (bananas, navel oranges, seedless grapes) and are propagated vegetatively. There is no end of interesting trivia in the produce section of your local grocery. Consult a botany text for further details.

4. The three-dimensional arrangements of tissue layers in roots, stems, and leaves are sometimes difficult to grasp from overhead transparencies alone. For smaller classes, the use of large models of these organs (available in most departments) will help show the three-dimensional arrangement of all the basic tissues, and their potential continuity from structure to structure. Secondary growth from the vascular and cork cambiums is also easier to demonstrate with models that show these structures. If you have a color video camera attachment on a dissecting microscope, cross sections of twigs of different age and of wood can be examined in front of a smaller lecture section (depending on your monitor size). This is particularly valuable once you have discussed the function of the two types of cambium using transparencies.

5. An interesting demonstration of the continuity of root and stem (and perhaps even leaf) vascular systems can be made by allowing a squash plant to decompose over winter. Pull up the old squash plant in your garden at the end of the summer and let it lie on the surface of the ground through the fall and into the following spring. Bacteria and fungi will decompose away the softer, cellulose walls first, leaving the pattern of the vascular bundles. At the junction of root and stem, quite a tangle occurs, but it is clear that the vascular systems of each part are completely connected. Be sure to discuss the biological process that resulted in this preparation.

Transparency Acetates

Figure 31.2	A comparison of monocots and dicots
Figure 31.3	The body plan of a flowering plant (a dicot)
Figure 31.5A	The structure of a plant cell
Figure 31.5B	Parenchyma cell
Figure 31.5C	Collenchyma cell (combined with Figure 31.5B)
Figure 31.5D	Sclerenchyma cells: fibers (left) and sclereids (right)
Figure 31.5E	Water-conducting cells
Figure 31.5F	Food-conducting cells (sieve-tube members)
Figure 31.6	The three tissue systems
Figure 31.7A	Locations of apical meristems, which are responsible for primary growth
Figure 31.7B	Primary growth of a root
Figure 31.7C	Primary growth of a shoot
Figure 31.8A	Secondary growth of a woody dicot stem
Figure 31.8B	Anatomy of a locust log

Figure 31.9A   The structure of a flower

Figure 31.9B   Life cycle of a generalized angiosperm

Figure 31.10   Gametophyte development and fertilization in an angiosperm (Layer 1)

Figure 31.10   Gametophyte development and fertilization in an angiosperm (Layer 2)

Figure 31.10   Gametophyte development and fertilization in an angiosperm (Layer 3)

Figure 31.11A   Development of a dicot plant embryo

Figure 31.11B   Seed structure

Figure 31.12B   The correspondence between flower and fruit in the pea plant

Figure 31.13A   Pea germination (a dicot)

Figure 31.13B   Corn germination (a monocot)

Reviewing the Concepts, page 642: Body plan of a typical flowering plant

---

Media

See the beginning of this book for a complete description of all media available for instructors and students. Animations and videos are available in the Campbell Image Presentation Library. Media Activities and Thinking as a Scientist investigations are available on the student CD-ROM and website.

Animations and Videos	Module Number
Root Growth in a Radish Seed Time-Lapse Video	31.9
Plant Fertilization Animation	31.10
Seed Development Animation	31.11
Fruit Development Animation	31.12

Activities and Thinking as a Scientist	Module Number
Web/CD Activity 31A: *Root, Stem, and Leaf Sections*	31.6
Web/CD Thinking as a Scientist: *What Are the Functions of Monocot Tissues?*	31.6
Web/CD Activity 31B: *Primary and Secondary Growth*	31.8
Web/CD Activity 31C: *Angiosperm Life Cycle*	31.10
Web/CD Activity 31D: *Seed and Fruit Development*	31.12
Web/CD Thinking as a Scientist: *What Tells Desert Seeds When to Germinate?*	31.13

CHAPTER 32

Plant Nutrition and Transport

Teaching Objectives

Introduction Describe the process, advantages, disadvantages, and examples of phytoremediation.

The Uptake and Transport of Plant Nutrients

32.1 Describe the experiments and conclusions of the work by van Helmont and Stephen Hales. Explain what happens to the materials that plants take up from the air and soil.

32.2 Compare the intracellular and extracellular routes of material movements into root xylem. Describe the function of the Casparian strip.

32.3 Explain how the transpiration-cohesion-tension mechanism causes the ascent of xylem sap in a plant.

32.4 Explain how guard cells control transpiration. Describe three cues that contribute to stomatal opening at dawn.

32.5 Explain how, when, and where phloem conducts sap.

Plant Nutrients and the Soil

32.6 Distinguish between micronutrients and macronutrients, and note examples of each. List the six macronutrients that make up about 98% of a plant's dry weight.

32.6 Explain how hydroponics help to determine which plant nutrients are essential.

32.7 Describe the signs of nitrogen, phosphorus, and potassium deficiency in plants.

32.8 Describe the properties of different soil layers. Explain how plants use cation exchange to absorb inorganic cations.

32.9 Explain how irrigation and the use of fertilizers impact agriculture. Describe techniques that minimize soil erosion and the buildup of salts in soils.

32.10 Compare the processes and products of organic and conventional agriculture.

32.11 Describe new strategies to improve the protein content of crops. Describe some of the benefits and concerns of genetic engineering of plants.

Plant Nutrition and Symbiosis

32.12 Explain how fungi help most plants absorb nutrients from the soil. Describe the significance of plant-fungus symbiosis to the evolution of life on land.

32.13 Explain how and why most plants depend upon bacteria to supply nitrogen.

32.14 Describe the special relationship between legumes and nitrogen-fixing bacteria.

32.15 Describe examples of parasitic and carnivorous plants. Explain why carnivorous plants are more commonly found in acid bogs.

Key Terms

adhesion	cohesion	macronutrients
Casparian strip	essential element	micronutrients
cation exchange	humus	mycorrhiza

nitrogen fixation	root pressure	transpiration
nodules	sugar sink	transpiration-cohesion-
phloem sap	sugar source	tension mechanism
pressure flow mechanism	topsoil	xylem sap

Word Roots

macro- = large (*macronutrient:* elements required by plants and animals in relatively large amounts)

micro- = small (*micronutrient:* elements required by plants and animals in very small amounts)

myco- = a fungus; **-rhizo** = a root (*mycorrhizae:* mutualistic associations of plant roots and fungi)

Lecture Outline

Introduction *Plants That Clean Up Poisons*

    A. Plants have an innate ability to accumulate metals at very high concentrations. Environmentalists use this unique characteristic when cleaning polluted soil and water (*phytoremediation*).

    B. Brake ferns (*Pteris vittata*) have been shown to preferentially absorb the toxin arsenic. This is very useful, particularly around wood treatment facilities that use arsenic. Other plants such as the sunflower have been used to clean up other environmentally hazardous sites. At the nuclear power plant in Chernobyl and at a car factory in Detroit, sunflowers were used to remove radioactive elements from water and lead from the soil.

    C. Phytoremediation is part of a broader technology called bioremediation, which uses prokaryotes and protists to clean toxic sites. Phytoremediation has several problems.

        1. The plants still need to be properly destroyed.

        2. There may be some evaporation of toxins through the leaves into the air.

        3. Animals that eat the toxic plants may be poisoned.

        4. The process is slow and may take several growing seasons.

I. The Uptake and Transport of Plant Nutrients

    Module 32.1 Plants acquire their nutrients from soil and air.

        A. *Review:* Mature plants are mostly composed of elements that were not obtained from soil, but rather CO_2 from the air and water from the soil. Also review the equation for photosynthesis (see Chapter 7, particularly the Opening Essay).

        B. A terrestrial plant has an efficient evolutionary design to obtain resources from terrestrial sources. A plant gets CO_2 from air through its leaves, and water, minerals, and some O_2 from the soil through its roots. All other materials are produced from mixtures of these raw materials and particularly from the sugars produced by photosynthesis (Figure 32.1A).

        C. Plants, like all aerobic organisms, obtain energy from the respiration of sugars. Leaves are net producers of O_2 and do not need to absorb more. Roots take up atmospheric O_2 through the soil for their respiratory needs.

D. Mineral forms of nitrogen, magnesium, and phosphorus (among others) are needed to make proteins, nucleic acids, phospholipids, ATP, chlorophyll, enzyme cofactors, and hormones.

E. The fact that some plants transport water from their roots to their highest leaves more than 100 m above the ground is astounding but explainable. It highlights the amazing evolutionary feat of plants to overcome the restrictions placed on them on land (Figure 32.1B).

Module 32.2 The plasma membranes of root cells control solute uptake.

A. Because of its large root surface area (particularly root hairs), a plant can absorb enough water and inorganic ions to survive and grow (Figure 32.2A).
Review: Passive transport (Modules 5.14) and the tissues of roots (Module 31.6).
Preview: Virtually all plants in the wild obtain nutrients and water through mycorrhizal fungal interconnections that may bypass root hairs. Root hairs are more important in laboratory seed cultures and fertilized agricultural plants (Module 32.12).

B. Substances enter roots in solution and make their way toward vascular tissue by three routes, intracellularly, extracellularly, and combinations of these two. In the end, nutrients must pass through at least one membrane before arriving at the vascular tissue. This allows plants to control the entry of substances into their roots (Figure 32.2B).

C. The *intracellular* pathway goes through the cell membrane of a root hair and then, by means of cytoplasmic continuity through plasmodesmata, throughout the cytoplasmic content of cortex cells and endodermal cells and finally into the xylem vessels.

D. The *extracellular* pathway goes through the hydrophilic cell walls of all epidermal and cortex cells and within the intracellular spaces. But it is forced, by the impervious waxy barrier called the **Casparian strip** in the walls of endodermal cells, through the endodermis and then into the xylem.

E. In reality, water and its dissolved solutes rarely travel just one pathway; rather they meander back and forth through both possibilities until they must pass through the selectively permeable barrier of the endodermis.

Module 32.3 Transpiration pulls water up xylem vessels.

Review: The properties of water, diffusion, and osmosis (Modules 2.9–2.11, 2.14, 5.14, and 5.16).

A. Getting water from the soil, against the force of gravity, up to the leaves where it is needed, is a major adaptation of land plants. Water and dissolved nutrients, **xylem sap,** travel in the xylem. Several mechanisms combine to produce forces that move the water.
Review: Xylem is composed of dead cells (Modules 17.1 and 31.5).

B. In some plants, root pressure pushes the column of water up the xylem. Root cell membranes actively pump inorganic ions into the xylem, and osmosis causes water molecules to follow.
Review: Active transport (Module 5.18).

C. The main motive force through xylem is by the **transpiration-cohesion-tension mechanism. Transpiration** is the evaporation of water from internal leaf cell surfaces and diffusion out stomata. Water molecules in xylem stick together by **cohesion** through hydrogen bonds, and the column of water in xylem is pulled up. The **adhesion** of water molecules to the cellulose molecules of the cell walls helps counteract the downward pull of gravity on the water column (Figure 32.3).

Module 32.4 Guard cells control transpiration.

   A. Transpiration works for and against plants. More than 200 L of water can be lost through transpiration in one day.

   B. Stomata are changeable openings in the leaf surface. Their size is regulated by two surrounding guard cells that change shape in response to changing environmental conditions (Figure 32.4).

   C. Guard cells buckle outward, opening the stomata; they actively pump K^+, and water follows by osmosis, increasing turgor pressure. Guard cells close the stomata when they lose K^+.
   Review: Osmosis and water balance (Modules 5.16 and 5.17).

   D. Three cues stimulate the stomata to open at dawn:

      1. Increased sunlight causes guard cells to take up K^+, and if the plant loses water too fast, the guard cells close.

      2. Decreased internal CO_2 has the same effect as increased sunlight.

      3. An internal daily timing mechanism (a biological clock) triggers K^+ uptake and stomatal opening in the morning and K^+ release and stomatal closing in the evening.
      Preview: This internal timing mechanism is a type of biological clock. The biological clocks of plants are discussed in greater detail in Module 33.10.

Module 32.5 Phloem transports sugars.

   A. The primary function of phloem is to distribute the sugars produced during photosynthesis throughout the plant. Phloem is composed of sieve-tube members arranged end to end, each bounded at the end with a sieve plate. Each sieve-tube member's plasma membrane is continuous with the next, so the phloem sap can flow easily from one cell to the next (Figure 32.5A).
   Review: The structure of phloem is also discussed in Modules 17.1 and 31.5.

   B. **Phloem sap** contains a watery solution of sucrose (principle element), inorganic ions, amino acids, and hormones.

   C. Phloem sap flows from a **sugar source** (an organ where sugar is made by photosynthesis or released from stored starch) to a **sugar sink** (an organ where sugar molecules are used, such as roots, buds, stems, fruits, tubers, and bulbs).

   D. The **pressure-flow mechanism** is the most widely accepted model for the movement of phloem sap. At the sugar source, sugar is loaded into the phloem by active transport. Water follows by osmosis, raising the water pressure. At the sugar sink, sugar leaves the phloem, and water follows by osmosis, lowering the water pressure. Phloem sap flows from source to sink down a gradient of hydrostatic pressure. Water is recycled from the sink to the sugar source through the xylem (Figure 32.5B).

   E. This model is supported by tests using natural phloem tappers, aphids. Their mouthpieces (stylets) are severed while they feed on sap. The closer the aphid stylet is to a sugar source, the faster the sap flows out and the higher the sugar content (Figure 32.5C).

II. Plant Nutrients and the Soil

Module 32.6 Plant health depends on a complete diet of essential inorganic nutrients.

   NOTE: A comparison can be made here with the nutritional needs of humans (Modules 21.14–21.19).

   A. Plants do not need a supply of organic nutrients because they make their own (autotrophs). All they need, in addition to raw materials for photosynthesis (CO_2 and water), are inorganic ions. Without the **essential elements,** a plant cannot complete its life cycle.

B. The most common symptoms of nutrient deficiency are stunted growth and leaf discoloration. Hydroponic culture can be used to determine which elements are essential (Figure 32.6).

C. Seventeen elements are essential in all plants. A few others are essential only in certain plant groups.

D. Nine of the essential elements are required in relatively large amounts and are known as **macronutrients.** Six are major components of organic compounds: carbon, oxygen, hydrogen, nitrogen, sulfur, and phosphorus (98% of a plants dry mass). Calcium, potassium, and magnesium constitute another 1.5% of a plant's dry mass.

E. Calcium is important in the formation of cell walls, in the functioning of certain proteins that help glue plant cells together in tissues, for the maintenance of cell membrane structure, and in regulating the selective permeability of cell membranes.

F. Potassium is an important cofactor for several enzymes and plays a role in maintaining osmotic balance and regulating guard cell function.

G. Magnesium is an important component of chlorophyll (center of porphyrin ring) and is a cofactor for several enzymes.

H. Eight essential nutrients are required in very small amounts and are known as **micronutrients.** Iron, chlorine, copper, manganese, zinc, molybdenum, boron, and nickel mainly function as components or cofactors of enzymes and are used repeatedly.
   Review: Cofactors are discussed in Module 5.7.

Module 32.7 Connection: You can diagnose some nutrient deficiencies in your own plants.

A. Growing plants in soil deficient in essential nutrients can produce plants of lower quality (in terms of nutritional value for humans, appearance, etc.) (Figure 32.7A).

B. The most common nutrient deficiencies seen in plants are those of nitrogen, phosphorus, and potassium.

C. Symptoms of many forms of nutrient deficiency are often distinct enough to allow visual determination of the deficiency. Compare the following affected tomato plants with healthy plants (Figure 32.7B).

D. Nitrogen deficiency (in the form plants can use, NO_3^- or NH_4^+) exhibits stunted growth and yellow-green leaves (Figure 32.7C).

E. Phosphorus deficiency (in the form plants can use, $H_2PO_4^-$ or HPO_4^{2-}) exhibits green leaves, but growth rate is greatly reduced and the new growth may be spindly and brittle (Figure 32.7D).

F. Potassium deficiency (in K^+ ions) exhibits yellow or dead brown spots or edges in localized areas on leaves. Stems and roots exhibit stunted growth (Figure 32.7E).
   NOTE: Commercial fertilizers give the values, in percent weight in the fertilizer, of nitrogen, phosphoric acid (H_3PO_4), and potash (K_2O). A fertilizer labeled 4-8-4 is 4% N, 8% H_3PO_4, and 4% K_2O.

Module 32.8 Fertile soil supports plant growth.

A. The structure and nutrient content of soil are important characteristics in plant root absorption. Soil structure is categorized according to horizons. The microscopic details of structure affect the availability of nutrients. There are three soil horizons, labeled A, B, and C.

B. The A horizon is the **topsoil.** It is subject to weathering and contains rock particles (such as sand and clay), living organisms, and high levels of decomposing organic matter called **humus.** This horizon is usually intensely active with the decomposing activity of bacteria, fungi, protozoans, and small animals. Most plant roots branch out in the A horizon and into the B horizon. The topsoil is the most important part of the soil.
NOTE: Much nutrient uptake takes place in the A horizon. It is also the region of most active mycorrhizae formation (Module 32.12).

C. The B horizon contains fewer organisms and less organic matter and is less subject to weathering.
NOTE: The lower levels of the B horizon represent the deepest regions at which water is obtained by plant roots and mycorrhizae.

D. The C horizon is broken-down rock that has been only slightly weathered.

E. Water, dissolved oxygen, and inorganic ions are removed by root hairs in direct contact with water films on soil particles (Figure 32.8B).

F. **Cation exchange** is the release of H^+ ions by root hairs to displace positive nutrient ions (such as Ca^{2+}, Mg^{2+}, and K^+) that naturally adhere to negatively charged clay particles and, thus, free these nutrients for absorption by the root hairs (Figure 32.8C).

G. Anions (such as NO_3^-) are not tightly bound to soil particles. This makes anions more readily available to plants. However, it also makes it more likely for anions to be leached out of the soil.

Module 32.9 Connection: Soil conservation is essential to human life.

A. Three agricultural practices are important for the conservation of the soil, proper irrigation, prevention of erosion, and prudent fertilization.

B. Irrigation makes possible the agricultural use of otherwise dry areas, but it has the disadvantages of overusing water and making the soil salty (Figure 32.9A). Modern drip irrigation methods are the most efficient at avoiding these problems.

C. Soil erosion by wind and water can be prevented by planting trees as windbreaks, terracing hillside crops, and using contour tillage (Figure 32.9B). Planting crops that provide ground cover (such as alfalfa and wheat) are better than maize or soybeans, which are planted in rows.

D. Most farmers use fertilizers containing nutrients that are either mined or produced by industrial processes. These fertilizers contain a mixture of N, P, and K that is rapidly released in soil and that may rapidly leach out to pollute groundwater. Organic fertilizers are of biological origin and release nutrients gradually.

E. GM plants (smart plants) are designed to inform the farmer when an essential nutrient is becoming deficient. This allows the farmer to more prudently apply fertilizers.
NOTE: Organic fertilizers also tend to help maintain beneficial soil structure, including humus.
Review: The environmental impact of agriculture (Module 19.11).

Module 32.10 Connection: Organic farmers must follow ecological principle.

A. Tomatoes at the farmers' market and at the "super" grocery store are both labeled "organic" (Figure 32.10). But how does one define and then guarantee that a product is in fact grown organically?

B. Organic farming uses the principles of ecology and is farming without pesticides or inorganic fertilizers. Natural fertilizers such as manure are used and predatory insects are added to fields to eat the unwanted insects.

C. Approximately 2 million acres (0.3% of the total cropland) in the United States are dedicated to organic methods of farming, and farmers are monitored to ensure that organic farming guidelines are followed (USDA-certified agencies). This is the fastest-growing segment of the agriculture industry but only provides 2% of the produce.

D. Organic farmers have four goals in mind:
  1. Replenish the soil as it is used.
  2. Create fields that are abundant and self-sustaining.
  3. Feed the world.
  4. Promote a healthy environment.

E. Some people are willing to pay more for safer, more nutritious, and better-tasting food. Organic farming has obvious environmental benefits. However, better organic farming practices need to be developed to improve plant and animal diversity in the fields and to improve crop yield.

Module 32.11 Agricultural research is improving the yields and nutritional values of crops.

A. The majority of people in the world have vegetarian diets, but the plants they eat are low in protein. Protein deficiency is the leading cause of malnutrition among humans (Module 21.16).

B. Therefore, increasing the protein content of such grains as rice would be most beneficial to a large portion of the world's population (Figure 32.11). Many high-yielding modern crop plants require very high levels of nitrogen fertilization, which is difficult to obtain in developing countries.

C. There are potential problems with GM plants; for example, there is a risk of escaping into the wild and overgrowing native species.

III. Plant Nutrition and Symbiosis

Module 32.12 Fungi help most plants absorb nutrients from the soil.

Review: The characteristics of fungi, particularly hyphae (Modules 17.15–17.22).

A. Mycorrhizae are structures formed by the mutualistic relationship between roots of plants and fungi (Figure 32.12). Virtually all plants in natural environments have mycorrhizae.

B. The plant supplies the fungus with required carbohydrates, while the fungus supplies the plant with increased efficiency of nutrient (particularly phosphorus) and water uptake. The fungus also secretes growth factors that promote root growth and produces antibiotics, which provide protection against pathogenic organisms found in the soil.

C. Farmers could increase mycorrhizae by adding fungal spores to the seeds at the time of planting.

D. Mycorrhizae are an early adaptation that probably helped the plants colonize the land. Ecosystem succession shows that colonizing plants have an abundance of mycorrhizae. *Preview:* Symbiotic relationships, such as mutualism, are discussed in Module 37.6.

Module 32.13 Most plants depend on bacteria to supply nitrogen.

Preview: The nitrogen cycle (Module 37.18).

A. All plants and, indirectly, all animals depend on the nitrogen supplies found in soil. Nitrogen is only available to plants as NH_4^+ (ammonium ions) and NO_3^- (nitrate ions).

B. Although nitrogen is 80% of our atmosphere, this gas is not usable by plants but must be converted to the organic form by one of three types of bacteria.

1. Nitrogen-fixing bacteria use **nitrogen fixation** (Module 16.16) to convert gaseous nitrogen (N_2) to ammonia (NH_3) (Figure 32.13).

2. Ammonifying bacteria convert organic forms of nitrogen to NH_4^+.

3. Nitrifying bacteria convert NH_4^+ to NO_3^-. Nitrate (NO_3^-) is the form of nitrogen most often used by plants because it is negative and readily released from soils.

C. After nitrate is absorbed, it is converted back to ammonium and used (along with the absorbed ammonium) in metabolic processes that require nitrogen (e.g., protein synthesis).

Module 32.14 Legumes and certain other plants house nitrogen-fixing bacteria.

A. Legume roots house nitrogen-fixing bacteria of the genus *Rhizobium* ("root living") in root swellings called nodules (Figure 32.14A). Bacteria living inside the plant cells are called bacteroid and live in vesicles (Figure 32.14B).

B. Nonlegume plants, such as alders, have root nodules containing the nitrogen-fixing bacteria actinomycetes.

C. The plant provides the bacteria with carbohydrates and other organic compounds, while the bacteria provide ammonium. Under ideal conditions, excess ammonium is produced and is secreted into the soil, enriching the soil.

D. Legume crops can be rotated with other crops or plowed into the soil prior to planting a second crop, both providing increased nitrogen to the soil. Legumes can be plowed under and they decompose as "green manure."

Module 32.15 The plant kingdom includes parasites and carnivores.

A. Dodder is a nonphotosynthetic plant that parasitizes other plant species using modified roots to tap the host plant's vascular tissue (Figure 32.15A).

B. Mistletoes are photosynthetic parasites of trees that supplement their diets by tapping into the host's vascular tissue (Figure 32.15B).

C. The sundew and Venus flytrap use ingenious insect traps formed from highly adapted leaves to trap, kill, and digest insects, thereby enhancing their supplies of nitrogen (Figures 32.15C and D). These carnivorous plants are found in bogs where nitrogen is limited because the acid conditions impede the decomposition of dead vegetation.

D. The structure-function relationship is well illustrated by the two carnivorous plants. The leaves have been modified to catch their prey.

Class Activities

1. I cannot keep alive plants that are kept in soil; I always either overwater or forget to water them and they end up dying; have your class consider the physiological basis of the death of these plants. I do like plants that do not require soil and can survive in water; have your class consider why these plants do not suffer from overwatering and how they obtain sufficient minerals to survive and thrive.

2. Foreshadowing the chapters concerned with the environment, have your students consider how transpiration might influence weather/climatic patterns.

Transparency Acetates

Figure 32.1A   The uptake of nutrients by a plant

Figure 32.2B   Routes of water and solutes from soil to root xylem

Figure 32.3   The flow of water up a tree (Layer 1)

Figure 32.3   The flow of water up a tree (Layer 2)

Figure 32.3   The flow of water up a tree (Layer 3)

Figure 32.4   How guard cells control stomata

Figure 32.5B   Pressure flow in plant phloem from a sugar source to a sugar sink (and the return of water to the source via xylem)

Figure 32.6A   A hydroponic culture experiment

Figure 32.8B   A close-up view of root hairs in soil

Figure 32.8C   Cation exchange

Figure 32.13   The roles of bacteria in supplying nitrogen to plants

Reviewing the Concepts, page 660: Transpiration and water uptake

Reviewing the Concepts, page 660: Bacteria in the soil convert atmospheric N_2 to forms usable by plants

Connecting the Concepts, page 660: Transport in plants

Media

See the beginning of this book for a complete description of all media available for instructors and students. Animations and videos are available in the Campbell Image Presentation Library. Media Activities and Thinking as a Scientist investigations are available on the student CD-ROM and website.

Animations and Videos	Module Number
Water Transport Animation	32.3
Transport of Xylem Animation	32.3
Transport of Xylem—Transpiration Animation	32.3
Translocation of Phloem Sap—Summer Animation	32.5
Translocation of Phloem Sap—Spring Animation	32.5
How Plants Obtain Minerals from Soil Animation	32.6
Sun Dew Trapping Prey Video	32.15

Activities and Thinking as a Scientist	Module Number
Web/CD Thinking as a Scientist: *How Are Water and Solute Potentials Calculated?*	32.3
Web/CD Activity 32A: *Transpiration*	32.4
Web/CD Thinking as a Scientist: *How Is the Rate of Transpiration Calculated?*	32.4
Web/CD Activity 32B: *Transport in Phloem*	32.5
Web/CD Activity 32C: *Absorption of Nutrients from Soil*	32.8
Web/CD Thinking as a Scientist: *Connection: How Does Acid Precipitation Affect Mineral Deficiency?*	32.8
Web/CD Activity 32D: *Connection: Genetic Engineering of Golden Rice*	32.11

CHAPTER 33

Control Systems in Plants

Teaching Objectives

Introduction   Describe the benefits and risks of soybeans in the human diet.

Plant Hormones

33.1   Describe the experiments and conclusions of the phototropism research performed by the Darwins, Boysen-Jensen, and Went. Explain why the role of auxin in grasses does not seem to be the same for sunflowers, radishes, and other dicots.

33.2–33.7   Describe the functions of the five major types of plant hormones.

33.8   Describe the uses of plant hormones in modern agriculture, and note the ethical issues associated with their use.

Growth Responses and Biological Rhythms in Plants

33.9   Define phototropism, gravitropism, and thigmotropism. Explain how these reactions occur, and describe their significance in plants.

33.10   Explain how biological clocks work and how they influence the lives of plants.

33.11   Distinguish between short-day plants and long-day plants. Explain why these terms are misleading.

33.12   Describe the roles of phytochromes in plants.

33.13   Describe some of the advances in botany that have resulted from the study of *Arabidopsis*.

Plant Defenses

33.14   Explain how plants defend themselves against herbivores. Describe the systemic acquired resistance defense response in plants.

33.15   Define zoopharmacognosy and explain its significance to human health.

Key Terms

abscisic acid	gibberellin	phototropism
auxin	gravitropism	phytochromes
biological clocks	herbivores	short-day plants
circadian rhythm	hormones	systemic acquired resistance
cytokinins	long-day plants	thigmotropism
ethylene	photoperiod	tropisms

Word Roots

aux- = grow, enlarge (*auxins:* a class of plant hormones, including indoleacetic acid, having a variety of effects, such as phototropic response through the stimulation of cell elongation, stimulation of secondary growth, and the development of leaf traces and fruit)

circ- = a circle (*circadian rhythm:* a physiological cycle of about 24 hours, present in all eukaryotic organisms, that persists even in the absence of external cues)

cyto- = cell; **-kine** = moving (*cytokinins:* a class of related plant hormones that retard aging and act in concert with auxins to stimulate cell division, influence the pathway of differentiation, and control apical dominance)

gibb- = humped (*gibberellins:* a class of related plant hormones that stimulate growth in the stem and leaves, trigger the germination of seeds and breaking of bud dormancy, and stimulate fruit development with auxin)

photo- = light; **-trop** = turn, change (*phototropism:* growth of a plant shoot toward or away from light)

Lecture Outline

Introduction *What Are the Health Benefits of Soy?*

    A. The dietary benefits of soy protein have started to catch on among Americans, as indicated by increased sales in the past decade.

    B. Soy protein contains all essential amino acids and is low in fat and high in fiber. Soy protein is a heart-healthy food and a good meat substitute. Soy products lower LDL and triglycerides (triacylglycerol) while maintaining HDL levels. But soy has its downside, too.

    C. All plants have phytochemicals, plant hormones that regulate the growth and development of plants. Soybeans contain a plant hormone (phytoestrogen) that is structurally similar to estrogen. One type of phytoestrogen called isoflavin has been shown to have some hormonal effects on women. Moderate amounts of estrogen can lessen menopausal symptoms, but too much increases the risk of breast cancer. Since soy products are considered a dietary supplement, they are not under strict FDA regulation (like drugs); therefore, the level of isoflavins varies widely between products.

    D. The risks and benefits of soy protein are still being investigated. This chapter examines the role of plant hormones such as isoflavins, with particular emphasis on plant movement, growth, flowering, fruit development, and defense.

I. Plant Hormones

    Module 33.1 Experiments on how plants turning toward light led to the discovery of a plant hormone.

        A. **Phototropism** is a response of plant shoots and seedlings to grow toward a source of light (Figure 33.1A). Examination of the cellular events during a phototropic response by a shoot tip shows that the cells on the darker side of the shoot have elongated faster than those on the light side of the shoot (Figure 33.1B).

        B. **Showing that light is detected by the shoot tip:** A series of classic experiments showed how a particular hormone controls the phototropic response. The series began with experiments by Charles Darwin and his son, Francis, in the late 1800s. They showed that grass seedlings bend toward light only if their tips are present and uncovered, suggesting that the tip was responsible for the sensing of light (Figure 33.1C). *NOTE:* Because these plant parts are mentioned in Chapter 31, indicate that these classical experiments were performed in young seedlings that still had the sheath that covers the young shoots of monocots.

C. In 1913, Peter Boysen-Jensen showed that a gelatin block placed between the plant tip and the lower plant would not inhibit the response, whereas a mica block would. This suggested that a chemical that could diffuse through the gelatin but not through the mica mediated the response (Figure 33.1C).

D. **Isolating the chemical signal:** In 1926, Fritz Went extended Boysen-Jensen's experiments to actually discover the hormone. He collected the hormone from severed shoot tips into agar blocks and then applied the agar blocks in various positions to decapitated seedlings growing in the dark. Agar blocks placed off-center caused the seedlings to bend, away from the side the block was on. Went called the diffusible substance auxin (Figure 33.1D).

E. Follow-up experiments showed that shoot tips secrete auxin in equal amounts in light or dark but that auxin diffuses from lighted sides of shoot tips to shaded sides. In the 1930s, biochemists identified the chemical structure of auxin.

F. Auxins have still not been shown conclusively to be the sole regulator of plant growth in light, there may be growth inhibitors that regulate growth of cells on the lighted side of the stem. The discovery of auxin was, however, the impetus for research on plant hormones.

Module 33.2 Five major types of hormones regulate plant growth and development.

A. **Hormones** are chemical signals that coordinate the parts of an organism. Hormones are produced by one part of an organism and transported to another part, where it triggers a response through a transduction pathway (Module 11.13). Only small quantities of hormones are needed to elicit a profound effect at the cellular and tissue level.

B. In general, hormones affect cell division, elongation, and development (cell differentiation). A general overview of hormones found in plants is presented in Table 33.2. Plant steroids (e.g., brassinosteroid) are not listed on this table.

C. All six types influence growth, and four affect development. The effects of a hormone depend on plant species, the site of action, the developmental stage of the plant, the concentration of the hormone at the target site, and the balance of concentrations of different hormones.

Module 33.3 Auxin stimulates the elongation of cells in young shoots.

A. **Auxins** are a class of chemicals that promote the elongation of developing seedlings. *Review:* The elongation of shoots is discussed in Module 31.7.

B. Indoleacetic acid (IAA) is the auxin that has been extracted from plants. The major site of auxin synthesis is the apical meristem of the shoot tips. When auxins are discussed in this chapter, assume it is in reference to IAA (Figure 33.3A).

C. Relatively high concentrations of IAA stimulate shoot cell elongation and inhibit root cell elongation. However, higher levels of IAA stimulate the synthesis of ethylene. Ethylene counters the effects of IAA and is the likely cause of the inhibition of shoot growth at higher IAA levels (Figure 33.3B).

D. Relatively low concentrations of IAA have no effect on shoot cell elongation but stimulate root cell elongation (Figure 33.3B).

E. One hypothesis about how auxin elicits its effect on cells is that auxins weaken cell walls. Auxins may stimulate certain H^+ pumps in plasma membranes. The increase in H^+ outside the plasma membrane but within the cell wall would stimulate enzymes that break bonds between cellulose molecules, thereby causing the walls to be more elastic and allowing cells to elongate in response to turgor pressure (Figure 33.3C).

F. Auxins can also trigger the development of vascular tissue and induce vascular cambium cell division and, thus, growth in stem diameter (Module 31.8). Auxins produced in seeds promote the growth of fruit tissues.

G. An agricultural use of auxin sprays is to promote fruit formation from seedless, unfertilized flowers (e.g., tomatoes). Synthetic auxins are also used as herbicides.

Module 33.4 Cytokinins stimulate cell division.

A. Cytokinins promote cell division (cytokinesis); are produced in actively growing tissues in roots, embryos, and fruits; and reach target tissues by flowing in xylem sap.

B. The effects of cytokinins are often influenced by the concentrations of auxins; it is the ratio of the concentrations of these two types of hormones that has the effect.

C. In unpinched plants, the balance of auxin (diffusing down from the shoot tip) to cytokinin (flowing in xylem up from roots) affects where axillary buds will begin to extend laterally and may also help coordinate the growth of root and shoot systems.

D. When a terminal bud is removed, the axillary bud growth is activated, still at the same concentration as when auxins dominate lateral buds inactivation (Figure 33.4).

E. The leading hypothesis to explain hormonal regulation of apical dominance is the direct inhibition hypothesis. This hypothesis proposes that cytokinins and auxins are in opposition to each other (act antagonistically). Some experiments contradict this hypothesis, and therefore, a modified hypothesis will be developed after more experimentation reveals the actual mechanism.

Module 33.5 Gibberellins affect stem elongation and have numerous other effects.

A. **Gibberellins** were first isolated from species of fungus of the genus *Gibberella* in Japan, where the fungus causes "foolish seedling disease" on rice plants. This disease is characterized by aberrant growth of rice shoots that causes elongation and weakening of the shoots. Dwarf pea plants grow to normal height when treated with gibberellins (Figure 33.5A).

B. Lower concentrations of gibberellins occur naturally in plants where the hormone functions as a growth regulator. More than 100 different gibberellins are known.

C. Gibberellins are made in tips of shoots and roots. Their main effect is to enhance the action of auxin on cell elongation and fruit development, and they have a role in seed development. In seeds, they seem to be the link between environmental cues and the metabolic processes required for the renewal of embryo growth during seed germination.

D. Gibberellins, in combination with auxins, are used to make apples, currants, and eggplants develop without fertilization. Gibberellins also influence Thompson seedless grape size and cluster pattern (Figure 33.5B).

E. In some plants, gibberellins are antagonistic to abscisic acid.

Module 33.6 Abscisic acid inhibits many plant processes.

A. **Abscisic acid (ABA)** is produced in buds and produces effects that are adaptive for inducing or maintaining seed dormancy during unfavorable times.

B. ABA does not have a primary effect on bud dormancy or leaf abscission as indicated by its name.

C. ABA seems to act as a growth inhibitor in seeds, particularly of annual plants, until a certain volume of rainwater washes the ABA out of the seeds. It may actually be the ratio of ABA to gibberellins that promotes germination. Seeds often require prolonged cold periods to allow sufficient ABA breakdown and removal of the inhibitory effect.

D. ABA also acts as a stress hormone, accumulating in leaves during times of drought, and causing stomata to close, thus reducing transpiration.

Module 33.7 Ethylene triggers fruit ripening and other aging processes.

A. The role of **ethylene** in fruit ripening was discovered when sheds warmed by kerosene stoves were used to ripen grapefruit. The gas was a by-product of the kerosene, which was absent from cleaner heaters.

B. **Fruit Ripening:** Ethylene is produced in tissues of ripening fruits. It has a positive-feedback effect on ripening by inducing programmed cell death (apoptosis). Starches and acids are converted to sugars, and cell walls are broken down, making the fruit softer (Figure 33.7A). This process, in addition to color changes, is adaptive and is used to attract animals to eat the fruit, thus promoting seed dispersal.

C. To retard ripening and fruit spoilage, growers flush out stored fruit with CO_2 to remove the accumulating ethylene.

D. **The Falling Leaves:** Ethylene probably also plays a role in the color changes in and falling of leaves during autumn. Pigment complexes are induced to change, and a breakable layer (abscission layer) of cells at the bases of leaves is induced to form when the shorter days and cooler temperatures of fall occur. Abscission is promoted by a change in the balance of ethylene to auxin (Figure 33.7B).

Module 33.8 Connection: Plant hormones have many agricultural uses.

Review: The roles of hormones were mentioned in the previous five modules. The additional uses below are also important.

A. Auxins are used to control (prevent) when plants will drop their fruit (Figure 33.8).

B. Ethylene is used to thin peaches and to loosen berries so that they can be picked by machines.

C. With auxins, gibberellins are used for producing seedless fruit (Module 33.5). In contrast, large doses of gibberellins promote early (first-year rather than second-year) flowering and seed production in biennial plants such as carrots, beets, and cabbage.

D. 2,4-D is a synthetic auxin applied to eliminate dicot weeds in monocot grain crop plantings. Dicots are more sensitive to the toxic effects of this compound than are monocots. One drawback to the use of 2,4-D is that a by-product of its production is dioxin, a compound known to be toxic to humans.

E. The economic and ethical issue of organically grown foods versus foods grown with chemicals such as synthetic plant hormones is still up for debate. Do we as a society choose cheap food produced with artificial chemicals and tolerate the potential risk, or do we pay more for organically grown foods?
Review: The economics and ethics of the use of such hormones (Module 32.10).
Preview: Biological magnification and the pesticide DDT (Module 38.4).

II. Growth Responses and Biological Rhythms in Plants

Module 33.9 Tropisms orient plant growth toward or away from environmental stimuli.

A. Plants are immobile and must have some mechanism of responding to the environmental cues that benefit their survival. Most plants respond to environmental cues by growth responses known as **tropisms.** Phototropism, gravitropism, and thigmotropism are irreversible growth responses to light, gravity, and touch, respectively.
NOTE: Differentiate the term tropism, or growth, from taxis, or movement. Taxis is a common form of response seen in animals and motile protists.

B. **Response to Light:** The mechanism for phototropism is the differential rate of cell elongation, largely under the control of auxin produced by shoot tips and differentially distributed in shoots by the effect of light and shade (Modules 33.1 and 33.3).

C. **Response to Gravity:** Plants show positive gravitropism in roots and negative gravitropism in shoots. The cellular mechanism is unknown but may involve the effect of gravity on starch grain-containing organelles in cells and their response to auxins (Figure 33.9A).

D. **Response to Touch:** Tendrils (modified leaves) and stems of climbing plants exhibit **thigmotropism,** directional growth in response to touch. Contact on one side of these structures elicits cell growth on the opposite side. This causes the structure to coil and grasp the object that contacts the plant (Figure 33.9B).

Module 33.10 Plants have internal clocks.

Review: The opening and closing of stomata discussed in Module 32.4 is an example of an internal clock.

A. **Innate Biological Rhythms and Their Fine Tuning by Environmental Cues:** Like animals, plants display rhythmic activities, particularly those that exhibit **circadian rhythms,** innate biological cycles of about 24 hours. Plants will continue these activities if placed in completely dark environments or in orbiting satellites. The molecular bases of **biological clocks** are not known (Figure 33.10).

B. Interestingly, most biological clocks are not precisely timed with the external environmental factors to which they keep the organism (plant or animal) tuned. For example, the sleep movements of plants kept in the dark exhibit 26-hour cycles. These imprecise timekeepers seem to be naturally reset each day by environmental cues.

C. **The Nature of Biological Clocks:** The biological clock of mammals is located in the hypothalamus (Module 28.15). For most organisms, the location and types of cells involved in biological clocks are not known. However, the biological clocks of all organisms may involve the synthesis of a protein that regulates its own production through feedback control. Once the protein concentration reaches a set level, it turns its own production off. There are genes found in many different organisms that encode a transcription factor that turns off the gene that codes for it when it is present at higher concentrations, and when the concentration of the transcription factor falls, that gene is turned on.

D. Another interesting aspect of biological clocks is that their timing is not temperature sensitive (this is an advantage), so since most chemical reactions are temperature dependent, the chemical bases of the timing must adjust for changes in temperature.

Module 33.11 Plants mark the seasons by measuring photoperiod.

A. Biological clocks may also function in seasonal events such as flowering, seed germination, and the onset and ending of plant dormancy during seasonal periods of environmental stress.

B. The relative lengths of day and night (**photoperiod** and, specifically, the length of the night) are the principal environmental cues for plants (Figure 33.11).

C. **Short-day plants** (e.g., chrysanthemums and poinsettias) flower in late summer or winter when light periods shorten. These plants respond to nighttime darkness of a critically long duration. A brief flash of light in the middle of this period will stop blossoming.

D. **Long-day plants** (e.g., spinach, lettuce, iris, many cereal grains, and other domesticated food plants) flower in late spring or early summer when light periods lengthen. These plants respond to nighttime darkness of a critically short duration. A brief flash of light in the middle of a longer period of darkness will induce blossoming.

Module 33.12 Phytochrome is a light detector that may help set the biological clock.

Review: The electromagnetic spectrum (Module 7.6).

A. **Phytochrome** is a protein that absorbs light. This protein has been found in all species of plants and algae examined to date and seems to help these photosynthetic organisms stay synchronized with seasonal changes in light conditions. It may also help trigger certain seasonal responses such as seed germination and flowering.

B. Phytochrome alternates between two forms that differ slightly in structure and wavelength of absorption, depending on which part of the spectrum has been most recently absorbed. Phytochrome is synthesized as P_r, and any P_{fr} that forms is converted to P_r in the dark. P_r is converted to P_{fr} at sunrise. A plant can measure photoperiod by keeping track of the sudden increase in P_{fr} (Figure 33.12B). By keeping track of the photoperiod, a plant can respond to the changes in the length of daylight as needed and, thus, flower, produce seed, and go dormant at the right time.

C. This can be tested experimentally by exposing plants to brief flashes of red light (660 nm) or far-red light (730 nm). The wavelength of the last flash of light affects a plant's measurement of night length. In long-day plants, if the last flash is red light (signifying sunrise, and the shortened night), flowering is induced. In short-day plants, if the last flash is far-red light (signifying sunset, and the continued lengthening night), flowering is induced (Figure 33.12A).

D. A phytochrome that absorbs blue light has been shown to regulate stomatal opening at daybreak and phototropism.

Module 33.13 Talking About Science: Joanne Chory studies the effect of light and hormones in the model plant *Arabidopsis*.

A. Dr. Joanne Chory is a professor of biology and a Howard Hughes Medical Institute Investigator at the Salk Institute for Biological Studies.

B. She has used the small, fast-growing plant *Arabidopsis* to investigate the role of signal-transduction pathways and how light regulates plant development. Chory has discovered the role of steroid hormones (brassinosteroids) and identified the receptor to these hormones.

C. The announcement in 2000 that the genome of *Arabidopsis* had been completely sequenced opened a new opportunity to investigate gene function. The information obtained from such research has led to improvements in agricultural practice.

D. Chory has demonstrated the structural and functional relationship with animal steroids. Her work on plant steroids is a good example of how evolution is the central theme of biology.

III. Plant Defenses

Module 33.14 Defenses against herbivores and infectious microbes have evolved in plants.

A. **Herbivores** are plant-eating animals.

B. **Defenses against Herbivores:** Plants have evolved several mechanisms to thwart herbivores, including physical defenses such as thorns and chemical defenses such as canavanine. Canavanine is similar enough to arginine to be incorporated into herbivore proteins in place of arginine; it is different enough from arginine that the function of such a protein will be abnormal and will lead to the death of an insect herbivore. Some plants recruit predatory animals for protection from certain herbivores (Figure 33.14A).

C. **Defenses against Pathogens:** The first line of defense against pathogens is the physical barrier provided by the epidermis (Module 31.6). Once infected, a plant will release microbe-killing chemicals and will make changes in its cell walls that will slow the spread of the pathogen.

D. Plants and their pathogens also illustrate the results of coevolution. Plants have many *R (resistance)* genes, and pathogens have *Avr (avirulence)* genes. It is thought that the products of these plant and pathogen genes are complementary. The result is that the area of the plant that is infected will be sealed off from the rest of the plant.

E. Another component of the response at the site of infection is **systemic acquired resistance.** In this instance, alarm hormones, one of which may be salicylic acid, are released at the site of infection. These hormones trigger signal-transduction pathways throughout the plant that result in the production of defensive chemicals (Figure 33.14B).

Module 33.15 Talking About Science: Plant biochemist Eloy Rodriguez studies how animals use defensive chemicals made by plants.

A. Dr. Eloy Rodriguez, a professor of plant biochemistry at Cornell University, is one of the world's leading authorities on defensive chemicals produced by plants. He is involved in a relatively new field of study called zoopharmacognosy, the study of how animals may medicate themselves with plants. Currently, Rodriguez's work focuses on the medicinal potential of rain forest plants.
Preview: The consequence of ecosystem destruction is the topic of Chapter 38.

B. There are numerous examples of defensive chemicals produced by plants that are now commonly used by humans. For example, aspirin was originally derived from willow trees and helps plants fight off infections.

Class Activities

1. Ask your students to try to find analogies between plant and animal hormones (Chapter 26) and plant and animal taxes (Chapter 35).

2. Plants have evolved various defenses against herbivores and pathogens, many of which have been coopted by humans (Module 33.15). Ask your students for examples of this as well as for speculation on the potential for future exploitation of plant defenses. Also, ask your students to consider plant defenses and animal/pathogen counters to these defenses in a coevolutionary sense.

Transparency Acetates

Introduction, page 662: Chemical structures of human estrogen and a phytoestrogen

Figure 33.1B	Phototropism in a grass seedling
Figure 33.1C	Early experiments on phototropism: Detection of light by shoot tips and evidence for a chemical signal
Figure 33.1D	Went's experiments: Isolation of the chemical signal (Layer 1)
Figure 33.1D	Went's experiments: Isolation of the chemical signal (Layer 2)
Figure 33.1D	Went's experiments: Isolation of the chemical signal (Layer 3)
Figure 33.1D	Went's experiments: Isolation of the chemical signal (Layer 4)
Table 33.2	Major types of plant hormones
Figure 33.3B	The effect of auxin concentration on cell elongation
Figure 33.3C	A hypothesis to explain how auxin stimulates cell elongation
Figure 33.7B	Abscission layer at the base of a leaf
Figure 33.11	Photoperiodic control of flowering
Figure 33.12A	The reversible effects of red and far-red light
Figure 33.12B	Interconversion of the two forms of phytochrome
Figure 33.14A	Recruitment of a wasp in response to an herbivore
Figure 33.14B	Defense responses against an avirulent pathogen

Reviewing the Concepts, page 679: Tropisms

Reviewing the Concepts, page 679: The timing of flowering is one of the seasonal responses to photoperiod

Connecting the Concepts, page 679: The five major classes of plant hormones

Media

See the beginning of this book for a complete description of all media available for instructors and students. Animations and videos are available in the Campbell Image Presentation Library. Media Activities and Thinking as a Scientist investigations are available on the student CD-ROM and website.

Animations and Videos	Module Number
Phototropism Video	33.9
Gravitropism Video	33.9
Mimosa Leaf Video	33.9

Activities and Thinking as a Scientist	Module Number
Web/CD Thinking as a Scientist: *What Plant Hormones Affect Organ Formation?*	33.2
Web/CD Activity 33A: *Leaf Abscission*	33.7
Web/CD Activity 33B: *Flowering Lab*	33.12

CHAPTER 34

The Biosphere: An Introduction to Earth's Diverse Environments

Teaching Objectives

Introduction Describe the unusual ecology of hydrothermal vent communities and how they were discovered.

The Biosphere

34.1 Define and distinguish among the different levels within ecosystems. Distinguish between biotic and abiotic components.

34.2 Define the biosphere. Explain what is meant by the patchy nature of the biosphere.

34.3 Describe the practices of the 1950s that were addressed in Rachel Carson's book *Silent Spring*.

34.4 Describe the abiotic factors that influence life in the biosphere.

34.5 Describe the adaptations of pronghorns that help them survive the environmental conditions of the open plains and shrub deserts of North America.

34.6 Explain how the input of solar energy and Earth's movement through space influences global climate patterns. Explain how landforms affect local climate.

34.6 Explain why the seasons of the year, prevailing winds, and ocean currents exist.

Aquatic Biomes

34.7 Describe the abiotic and biotic characteristics of the different ocean zones and adjacent aquatic biomes.

34.8 Describe the different types of freshwater biomes.

34.8 Explain how the properties of a river change from its source to its outlet and how this impacts the biotic components of this biome.

Terrestrial Biomes

34.9 Explain why species may appear similar in widely separated biomes.

34.9 Explain how fire is a crucial factor in some biomes.

34.9–34.17 Describe the types of characteristics used to define terrestrial biomes. Then use these characteristics to define the major terrestrial biomes: tropical forests, savannas, deserts, chaparral, temperate grasslands, temperate forests, coniferous forests, and tundra.

34.18 Compare the impact of hurricanes and humans on tropical rain forests in Puerto Rico.

Key Terms

abiotic components	biomes	chaparral
aphotic zone	biosphere	community
benthic zone	biotic components	coniferous forests

continental shelves	ocean currents	temperate grasslands
coral reefs	organism	temperate zones
desertification	pelagic zone	trade winds
deserts	permafrost	tropical forests
doldrums	photic zone	tropics
ecology	phytoplankton	tundra
ecosystem	population	westerlies
estuary	prevailing winds	wetland
habitats	savanna	zooplankton
intertidal zone	temperate broadleaf forests	

Word Roots

a- = without; **bio-** = life (*abiotic components:* nonliving chemical and physical factors in the environment)

estuar- = the sea (*estuary:* the area where a freshwater stream or river merges with the ocean)

inter- = between (*intertidal zone:* the shallow zone of the ocean where land meets water)

pelag- = the sea (*oceanic pelagic biome:* most of the ocean's waters far from shore, constantly mixed by ocean currents)

perman- = remaining (*permafrost:* a permanently frozen stratum below the arctic tundra)

-photo = light (*aphotic zone:* the part of the ocean beneath the photic zone, where light does not penetrate sufficiently for photosynthesis to occur)

Lecture Outline

Introduction *A Mysterious Giant of the Deep*

    A. The ocean is a very special environment.

        1. Exploration of the ocean's depths requires special submersibles such as Alvin, seen in Figure A. Unusual new species, such as giant squids have been discovered at these depths.
Review: Continental drift and the location of crustal plates (Modules 15.3).

        2. Off the coast of Baja California between crustal plates, at depths of more than a mile and in complete darkness, hydrothermal vents release hot, nutrient-rich gases (Figure B).

        3. Around these vents are groups of organisms, the most obvious of which are large, yard-long tube worms. A variety of other animals, including shrimps, crabs, clams, and a few fishes, also live here (Figure C).

        4. Most of the prokaryotes in hydrothermal vents are chemoautotrophs (Module 16.11). Ultimately, all the other organisms depend on the food made by these prokaryotes because energy sources dependent on sunlight never make it in any appreciable quantity to these depths.

        5. This setting hints at many of the topics concerning populations, communities, and nutrient cycling that ecologists study.

B. **Ecology** is the scientific study of the interactions between organisms and their environments.

1. Dealing with humankind's gravest biological crises hinges on a firm understanding of ecological principles.

2. This unit starts with an overview of Earth's different biological settings, details the principles and mechanisms of ecology, and ends with a discussion of the impact of human societies on the biosphere.

Module 34.1 Ecologists study how organisms interact with their environment at several levels.

Review: The hierarchical organization of life (Module 1.1) and the scientific process (Modules 1.7 and 1.8).

A. At the **organism** level, the focus is on how an individual organism interacts with aspects of its immediate surroundings through either its physiology or behavior (Figure 34.1).

B. At the **population** level, ecologists focus on functioning among all the members of an interbreeding group within a particular geographic area.

C. Studies at the **community** level focus on all the organisms of all species and their interactions within one particular area.

D. The **ecosystem** level of study adds the nonliving factors (**abiotic components,** including temperature, energy, water, inorganic nutrients, and other chemicals) to the picture, in addition to relationships among the living factors (**biotic components**).

E. Ecology can be enormously complex because it studies multidimensional problems. Ecological research still employs the scientific process (hypotheses, tests, and observations) but must often take into account the complexities produced by the multidimensional nature of ecological interactions. Studies can be done on idealized collections of organisms or environments assembled in artificial setups in the laboratory, or by a careful examination of natural systems. Mathematical and computer models are devised to test large-scale experiments that could not be performed in the lab or field.

I. The Biosphere

Module 34.2 The biosphere is the total of all of Earth's ecosystems.

A. The **biosphere** includes the atmosphere to an altitude of a few kilometers, the land to a soil depth of a few meters, all lakes and streams, and the ocean to a depth of several kilometers.

B. The biosphere is isolated by space and is totally self-contained except for energy input from the sun and heat loss to space (and input of solid matter in the form of meteorites) (Figure 34.2A).

C. The biosphere is erratic on many levels. At each level, the randomness is a result of variability of **habitats** (specific environments where organisms live) (Figure 34.2B).
Preview: Randomness and human impact on this pattern are discussed in Chapter 38.

Module 34.3 Connection: Environmental problems reveal the limits of the biosphere.

Preview: Environmental issues are the subjects of Chapter 38.

A. Technological solutions, particularly those using chemicals, to agricultural and other problems during the past 50 years have had environmental impacts.

B. Rachel Carson, author of *Silent Spring* (Figure 34.3), was one of the first observers to realize the global dangers of the use of agricultural chemicals such as DDT.
Preview: See Module 38.4 for a discussion of the environmental impact of DDT and other pollutants, such as CFCs.

C. Environmental degradation, famine, species endangerment, and extinction have been tied to many human activities, including land misuse, expanding human population, incursions on natural habitats, and the poisoning of soil and water by toxic wastes.

Module 34.4 Physical and chemical factors influence life in the biosphere.

A. **Solar energy** powers most surface terrestrial and shallow-water ecosystems. Ecosystems such as hydrothermal vents and dark caves are dependent on energy extracted from inorganic materials by prokaryotes. In nearly all environments, the availability of light is a critical factor that affects the distribution of photosynthetic organisms and their dependents. In aquatic environments, most photosynthesis occurs near the surface.

B. **Water** is essential to all life. In aquatic environments, water balance must be maintained in diverse ionic concentrations. In terrestrial environments, water must be conserved. *Review:* Osmoregulation (Modules 25.5–25.7).

C. **Temperature** affects rates of metabolism and the functioning of enzymes. Metabolism usually occurs above 0°C and below 45°C, although some organisms can survive freezing or live at temperatures around boiling. *Review:* Thermoregulation (Modules 25.1–25.4).

D. **Wind** brings nutrients to some organisms, but it can cause damage, increase evaporation, and lower effective temperatures.

E. Soil structure, pH, and nutrient content are important factors determining where plants and other soil-dwelling organisms can live.

F. Fires and other catastrophes are infrequent and unpredictable in most ecosystems (Figure 34.4). In grasslands and drier forests, fire may play an important recurring role in modifying the physical, chemical, and biological parameters, enough so that some plants have adapted to frequent fires.

Module 34.5 Organisms are adapted to abiotic and biotic factors by natural selection.

Review: Evolutionary principles are discussed in Chapter 13.

A. Species exist in a given area because they evolve there or disperse there. In either case, unique adaptations that fit the local environment allow each species to live there.

B. Each organism can usually tolerate environmental fluctuations only within the set of conditions to which it is adapted. For example, the pronghorn is a highly successful herbivore that evolved on the open plains of North America (Figure 34.5).

C. The abiotic factors of the pronghorn's environment include extreme daily and seasonal temperature fluctuations, aridity, and wind. The pronghorn is well insulated by a coat of hollow hairs and can obtain all the water it needs from the vegetation it eats.

D. Some biotic factors to which the pronghorn is adapted include its diet of coarse grasses and woody shrubs and its predators—wolves, coyotes, and cougars. Pronghorns have teeth adapted for biting and chewing these plants and a ruminant-type digestive system that depends on the chemical digestion of cellulose by prokaryotes. Pronghorns can escape their predators by means of great speed and endurance, are camouflaged, have keen eyesight, and increase their environmental awareness by living in herds.

Module 34.6 Regional climate influences the distribution of biological communities.

A. Because of Earth's curvature, different latitudes receive different amounts of solar energy. This uneven heating drives winds and water currents. Seasonal differences in temperature exist because Earth is tilted on its axis (Figures 34.6A and B). The **tropics** (between latitudes 23.5° N and 23.5° S) have the most yearly input and the least seasonal variation in solar energy.

B. Uneven surface heating affects wind patterns and rainfall. Air over equatorial areas rises, forming clouds and rain but no wind, known as the **doldrums** (Figure 34.6C). High-altitude air masses spread to the north and south, descend at about 30° latitude, and flow on the surface both north and south. The area around 30° includes the world's major deserts because these sinking air masses are very dry. The **trade winds** flowing toward the equator are generally easterly (east to west) because of the high spin of Earth's surface at the tropics. The winds flowing through the **temperate zones** to the poles trend west to east **(westerlies)** because of the slower spin of the surface at the higher latitudes (Figure 34.6D).

C. **Ocean currents** are produced from a combination of the prevailing winds, Earth's rotational spin, unequal heating of surface water, and the shapes of continents. The flow of warm and cold currents can have a major effect on regions with water of contrasting temperature (Figure 34.6E).

D. Landforms also affect local climate by influencing wind speed and precipitation. For example, moist air flowing off the Pacific Ocean across the mountains of Pacific northwestern North America produces, first, relatively warm, extremely wet climates and then, in the rain shadow of the Cascade Range, continental climates that are almost desertlike (Figure 34.6F). The rain forests and deserts of Washington State are ecosystems commonly found throughout the world. They are referred to as **biomes.** Biomes are grouped into two types, aquatic or terrestrial.

II. Aquatic Biomes

Module 34.7 Oceans occupy most of Earth's surface.

A. Evaporation from the ocean surface loads the air with moisture that provides most of the world's precipitation. Photosynthesis of marine algae provides much of the biosphere's O_2.

B. The **intertidal zone** characterizes all areas exposed to fluctuations in tidal height. Most pronounced are the intertidal zones of temperate coastlines with rocky shores, which may include tidepools (Figure 34.7A). The **continental shelf** is that portion of a continent under water (Figure 34.7B).

C. The **pelagic zone** of the open ocean includes all the water and is a major habitat for **phytoplankton** and **zooplankton** and highly motile marine invertebrates, fishes, and mammals. It is divided between the photic zone, where photosynthesis can occur and which is usually rich in life forms, and the aphotic zone, which is generally less rich in life forms.

D. The seafloor is called the **benthic zone** and is characterized by communities of invertebrates and fishes. Depending on its depth, it may include photosynthetic organisms.

E. Underlying the **photic zone** is the **aphotic zone,** the most extensive part of the biosphere. The aphotic zone contains a diverse array of life whose sources of energy include organic remains that sink from the photic zone and the hydrothermal vents discussed earlier (Opening Essay).

F. **Coral reefs** are a diverse ecosystem found in tropical waters above the continental shelf. Coral reefs are extremely fragile and are destroyed easily by pollution, native and introduced predators, and souvenir collectors (Figure 34.7C).

G. **Estuaries** are flat, shallow areas where broad expanses of fresh water meet seawater (Figure 34.7D). They are among the most productive of all environments on Earth. Estuaries and intertidal zones are among the most threatened ecosystems as a result of overharvesting, pollution, and the removal of habitat by human development of coastal areas. Laws in many countries now severely regulate activities in these areas in an attempt to restore and conserve these regions.

H. Mudflats and salt marshes are two types of **wetland** that border estuaries. Wetlands have characteristics intermediate between aquatic and terrestrial ecosystems. Most wetlands have permanently or periodically saturated soils.
NOTE: Most wetlands have specialized vegetation, can be highly productive, or play pivotal roles in the maintenance of nearby aquatic ecosystems.

Module 34.8 Freshwater biomes include lakes, ponds, rivers, streams, and wetlands.

A. Light and the scarcity of dissolved inorganic ions have a major effect on ponds, lakes, rivers, and streams.
Review: Osmoregulation (Module 25.4).

B. All but the most shallow ponds and lakes have photic and aphotic zones. Because of the lack of currents, environments in the aphotic and benthic zones may be low in, or lack, oxygen.

C. Temperature stratification has important effects on oxygenation and on organismal distribution in lakes and ponds, particularly in temperate zones. Stratification can impede the mixing of surface and deep water, except during times when surface temperatures are changing rapidly, during spring and fall.

D. The presence and distribution of inorganic ions (particularly nitrogen and phosphorus) can limit organismal growth and distribution. Increased amounts of nutrients affected by inputs from sewage or agricultural runoff can lead to phytoplankton blooms. When these algae die and decompose, a pond or lake suffers from oxygen depletion.
NOTE: Of particular danger is the increase in respiration by blooms overnight. This can deplete oxygen on a daily cycle and lead to the suffocation of many associated organisms, including fish.

E. Streams and rivers support different communities than ponds and lakes. Near sources, water is usually cold, clear, and low in nutrients, and currents are swift. Near outlets, water is usually warmer, murkier, and high in nutrients, and currents are slower. These differences support different species (Figure 34.8A).

F. Freshwater wetlands are similar to the intertidal zones with respect to the diversity of species and the protective qualities for the environment. They are easily harmed, and efforts are under way to protect and restore freshwater wetlands (Figure 34.8B).

III. Terrestrial Biomes

Module 34.9 Terrestrial biomes reflect regional variations in climate.

A. Biomes can be divided into nine major types (Figure 34.9).

B. Biomes are usually named for their predominant vegetation but are characterized by distinct groups of organisms from all kingdoms.

C. Each biome is a type, not a distinct assemblage.

D. Biomes are distributed in broad patterns across planet Earth. Some occur in wide bands. Others are found in widely separated areas. The assembly of species found in the separated examples of the same type may show convergence of traits in evolutionarily unrelated forms of plants and animals.

E. Biomes do not abruptly change from one to another, but grade into each other.
NOTE: Such biome gradients are referred to as ecoclines.

F. Fires are important in maintaining certain biomes, such as grasslands.
Preview: Module 37.8 discusses the role of fire in ecosystems.

G. Many natural biomes have been broken up by human activity (Chapter 38).

Module 34.10 Tropical forests cluster near the equator.

A. **Tropical forests** are found near the equator where temperatures are warm, and days are uniformly 11–12 hours long year-round in the tropical forest. Rainfall is variable and defines subtypes of this biome.

B. Tropical thorn forests are common in equatorial lowlands, such as eastern Africa and northwestern India. They are characterized by scarce rainfall. The plants found here are thorny shrubs and trees.

C. Tropical deciduous forests dominate areas where there are distinct wet and dry seasons of about equal length, such as central West Africa, India, and Southeast Asia. The deciduous trees and shrubs of these forests drop their leaves during the dry season and releaf during the wet season.

D. Tropical rain forests are the most complex of all biomes, with very high diversity (particularly of plant species—as many as 300 tree species per hectare) and complex structure (Figure 34.10). Larger animals are tree dwellers, and there is little organic soil because of high decomposition and recycling rates. Tropical rain forests are stratified, with an upper canopy of the largest trees, a lower layer of trees, the shrub understory, the herbaceous plants at ground level, the forest floor, and the root layer. Tropical rain forests occur in humid equatorial areas (e.g., Indonesia and the Amazon River basin) where rainfall ranges between 200 and 400 cm per year and there is a short season of reduced rainfall.

E. The impact of humans on the tropical rain forest is currently of great concern. The deforestation of these areas may cause large-scale changes in world climate, as well as the loss of numerous species (Chapter 38).

Module 34.11 Savannas are grasslands with scattered trees.

A. **Savannas** cover wide areas of the tropics in South America, central and southern Africa, and temperate North America and have between 30 and 50 cm of rain each year (Figure 34.11).

B. In temperate North America, the grasslands of the west merge with the temperate forests of the east.

C. Savannas are simpler in structure and lower in diversity than tropical forests and are characteristic of areas of low but consistent rainfall.

D. Frequent fires and grazing animals inhibit invasion by trees and maintain the wind-pollinated grasses and nonwoody insect-pollinated dicots.
Preview: Module 37.8 discusses the role of fire in ecosystems.

E. Rapid grass growth makes the savanna home to many of the world's largest herbivores and their predators. Particularly famous are those of Africa (e.g., giraffes, zebras, antelope, baboons, lions, and cheetahs) and Australia (e.g., kangaroos). Savanna habitat in North America (home to bison, deer, black bear, coyotes, and wolves) has largely been replaced by farms. During the seasonal drought, large mammals must migrate to find suitable grazing and water.

F. Other animals characteristic of this region are burrowing animals (e.g., mice, moles, gophers, snakes, ground squirrels, worms, and arthropods), which must go underground to find shelter in a region with few trees.

Module 34.12 Deserts are defined by their dryness.

A. **Deserts** have daytime temperatures reaching 54°C, and nighttime temperatures dropping below freezing. Rainfall is less than 30 cm per year, and evaporation is rapid. Rainfall often occurs at one short time (or not at all, in some years) (Figure 34.12).

B. Deserts are centered at about 30° north and south latitudes in regions of descending, dry air masses. Most famous are the Sahara (where evaporation exceeds rainfall), Arabian, and Kalahari Deserts and the desert areas of North America in Mexico and the southwestern United States. Areas in rain shadows of mountains in more temperate areas may also be deserts.

C. Cycles of growth and reproduction are keyed to rainfall. Desert plants are adapted to conserve water and to produce great numbers of seeds that may remain dormant for several years before rain triggers germination. Desert animals are adapted to drought and temperature extremes. Many are burrowers and seed-eaters (e.g., ants, birds, and rodents). Lizards, snakes, and hawks are important predators.

D. The size of many deserts is increasing (**desertification**), principally because of the pressures of overgrazing and dry-land farming. This process is especially evident in the savannas of central Africa.

Module 34.13 Spiny shrubs dominate the chaparral.

A. The climate of the **chaparral** results from cool, offshore ocean currents that produce mild, rainy winters and long, hot, dry summers (Figure 34.13).

B. Important regions of chaparral include regions around the Mediterranean, coastal Chile, southwestern Africa, southwestern Australia, California, and northwestern Mexico (all chaparrals are mid-latitude coastal areas).

C. Perennial shrubs and annual plants are adapted to periodic fires and require occasional fires to maintain their overall structure.
Preview: Module 37.8 discusses the role of fire in ecosystems.

D. Characteristic animals include browsers (e.g., deer), fruit-eating birds, and seed-eating rodents. Lizards and snakes are important predators.

Module 34.14 Temperate grasslands include the North American prairie.

A. **Temperate grasslands** are mostly treeless. This biome is maintained in regions with relatively cold winter temperatures, seasonal drought, occasional fires, and grazing by large mammals (Figure 34.14). These factors prevent the establishment of woody shrubs and trees.
Preview: Module 37.8 discusses the role of fire in ecosystems.

B. Temperate grasslands include areas known as veldts in South Africa, pampas in Argentina and Uruguay, steppes in Asia, and prairies in central North America.

C. The area covered by grasslands increased dramatically following the ice age. In North America, little native grassland remains because vast portions of it are used for grain production.

D. The amount of rainfall determines the height of the grassland vegetation. In addition to grazing mammals (e.g., bison and pronghorn of North America, gazelles and zebras of Africa, and wild horses and sheep of Asia), common animals include burrowing animals and carnivores such as badgers, skunks, and foxes. The rich soil supports a great diversity of microorganisms, annelids, arthropods, and burrowing mammals.

Module 34.15 Broadleaf trees dominate temperate forests.

A. **Temperate broadleaf forests** occur where there is enough precipitation to support trees. The seasonal temperature range can be great, ranging from −30°C to +30°C (Figure 34.15).
   Review: These forests are threatened by global warming (Modules 7.13 and 38.5).

B. Temperate forests are in the eastern United States, most of central Europe, and parts of eastern Asia and Australia. A small amount can be found in southern South America. In many temperate zones, human occupation of this biome has drastically altered the region.

C. Worldwide, the mix of broadleaf tree species varies. Trees that dominate include maples, oaks, hickory, and beech. The diversity of species may be high, but not nearly as high as in tropical rain forests. The growing season usually lasts 5–6 months, and the trees become dormant in autumn. Leaf drop conserves water during cold, sometimes dry, winters.

D. Temperate forest soils are rich in organic and inorganic nutrients and support a diversity of species.

E. Animal life is diverse because of the diverse habitats and includes arthropods, birds, and mammals (e.g., whitetail deer, bobcats, foxes, black bears, and mountain lions).

F. Unlike drier areas, temperate forests tend to recover after a disturbance.
   Preview: The role of disturbances in community maintenance is discussed in Module 37.7.

Module 34.16 Coniferous forests are often dominated by a few species of trees.

A. **Coniferous forests** are dominated by cone-bearing trees such as spruce, pine, fir, and hemlock.

B. Prior to human disturbance, much of the southeastern United States was dominated by coniferous forest.

C. Fire is essential to this biome. Without periodic fires, deciduous trees will tend to replace the conifers.
   Preview: Module 37.8 discusses the role of fire in ecosystems (also see Module 37.7).

D. The taiga forms a broad band across North America and Eurasia (Figure 34.16). In more southerly regions, it is located at higher elevations, below alpine areas. There is little taiga in the southern hemisphere.

E. Harsh winters; short, warm summers; and considerable precipitation, often as snow, characterize the region. Snow insulates the thin and acidic soil during the winter.

F. Taiga is usually characterized by a few species of conifer, whose shape and resiliency protect them from heavy snow loads. Scattered deciduous trees (birch, willow, aspen, and alder) are common, especially near openings.

G. Animals are adapted to cold winters, often remaining active in tunnels under the snow in winter (e.g., mice). Squirrels and birds feed on conifer seeds. Browsers include deer, moose, elk, snowshoe hares, beavers, and porcupines. Predators include bears, wolves, lynxes, and wolverines.

H. Actually, northwestern North American coniferous forests are temperate rain forests (Chapter 31, Introduction). Warm, moist air from the Pacific Ocean supports this biome. In particularly wet areas, both broadleaf trees and conifers are dominant.

Module 34.17 Long, bitter-cold winters characterize the tundra.

A. **Tundra** is found from the northern edge of the taiga to the northern limits of land and encircles the North Pole. Alpine tundras occur at high elevation, above the treeline and below permanent rock and ice, throughout all climatic regions (Figure 34.17).

B. Vegetation is dominated by low-growing herbs and shrubs, and lichens and bryophytes. During short but warm summers, vascular plants grow and flower quickly.

C. The arctic tundra is characterized by **permafrost,** a permanently frozen layer of ground beginning a few meters deep and ranging from several meters to more than a kilometer in depth. In many tundra areas, there is little precipitation, which is mostly snow. But poor drainage due to permafrost and slow rates of evaporation retain the moisture and keep the soil saturated.

D. Animals are adapted to the cold by thick fur, or by migratory behavior. Large herbivores include musk ox and caribou. The main smaller mammal is the lemming. There are a few predators, such as the arctic fox and the snowy owl. Many species found in the tundra, especially the birds, use it as a summer breeding ground. Huge populations of blood-eating insects, such as the mosquito, develop in mid-summer and then experience an abrupt decline in population size as winter approaches.
Preview: Population dynamics (Chapter 36).

Module 34.18 Talking about Science: Ecologist Ariel Lugo studies tropical forests in Puerto Rico.

A. Dr. Ariel Lugo is a tropical ecologist who works in Puerto Rico (Figure 34.18B). He tempers his concerns about the rain forest organisms with an understanding of the social and economic needs of the people who live in and use these forests.

B. The main force causing deforestation at present is not the need for lumber or the destructive effects of a hurricane (Figure 34.18A), but the need for land to grow food. Unfortunately, in the tropics, once the forest is cut, the remaining land can be farmed only a short time before it is infertile. Increasing populations in tropical areas also adds to the problem.

C. Lugo believes it is critical that land use in these areas remains sustainable, and this depends on the cultural awareness of the people living there. Any deforestation that occurs needs to be planned, controlled, and integrated into the ecosystem mechanisms in the area to avoid losing species and degrading soil and water resources.

Class Activities

1. Have your students consider the biome in which their community exists. Have them consider how this biome has been altered by human activity and how this has affected other biomes.

2. Ask your students to compare latitudinal and altitudinal biome gradients.

Transparency Acetates

Figure 34.6A   How solar radiation varies with latitude

Figure 34.6B   How Earth's tilt causes the seasons

Figure 34.6C   How uneven heating causes rain and winds

Media

See the beginning of this book for a complete description of all media available for instructors and students. Animations and videos are available in the Campbell Image Presentation Library. Media Activities and Thinking as a Scientist investigations are available on the student CD-ROM and website.

Animations and Videos

	Module Number
Hydrothermal Vent Video	34.7
Tubeworms Video	34.7
Coral Reef Video	34.7

Activities and Thinking as a Scientist

	Module Number
Web/CD Activity 34A: *Connection: DDT and the Environment*	34.3
Web/CD Thinking as a Scientist: *How Do Abiotic Factors Affect Distribution of Organisms?*	34.4
Web/CD Activity 34B: *Adaptations to Biotic and Abiotic Factors*	34.5
Web/CD Activity 34C: *Aquatic Biomes*	34.8
Web/CD Activity 34D: *Terrestrial Biomes*	34.17

CHAPTER 35

Behavioral Adaptations to the Environment

Teaching Objectives

Introduction Describe the adaptations of impalas that have led to their prolonged success.

The Scientific Study of Behavior

35.1 Define and distinguish between (a) the broad study of behavior and behavioral ecology and (b) proximate and ultimate causes of behavior.

35.2 Describe the adaptive advantage of innate behaviors. Describe examples of fixed action patterns, noting the sign stimulus and adaptive advantage of each.

35.3 Explain why the "nature versus nurture" question is misleading.

Learning

35.4–35.11 Define the seven types of learning, and note the adaptive advantages and examples of each.

35.6 Describe the problems that imprinting creates for captive breeding programs. Explain how these challenges were addressed for whooping cranes.

35.7 Define and compare kinesis, taxis, and the use of landmarks in animal movements.

35.8 Describe the ways that animals navigate during migrations.

Foraging and Mating Behavior

35.12 Define and describe examples of a search image and optimal foraging.

35.13 Compare monogamous and polygamous relationships. Describe the circumstances that would favor each system, and provide examples of each.

35.14 Explain how courtship rituals are adaptive.

Social Behavior and Sociobiology

35.15 Define and describe examples of social behavior and sociobiology.

35.16 Define a territory and describe ways that territories are used, identified, and defended.

35.17 Define agonistic behavior and describe an example. Explain how agonistic behavior is adaptive.

35.18 Explain how dominance hierarchies are maintained and adaptive.

35.19 Describe dominance hierarchies and reconciliation behavior in chimps.

35.20 Compare the different types of signs used by nocturnal mammals and diurnal birds. Describe the complex social signals used in animal societies, including honeybees.

35.21 Define and distinguish among altruism, kin selection, and reciprocal altruism. Describe examples of each.

35.22 Explain how genes and culture influence human social behavior.

35.23 Describe the fields of sociobiology and evolutionary psychology. Describe how biodiversity is threatened.

Key Terms

agonistic behavior	imprinting	reciprocal altruism
altruism	inclusive fitness	search image
associative learning	innate behavior	sensitive period
behavior	kin selection	sign stimulus
behavioral ecology	kinesis	signal
cognition	landmarks	social behavior
cognitive map	learning	social learning
communication	migration	sociobiology
culture	monogamous	spatial learning
dominance hierarchy	optimal foraging theory	taxis
fixed action patterns (FAPs)	polygamous	territory
foraging	promiscuous	trial-and-error learning
habituation	proximate questions	ultimate questions

Word Roots

agon- = a contest (*agonistic behavior:* a type of behavior involving a contest of some kind that determines which competitor gains access to some resource, such as food or mates)

kine- = move (*kinesis:* a change in activity rate in response to a stimulus)

socio- = a companion (*sociobiology:* the study of social behavior based on evolutionary theory)

Lecture Outline

Introduction *Leaping Herds of Herbivores*

    A. The impala is a small, graceful grazer of the African grassland. It has not changed in more than 8 million years, yet it is the most successful and most commonly preyed upon animal of the savanna.

    B. Behavior is the key to the impala's success. It will form large herds when food and water are plentiful, disperse during drought, warn others of its kind when predators are near, and allow other impalas or birds (the oxpecker) to remove blood-sucking ticks from its face and ears. Impalas will eat almost any vegetation and can go days without water.

    C. The study of animal behavior is essential to understanding animal evolution and ecological interactions.

I. The Scientific Study of Behavior

    Module 35.1 Behavioral ecologists ask both proximate and ultimate questions.

    A. **Behavior** refers to any observable activity that an animal performs.

    B. Early workers in the field of behavioral biology were von Frisch, Lorenz, and Tinbergen, all Nobel laureates.

       1. Von Frisch pioneered the use of experimental methods in behavior, studying food hunting by honeybees.

2. Lorenz, the "father of behavioral biology," compared behaviors in various animals and found that different stimuli often elicited different behavior.

3. Tinbergen studied the relationship between innate (genetically programmed) behavior and learning.

C. Tinbergen is best known for his paper in which he proposed that to fully understand any behavior, one must consider both the mechanism underlying the act and its evolutionary significance. This approach is known as **behavioral ecology,** the study of behavior from an evolutionary approach.

D. Behavioral ecologists ask two levels of questions when observing behavioral activity. The **proximate question** focuses on the behavior in terms of immediate activities triggered by environmental stimuli (asks the question "how"). The **ultimate question** focuses on the evolutionary context of the behavior (asks the question "why").

Module 35.2 Early behaviorists used experiments to study fixed action patterns.

A. **Fixed action patterns (FAPs)** are a type of **innate behavior,** which is behavior performed the same way by all members of a species. FAPs are essentially unchangeable behavioral sequences that can be performed only as a whole and, once started, must be completed. The stimulus that triggers an FAP (i.e., is the proximate cause of the behavioral sequence) is called a **sign stimulus.**

B. For example, the graylag goose exhibits an FAP when she retrieves an egg that rolls out of her nest. She stands up, extends her neck, and sweeps her head from side to side, using her beak to bring the egg back. If an experimenter moves the egg aside while it is being brought back, the goose will continue the behavior (without the head swinging) until she sits down in the nest again, at which time she will notice that the egg is still outside (Figure 35.2).

C. FAPs are particularly important in animals with life spans too short to allow for learning and in newborn vertebrates, where, in the context of the ultimate question, such behavior ensures that the young will obtain food from the parents (or directly from the environment) without any learning.

D. FAPs can be discussed in a behavioral ecology context when considering that inappropriate behaviors lead to death and only genes that promote appropriate behavior are passed on to the next generation.

Module 35.3 Behavior is the result of both genes and environmental factors.

A. The relationship between genes and behavior is complex. Most genetically programmed behaviors have some aspect that can be changed by experience. How much behavior is governed by genes and how much by experience is a classic debate.

B. Both genes and the environment influence behavior. The question is the relative influence of each over any trait, including behavioral ones. The prairie vole and the mountain vole vary in their behavior after mating and after the birth of their pups. The female prairie voles also have different levels of oxytocin than the female mountain voles do. Similarly, the male prairie vole has increased levels of vasopressin compared to the male mountain vole (Figures 35.3A and B).

C. Genetic studies were done to test the effect of inserting the prairie vole gene for vasopressin in mice. The results of the study indicate that the gene for vasopressin was responsible for the observed behavior of the mice that was similar to the prairie vole.

D. A cross-fostering experiment was done with mice that were either aggressive or not aggressive. Those that came from the aggressive species were placed in the nonaggressive nest and vice versa. The behaviors observed indicated that aggression was a learned behavior.

E.   The complementary results of these studies indicate that behavior is a combination of both genetics and environmental factors.

II. Learning

Module 35.4 Learning ranges from simple behavioral changes to complex problem solving.

A.   **Learning** is modification in behavior resulting from specific experience. The different types of learning reflect the complexity of the changed behavior (Table 35.4). Learning empowers animals to change their behavior in response to environmental changes.

B.   **Habituation** happens when an animal learns not to respond to an unimportant stimulus. This is one of the simplest forms of learning and is common in all animals. It is highly adaptive because it prevents animals from wasting energy on pointless activity. For example, if a hydra is repeatedly touched, it will eventually stop contracting (the normal response).

C.   Habituation increases fitness because it focuses the energy expended by an animal on survival and reproduction.

Module 35.5 Imprinting is learning that involves both innate behavior and experience.

A.   **Imprinting** is learning to perform a response during a limited time period, and the learned behavior is irreversible. The **sensitive period** is the limited time when an animal must learn. Its learned component is the imprinting itself. Imprinting is particularly important in the formation of bonds between animals.

B.   Lorenz's most famous study showed that graylag goslings would imprint on him as a mother figure if, during the first two days after hatching, the geese saw him and not the mother. The specific imprinting stimulus was found to be the movement of an object (normally the parent) away from the hatchlings (Figure 35.5A).

C.   Salmon imprint on the complex of odors unique to the stream they hatch in so that, as adults, they can return to that same stream to spawn (Chapter 29, Opening Essay).

D.   Each species of songbird has its own unique song. Song imprinting occurs in birds learning the mating call of each species. During a critical period of 10–50 days after hatching, a bird imprints on the calls of its own species (Figure 35.5B).

E.   Birds raised in isolation who do not hear their species' song until after 50 days do not learn to sing normally, whereas isolated males played tapes of their species' song during the critical period do learn to sing normally.

F.   Studies of the white-crowned sparrow demonstrate that there is a genetic component to their song. Isolated males who were exposed to the songs of species other than their own did not learn those songs; rather, they sang an abnormal song.

G.   Humans have a sensitive period for learning vocalization. Children are much better at learning a foreign language than adults.

Module 35.6 Connection: Imprinting poses problems and opportunities for conservation programs.

A.   Breading endangered animals in captivity in an effort to increase their chance of survival is a difficult task due to problems related to imprinting.

B.   If the parents are available after birth, imprinting is less of a problem. However, if the parents are not available, proper imprinting is limited.

C.   An imprinting experiment with a whooping cranes recovery project required the use of a lightweight plane. The plane was to become the surrogate mother and eventually lead the young birds on their first migration to Florida (south for the winter).

D. The program was successful; the young whooping cranes bonded with the plane (as mother) and migrated to Florida for the winter. Subsequent trips have led several more generations to Florida, and the whooping crane count is approximately 300 birds in the wild.

Module 35.7 Animal movement may be a simple response to stimuli or behavior with a response.

A. **Kinesis** is a random movement in response to a stimulus. The activity is repeated until the organism finds itself in a more favorable environment. Human body lice are more active in dry areas and less active in wet areas.

B. Orientation behavior involves directed movements toward (positive) or away from (negative) a stimulus. Such directed movement is known as **taxis.** Numerous taxes are named from the stimuli that elicit the behavior (photo-, geo-, chemo-, rheo-). Thus, positive rheotaxis is exhibited by fish swimming upstream (Figure 35.7A). Taxis is a more efficient behavioral response than kinesis.
NOTE: Even prokaryotes and protists exhibit kinetic and taxic behaviors. Distinguish between a taxis (movement) and a tropism (growth) (as seen in plants; Module 33.9).

C. **Landmarks** are used by animals to find their way from place to place, and each animal must learn the particular landmarks that are unique for that location (Module 35.7B). The capacity to learn by landmarks is called spatial learning and is an advantage when navigating through an environment.

Module 35.8 Movements of animals may depend on internal maps.

A. Animals use **cognitive maps,** internal representations of spatial relationships, to navigate through the environment. The most extensive studies of cognitive maps have been made of animals that undergo seasonal migration.

B. The family of birds including jays, crows, and nutcrackers use cognitive maps to store and then retrieve their cache.

C. Seasonal **migration** is the regular movement from one place to another during a particular time of the year. Animals usually migrate to areas that are more suitable for feeding or reproducing.

D. Gray whales migrate north in summer to rich feeding grounds on the coast of Alaska, and south in winter to shallow lagoons off Baja California (Mexico), where they breed and produce offspring before the next northward migration. They have been shown to use coastal landmarks for orientation.
Preview: The impact of human activities on migration and dispersal is discussed in Chapter 38.

E. Insect-eating birds winter in the tropics and summer at high latitudes. Many have been shown to navigate using the positions of stars and the sun. Unless birds use the North Star as a fixed landmark, such navigational skills require that the animals internally adjust their sensors to take into account the daily changes in direction of stars and the sun (Figure 35.8).

F. Some maps used by animals are purely genetic. The monarch butterfly migrates thousands of kilometers to a place it has never been.

Module 35.9 Animals may learn to associate a stimulus or behavior with a response.

A. **Associative learning** is learning that a particular stimulus, or behavioral response, is linked to a reward or punishment.

B. Classical conditioning is producing a behavioral response when a reward or punishment is associated with an arbitrary stimulus. Eventually the response is elicited without the reward or punishment (B. F. Skinner).

C. Natural associations occur by **trial-and-error learning,** where, over time, an animal associates the positive or negative results of a certain type of behavior with the reward or punishment it brings (Figure 35.9).

Module 35.10 Social learning involves observation and imitation of others.

A. **Social learning** is learning by observing the behavior of others. Predatory behaviors are passed from mother to young by observing the hunting habits exhibited by the mother.

B. The vervet monkey is another good example of learned behavior and the different (correct) calls that are used for various types of communication (Figure 35.10).

Module 35.11 Problem-solving behavior relies on cognition.

A. **Cognition** is the ability of an animal's nervous system to perceive, store, process, and use information provided by the senses. The ability to think or problem solve occurs mostly in primates, dolphins, and some birds.

B. Dogs solve problems by trial and error or by remembering a prior experience, not by thinking (as is seen in chimpanzee behavior) (Figure 35.11A).

C. Some birds, such as ravens, demonstrate the capacity to solve problems (Figure 35.11B).

III. Foraging and Mating Behaviors

Module 35.12 Behavioral ecologists use cost-benefit analysis in studying foraging.

A. **Foraging** is the food-obtaining behavior that includes recognizing, searching for, securing, and eating food.

B. Some animals are feeding generalists. For example, the gulls will eat many foods. While other animals are feeding specialists such as the koalas, which eat only eucalyptus leaves (Figures 35.12A and B). Most animals can be classified somewhere in between these two extremes. An animal is said to have a **search image** when it concentrates on feeding on an abundant food item to the exclusion of other food.

C. **Optimal foraging theory** states that feeding behavior should provide maximum energy (or nutrient) gain for minimum energy and minimal time of exposure to predators.

D. Optimal foraging depends on the animal's compromising among a number of trade-offs involved with choosing one feeding-behavior pattern over another. Different foods have different digestibilities. Further, prey differ in their relative sizes, population densities, and ease of capture, and these factors may change through time. Searching for one type of food might expose an animal to more predation. Natural selection causes animal behavior to evolve in a direction that optimizes foraging over the entire range of possible environments and preys the animal could forage for. An animal may switch foraging behaviors, depending on conditions.

Module 35.13 Mating behaviors enhance reproductive success.

A. Mating behaviors that improve the chance of passing on genes to the next generation are selected for. There are three common mating systems that are used by animals:

   1. In **promiscuous** mating, no strong bonds or committed relationship is formed.

   2. In **monogamous** mating, mates remain together for an extended period of time.

   3. In **polygamous** mating, one individual mates with several different individuals.

B. Examining the habits of a given species and the needs of the young will explain the mating system used by the species. Birds provide a good example of the mating system used based on the needs of the young. Many birds are born very helpless and require large amounts of food. This requires the efforts of a mating pair (monogamous system). However, if the young chicks are born and can quickly forage for themselves, the need of two parents is diminished (e.g., pheasants and quail) and a polygamous system is used.

C. Certainty of paternity is a factor that can influence mating behavior. If the act of fertilization is internal and there is a significant time lapse before birth or egg laying occur, the certainty of the father is in question. The male jawfish fertilizes the eggs then sucks the eggs into its mouth to care for the eggs that were certainly fertilized by its sperm (Figure 35.13).

Module 35.14 Mating behavior often involves elaborate courtship rituals.

A. Courtship rituals signal that certain individuals are not threats to others but are the correct species and sex and are physically fit for mating.

B. Courtship rituals often contain actions that signal appeasement. For example, all loon courting behavior consists of appeasement gestures. During their courtship, loons turn their heads away, dip beaks, and submerge heads and necks, and the male turns his head backward and down as a final invitation to land to mate (Figure 35.14).

C. Many other animals go through group courtship rituals. Sage grouse males congregate in a lek, an area where they strut in front of watching females. All the females choose among all the males, usually mating with only a few of the most dominant individuals. If there is a positive correlation between a male's display and his evolutionary fitness (as behavioral ecologists think), such behavior will give a female the best chance at passing on her genes (Module 13.17).

IV. Social Behavior and Sociobiology

Module 35.15 Sociobiology places social behavior in an evolutionary context.

A. **Social behavior** is broadly defined as any interaction between two or more animals, usually of the same species. Much of social behavior is highly adaptive because it can affect the growth and regulation of populations.

B. Many social behaviors involve interactions between two or more individuals. Courtship, aggression, and cooperation have social elements. A key element of all types of social behavior is some form of communication.

C. The research discipline that focuses on the adaptive advantage of social behavior and how certain behaviors are preferentially selected over others through natural selection is called **sociobiology.**

Module 35.16 Territorial behavior parcels space and resources.

A. A **territory** is an area, usually fixed in location, inhabited by an individual and defended from occupancy by other individuals of the same species. The sizes of territories depend on species, use, and the total size of the area out of which the territories are parceled. Not all animals are territorial.
    Preview: Population distribution patterns, some that are a result of territoriality, are discussed in Module 37.2.

B. When space is at a premium, breeding birds maintain tiny nesting territories by agonistic behavior (Figure 35.16A).

C. Large hunters defend much larger territories for hunting and mating activities. They maintain—and spend considerable time proclaiming—their territorial boundaries, either by calling (birds, sea lions, squirrels) or marking (defecation by jaguars, scent marking by cheetahs and other cats) (Figure 35.67B). Marked territories reduce undesirable confrontations.

D. Territorial animals gain exclusive use of the resources in their territories, gain familiarity with one area, and are better able to raise young without interference from other individuals.

Module 35.17 Rituals involving agonistic behavior often resolve confrontations between competitors.

A. **Agonistic behavior** includes behavior that settles disputes among members of populations through displays or actual combat. It may involve tests of strength, posturing, or ritualized contests (Figure 35.17).

B. In most cases, agonistic behavior ends when one individual stops threatening, becomes submissive, and enters into some kind of surrender behavior. Further aggressive activity is inhibited.

C. Agonistic behavior is adaptive because the inhibition of aggressive activity minimizes the potential for damage that could adversely affect the reproductive success of both individuals.

Module 35.18 Dominance hierarchies are maintained by agonistic behavior.

A. The pecking order established among hens in a hen yard is an example of a **dominance hierarchy,** the rank among individuals based on social interaction. No hen will peck the alpha (top-ranked) hen, while all other hens will peck the omega hen (lowest-ranked). The alpha hen gets first access to resources such as food, water, and nesting sites (Figure 35.18).

B. In a dominance hierarchy, the position of each animal is fixed for extended periods of time. By establishing the set pattern, the animals in the social group do not need to constantly waste energy testing each other's status and can devote their energies to other activities such as finding food, watching for predators, locating a mate, and caring for young.

C. Dominance hierarchy is a common social behavior among vertebrates. The wolf pack has an alpha (dominant female) that controls breeding based on resources.

Module 35.19 Talking about Science: Behavioral biologist Jane Goodall discusses dominance hierarchies and reconciliation behavior in chimpanzees.

A. Dr. Jane Goodall has studied chimpanzees in their natural habitat in eastern Africa since the early 1960s (Figure 35.19A). She promotes better understanding of primate behavior and pushes for better living conditions for animals kept in zoos or medical research laboratories.

B. The closest living relatives of humans are chimpanzees. Dominance hierarchies are an important part of chimpanzee life. Adult males expend considerable effort improving or maintaining their social status, often by using agonistic charging displays. Higher-ranked males have preferred access to the best food, resting places, and mates, but other behaviors provide complex solutions to many social conflicts that do not always end with the dominant male having all the advantages (Figure 35.19B).

C. Females develop a different hierarchy. High status allows them to use the best food items. A high-ranking female's offspring start out in their social groups with higher social rankings.

D. Reconciliation behavior has adaptive advantages. The family group of chimps must cooperate to survive. So when tensions are high among members of the family, some gesture of reconciliation is offered to calm the situation (Figure 35.16B). Goodall states that the single most important social behavior is grooming. It improves bad relations and maintains good ones. Maybe we can learn something from our primate cousins!

E. Goodall's research has led her to conclude that chimpanzees are conscious.

Module 35.20 Social behavior requires communication between animals.

A. A **signal** is used by an animal, according to behavioral ecologists, to communicate with and elicit a change of behavior in another animal. The signals used may be sounds, odors, visual displays, or touches. In general, the more complex the social organization of a species population, the more complex the signaling needed to maintain it (Figure 35.20A).

B. The types of signals used by a species are determined by the lifestyle. Nocturnal animals use sound and odor, while diurnal animals use sound and sight, to communicate.

C. Aquatic animals also use signals. Erect fins ward off intruders, and electrical signals indicate hierarchy or status. Whales communicate with their songs, which can be heard many kilometers away and are used to locate each other.

D. Social insects exhibit some of the most complex social systems. A colony of honeybees includes more than 50,000 individuals, mostly sterile workers that maintain the health of the hive by feeding, caring for young, and doing defensive behaviors. Pheromones released by the queen bee help maintain social order. Other pheromones can signal the need for aggressive or defensive behavior. Feeding activities, in particular, involve complicated communication to pass on the locations of food sources.

E. Von Frisch first described the signaling system, hypothesizing that two types of behavior signaled two types of food. Signaling in the dark hive mostly involves physical contact and sound.

F. "Round dances" indicate that food is near. "Waggle dances" indicate the distance and direction of the food. The waggle's speed indicates distance, and the angle relative to the hive's vertical position indicates direction relative to the horizontal position of the sun (straight up is equivalent to flying directly toward the sun). An internal clock must also be involved because the bees maintain their sense of where the food is even if several hours of sunless storm interrupt feeding (Figure 35.20B).

Module 35.21 Altruistic acts can often be explained by the concept of inclusive fitness.

A. **Altruism** is behavior that reduces an individual's fitness while increasing the fitness of a recipient. For example, naked mole rats have a social structure resembling that of honeybees. The queen mates with three males (kings), while the rest of the colony consists of nonreproductive males and females who care for the queen and kings (Figure 35.21A). *NOTE:* The example given of altruistic behavior in honeybee hives is a special case. In a sense, the whole hive is one individual with adaptive behavior among its parts. The hive is composed of one reproductive queen and thousands of sterile workers. The workers function like cells of other organisms, where the loss of one is not missed by the whole.

B. At first glance, altruism seems nonadaptive. However, it is thought to have evolved by either of two mechanisms: kin selection or reciprocal altruism.

C. A Belding's ground squirrel will sound an alarm to warn other squirrels that a predator is near. This is not good for the individual that sounds the alarm because it reveals its location to the predator (Figure 35.21B). The idea of helping others (a relative) pass on their genes instead of passing on their own genes is called **inclusive fitness.**

D. **Kin selection** states that altruistic behavior would evolve in groups of related individuals because it increases the number of copies of a gene common to the whole group. For example, the great majority of the individuals in a naked mole rat colony are closely related. The queen appears to be either a sibling, daughter, or mother of the kings; the nonreproductive individuals are either the queen's direct descendants or her siblings. Hence, by promoting the reproductive success of the queen and kings, the nonreproductive individuals are increasing the probability that copies of their own genes will be represented in the next generation.

E. **Reciprocal altruism** is an altruistic act repaid at a later time by the beneficiary of the act (or social associates of the beneficiary). For instance, chimpanzees will sometimes save the life of a nonrelative. If a future "repaying in kind" always (or usually) follows, the altruistic behavior increases the fitness of an individual in the long run.

Module 35.22 Connection: Both genes and culture contribute to human social behavior.

Review: The evolution of human culture (Modules 19.9–19.12).

A. Group behavior, like individual behavior, has genetic and environmental components. **Culture** is a component of the environment and is defined as a system of information transfer through social learning or teaching that influences the behavior of individuals in a population.

B. A recent study published by the National Academy of Sciences in 2003 sought to answer the question "Do opposites attract?" (Figure 35.22). Almost 1,000 heterosexual men and women were asked to rank ten attributes based on importance of choosing a long-term partner. They were then asked to evaluate themselves on these same attributes. Results from the study refute the old adage and indicate that "likes attract."

C. Just as the genetics of a population will evolve over time, social behavior evolves.

Module 35.23 Talking about Science: Edward O. Wilson promoted the field of sociobiology and is a leading conservation activist.

A. Dr. E. O. Wilson's 1975 book, *Sociobiology: The New Synthesis,* promotes the idea that social behavior is genetically based and undervalued in the scientific study of social behavior (Figure 35.23). Most of the book deals with nonhumans; however, two chapters discuss humans. This book rekindled the old debate about which most strongly influences human behavior: genes (nature) or learning (nurture).

B. In the 25th anniversary edition of *Sociobiology,* Wilson explains that research in the areas of neurobiology and human genetics improves our understanding of human behavior. A new field of research has emerged from sociobiology called evolutionary psychology. Another area of research that is becoming increasingly important for society is evolutionary biology.

C. In a more recent book, *The Diversity of Life,* Wilson discusses a "biodiversity ethic." This ethic holds that humans should never knowingly allow a species to go extinct if measures to save it can be implemented. He holds that biodiversity has an inherent value to humans apart from the physical welfare it provides.

D. In Wilson's latest book, *The Future of Life,* he describes the intrinsic value of biodiversity and explains that it makes good economical and ethical sense to preserve all forms of life. The cause of the current biodiversity crisis, according to Wilson, is a result of two factors:

1. The population explosion.

2. The ever-increasing demand for energy.

E. One thing that may help this crisis is the education and empowerment of women. As women become better educated, they choose to have children at a later stage in life, which postpones the next generation and reduces the birth rate.
Preview: Human impact on the biosphere (Chapter 38).

Class Activities

1. Demonstrations of behavior are the clearest way to describe and explain the principles. Although social behaviors (other than those of students) are difficult to demonstrate in a classroom, individual types of behavior can sometimes be shown, particularly by animals that are familiar with their laboratory homes. In small classrooms or laboratory settings, reptiles and fish will show territorial, agonistic, and mating behaviors.

2. Animals often follow chemical trails. Markers with various odors can be purchased at relatively low cost. These markers can be used to create a chemical trail that can be followed by blindfolded students. It is interesting to compare how well such trails are followed by females relative to males, smokers relative to nonsmokers, those with allergies relative to those without allergies, etc.

3. As college students your students will definitely be interested in an examination of human mating behaviors. Assign your students to groups to research such mating behaviors in different human cultures.

Transparency Acetates

Figure 35.2   A graylag goose retrieving an egg—a fixed-action pattern
Table 35.4   Types of learning
Figure 35.7A   Positive rheotaxis of a trout
Figure 35.7B   Nest-locating behavior of the digger wasp
Figure 35.8   An experiment demonstrating star navigation
Figure 35.14A   Courtship and mating of the common loon
Reviewing the Concepts, page 724: Innate behavior: fixed action patterns (FAPs)
Reviewing the Concepts, page 724: Imprinting
Connecting the Concepts, page 724: Behavioral ecology

Media

See the beginning of this book for a complete description of all media available for instructors and students. Animations and videos are available in the Campbell Image Presentation Library. Media Activities and Thinking as a Scientist investigations are available on the student CD-ROM and website.

Animations and Videos	Module Number
Ducklings Video	35.5
Chimp Cracking Nut Video	35.11
Albatross Courtship Video	35.14
Blue-Footed Boobies Courtship Video	35.14
Giraffe Courtship Video	35.14
Snake Ritual Wrestling Video	35.17
Wolves Agonistic Behavior Video	35.17
Chimp Agonistic Behavior Video	35.18

Activities and Thinking as a Scientist	Module Number
Web/CD Thinking as a Scientist: *How Can Pillbug Responses to Environments Be Tested?*	37.7
Web/CD Activity 37A: *Honeybee Waggle Dance*	37.20

Population Dynamics

Teaching Objectives

Introduction Explain how starlings made it to North America and what has occurred since their introduction.

36.1 Define a population and describe several examples.

Population Structure and Dynamics

36.2 Define population density and describe techniques to measure it.

36.2 List the main types of dispersion patterns, and explain why each occurs.

36.3 Explain how life tables are used to track mortality and survivorship in populations. Compare Type I, Type II, and Type III survivorship curves.

36.4 Describe and compare the exponential growth model and the logistic growth model, illustrating both with examples. Explain the concept of carrying capacity.

36.5 Describe the factors that regulate growth in natural populations.

36.6 Define boom-and-bust cycles, explain why they occur, and note examples.

Life Histories and Their Evolution

36.7 Explain how life history traits vary with environmental conditions and with population density. Compare r-selection and K-selection, and indicate examples of each.

36.8 Describe the inherent problems of managing populations.

The Human Population

36.9 Explain how the human population is changing and the impact this has had and continues to have on Earth. Use the concept of an ecological footprint to compare the impacts of humans living in different countries.

36.10 Explain how the age structure of a population can be used to predict changes in population size and social conditions.

Key Terms

age structure	intrinsic rate of increase	population density
carrying capacity	K-selection	population ecology
clumped	life history	random
demographic transition	life tables	r-selection
density-dependent	limiting factors	survivorship curves
dispersion pattern	logistic growth model	sustainable resource
ecological footprint	maximum sustained yield	management
exponential growth model	population	uniform

Word Roots

demo- = people; **-graphy** = writing (*demography:* the study of statistics relating to births and deaths in populations)

Lecture Outline

Introduction *The Spread of Shakespeare's Starlings*

    A. Originally native to Europe and Asia, starlings are now abundant and destructive pests across North America.
Preview: The impact of introduced species is discussed in Module 38.3.

    B. Starlings were brought to New York City by a private group of citizens for arbitrary reasons at a time when importing foreign species was not regulated. Without native predators, parasites, or competitors, the starling population rapidly spread across the United States.

    C. Such uncontrolled population growth has features in common with that of the human population on a global scale.
NOTE: In general, this picture is also one seen commonly wherever nonnative species are introduced. Other examples include the introduction of rabbits into Australia and the kudzu vine to the southern United States.

    D. **Population ecology** is concerned with the changes in population size and structure over time and the factors that regulate these changes.

Module 36.1 Population ecology studies how and why populations change.

    Review: Populations and their place in the hierarchical organization of life are first discussed in Module 1.1.

    A. Ecologists define a **population** as an interacting group of individuals of a single species that use common resources, most likely will interbreed, and are regulated by the same natural phenomena.

    B. Ecologists might restrict their definition to just the individuals in a very small but contained area, such as all the sea anemones of one species in one tidepool. Or they may expand their view to include all the individuals over the face of Earth—for instance, the human population as it is exposed to the disease-causing HIV.

I. Population Structure and Dynamics

Module 36.2 Density and dispersion patterns are important population variables.

    A. **Population density** is the number of individuals of a species per unit area or volume.

    B. Density and dispersion patterns can be compared between populations occupying different areas to contrast growth, stability, or other parameters.

    C. Population density is usually measured by counting the number of individuals in a subsample and estimating the number (relative to a unit of volume or area) in the whole population.

    D. **Dispersion pattern** refers to how the individuals in a population are spaced within their areas.

E. A **clumped pattern** shows local aggregations in patches, usually resulting from an unequal distribution of resources for plants and animals or from associations with mating and social behavior for animals (Figure 36.2A).

NOTE: An example of a clumped distribution is the higher concentration of humans found in and near cities.

F. A **uniform pattern** shows an even distribution over an area and usually results from interactions among individuals, such as competition for resources by plants, secretion of chemicals by plants that inhibit growth, or territorial behavior of animals (Figure 36.2B).

Preview: Territoriality, which can be responsible for a uniform population distribution, is discussed in Module 35.16.

G. A **random** type of dispersion shows a patternless, unpredictable distribution. Such patterns are rare but might be seen in, for example, clams distributed across a sandy ocean bottom, where the factors affecting them are numerous and complexly interrelated.

H. Dispersion estimates are important tools used to analyze populations. They are used to monitor changes in populations and to compare growth and stability of one area to another.

Module 36.3 Life tables track mortality and survivorship in populations.

A. **Life tables** relate these rates to size classes, usually grouped by decades for human life tables (Table 36.3).

B. Data from life tables can be graphed to illustrate three basic **survivorship curves** (Figure 36.3).

C. Type I is characteristic of species (whales, elephants, and humans) that have low birth rates, low infant mortality, and good care for the young.

D. Type II is characteristic of intermediate species (squirrels, lizards, and hydras).

E. Type III is characteristic of species (oysters and sea lettuce) that have high birth rates, high infant mortality, and little or no care for the young.

F. Mathematical models are used by population ecologists to describe and predict population growth.

Module 36.4 Idealized models help us understand population growth.

A. Mathematical equations of population growth provide useful starting points for studying populations and have stimulated many experiments and controversies. For the following two models, these abbreviations are used:

1. G = growth rate.
2. N = number of individuals in the population at the time the growth rate is studied.
3. r = **intrinsic rate of increase** (estimated by subtracting the death rate from the birth rate).
4. K = carrying capacity (the maximum number of individuals of a particular species that can be supported by a particular environment).

B. **Exponential Growth Model.** This models the growth of a population under ideal conditions with unlimited resources. The rate of growth is exponential and depends on the number of individuals in the population:

$$G = rN$$

The graph shows a J-shaped curve, representing population size increasing without limit **(exponential growth model)**. As N increases, so does G. This type of growth, if exhibited by a bacterium growing in an unlimited environment, would result in an inconceivably large number of bacteria in less than two days (Figure 36.4A).

C. In nature, population growth is rarely, if ever, best modeled by an exponential growth equation. There are always factors in the environment that limit population growth (population-limiting factors).

D. **Limiting Factors and Logistic Growth Model.** As with the exponential growth model, this is an idealized model of population growth. However, the logistic model takes limits to population growth into consideration. The rate of growth is exponential in the beginning, but limited by how close the population size (N) is to a critical size, the carrying capacity (K):

$$G = rN[(K - N)/K]$$

E. More accurately defined; **carrying capacity** is the largest population that a defined area can sustain during a given period without harming the environment. The graph shows a lazy-S-shaped (**logistic growth model**) curve (Figure 36.4C). At first population size increases slowly; N is very small relative to K, and $(K - N)/K$ is near 1; then the population size increases rapidly. As the population size approaches K, the growth rate slows down; as N approaches K, the value of $(K - N)/K$ approaches zero and the value of G also approaches zero. This type of growth is typical of all organisms growing in limited environments. For example, actual data from a population of fur seals follow this model (Figure 36.4B).

F. The growth rate of a population results from the combination of birth rate and death rate at any one time. Growth rate rises if birth rate rises or death rate falls. Growth rate falls if birth rate falls or death rate rises.
NOTE: The growth rate discussed above is assuming there is no emigration or immigration.

Module 36.5 Multiple factors may limit population growth.

A. **Density-dependent** factors affect a greater percentage of individuals as the density of individuals (number per unit area) increases. Food supplies that become limited and the buildup of toxic wastes often depress growth rates by increasing the death rate, decreasing the birth rate, or both. The rate of the population growth is said to be density-dependent.

B. An example of the action of density-dependent factors is the decrease in clutch size as the number of female song sparrows increased (Figure 36.5A).

C. Clear-cut cases of density-dependent factors operating in nature are sometimes hard to determine because of the many conflicting factors. The white-footed mouse is a good example of how the density of a population can limit the population growth.

D. Density-independent factors limit population size, no matter what the size, and are often abiotic factors such as fires, floods, storms, seasonal changes in temperature or moisture, or disruption by human activity.

E. An example of the action of density-independent factors is the exponential growth then sudden decline in mid-summer of populations of leaf-sucking aphids due to drying conditions (Figure 36.5B).

F. Over the long term, most populations are regulated by a mixture of density-dependent and density-independent factors, and the distinction between these two types may not be clear (Figure 36.5C).

Module 36.6 Some populations have "boom-and-bust" cycles.

A. Potential density-dependent factors suggested for population cycles (in addition to food supply and predation) include stress from crowding (e.g., lemmings).

B. Populations of predators and prey often show periodic cycles, such as the 10-year cycle for the lynx and the snowshoe hare in the taiga of North America. Note that the cycles of both animals have about a 10-year period (Figure 36.6).

NOTE: The numbers of prey are much larger than those for predators (note the two different Y axes), relative differences that hold true for these two different trophic levels across community types (see Module 37.13). Also notice that the hare population generally peaks before the lynx, and once the hare population falls, the lynx population follows. This leads into the following discussion.

C. For the lynx and many predators, the availability of prey often determines population changes.

D. For the hare, however, the force of predation may not be the determining factor. Hare populations cycle whether or not lynxes are present. There is evidence that the 10-year cycle of the snowshoe hare population is due to both the effects of predation and fluctuations in the hare's food supply.

E. Predator population cycles always lag behind prey population cycles. Predators reproduce more slowly than prey and take longer to increase the total population. As the predator population increases, more pressure is placed on the prey population, thus decreasing their numbers. This causes stress on the predator population, which then starts to decline.

II. Life Histories and Their Evolution

Module 36.7 Evolution shapes life histories.

A. **Life history** is the series of events of an organism's existence—birth, reproduction, and death. Aspects of life history that influence growth rate include age at first reproduction, number of offspring, and amount of parental care. Each of these traits is shaped by natural selection.

B. Life histories that are characterized by reproducing early in life, yielding many offspring (big-bang reproduction), generally exhibiting high mortality rates (a Type III survivorship curve; Figure 36.3), and having populations showing exponential growth during favorable times are indicative of *r*-selection, the intrinsic rate of population increase. Such populations live in unpredictable environments and are controlled by density-independent factors. Examples include dandelions, molds, and the agave (Figure 36.7A).

Preview: r-selection-type species are often first to recolonize in secondary succession (Module 37.7).

C. Life histories that are characterized by reproducing later in life, yielding fewer offspring, generally experiencing low mortality rates (a Type I survivorship curve; Figure 36.6), and having populations showing stability over time are of the *K*-selection type, close to carrying capacity. Such populations are held near carrying capacity by density-dependent factors. Examples include many larger vertebrates such as polar bears and whales.

D. An example is given of two different guppy populations evolving under two different regimes of predation. Killifish and cichlids both prey on guppies. Killifish eat mainly small, immature guppies. Cichlids eat mainly large, mostly mature, guppies. When preyed upon by cichlids, guppies tend to be smaller, mature earlier, and produce more offspring than they do in areas without cichlids. The heritability of these life history traits is demonstrated by the retention of these characteristics over the course of several generations in predator-free environments. Another experiment involved taking guppies from populations preyed upon by cichlids, removing them from that environment, and subjecting them to a pattern of predation in which small guppies were preyed upon.

The results were that within two years the female guppies matured later and produced fewer, larger offspring (Figure 36.7B).

Review: These experiments are good examples of the scientific approach to problem solving (Modules 1.7 and 1.8) and the effects of directional selection (Module 13.16).

Module 36.8 Connection: Principles of population ecology have practical applications.

A. The practice of harvesting crops without damaging the resources is called **sustainable resource management** and is practiced and promoted by wildlife managers, fishery biologists, and foresters.

B. **Maximum sustained yield** promotes the concept of harvesting at a level that is constant without forcing the population into decline. This idea is illustrated in Module 36.4. Populations grow best when resources are plentiful and the number of individuals in the population is at an intermediate level.

C. Ecological principles are unfortunately not used when decisions are being made to overharvest a crop. A prime example is the overharvesting of northern cod. As a result of poor planning and a total disregard of ecological principles, the cod fisheries of Newfoundland have collapsed (Figure 36.8A).

D. Integrated pest management (IPM) programs use several approaches in an attempt to control the population of a pest. A combination of chemical, biological, and cultural methods is employed with the objectives of minimizing environmental damage and reducing health risks while controlling the pest population.

III. The Human Population

Module 36.9 Connection: Human population growth has started to slow after centuries of exponential increase.

A. The worldwide human population grew relatively slowly (with a 25% setback during the bubonic plague) until it was about 500,000,000 in 1650. Between 1650 and 1850 (200 years), the population doubled to 1 billion. Between 1850 and 1930 (80 years), the population doubled to 2 billion. Between 1930 and 1975 (45 years), the population doubled to 4 billion. Presently there are approximately 6.4 billion people on Earth (Figure 36.9A). The world population is projected to reach 9.3 billion by 2050.

B. Most of human history saw replacement reproduction. But with the advent of better nutrition, medicine, and sanitation facilities (particularly clean drinking water), more people are reaching maturity. The world growth rate has been exponential for more than 360 years.

C. Human population cannot continue to grow forever in a limited environment; the human population will stop growing. The question is, at what carrying capacity or as a result of what unforeseen biotic or abiotic catastrophe will the population stop growing? Fortunately, or we can hope (depending on one's view of human nature and ingenuity), humans can deliberately choose at what level to control the human population.

NOTE: Regarding carrying capacity, debate must also concern the quality of life of humans and of the remaining species on Earth (Chapter 38).

D. A new method of estimating the potential for human population growth is called an **ecological footprint.** This is a multiparameter method of estimating the amount of land needed to support one human in a particular lifestyle (Figure 36.9B). In 1997, Americans required 5 times the ecological footprint available per person on earth.

E. Several questions can be raised and discussed by the class.

   1. What will the maximum carrying capacity be for the Earth, or have we reached it already?

   2. Are Americans and people of other developed nations, such as those in Europe, willing to change their lifestyle to fit into the available ecological footprint?

   3. How close to each other are humans willing to live (Figure 36.8C)?

Module 36.10 Birth and death rates and age structure affect population growth.

A. A country (e.g., Sweden) obtains zero population growth (ZPG) when the rate of birth equals the death rate. Most developed countries are approaching or have obtained such growth patterns, but others, such as Mexico, are still in the process of **demographic transition** (Figure 36.10A). Even in a country such as China (which has very strict population laws), with a birth rate of 1.7 children per female, the population will continue to increase due to a lag in the rate of decline.

B. A typical population has three main age groups: prereproductive (under 15 years old), reproductive (15–45 years old), and postreproductive (45 years and older). In each diagram, all the bars add up to 100, the vertical "steps" represent age groups by 5-year intervals, and the left and right halves divide the population by gender (Figure 36.10B).

C. **Age structure** is the portion of individuals of a given age within a population. Human population age structures can also show differences in social conditions, as in the comparison of age structures of the populations of Italy, the United States, and Afghanistan. Italy has a stable structure and relatively low birth rate, with older people continuing to represent a larger portion of the entire population than even the United States. Afghanistan population structure shows the effects of a predominantly young population and explosive population growth (Figure 36.10B).

D. Other factors that impact age structure and the comparison among countries are *infant mortality* and *life expectancy at birth*. Afghanistan has an infant mortality rate of 143 and a life expectancy at birth of 47 years. Japan has an infant mortality rate of 3 and life expectancy at birth of 81 years.

E. Human populations are unique in being able to voluntarily regulate reproduction. Reduced family size and, especially, delayed reproduction decreases population growth rates. A key component to reducing a developing county's population is the education of its women. As women become better educated, they choose to have fewer children and start at a later age. This is politically and socially a hot button.

F. The impact of the global human population growth on Earth is discussed in Chapter 38.

Class Activities

1. Modules 36.9 and 36.10 should provoke much discussion and debate: Discuss the economic impact of an aging population—fewer working individuals supporting a larger number of retired individuals. How might this affect the politics of immigration (note that predications based on age structure diagrams do not consider migration)? What is the ultimate carrying capacity of this planet for humans? What, if anything, should be done to limit human population growth? What are the moral and ethical issues involved? Ask students how they think these issues will affect their quality of life. The future of social security has been a prominent issue in political discussions.

2. Consider how humans have impacted the life histories of both domesticated and nondomesticated plants and animals.

3. Have your students consider pest management in terms of local (or their own) lawns/gardens/farms/parks. How might they manage these areas without using (or by minimizing the use of) pesticides?

Transparency Acetates

Chapter 36 Introduction, page 726: The spread of starlings across North America

Table 36.3	Life table for the U.S. population in 1999
Figure 36.3	Three types of survivorship curves
Figure 36.4A	Exponential growth of bacteria
Figure 36.4B	Growth of a population of fur seals
Figure 36.4C	Logistic growth and exponential growth compared
Figure 36.5A	Decrease in song sparrow clutch size as population density increases
Figure 36.5B	The effect of an abiotic factor (climate) on aphid population size
Figure 36.5C	Fluctuations in a song sparrow population, with periodic catastrophic reductions due to severe winter weather
Figure 36.6	Population cycles of the snowshoe hare and the lynx
Figure 36.7B	Effect of predation on life history traits of guppies
Figure 36.8	Collapse of northern cod fishery off Newfoundland
Figure 36.9A	The history of human population growth
Figure 36.9B	Ecological footprint in relation to ecological capacity
Figure 36.10A	Demographic transition in Mexico
Figure 36.10B	Age structures for the human population of Afghanistan, the United States, and Italy for 2003

Reviewing the Concepts, page 740: Three types of survivorship curves

Connecting the Concepts, page 740: Idealized exponential and logistic growth curves

Connecting the Concepts, page 740: Demographic transition for a hypothetical country

Testing Your Knowledge, page 741: Dispersion patterns

Media

See the beginning of this book for a complete description of all media available for instructors and students. Animations and videos are available in the Campbell Image Presentation Library. Media Activities and Thinking as a Scientist investigations are available on the student CD-ROM and website.

Activities and Thinking as a Scientist	Module Number
Web/CD Activity 36A: *Techniques for Estimating Population Density and Size*	36.2
Web/CD Activity 36B: *Investigating Survivorship Curves*	36.3
Biology Labs On-Line: *Population Structure and Dynamics*	36.5
Web/CD Activity 36C: *Human Population Growth*	36.9
Web/CD Activity 36D: *Analyzing Age-Structure Diagrams*	36.10
Biology Labs On-Line: *The Human Population*	36.10

CHAPTER 37

Communities and Ecosystems

Teaching Objectives

Introduction   Describe the interrelationships of the wasps that parasitize the cabbage white butterfly.

Structural Features of Communities

37.1   Describe the four properties of a community.

37.2   Define the concepts of interspecific competition, the competitive exclusion principle, resource partitioning, and a niche.

37.3   Define predation and describe the different strategies of predators and prey. Distinguish between Batesian and Müllerian mimicry.

37.4   Define a keystone species, and describe two examples.

37.5   Explain why most plants have a variety of chemicals, spines, and thorns for defense against herbivores. Define coevolution and describe two examples.

37.6   Describe three types of symbiotic relationships, noting examples of each.

37.7   Explain how disturbances can be beneficial to a community. Distinguish between primary and secondary succession.

37.8   Describe the roles of fire in shaping ecosystems.

37.9   Identify and compare the trophic levels of terrestrial and aquatic food chains.

37.10   Explain how food chains interconnect to form food webs.

Ecosystem Structure and Dynamics

37.11   Compare the movement of energy and chemicals in ecosystems.

37.12   Compare the primary production of tropical rain forests, coral reefs, and open ocean. Explain why these differences exist.

37.13–37.14   Describe the movement of energy through a food chain. Explain why there are more producers than consumers and why eating meat is considered to be a great luxury.

37.15–37.19   Explain how water, carbon, nitrogen, and phosphorus are cycled within ecosystems.

Ecosystem Alteration

37.20   Describe what we have learned from the experiments at the Hubbard Brook Experimental Forest.

37.21   Define cultural eutrophication and explain how it is caused.

Key Terms

abiotic reservoir	commensalism	detritivores
Batesian mimicry	community	detritus
biogeochemical cycles	competitive exclusion	disturbances
biomass	principle	ecological succession
chemical cycling	decomposers	ecosystem
coevolution	decomposition	energy flow

food chain	parasitism	producers
food web	pathogens	quaternary consumers
herbivores	predation	resource partitioning
interspecific competition	predator	secondary consumers
keystone species	prey	secondary succession
Müllerian mimicry	primary consumers	species diversity
mutualism	primary production	symbiotic relationship
niche	primary succession	tertiary consumers

Word Roots

mutu- = reciprocal (*mutualism:* a symbiotic relationship in which both the host and the symbiont benefit)

Lecture Outline

Introduction *Dining In*

    A. A special food chain.

        1. Some insects go to extremes of interdependence. For example, chalcid wasps parasitize the eggs of ichneumon wasps, which have been laid in Apanteles wasp eggs, which have been laid in *Pieris* (cabbage butterfly) caterpillars (which eat cabbages) (chapter-opening photos).

        2. One would be tempted to think such food chains could go on forever, as suggested by Jonathan Swift's poem about fleas on fleas. However, there are good reasons this cannot be so.

    B. This chapter focuses on two interrelated levels of ecology:

        1. Community structure and function depend on the interactions among organisms.

        2. Ecosystem structure and function depend on the interactions of the community with its abiotic environment.

I. Structural Features of Communities

    Module 37.1 A community includes all the organisms inhabiting a particular area.

    A. A **community** is an assemblage of all populations of organisms living close enough together for population interaction (Figure 37.1). The four main properties of a community are presented below.
       Review: The hierarchical organization of life (Module 1.1).

        1. **Species diversity** refers to the variety of species present and has two components: richness (the number of different species) and relative abundance (the number of individuals of each species). A community with individuals divided equally among four species is very different from a community with the same species unequally represented.

        2. The nature of the dominant organisms is an important property. This can involve either vegetation or animals. The dominant species in Figure 37.1 are the grasses.
          NOTE: Another example is the dominance of mosses, shrubs, grasses, and lichens in alpine tundras and the clumps of different vegetation groups (Module 34.17).

3. The response to a disturbance by a community illustrates the stability of the community, the ability to resist change, and the return of the original species' composition and structure.

4. The fourth property of communities is their **trophic structure,** the nutritional relationships among all the components (Modules 37.9–37.11).

B. There are four interspecific interactions that tie populations together in communities: competition, predation, herbivory, and symbiosis. These interactions are all influenced by evolution through natural selection.

Module 37.2 Competition may occur when a shared resource is limited.

Review: Population growth models (Module 36.4).

A. **Interspecific competition** occurs when two species are competing for the same resources. Competition between two species can inhibit the growth of both populations, sometimes to the point where one is eliminated.

B. In the 1930s, Gause studied interspecific competition between two species of paramecium. When grown in separate cultures with the same amount of food being added each day, each species' population followed a logistic growth curve (Module 36.4). When grown together, one species of paramecium eliminated its competitor.

C. The ideas embodied in Gause's experiments have been termed the **competitive exclusion principle.** In modern wording, this principle states that populations of two species cannot coexist if their niches are too similar.

D. A population's **niche** is its role in its community, the total of a species' relationships to the biotic and abiotic factors of its habitat. The concept of niche is a theoretical construct that is difficult to assess in nature.
   NOTE: Compared to an organism's habitat (its address), its niche is like an organism's occupation. Although this analogy is not perfect, it clarifies the fact that habitat and niche refer to different characteristics of a species.

E. Niche and interspecific competition are demonstrated by two species of suspension-feeding barnacles in the genera *Chthamalus* and *Balanus. Chthamalus* normally lives higher on intertidal rocks, but if *Balanus* is removed, **Chthamalus** will live lower. Ecologists conclude that *Chthamalus*'s lower boundary is determined by competition, and the upper boundaries of both species are determined by how well a species resists drying out (Figure 37.2A).

F. Competition between two very similar species for the same resources will have either of these two results:
   1. One species will become extinct.
   2. One of the species will change enough to use a different set of resources.

G. This process of niche differentiation between two similar species in one community is called **resource partitioning** (Figure 37.2B).

Module 37.3 Predation leads to diverse adaptations in both predator and prey.

A. The **predator** is the eater, and the **prey** is the eaten (including plants). No species is entirely free of predation, at least when young. **Predation** is the interaction between species when one kills and eats the other species.

B. Adaptations to assist in eating or avoid being eaten are requirements for survival to reach sexual maturity.

C. Camouflage, the blending in of an organism with its background, is common among animals (Figure 37.3A).

D. Defense mechanisms against predators include size, fleeing, hiding, mimicry, and the production of defensive structures (e.g., spines or armor) or chemicals (e.g., skunk sprays and alkaloids in poison-arrow frogs). These mechanisms evolve by natural selection influenced by predator-prey interaction (Figure 37.3B).

NOTE: In addition, predators (and parasites) often remove the weaker or infirm individuals of their prey, thereby helping improve the prey's genetic stock or, at least, the overall health of the prey population, and helping keep the prey population size below levels at which it may outstrip its food supply.

E. Mimicry protects the mimic (of a distasteful or dangerous species) from consumption. **Batesian mimicry** is shown by a harmless species (in lower numbers) mimicking a dangerous species (Figure 37.3C). **Müllerian mimicry** is shown by two unpalatable species, each of which gains advantage from the other warning off predators (Figure 37.3D). The snapping turtle also uses mimicry to catch fish (its tongue looks like a wriggling worm).

Module 37.4 Predation can maintain diversity in a community.

A. **Keystone species** exert a strong influence over the community because of their ecological role. This is illustrated in the sea star experiment conducted by Paine (Figure 37.4A). Keystone species help maintain community diversity by consuming, and reducing the density of, prey that are very strong competitors.

B. In the experiments by Paine, the predatory sea star *Pisaster* is removed from a community, its main prey, *Mytilus* (a mussel), outcompetes many other shoreline organisms (e.g., barnacles and snails), and community diversity declines.

C. The sea otter is a keystone species that is currently being preyed upon by killer whales; scientists think this is a result of overfishing in the northern Pacific Ocean. Killer whales normally eat sea lions and seals, which normally eat fish. The fish population has declined due to overfishing, which causes the ripple effect and the decline in the sea otter population (Figure 37.4B).

Module 37.5 Herbivores and the plants they eat have various adaptations.

A. **Herbivores** are animals that eat plants or algae. The sea urchin is an herbivore that eats kelp (Figure 37.4B).

B. Plants, unlike animals, cannot flee from predators. They have evolved specialized mechanisms of defense, such as thorns and spines. Plants also produce toxic chemicals such as strychnine, nicotine, morphine, opium, mescaline, and tannins. Some plants have evolved chemicals that induce abnormal development in the insects that eat them.

C. **Coevolution** is a series of interdependent adaptations of two species. An example of coevolved features is the evolution of toxic chemicals in the leaves of *Passiflora* that protect the plant from consumption by most insects, and the coevolution of special enzymes in the butterfly *Heliconius,* which can eat *Passiflora*. Furthermore, some species of *Passiflora* produce sugar deposits on leaves that look like *Heliconius* eggs, thereby causing the butterfly to avoid laying eggs on them (Figure 37.5).

Review: The coevolution of plants and animals is discussed in Module 17.13.

Module 37.6 Symbiotic relationships help structure communities.

A. A **symbiotic relationship** is an interaction between two or more species in which one or more species lives in or on another.

NOTE: The distinction between each of the following categories of symbiosis is inexact. It is often difficult to determine the precise nutritional or other benefits provided by, or harm caused by, a symbiotic relationship. The categories are derived by ecologists to simplify discussion of some complex interrelationships.

B. **Parasitism** is much like predation, but the parasite is usually smaller than the host species. The parasite gains and the host loses from the relationship. Natural selection favors parasites that have adaptations to find and feed on hosts. Coevolution of host and parasite often takes place so that the hosts have adaptive defenses against parasites. *NOTE:* The worst harm done by parasites is on nonnative hosts, which have not coevolved with the parasite. The fungal pathogens that cause Dutch elm disease and chestnut blight are two such parasites that have ravaged native tree populations in North America.

C. **Pathogens** are disease-causing microbes; they are similar to parasites but can be lethal to the host. The myxoma virus (a rabbit pathogen) was introduced in 1950 to control the exploding rabbit population in Australia. After 40 years of coevolution, rabbits are better able to resist infections, and the most virulent virus strains are absent, having died off with the rabbits they killed (Figure 37.6A). A new viral pathogen was introduced in 1995 with renewed success.
Preview: Introduced species often pose a threat to native species (Module 38.3).

D. **Commensalism** involves close relationships between organisms in which one benefits and the other neither gains nor loses. An example is the relationship between certain insect-eating birds and grazing cattle. The cattle flush out insect prey that the birds consume. It is not clear how, if at all, the cattle benefit.
NOTE: Another example is an owl roosting in an abandoned woodpecker hole. In commensal relationships, the neutral species may be neutral only in our present understanding, but may, in fact, gain or lose from the relationship.

E. **Mutualism** benefits both partners. Nitrogen-fixing bacteria gain a home, and their nodule-forming legumes gain nitrogen (Module 32.13). The acacia tree gains protection from plant pests by catering to its *Pseudomyrmex* inhabitants. These ants live in hollow thorns and eat sugar and protein-rich swellings as the tree grows. If the ants are removed, the tree dies (Figure 37.6B).

Module 37.7 Disturbance is a prominent feature of most communities.

A. Traditionally, biological communities have been viewed as being stable, with interactions among the components acting to maintain the community. On a local scale, however, change may be more common than stability. An updated model describes communities in constant flux responding to change.

B. **Disturbances** are events that damage communities, remove organisms, and alter the available resources. Natural disturbances such as fire, storm, drought, and freezing temperature have an impact on the community. Human activity can also disturb communities.

C. Disturbances can have both negative and positive effects. Small-scale disturbances often have positive effects. For example, a depression left by an uprooted tree may fill with water and be used as an egg-laying site by frogs. Small-scale disturbance may increase environmental variability, thus increasing diversity.
Preview: The negative impact of human disturbance is the topic of Chapter 38.

D. **Ecological succession** is the transition in the species composition in a community over time, following the destruction of the original community by flood, fire, glacial retreat, or other natural or human disturbance.
NOTE: In succession it is important to emphasize that it is the organisms themselves that influence the transition in both the biotic and abiotic factors.

E. **Primary succession** occurs in virtually lifeless areas that have no soil. An example is a newly formed volcanic island. Another example of primary succession is the land exposed after a glacier retreats. Frequently, the first colonizers are autotrophic microorganisms. Often, the first large photosynthesizers found on the barren ground are lichens and mosses. The decomposition of these organisms gradually forms soil. Once soil is present, the lichens and mosses are overgrown by other plants, such as grasses, shrubs (mat-forming *Dryas*), and trees (spruce and hemlock) from seeds that have been blown in or carried in by animals. This gradual process of succession to the community making up the biome can take hundreds of years (Figure 37.7).

F. **Secondary succession** occurs when a previously existing community was destroyed, but the soil was left intact. An example is a forest that was cleared for farmland and was later abandoned; this can be seen in areas of the eastern United States. If the area remains undisturbed and secondary succession takes place, the land will eventually give way to a forest.

G. Today, humans are the single greatest factor affecting community change and succession. *NOTE:* Examples can be seen in overgrazing in parts of Africa, resulting in desertification. Logging in the United States and Europe has reduced large tracts of forest to patchy woodlands. The grasslands of the midwestern United States have been converted to farmland. The tropical rain forest in the southern hemisphere is being cleared for lumber and pastureland.
Preview: Human impact on the environment (Chapter 38).

Module 37.8 Talking about Science: Fire specialist Max Moritz discusses the role of fire in ecosystems.

A. Dr. Max Moritz is a wildland fire specialist with the College of Natural Resources at the University of California (Figure 37.8A). One of his special interests is fire in the chaparral ecosystems that mark much of the American West (Figure 37.8B).

B. Until recent decades, the benefits of wildfires were poorly understood. People have long tried to suppress wildfires, but it is now known that, in some ecosystems, low-intensity wildfires deter more destructive high-intensity wildfires by not allowing the fuel (trees and brush) to grow large. In addition, wildfires are important to the plant nutrient cycle. Some species of chaparral plants actually require the heat and chemical effects of fire for seed germination.

C. Through his research, Moritz hopes to help people understand the ways they influence wildfires (through building, logging, grazing, and landscape defragmentation) and to teach people how to live wisely in fire-prone ecosystems.

Module 37.9 Trophic structure is a key factor in community dynamics.

A. The trophic structure of a community is the pattern of feeding relationships that determines the flow of energy and the routes of elements that are cycled.

B. The transfer of food from trophic level to trophic level is called a **food chain** (Figure 37.9). Food chains differ for each community type. Natural food chains are never single, unbranched chains (as implied by the diagrams).

C. In a terrestrial food chain, the trophic levels include the following:
   1. **Producers** (autotrophic plants).
   2. **Primary consumers** (herbivores that consume the producers; e.g., grasshoppers).

3. **Secondary consumers** (e.g., a mouse eating an herbivorous insect).

4. **Tertiary consumers** (e.g., a snake eating a mouse).

5. **Quaternary consumers** (carnivores that consume the next lower consumer level; e.g., a hawk).

D. In the illustrated aquatic food chain, the trophic levels are the same, but the players are different.

E. **Detritivores,** or **decomposers,** derive their energy from the breakdown of **detritus,** organismal waste and parts of dead organisms. Detritivores include, principally, fungi and bacteria (essential to all life on Earth) but also small animals and prokaryotes. The larger detritivores break apart the material physically and alter it chemically. The smaller detritivores function in **decomposition,** the breakdown of organic chemicals to inorganic chemicals.

Module 37.10 Food chains interconnect, forming food webs.

A. A **food web,** which is a network of interconnected food chains, is a more realistic representation of the trophic structure of a community (Figure 37.10). Consumers usually eat more than one type of food. Each food type is consumed by more than one type of consumer. Detritivores feed on the dead remains of all (different detritivores are selective).

B. The arrows in a food web diagram outline an ecosystem's overall flow of chemical nutrients and energy, but the diagram still simplifies the relationships among organisms because the individual species at all the trophic levels are usually not represented.

II. Ecosystem Structure and Dynamics

Module 37.11 Ecosystems ecology emphasizes energy flow and chemical cycling.

Review: The distinction between autotrophs and heterotrophs (Module 16.11) and the laws of thermodynamics (Module 5.2).

A. An **ecosystem** includes all the organisms in a community and the interaction of those organisms with their abiotic environment. An ecosystem has two dynamic processes: energy flow and chemical cycling.

B. **Energy flow** is the one-way passage of energy through the components of the ecosystem, usually starting with photosynthesis by autotrophs and proceeding through heterotrophs. Every use of chemical energy by an organism involves loss of heat to the surroundings (Figure 37.11).

C. An exception to the sun being the ultimate source of energy for an ecosystem, as for example hydrothermal vent ecosystems, is discussed in Chapter 34 (Opening Essay; Module 34.7).

D. **Chemical cycling** is the circular movement of elements among the biotic and abiotic parts of an ecosystem (or among components of many ecosystems).

Module 37.12 Primary production sets the energy budget for ecosystems.

A. The Earth receives approximately 10^{19} kcal of solar energy per day (equal to the energy released by 100 million atomic bombs). Only 1% of the visible light that reaches Earth is converted into chemical energy by autotrophs via photosynthesis. On a global scale, this adds up to 170 billion tons of organic matter each year.

B. **Biomass** is the amount of organic material in a collection of living organisms or their remains. The rate at which producers convert solar energy to chemical energy in a given time period is called **primary production.**

C. There is a wide variety in the amount of production by producers when comparing ecosystems. Table 37.12 compares the primary production of several ecosystems.

Module 37.13 Energy supply limits the length of food chains.

A. The energy available along a food chain drops by an average of between 80% and 95% at each trophic level.
   Review: Module 5.2 discusses the first and second laws of thermodynamics.

B. The energy reduction between several trophic levels produces an energy pyramid (Figure 37.13). Food chains are limited to three to five levels because at the end of a food chain, little energy is available.
   Preview: Since some toxins, such as DDT, persist in the food chain, they become increasingly concentrated at higher trophic levels. The result is biological magnification (Module 38.4; also see Module 34.3).

Module 37.14 Connection: A production pyramid explains why meat is a luxury for humans.

A. Humans are omnivores. Among other foods, we eat fish (as tertiary or quaternary consumers), meat (as secondary or tertiary consumers), and plants (as primary consumers).

B. Humans have about ten times more energy available when we eat grain than when we eat grain-fed beef (Figure 37.14).

C. Meat production is expensive both economically and environmentally because it requires more land to be cultivated, more water for irrigation, and more chemical fertilizers and pesticides.

Module 37.15 Chemicals are recycled between organic matter and abiotic reservoirs.

A. There are virtually no extraterrestrial sources of water or other nutrients that life requires.

B. The process of cycling chemicals between abiotic sources and an ecosystem's biotic components is called a **biogeochemical cycle.** The point in the cycle where the chemicals are stockpiled outside the living organisms is called an **abiotic reservoir.**

C. A typical cycle has four steps (Figure 37.15).
   1. Producer incorporates chemical from abiotic reservoir into organic compound.
   2. Consumer feeds on producer.
   3. Consumer and producer return waste products to environment.
   4. Decomposers convert organic waste compounds back to inorganic form, and they are stored in the air, soil, or water.

D. Biogeochemical cycles can bypass the producer and consumer steps (e.g., the evaporation of water from a pond back to the atmosphere only to fall as rain again elsewhere). The cycles can be local, as with phosphorous, or global, as with water.

E. The four abiotic reserves discussed in the next four modules are: water, carbon in the air, nitrogen in the air, and phosphorus in rocks.

Module 37.16 Water moves through the biosphere in a global cycle.

A. Water is essential for life because all organisms are composed mostly of water and water makes the environment suitable for life. The cycling of water is driven by heat from the sun through the processes of precipitation, evaporation, and transpiration (Figure 37.16).

B. The principal abiotic reservoir is the ocean. The atmospheric reservoir is mobile and gives the water cycle its global character. Over the ocean, evaporation exceeds precipitation, and there is a net movement of water vapor onto land. On land, precipitation exceeds evaporation and transpiration, and there is a net movement of liquid water into the ocean.

C. By removing forests and overirrigating, humans can have major impacts on the water cycle. Water vapor leaving land will be altered when tropical rain forests are removed. When land is overirrigated, evaporation will increase and groundwater supplies will decrease.

Module 37.17 The carbon cycle depends on photosynthesis and respiration.

Review: Equations for photosynthesis and cellular respiration (Figures 7.4A and B).

A. Carbon is the major element in all organic compounds. The principal abiotic reservoir is the atmosphere, which cycles globally. Within the biosphere, carbon moves along food chains between trophic levels. Carbon returns to the atmosphere as respired CO_2 (Figure 37.17).
NOTE: Carbon cycle pathways are similar to food chain pathways because energy-storage molecules are all carbon-based compounds.

B. The reciprocal processes of photosynthesis and respiration are responsible for the movement of CO_2 from the abiotic and biotic world.
Preview: The burning of fossil fuels and wood has contributed to increased atmospheric levels of CO_2, and this may cause global warming (Module 38.5).

Module 37.18 The nitrogen cycle relies heavily on bacteria.

Review: Nitrogen fixation and other nitrogen-cycling processes involving prokaryotes (Modules 16.17, 32.13, and 32.14).

A. Organisms use nitrogen during the anabolic processes of proteins and nucleic acids synthesis. The principal abiotic reservoir is the atmosphere, which cycles globally. However, gaseous nitrogen (80% of the atmosphere) is only available directly to certain nitrogen-fixing prokaryotes (Figure 37.18).

B. Plants can use nitrogen only in the form of NO_3^- (nitrate) or NH_4^+ (ammonium). Nitrogen-fixing bacteria convert atmospheric N_2 to NH_3 (ammonia), which then becomes NH_4^+. Nitrifying bacteria convert NH_4^+ into NO_3^-. NO_3^- is the main source of nitrogen for plants. Animals must eat plants or other animals to get usable nitrogen.

C. Fungi and prokaryotes decompose nitrogen-containing detritus to NH_4^+. Nitrogen is lost from the biotic cycling by the action of denitrifying bacteria converting soil NO_3^- into atmospheric N_2.
NOTE: Denitrification is anaerobic. Losses occur in agricultural areas where soil structure has broken down and becomes waterlogged and anaerobic.

D. Most nitrogen cycling by bacteria involves the inner cycle in Figure 37.18. Not shown in the figure are the NH_4^+ and NO_3^- made in the atmosphere, which reach the ground in precipitation and dust. Such sources are important in some ecosystems.

E. Sewage-treatment facilities and agricultural runoff release large amounts of biologically usable nitrogen into groundwater, streams, and lakes, resulting in increased algae growth (eutrophication) and the buildup of excess nitrogen compounds in water. Nitrates in drinking water are converted to nitrites, which can be toxic to humans.
NOTE: A considerable amount of nitrogen fixation occurs in the combustion of fossil fuels and in synthetic fertilizers produced by industrial nitrogen fixation, pathways not shown in the figure.

Module 37.19 The phosphorus cycle depends on the weathering of rock.

A. Phosphates are used by organisms to synthesize nucleic acids, phospholipids, and ATP, and are in bones and teeth. The main abiotic reservoir of phosphorus is rock. The cycling time for this reservoir is extremely slow because it requires that phosphates precipitate out into sediments, reform into rock, uplift, and be available again from rock weathering.

B. Abiotic pools of inorganic phosphates in soil solution are often limiting in ecosystems (Figure 37.19). The biotic cycling of phosphate starts with plant uptake of the phosphate ions.

C. Phosphates from fertilizer (made of crushed rocks) and pesticides can be in excess in runoff, leading to eutrophication of streams and lakes.

III. Ecosystem Alteration

Module 37.20 Connection: Ecosystem alteration can upset chemical cycling.

A. Since 1963, the Hubbard Brook Experimental Forest, a deciduous forest in the White Mountains of New Hampshire, has been studied by a team of scientists. The Hubbard Brook Forest consists of several watersheds. Long-term studies such as this one are essential for gaining an understanding of the dynamics of an ecosystem.

B. This study involves monitoring the water and nutrient dynamics that occur under natural conditions and after human intrusion.

C. From undisturbed forests, 60% of water entering as precipitation leaves the watershed in runoff, while transpiration and evaporation lose the remaining 40%. The flow of nutrients into and out of the watershed is nearly balanced, with small gains in some, particularly nitrates, in most years (Figure 37.20A).

D. In 1966, one of the watersheds was completely logged and sprayed with herbicide for three years to prevent the regrowth of plants. All the original plant material was left in place. Amounts of water and nutrients in runoff were monitored and compared to an unaltered watershed (Figure 37.20B).
   NOTE: In the background of Figure 37.20B, experimental setups of other logging methods can be seen, particularly strip-cutting on the left.

E. In the altered watershed, runoff increased 30–40%, apparently because there were no plants to absorb and transpire water from the soil. Further, there were huge losses of nutrients. For example, after the cutting, nitrate losses were 60 times greater than in the undisturbed watershed (Figure 37.20C).

F. One interesting finding from this study is that even before the study at Hubbard Brook began, none of the watersheds were free from human impact. For example, since the 1950s, acid precipitation has dissolved and carried away most of the Ca^{2+} in the soil. The result of lost calcium may have stopped tree growth.
   Review: The effects of acid precipitation on the environment are discussed in Module 2.16, and the effects of pH on enzyme activity are discussed in Module 5.7.

G. A new study to investigate the effects of calcium loss on tree growth was recently begun by spraying selected areas with calcium from helicopters. Preliminary results indicate an increase in soil pH, nitrate concentrations, and soil respiration. More time will be needed to verify renewed tree growth.

Module 37.21 Talking about Science: David Schindler talks about the effects of nutrients on freshwater ecosystems.

A. Dr. David Schindler is a professor of ecology at the University of Alberta and was involved in environmental research that resulted in the banning of phosphates in detergents (Figure 37.21A).

B. **Cultural eutrophication** involves the increase of nutrients above natural levels in aquatic ecosystems (Figure 37.21B).

C. Increases in nutrients in runoff ultimately end up flowing into aquatic ecosystems, where they can lead to eutrophication. This causes the ecosystems to become more productive and results in changes in the kinds and relative numbers of organisms.

D. Algal producers bloom in eutrophic conditions. This increases oxygen production during the day but greatly reduces oxygen levels at night, when the algae respire. Increased production of organisms causes increased respiration by decomposers and the development of anaerobic conditions in lake-bottom sediments. Over time, all aerobic organisms may suffer and eventually die out.

E. Other freshwater problems were listed by Schindler. Global warming was one. Another problem is the buildup of acidity following acid rain, particularly in those lakes that do not have natural buffering (Module 2.16). Failure to treat sewage runoff from large-scale cattle and hog farms causes eutrophication. Also, cattle and hogs have some of the same intestinal microbes as humans, yet their sewage flows freely into streams and rivers.

Class Activities

1. In most areas of the United States, successional changes in community structure occur and can be demonstrated. Demonstrate local changes by using slides of sites representing different time periods, or by visiting the sites with students and discussing the changes with them there. Have students measure or estimate the following at each site (or, with slides, during lecture): overall diversity of species; density and dispersion of the dominant vegetation; trophic level represented by each dominant organism; total biomass in the community; depth of the litter layers and organic soil; examples of parasitic, mutualistic, or commensal relationships; and overall resistance of the community to catastrophic occurrences.

2. Construct a glassware-tubing device to demonstrate the flow of energy through three trophic levels in an ecosystem to show how little energy is available after the third level. Use Y-shaped tubes to divide the output of a corked flask into flow that goes to the next flask and flow that goes to the sink (energy in heat, respiration, and waste). Use a valve in the line to the next flask to adjust its flow to about 10% of the waste flow. Spinning-ball gauges at the start and between each flask will show the drop in available energy, and the output from the third flask will be a mere trickle. Charge up the entire system with water before lecture, and hook up the first flask with an "energy source" from the sink or other water supply.

3. Have your students consider how human activities have disrupted the biome in which they live. Divide your students into groups; have each group consider a different aspect of the ecosystem (e.g., one group considers energy flow, another considers the carbon cycle, another considers the nitrogen cycle, etc.) and how it has been impacted by human activity. The groups should soon notice the need to interact with other groups, as these flows and cycles interact with one another.

Transparency Acetates

Figure 37.2	A test of competitive exclusion: two species of barnacles on intertidal rocks
Figure 37.2B	Resource partitioning among seven species of *Anolis* lizards
Figure 37.4B	Predation by killer whales on sea otters, allowing sea urchins to overgraze on kelp
Figure 37.9	Two food chains

Figure 37.10   A food web

Figure 37.11   A terrarium ecosystem

Figure 37.12   Net primary production of various ecosystems

Figure 37.13   An idealized pyramid of production

Figure 37.14   Food energy available to the human population at different trophic levels

Figure 37.15   A general model of nutrient cycling

Figure 37.16   The global water cycle

Figure 37.17   The carbon cycle

Figure 37.18   The nitrogen cycle

Figure 37.19   The phosphorus cycle

Figure 37.20C   The loss of nitrate from a deforested watershed

Reviewing the Concepts, page 762: An ecosystem includes a community and the abiotic factors with which it interacts

Connecting the Concepts, page 762: A community's interactions

Connecting the Concepts, page 763: Ecosystem dynamics

Media

See the beginning of this book for a complete description of all media available for instructors and students. Animations and videos are available in the Campbell Image Presentation Library. Media Activities and Thinking as a Scientist investigations are available on the student CD-ROM and website.

Animations and Videos   Module Number

Clownfish and Anemone Video   37.6

Activities and Thinking as a Scientist   Module Number

Web/CD Thinking as a Scientist: *How Are Impacts on
    Community Diversity Measured?*   37.1

Biology Labs On-Line: *Structural Features of Communities*   37.5

Web/CD Activity 37A: *Interspecific Interactions*   37.6

Web/CD Activity 37B: *Primary Succession*   37.7

Web/CD Activity 37C: *Food Webs*   37.10

Web/CD Activity 37D: *Energy Flow and Chemical Cycling*   37.11

Web/CD Thinking as a Scientist: *How Do Temperature
    and Light Affect Primary Production?*   37.12

Web/CD Activity 37E: *Energy Pyramids*   37.14

Web/CD Activity 37F: *The Carbon Cycle*   37.17

Web/CD Activity 37G: *The Nitrogen Cycle*   37.18

Web/CD Activity 37H: *Water Pollution from Nitrates*   37.18

CHAPTER 38

Conservation Biology

Teaching Objectives

Introduction   Describe the goals of conservation biology and the particular challenges of managing tigers in Asia.

The Biodiversity Crisis: An Overview

38.1   Describe the three components of biodiversity. Explain how human activities are a threat to biodiversity. Distinguish between endangered species and threatened species.

38.2   Explain why biodiversity is vital to human welfare. Explain why Madagascar is such an important island country.

38.3   Describe the three greatest threats to biodiversity, noting examples of each.

38.4   Explain how humans have polluted the environment and helped thin the ozone. Describe the consequences of these actions.

38.5   Describe the causes and consequences of global warming.

Conservation of Populations and Species

38.6   Compare the small-population approach to the declining-population approach to the study and conservation of endangered species.

38.7   Explain why the efforts to save the red-cockaded woodpecker from extinction are a good model for future conservation efforts.

Managing and Restoring Ecosystems

38.8   Describe the goals of landscape ecology. Describe the significance of edges and movement corridors in maintaining biodiversity.

38.9   Describe the significance of biodiversity hot spots. Describe the challenges of protecting species that migrate or otherwise require great ranges.

38.10   Describe the goals of the Yukon to Yellowstone Initiative. Explain why wolves are considered to be a keystone species.

38.11   Explain how restoration ecology, including bioremediation and biological augmentation, helps return degraded ecosystems to near-natural, predegraded states. Describe examples of both approaches.

38.12   Describe the goals and expected outcomes of the Kissimmee River Project.

38.13   Explain how zoned reserves are being used to protect ecosystems. Describe the success and ongoing challenges in Costa Rica.

38.14   Explain why sustainable development is the ultimate goal for the long-term prosperity of human societies and the ecosystems that support them.

Key Terms

biodiversity	conservation biology	ozone layer
biodiversity crisis	endangered species	restoration ecology
biodiversity hot spots	endemic species	sustainable development
biological augmentation	global warming	threatened species
biological magnification	landscape ecology	zoned reserve
bioremediation	movement corridor	

Lecture Outline

Introduction *Saving the Tiger*

    A. Focus on the human destruction of habitat and conservation efforts in the struggle to save the tigers.

        1. The tiger population was estimated to be around 100,000 worldwide 100 years ago. There are now approximately 5,000 remaining, and 3 of the 8 species are extinct.

        2. Intense conservation efforts by the government of Myanmar have begun to save the tiger population in the Hukawng Valley. Estimates from 2001 placed the tiger population in the 6,500 sq. km reserve at 150 to 200.

        3. The Myanmar government increased the reserve size to 20,000 sq. km to provide more habitat for the tiger and its prey. Wildlife biologists hope to see a tenfold increase in the tiger population in the next decade.

    B. The story of the tiger illustrates the **biodiversity crisis** (a rapid decrease in plant and animal diversity) that is threatening life on Earth.

    C. **Conservation biology** is an attempt by biologists to reverse the destructive trends of habitat and species destruction. The approach can be on a single species, as with the tiger, or very broad, attempting to assess and protect many species at once.

    D. This chapter focuses on the biodiversity crisis and approaches used by conservation biologists to slow the loss of species. Conservation biology touches all levels of ecology, from a single species (the tiger) to the habitat in which it lives (the Hukawng Valley reserve).

I. The Biodiversity Crisis: An Overview

    Module 38.1 Human activities threaten Earth's biodiversity.

    A. The high rate of species loss is a direct result of human activity. Humans are altering trophic structure, energy flow, chemical recycling, and natural disturbances.

    B. There are approximately 10 million to as many as 80 million different species in the world. Scientists have named about 1.5 million species. The rate of species loss is estimated to be 1,000 times higher than at any time in the past 100,000 years.

    C. Biodiversity has three components: genetic, species, and ecosystem diversity.

        1. *Genetic diversity* within and among populations of a species is dependent on the raw material provided by the genes. If a population is lost, there is a reduction in the available material used for adaptation to environmental changes. Extreme decreases in genetic diversity endanger the survival of a species.

        2. *Species diversity* is the variety of species in an ecosystem and is a popular scientific, as well as political, topic. The ESA defines an **endangered species** as one that

is close to extinction in all or most of its range. The ESA also defines **threatened species** as those that are close to becoming endangered in the near future.

3. *Ecosystem diversity* is described as the interaction of populations of different species within an ecosystem. Removal (extinction) of a species in an ecosystem can adversely affect the remaining species, particularly if the lost species is a keystone predator like the tiger. Altered patterns of chemical and energy flow in one ecosystem can affect the entire biosphere (phytoplankton remove CO_2 and thus moderate the greenhouse effect).

D. Destruction of tropical rain forests dramatically illustrates ecosystem damage (Figure 38.1A). Coral reefs have been decimated, and it is estimated that 40% to 50% of all coral reefs will be gone in the next 30 to 40 years (Figure 38.1B).

Module 38.2 Biodiversity is vital to human welfare.

A. Human activities are altering the biosphere at a rapid rate. These changes are threatening the survival of species on which we are dependent for survival. For example, humans depend on other species for oxygen, food, clothing, soil fertilizer, etc.

B. Twenty-five percent of prescription drugs dispensed by U.S. pharmacies contain substances derived from plants. Accompanying the loss of biodiversity is the loss of potential benefit to humans. For example, in Madagascar, there are plants that have potential as treatment for cancers (the rosy periwinkle; Figure 38.2).

C. Madagascar is home to 200,000 plant and animal species. In the 2,000 years humans have lived on Madagascar, 80% of its forests and 50% of its native species have been lost. This loss of biodiversity (and its potential) is not unique to this island.
Review: The impact of humans on Madagascar is also discussed in Module 19.1.

D. The loss of species means the loss of genetic diversity and lost opportunities that we have not been able to realize. PCR is a good example of how scientists have discovered useful biomedical products through a process called bioprospecting.

E. In an attempt to facilitate understanding the true value of the ecosystem, a team of ecologists and economists estimated the value of ecosystems in terms of cost for services rendered. They estimated the value of a wetland in 1997 at 33 trillion U.S. dollars per year. That same year the total gross national product of the U.S. was 18 trillion U.S. dollars.

Module 38.3 Habitat destruction, introduced species, and overexploitation are the major threats to biodiversity.

A. Habitat destruction by humans poses the single greatest threat to biodiversity. Agriculture, residential development, overpopulation, forestry, mining, and environmental pollution all contribute to habitat destruction (Figure 38.1A). According to the IUCNNR, habitat destruction is directly responsible for 73% of all species in modern history becoming extinct, endangered, or threatened.

B. The next greatest threat to biodiversity is the competition between native and introduced (exotic) species. Nonnative species, introduced either intentionally or unintentionally into a new community, frequently fail to survive. However, when they do survive, the absence of their native predators allows their populations to drastically increase.

C. Examples of introduced species in North America are house sparrows, starlings, rock doves (pigeons), and the kudzu vine (Figure 38.3A).

D. In Lake Victoria, about 200 native species went extinct with the introduction of the Nile perch. The Nile perch was introduced to provide food to the growing human population of eastern Africa. Instead, the Nile perch wiped out the smaller native species and critically reduced its own food supply.

E. Biodiversity is also threatened when wildlife is harvested past the rate of repopulation. Some examples of species that have been drastically reduced in numbers through excessive human activity (hunting, poaching, commercial harvesting) are the American bison, Galápagos tortoises, tigers, whales, and the North Atlantic bluefin tuna (Figure 38.3B). Illegal wildlife trade also threatens many species (e.g., demand for rhinoceros horns, grizzly bear gallbladders, and elephant tusks).

Module 38.4 Connection: Pollution of the environment compounds our impact on other species.

A. The biodiversity crisis is worsened by the pollutants that humans release into the environment. Pollution can have a local effect, for example, environmental damage that occurs during an oil spill.

B. Likewise, pollutants can have a far-reaching effect. Air pollutants emitted into the atmosphere in one place can have effects on environments thousands of miles away. *Review:* Acid precipitation (Module 2.16).

C. The ozone layer has been thinning since 1975. The reduction in this protective layer may cause increases in skin cancer and cataracts and may have deleterious effects on the phytoplankton in the oceans. The destruction of the ozone is thought to have resulted from the use of CFCs.
Review: CFCs and the ozone layer are discussed in Module 7.14.

D. Excessive runoff of nutrients into surface water supplies has resulted in dead zones at the mouths of rivers that extend far out into the ocean. As many as 150 dead zones worldwide have been documented.

E. DDT and other such chemical pesticides have adverse effects on nontarget species. As DDT is passed up a food chain it becomes increasingly concentrated in animal tissue, in a phenomenon called **biological magnification.**
Review: Food chains and energy flow through ecosystems (Modules 37.9 and 37.13).

F. A poignant example of biological magnification is seen in the Great Lakes where the chemical PCB is passed up the food chain and found to be 5,000 times higher in herring gull eggs than in the phytoplankton (Figure 38.4).

G. Never-seen-before synthetic chemicals are causing a pollution crisis because microbes cannot degrade them or they are degraded into an even more toxic substance. Mercury is a prime example of the latter point. Aquatic microbes convert mercury into methyl mercury, which is extremely toxic (and soluble) and accumulates in fish.

Module 38.5 Connection: Rapid global warming could alter the entire biosphere.

Review: The introduction to global warming, the carbon cycle, and the equations for cellular respiration and photosynthesis (Modules 1.9, 5.21, 6.3, 7.4, 7.13, and 37.17).

A. Global warming has been accepted by most of the scientific community as a reality. Now the debate is centered around how severe the effects of global warming will be on the world.

B. Since the industrial revolution, CO_2 concentrations have steadily risen. Carbon dioxide concentration in the atmosphere, as measured in Hawaii, has increased dramatically (17%) in just more than 40 years (Figure 38.5A).

C. CO_2 is one of the greenhouse gases. CH_4 and NO are also greenhouse gases released from fossil-fuel burning, among other sources. CO_2 is good, in moderation, because it is estimated that without the heat trapped by the CO_2 put into the atmosphere by natural phenomena, the average temperature of Earth would be $\approx -18°C$ (the **greenhouse effect,** Figure 38.5B).

D. Global warming results from an excess amount of these gases. However, some climatologists are predicting that, at the current rate of increase of greenhouse gases, atmospheric temperatures could rise about 2°C by the end of the 21st century.

E. A 2°C rise in global atmospheric temperature could melt polar ice caps and raise sea levels significantly. Environmentally sensitive and heavily populated coastal regions would be flooded. Such warming may also alter precipitation patterns and the grain belts of the United States may become much drier and unable to support crops.

F. Recent studies have shown that many species are adapting to global warming while others are struggling. The polar bears along the Hudson Bay have a shorter hunting season and have less stored fat than they had decades before. Some polar bears are even starving (Figure 38.5C).

G. Some experts suggest that increases in greenhouse gases will affect cloud cover, which would tend to decrease temperature. Other experts are calling for drastic reductions in fossil fuel usage.

H. Worldwide cooperation and individual efforts are needed to reverse the warming trend. An international agreement (the Kyoto Protocol) among 189 countries outlines a plan to reduce greenhouse gas emissions. Noticeably missing from this agreement is the United States.

I. Heat waves, reduced farm productivity, and the spread of tropical diseases such as malaria may become major consequences of global warming. The loss of species is still increasing in intensity.

II. Conservation of Populations and Species

Module 38.6 Two ways to study endangered populations are the small-population approach and the declining-population approach.

A. When habitats are patchy, the distribution of the subpopulations of a species' population is often patchy. Gene flow among subpopulations varies with the degree of isolation.

B. Habitat degradation has increased the degree of population fragmentation that naturally occurs as a result of environmental patchiness. Human activities, such as logging, have created patchy environments and population fragments where they did not previously exist (Figure 38.6A). Populations of the northern spotted owl (Figure 38.6B) declined with logging of the coniferous forests they inhabit.
Review: The impact of logging on coniferous forests is discussed in Module 17.14.

C. Two approaches explain the biology of the extinction process:
1. The *small-population approach* states that a population reaches a critical level of smallness due to a variety of factors, such as the loss of habitat, then spirals down, as in a vortex, toward extinction. The key factor driving the extinction vortex is the loss of genetic variation, which a population depends on for adaptation to environmental changes.
2. The *declining-population approach* is proactive and tries to identify, diagnose, and halt a declining population before it reaches a critical level. This process requires a careful, logical approach to determining the cause of the decline before recommending corrective actions.

Module 38.7 Identifying critical habitat factors can guide conservation efforts.

A. Critical factors determine if a habitat is suitable for the recovery of the red-cockaded woodpecker.

B. The red-cockaded woodpecker is dependent on the presence of mature living pine trees for nesting sites (Figure 38.7A). This species also depends on fire to keep the undergrowth below 15 feet in height among the pines (Figures 38.7B and C). A proactive approach of controlled fires and the excavation of new nests in pines were used to help return this species to a sustainable level.

C. A side benefit of the management of one species was increased species diversity.

D. Conservation biologists recognize it is often necessary to consider a species' worth relative to the concerns of the community as a whole. A keystone species is often the species that needs the most intervention to save the community.

III. Managing and Restoring Ecosystems

Module 38.8 Sustaining ecosystems and landscapes is a conservation priority.

A. Past conservation efforts were focused on saving individual species. Now the focus is on saving entire ecosystems and landscapes. **Landscape ecology** is the use of ecological principles to the study of the structure and interaction of several ecosystems. One goal of landscape ecology is to understand the patterns of landscape use—past, present, and future—and to promote biodiversity as part of the land-use strategy.

B. Edges differ from the habitats on either side of them. Thus, they support communities that differ from those found in either habitat. Human activities can create edges (Figure 38.8A).

C. The brown-headed cowbird is an edge-adapted species (Figure 38.8B). It forages for insects in open fields and parasitizes the nests of forest birds.

D. Movement corridors may connect fragmented habitats. Some movement corridors are artificial constructs (Figure 38.8C). Movement corridors can be beneficial in promoting dispersal, and are particularly important to species that migrate. However, movement corridors may facilitate the spread of disease, particularly among small populations. The value of movement corridors must be studied further.
   NOTE: Promoting dispersal in movement corridors promotes gene flow.

Module 38.9 Protected areas are established to slow the loss of biodiversity.

A. Conservation biologists are using their understanding of populations, communities, ecosystems, and landscape biology to better protect **biodiversity hot spots** (small areas with high concentrations of endangered or threatened species).

B. Many species found in biodiversity hot spots are **endemic species** (species not found anywhere else) and as such are particularly sensitive to environmental degradation and consequent extinction.

C. The "hottest" spots seen in Figure 38.9A cover less than 1.5% of the land yet are home to 1/3 of all the species on Earth. Because these hot spots are particularly sensitive to habitat destruction, loss of species could be as high as one-half within the next 10 to 15 years given the current rate of human development.

D. Conservation of relatively small biodiversity hot spots should not detract from conservation efforts over wider areas.

E. Uneven patterns of species distribution are seen during seasonal migration. For example, monarch butterflies winter in central Mexico and spend their summers in the United States and Canada. Migrational patterns increase the complexity of species conservation; habitat preservation must consider the entire area associated with the migratory pattern.

F. Another example of a migratory species is the loggerhead turtle (Figure 38.9B). This species feeds and mates at sea, but the females lay their eggs on specific beaches. Many juveniles and adults drown at sea, caught in fish and shrimp nets. Eggs, buried in shallow pits, are vulnerable to predation as well as to residential and commercial development of the beaches.

G. Approximately 7% of the world's land has been set aside as reserves. The question is, which is better, large tracts of land or many small reserves? Current indications are that for some species such as the tiger, bigger (land reserve) is better. But the reality is that more land will most likely not be placed into reserve, and therefore, alternatives must be developed.

Preview: Zoned reserves and linked reserves (Modules 38.13 and 38.10).

Module 38.10 Connection: The Yellowstone to Yukon Conservation Initiative seeks to preserve biodiversity by connecting protected areas.

A. The Y2Y Initiative is an ambitious effort to link parks and reserves with protected corridors from Alaska to Wyoming (Figure 38.10A).

B. Wildlife reserves are effective as long as the animals remain on the protected land. However, studies have shown that reserves do not provide large enough ranges for signature species, and once off the protected lands, the animals are vulnerable (Figure 38.10B).

C. The reintroduction of the gray wolf to Yellowstone National Park was controversial but has been a huge success (Figure 38.10C). The initial number of 60 wolves has increased to approximately 300. The effect throughout the park has been dramatic, affecting as many as 25 species.

D. Reintroduction programs and migration from Canada have brought the gray wolf back to Idaho and Montana. Despite the overpopulation of deer and elk and the success at Yellowstone, local and political resistance still persist to the presence of wolves in states where they once roamed freely.

Module 38.11 The study of how to restore degraded habitats is a developing science.

Review: The role of prokaryotes in bioremediation is discussed in Module 16.16.

A. Abandoned land that has been degraded or land that has been damaged by toxic chemicals is in need of restoration. The expanding field of **restoration ecology** uses ecological principles to return land to its predegraded state.

B. Prokaryotes, fungi, lichens, and plants are used in **bioremediation** (the use of living organisms to restore ecosystems). Lichens that concentrate uranium are being studied for possible use in cleaning areas contaminated as a result of mining activities (Figure 38.11A).

C. Another tool of restoration ecology is **biological augmentation,** a process whereby the growth of plants, such as legumes, is encouraged to replenish nutrient-depleted soil (Figure 38.11B).

D. Restoration ecology is still in the experimental stages with no particular method proven best. Therefore, multiple methods are being investigated (the scientific process at work; Modules 1.7 and 1.8).

Module 38.12 Connection: The Kissimmee River Project is a case study in restoration ecology.

A. The Kissimmee River Project (started in 1992) is the largest landscape restoration project ever attempted and will reclaim 27,000 acres of wetland and restore the original channel.

B. Phase one was completed in 2004. The effects were seen almost immediately, with ducks and birds returning in droves. Fish that require high levels of dissolved oxygen have repopulated the waters, and native vegetation has filled the marshes again.

C. The project's cost is being shared 50-50 by the state of Florida and the federal government at a price tag of 578 million dollars. Economic benefits to recoup the cost of restoration will be realized through other means such as increased recreation (hunting and fishing) and ecotourism.

Module 38.13 Connection: Zoned reserves are an attempt to reverse ecosystem disruption.

A. Few, if any, ecosystems are unaffected by humans.

B. **Zoned reserves** are extensive regions of land that include one or more undisturbed areas. Within these areas, species and ecosystem processes involving them can be conserved. *Review:* Global warming will make managing reserves very difficult (Module 7.13).

C. Countries exchange political and economic favors for establishing these areas. Costa Rica has become a world leader in establishing zoned reserves (Figure 38.13A).

D. Local education about the ecological and economic benefits is needed, and buffers must be established around the margins of zoned reserves where social and economic climates are more compatible with the conservation of resources within the reserves.

E. Commitment to the conservation project by the Costa Rican government, nongovernmental organizations, and local citizens has helped this project succeed. Success can be measured in a variety of ways, but one is in the living conditions of the Costa Rican people (Figure 38.13B). Life expectancy, literacy, and infant mortality have all improved.

F. The program still faces challenges. The increase in the population from 4 million to 6 million by 2050 will place an increased demand for resources. Sustainable development must be continued.

Module 38.14 Sustainable development is an ultimate goal.

Review: The challenges of the sustainable development of coniferous and tropical forests (Module 17.14).

A. **Sustainable development** is defined as the long-term prosperity of human societies and the ecosystems that support them. Sustainable development will require changing the human mindset. For the sake of future generations, the natural processes upon which humans are dependent must be preserved.

B. The Ecological Society of America endorses a research project called the Sustainable Biosphere Initiative. It has one goal: to acquire the necessary information about the biosphere to develop, manage, and conserve the Earth's resources in a responsible manner.

C. Cross-discipline research and education will be required to promote sustainable development and at the same time reverse the biodiversity crisis (Figure 38.14).

D. The condition of the biosphere is precarious at best, and a reversal of the current situation will require personal, scientific, and political efforts of enormous proportions. But failure to act will result in the demise of the biosphere as we know it.

Class Activities

1. This chapter provides the best opportunity to get students involved. Encourage involvement on a personal level (recycling) or on a larger level (e.g., volunteering in litter pickup). Ask the students what, if anything, needs to be done to preserve the environment. What are the relative merits of environmental and economic (both pro- and anticonservation) arguments?

2. Invite a representative of an environmental society, such as the Sierra Club, to speak to the class; invite speakers from contrasting groups on both sides of these issues.

3. Ask your class to identify edges and corridors in their local environment. What animals and plants exploit these edges and corridors, and how might these animals (including humans) and plants be affected by further disruption of the local environment? by attempts at restoration of the local environment?

Transparency Acetates

Figure 38.4   Biological magnification of the pesticide DDT in a food chain

Figure 38.5A   The increase of atmospheric CO_2 and temperature variation at Mauna Loa, Hawaii, since 1958

Figure 38.5B   Global warming and factors influencing it

Figure 38.9A   Earth's terrestrial biodiversity hot spots (purple)

Figure 38.10A   Map of Yellowstone to Yukon ecoregion with protected areas shown in green

Figure 38.13A   Zoned reserves in Costa Rica

Reviewing the Concepts, page 782: Threats to biodiversity

Connecting the Concepts, page 782: Conservation biology

Media

See the beginning of this book for a complete description of all media available for instructors and students. Animations and videos are available in the Campbell Image Presentation Library. Media Activities and Thinking as a Scientist investigations are available on the student CD-ROM and website.

Activities and Thinking as a Scientist	Module Number
Web/CD Activity 38A: *Connection: Madagascar and the Biodiversity Crisis*	38.2
Web/CD Activity 38B: *Connection: Fire Ants as an Exotic Species*	38.3
Web/CD Activity 38C: *Connection: DDT and the Environment*	38.4
Web/CD Activity 38D: *Connection: The Greenhouse Effect*	38.5
Web/CD Thinking as a Scientist: *Connection: How Are Potential Restoration Sites Analyzed?*	38.11
Web/CD Activity 38E: *Conservation Biology Review*	38.14

Major Changes in the Fifth Edition of *Biology: Concepts & Connections*

Chapter 1, "Biology: Exploring Life," has a new opening essay on the brown pelican, pictured on the cover of this book. A new module (1.3) highlights cells as the structural and functional units of life and introduces the concepts of emergent properties and biological systems. Module 1.8, on hypothesis-based science, more fully develops the everyday (broken flashlight) example and now includes research on mimicry in king snakes.

Unit I, The Life of the Cell, the book's introduction to the basic chemistry, structure, and energetics of cells, has benefited from a number of new chapter-opening essays, art improvements, and reordering and refocusing of many modules. Chapter 2 includes a new Connection module on trace elements as common additives to food and water. Hydrogen bonds are now covered in a separate module (2.10), as a prelude to the major section on water's life-supporting properties. The new opening essay in Chapter 3 uses the topic of lactose intolerance to introduce organic molecules. Chapter 4 includes a better visual and descriptive comparison of prokaryotic and eukaryotic cells. In Chapter 6, the modules on oxidation-reduction reactions and ATP generation have been combined and restructured. The presentation of fermentation (6.13) has been heavily revised. Chapter 7 has a new opening essay on energy plantations, and the photosynthesis art has been restructured. A mechanical analogy has been added to Module 7.9 to help explain electron flow in the light reactions.

Unit II, Cellular Reproduction and Genetics, incorporates important recent advances in the field. New chapter introductions discuss the rescue of extremely rare plant species (Chapter 8), the cloning of endangered animals (Chapter 11), and the use of DNA in forensic investigations (Chapter 12). Chapter 8 incorporates advances in our understanding of binary fission (8.3), the G0 stage of the cell cycle (8.9), the causes of Down syndrome (8.20), and sex chromosome nondisjunction syndromes (8.22). Chapter 9 contains a heavily revised module on options for fetal genetic testing (9.10). The discussion of non-Mendelian genetics has been reorganized and includes a new module discussing the role of the environment (9.16). The final section of Chapter 10, now called "Microbial Genetics," includes coverage of both viruses (with an update on emerging viruses, such as SARS) and bacteria (10.22 and 10.23, formerly in Chapter 12). In Chapter 11, a new section called "Animal Cloning" highlights the differences between reproductive and therapeutic cloning. Chapter 12 has been largely revised, as reflected in its new title, "DNA Technology and Genomics." Modules on applications of DNA technology are now located immediately after the modules that present the corresponding methods. A new module (12.17) presents recent advances in genomics and proteomics. A new Talking About Science module (12.20) features a discussion of the Human Genome Project with Eric Lander.

Unit III, Concepts of Evolution, has been extensively reorganized and updated. In Chapter 13, Module 13.2 ("Darwin proposed natural selection as the mechanism of evolution") now follows directly from the account of Darwin's travels in Module 13.1. Module 13.4 refines and expands the discussion of the molecular evidence of evolution and includes a new figure on comparative embryology. Module 13.12, on sources of genetic variation, now includes recombination in bacteria and viruses. The revised opening essay for Chapter 14 describes new research on the mosquito species that spreads West Nile virus. A new Module 14.1 distinguishes microevolution and macroevolution. Material on macroevolution has been moved from Chapter 15 and expanded into a new three-module section at the end of Chapter 14. Module 14.11 includes a figure on the range of complexity of eyes in molluscs to illustrate the concept of gradual refinement in the evolution of complex structures. Module 14.12, on the role of changes in developmental genes in evolution, includes a discussion of homeotic genes. In Chapter 15, the modules on phylogeny and systematics are heavily revised, with updated information on molecular systematics. Module 15.8 explains how cladistic analysis includes birds in the reptilian clade, a classification now adopted by this book.

Unit IV, The Evolution of Biological Diversity, has been revised within an updated phylogenetic framework. In Chapter 16, the discussion of hypotheses about the origin of life now includes protobionts and their nutrition (16.6). Several modules describing general prokaryote characteristics now precede expanded coverage of various groups of archaea and bacteria. The revised protist section follows a tentative phylogeny of protist clades. The coverage of plants in Chapter 17 now begins with their evolution from green algae (17.1) and adaptations for life on land (17.2). The section on fungi in Chapter 17 has been rearranged and expanded to cover basic aspects of fungal life cycles and reproduction, a tentative phylogeny, and details of the life cycles of two fungal groups. A new module (17.21) presents leaf-cutting ants as an example of a mutualistic relationship between fungi and animals. In Chapter 18, two new modules (18.3 and 18.4) provide an overview of animal body plans and how they have been used to infer phylogenetic relationships. Another new module (18.15) presents a cladogram of the chordates. Lampreys are now covered in a separate module (18.16), and the coverage of chondrichthyans, ray-finned fishes, and lobe-fins has been updated (18.17). The characteristics and major groups of mammals are more fully described in Module 18.21. Chapter 19 has been significantly revised to reflect more current understanding of primate and human evolution. Two new Connection modules discuss the evolution of human skin color and human language.

Unit V, Animals: Form and Function, has been enhanced with improved art and more relevant connections to everyday life. New chapter introductions discuss the controversy surrounding AIDS vaccine trials (Chapter 24) and the increased use of fertility drugs (Chapter 27) as well as research on whether elephants really run (Chapter 30). New Connection modules discuss artificial tissues (Chapter 20); the Heimlich maneuver, vitamin requirements, obesity and evolution, and fad diets (all in Chapter 21); anemia and blood doping (Chapter 23); hydration needs ("Do we need to drink eight glasses of water each day?") and alcohol's effects on the liver (both in Chapter 25); the potential abuse of human growth hormone by athletes (Chapter 26); mental illnesses and other neurological disorders (Chapter 28); changes in taste perception with age (Chapter 29); and osteoporosis (Chapter 30). In addition, the presentation of the concepts underlying the applications has been improved. For example, in Chapter 24, "The Immune System," a new discussion of helper T cells (24.11) prepares the students for a new Connection module offering a detailed description of how HIV affects immunity (24.12). And the revised discussion of clonal selection (24.7) has a large new figure to help clarify this difficult topic for students. In Chapter 27, the topic of hormonal regulation of the menstrual cycle has been reworked to provide better text/art integration (27.5). Chapter 28 has a more current organization of the vertebrate peripheral nervous system (28.12).

Unit VI, Plants: Form and Function, opens with a new Talking About Science module featuring plant biologist Natasha Raikhel. The discussion of plant anatomy contains new connections to what students actually see in their food (31.4 and 31.12). A new summary figure (31.6) helps students visualize the organization of plant tissue systems throughout a plant body and its individual organs. In Chapter 32, a new section ("Plant Nutrition and Symbiosis") has improved coverage of symbiotic relationships. Chapter 33 has an updated discussion of the role of hormones in apical dominance (33.4).

Unit VII, Ecology, has been updated with current ecological data, fresh photos, and new and revised Talking About Science and Connection modules. The chapter on animal behavior, which is now Chapter 35, opens with an essay on impalas and includes two new Connection modules (imprinting of whooping cranes on ultralight aircraft and a human mate choice study). Module 35.3 includes new research on monogamous prairie voles in discussing the influence of genes and environment on behavior. New modules include 35.10, on social learning, and 35.13, on mating systems and parental care as they relate to the needs of offspring and the certainty of paternity. In Chapter 36, Modules 36.9 and 36.10, on human population growth, have new material on demographic differences between developing and developed countries. Chapter 37, on communities and ecosystems, includes a new module on herbivory (37.5) and one on primary production (37.12). Module 37.2 includes a new figure illustrating resource partitioning in Anolis lizards, and Module 37.15 has a figure presenting a general model of nutrient cycling in ecosystems. Max Moritz describes the role of fire in some ecosystems in a new Talking About Science module. Chapter 38 begins with a new essay on tiger conservation in Myanmar and updated information on the biodiversity crisis in Module 38.1. Module 38.4 has new material on biomagnification, dead zones, and mercury pollution. Two new Connection modules describe the Yellowstone to Yukon Conservation Initiative and the Kissimmee River Restoration Project.